Science and Society

Science and Society

Edited by

NORMAN KAPLAN

Rand McNally & Company

Chicago

RAND McNALLY SOCIOLOGY SERIES

Edgar F. Borgatta, Advisory Editor

Alford, *Party and Society*

Borgatta and Sperling, *A Workbook for the Study of Social Interaction Processes*

Christensen, ed., *Handbook of Marriage and the Family*

Demerath, *Social Class in American Protestantism*

Faris, ed., *Handbook of Modern Sociology*

Hadden and Borgatta, *American Cities: Their Social Characteristics*

March, ed., *Handbook of Organizations*

Nye and Hoffman, *The Employed Mother in America*

Scott, *Values and Organizations: A Study of Fraternities and Sororities*

Warren, *The Community in America*

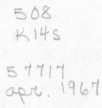

PRINTED IN THE U.S.A. BY RAND McNALLY & COMPANY

Preface

The idea for this volume began to take on some reality several years ago when I was still at Cornell University. It was brought to fruition while I was at the University of Pennsylvania. To my friends, colleagues and former students at both universities, I owe a great debt for their advice and encouragement. My own interests in the sociology of science first began to develop in a seminar I had with Professor Robert K. Merton at Columbia University nearly two decades ago. These interests were nurtured in a very practical fashion by a series of grants from the National Institutes of Health, and although these are not directly connected with this volume, without their help to pursue research interests in this area, I might never have contemplated the need for such an undertaking.

It goes without saying that this volume could not exist except for the many contributors and their publishers who have so generously granted their permission to be included here. Full acknowledgement and citation of original sources are made on the title page of each contribution. I should also like to thank Daniel A. Greenberg for his advice and critical comments on an earlier version of this book. Kay Nadel, Beverly Porter, and Martha Lodge helped with the bibliography at various stages. Barbara Hockey Kaplan has helped and encouraged me in so many ways as to make it impossible to single out any particular contributions for which she can be thanked adequately. Finally, I owe a debt to Rand McNally and especially to John Applegath and Ed Borgatta for having the courage and foresight to publish this book before the sociology of science has achieved much formal recognition in the universities. Specific thanks must go to Shirley McAvinchey of Rand McNally who went over each word so carefully. I assume full responsibility to all the contributors for the company in which they have been placed, and to all the readers, for any errors which may still be present.

Program of Policy Studies in Science and Technology
The George Washington University
Washington, D.C.
July 1, 1965

Table of Contents

IV. NATIONAL SCIENCE ESTABLISHMENTS

V. SCIENCE AND POLICY

VI. PROLOGUE TO THE FUTURE

ix

Science and Society: An Introduction

Science has always been intimately related to society. Just how intimate these relations are has only recently become widely recognized. The exact nature of these connections—the ways in which society affects the development and the pursuit of science and the ways in which science (and not just its technological by-products) affects the development of society—is only now beginning to be explored in any depth. There have been, of course, scattered commentaries, speculations, and even serious studies of some facets of this interconnection over the years. But it has been only in the last decades that it became so clear that studies of the relations of science and society could no longer be neglected.

Even so, only a slow start has been made. There is still no generally accepted label identifying studies of science and society. There is still no single identifiable academic discipline specializing in such studies. Sociologists, political scientists, economists, historians, and, perhaps not so strangely, the "hard" scientists themselves have all shown some concern. They have tried to identify the boundaries of such a field of study. They have sought to outline some dimensions of problems considered worthy of study. They have identified trends and changes within science itself and in relation to the larger society. They have raised "cries of alarm" about different ways of supporting or organizing scientific research. They have recorded their experiences and observations of how science and society are related. But almost all would agree that there is still a very long way to go.

Who now needs to know something of the relations of science and society? The answer, especially in a democratic society, is that it is difficult to think of anyone who does not need to know. With national governments increasingly assuming the role of the single most important and most beneficent "patron" of the sciences, the members of the government, directly, and the public at large, somewhat indirectly, now need to know something of the nature of science, scientists, and the research they support.

Although we are all involved, directly or indirectly, in the effects of science and in the effects of society upon science, the knowledge and understanding of the underlying processes may differ considerably according to the specific kind of involvement. The research administrator of a federal agency may have a different perspective from that of a natural scientist applying for a grant. The lay citizen may want to examine his own attitude toward the space race for the moon, or he might wonder whether it is

1

"better" to support the research effort in cancer or heart disease or muscular dystrophy when private agencies promoting each of these research campaigns solicit him for funds. The congressman may wonder whether public funds can rightly and properly be appropriated to study the mating habits of some species of the fly—or he may wonder whether his constituents will wonder. The extent to which the present modes of research support encourage the trend toward "big" science and concentration of research efforts in a few large centers at the expense of the individual scientist and the smaller centers may worry some scientists as well as congressmen and other government officials. The extent to which basic work in science is being crowded out by the more immediately practical, the more "saleable," and the more glamorous technology and development work may be of concern to still others.

What do we need to know to make intelligent decisions, to make reasonable choices, and to enhance our understanding of the potential effects and ramifications of different modes of action? Surely it would be of some help to understand the nature of science itself, but a deep understanding of much of science is beyond most of us in many senses. Even the molecular biologist may not understand fully all that is happening in nuclear physics. Is it possible to know and understand science in the same way that all of us—laymen or professional scholars—can know and understand (and appreciate) Shakespeare? The answer is not entirely clear, although many have argued that it is essential to make the effort. Indeed, as Leland Haworth argues in his paper which appears here, it is the duty of the scientist to interpret science for the layman. And undoubtedly the newspapers and the popular press carry more science news, usually reported at a high level of accuracy and reliability, than ever before. But I often wonder whether it is possible, even for the highly educated layman, to grasp more than vaguely and somewhat superficially the substance of scientific findings. In any event, none of the selections included in this book has the primary purpose of conveying the actual substance of scientific knowledge and theory to the layman. Instead, the main goal is to present a more or less coherent view of the *connections* between science and society.

While there are no discussions of the technical substance of nuclear physics, several of the papers discuss nuclear physics as an area of science to be supported in competition with other areas. Or they may touch upon the changes within science—the changing patterns of organization and support—which the nature and requirements of research in nuclear physics are helping to bring about. This includes the large scale of the effort required as a consequence of the huge and expensive particle accelerators, which in turn enhances the tendency toward team research. Without necessarily understanding how or why or whether the recent discovery of the negatively charged omega-minus particle confirms Murray Gell-Mann's theory, it is still possible to understand something of the nature of the experimental research which had to be undertaken to test this theory and the complex arrangements necessary for its support.

In other words, this book is not intended to convey a "popularized" version of the technical nature of science. I do not argue that it is impossible or unnecessary for the layman to acquire a background in the technical nature of science. I contend only that it is very difficult to do so. *And even more important,* I am arguing that understanding the substance of science is *not* a sufficient basis for understanding the role of science in society. In fact, I would submit that the natural and physical scientists are themselves not expert in the understanding of the interrelations of science and society simply by virtue of their *expertise* in science. There is a developing field of knowledge *about* science and its interrelations with society which must call upon the concepts and methods of sociology, economics, political science, psychology, history, and perhaps even several other fields of knowledge as well. This new field is not the monopoly of any existing discipline by any means.

With this in mind, I have tried to present here selections from the growing body of literature about science and its interrelations with society. These selections represent a cross section of the "state of the art." Ten years ago, the cross section which might have been selected from the available literature would have had a very different appearance. It is hoped that a few years from now our knowledge of this field will have advanced so that much of what appears in this book will be of interest primarily to historians. The papers included here are all very recent. Of the thirty-nine selections included here, only three were published before 1959 (four more were published during 1959).

Almost half of the authors included here had their training originally in the physical or natural sciences, although many of these men are now engaged in research administration or in science policy positions. The remainder of the authors represent a broad spectrum of social-science backgrounds except for two who are professional journalists.

The underlying theme, then, of this volume revolves around the interrelations of science and society. In the first section, labeled "prologue to the present," selections have been included which provide some background, primarily historical, for an understanding of these interrelations. Two kinds of background are explored: the first seeks to lay out some of the dimensions and problems of an emerging field—identified in one paper as the "science of science" and in another by a nonsociologist as the "sociology of science." The second aspect of this background places more emphasis on the emerging substantive problems of this field. The opening selection, for example, is a brief account of a not very distant period in our history when the scientists, and science, were so uninvolved in the wars between nations that they could and did communicate freely with each other although the nations of which they were citizens were on opposite sides in various wars. This is a dramatic, but not unimportant, illustration of one aspect of the interrelations of science and society.

Another facet of this relationship, at once more direct and of more immediate relevance today, is the role of the universities in responding to the challenges of modern science. Universities were not always so intimately bound up with the promotion and development of science. Some resisted mightily and others capitulated reluctantly; the pattern differed in the many universities of the various countries. The timing differed too; science became welded into the university structure earlier in Germany—during the early part of the nineteenth century—and variations of this pattern spread to other nations. But it took time and the pattern was never duplicated exactly as it moved from one country to another. It was not until the turn of the century that science gained a firm beachhead in the American universities and whatever the timing, much seemed dependent upon the character of the educational system as a whole, its relation to the social class system and to a host of other social factors. When we look at the relations of modern science and the universities today we are apt to forget how recent the present adjustments and how differently the problem was viewed just a few decades ago. The changes involved were not always so abrupt or dramatic or obvious, but they have been crucial for the development of modern science. And it is these changes which are the primary focus of the other papers in this section.

Many more selections might have been included on the background of the current problems of science and society. Some references, a few quite extensive in nature, are scattered through a number of other selections included in this volume. Other references are included in the bibliography. But, the limitations of space aside, the decision to include so few historical selections was a deliberate one. While there is much to be learned from history, and while there is a real need for even more historical studies focusing more directly on the extrinsic relations of science, I would argue that the past is not a wholly adequate guide to the future in the study of science and society. Science itself has changed too much, and its relations to society have changed even more radically.

The theme of change is carried through the second section which focuses on the nature of science as a social institution. By this we mean the norms and values which affect the behavior and attitudes of scientists as they are engaged in the activities identified with science. The institutional aspects of science are determined by both its intrinsic technical nature and

nce, by itself, is obviously not the only or immediate answer, bu
newly developing nations should not have to repeat the experi
more industrialized nations, and certainly not on the same tim
for the more developed nations with the most advanced scientifi
nts, the results of science will not be automatic panaceas, even
ntific problems themselves.

last few selections, the changes in the internal nature of science
in its external relations are examined for their effects on science
years ahead. Big science will undoubtedly affect the future char-
and direction of science. It will affect the role of the scientist in
atory and his role in the larger society. Above all, the changes in
ill affect us all, and it is time that we started to prepare to under-
at is happening. A good beginning is made in these essays, but the
e can learn more of what is involved and support systematic re-
this area, the sooner will these essays be superseded by new and,
y, better knowledge.

its external relations with the larger society. The balance between these two determinants is still only barely understood. Presumably, the intrinsic technical requirements impose certain limits on the extent to which external, nonscientific considerations can influence the shape of scientific activities. But, on the other hand, it seems clear that there are rather wide boundaries within which science can flourish (both relatively and absolutely however it may be defined) as witnessed by the fact that science has flourished within a variety of political, economic, and social systems.

The selections included in the second section touch on only a few of the basic problems involved in trying to understand science as a social institution. They are, I think, among the more important as well as the more highly developed in terms of the work already accomplished. These selections center around the norms and values of science, the nature of scientific activity as it is affected by both intrinsic and extrinsic factors, the problems of trying to define basic research, and the nature of the social system within science which supports this kind of activity.

Scientific research is conducted within a variety of laboratories around the world. Some are quite small and uncomplicated, while others are very large and quite complex in organization. These laboratories are supported and maintained in a variety of ways. There are private and public laboratories. Some are independent of any other institutional affiliation, others are attached to, or may be a part of, larger organizations which have many other goals in addition to the conduct of research. This includes university laboratories as well as those in industry and government.

It is probably true that the scientist, viewing his technical tasks at the laboratory bench, would be equally at home in almost any kind of society. However, his freedom to work on particular problems, the ease or difficulty of obtaining the necessary support and facilities, and a host of other related factors would be affected by the place of the laboratory within the larger society. The society does have an effect on the internal organization of the laboratory, and this in turn affects the substantive progress of science. The selections included here focus on some aspects of this problem.

As laboratories have become larger and more complex and as they have moved into formerly "alien" environments, considerable attention has been given to the various problems of the internal organization of laboratories. The bibliography to this section provides some indication of the wealth of work already accomplished. This is also attested by the fact that there are quite a few collections, and even textbooks, devoted specifically to this area. It is for this reason that the more specific and the more technical papers on laboratory organization have not been included in this volume. Those which have been included are addressed to the more general problems of laboratory organization which are especially relevant for an understanding of the interaction of science and society. The professional actively engaged in the study of laboratory organization will, it is hoped, find these selections valuable in providing a larger frame of reference. But those interested in more detailed findings, methodological problems in studying laboratories, and related problems will have to go to the growing technical literature to find what they need.

In the fourth section we move toward a more macroscopic view of the organization of science at the level of whole societies. An underlying hypothesis is that the nature of these "national science establishments" is, to a significant extent, determined by the general nature of science as an institution as this is molded by the nature of the society as a whole. Further, it is suggested that the particular nature of the national science establishment affects the internal organization of the research laboratory and, more generally, the effectiveness and rate of progress of scientific activities within any particular society. Thus it is necessary to know something about both the internal organization and the external relationships of scientific research activities. In the previous section, some of the basic problems of the internal organization of research were presented. In this section, the external relationships are examined.

In the first three papers certain aspects and problems of the national organization of science in the United States are discussed. The remaining papers deal primarily with Europe or specific countries in Europe. All of them illustrate forcefully the intimate interconnections of a number of characteristics of the society to the particular kind of national science establishments. These papers also illustrate the importance of approaching the study of the social aspects of science from a comparative, cross-national perspective. If it were not for the limitations of space and the desire to explore other related problems, many more selections dealing with the national organization of science, ranging from Australia to Yugoslavia, might well have been included. A number of the more important of such national studies are listed in the bibliography.

From a consideration of national science establishments it is but a short step to the area of science policy. Until quite recently, there was little explicitly relating the particular nature of a national science establishment to concrete policies of national governments or any other bodies. The big change has been the recognition, especially by national governments, of the necessity to plan the development of science and to integrate this planning with over-all national policies. It is in this area of science policy, especially, that the past is a poor guide to the present as well as the future. Policies are being contemplated and formulated today with almost no direct precedents upon which to rely. Under the pressures for immediate action, policies are being made, often in reaction to specific crises and without the benefit of a

more developed body of knowledge included in this section indicate, we know all the relevant dimensions of th

It is becoming increasingly clear, ceptually distinct and yet intimately re on the one hand, the problems of form On the other hand, there are the probl of a science policy. A policy for scienc development of science. It involves such money for basic research, whether to prov for mental health, whether the current l ences is entirely adequate, and so on. A r explicit recognition of the role of science i including the political, social, and econon potential, affect the kinds of political, socia can be made, a fact which emerged most cl troversy over testing nuclear devices. But importance of science for certain national g concerning the internal development of s affected.

Aside from these considerations, the m effects on the internal development of science For example, choices must be made on the leve to concentrate this effort. In the United States, into a policy of encouraging more basic resea while other countries may seek to accomplish t government-operated laboratories. Whichever c consequences not only for the development of s variety of other institutions in the society. One of here is the changing role of the universities as res in relation to their other functions in a society. In to conceive of very many aspects of a society upo impinge. And because of this, it is all the more something about intelligent planning for science.

In the final section, the selections included stres problems in the years ahead as new adjustments are and society. Of considerable interest is the increasin necessity) for international cooperation, especially in scale and very expensive research in certain areas have a more long-range effect on the relations among area of basic concern is the actual and potential rol the development of the newer, and largely prescie

world. Scie clearly the ences of th scale. Ever establishm for the sci

In th as well as itself in t acteristics the labor science stand wh sooner search i hopefull

PART I

Prologue to the Present

The history of the changing relations between society and science has yet to be written. Science and society were probably never more intimately bound up with each other than they are today. Yet we have only fragmentary knowledge of how this came to be so. This is especially true for our knowledge of how society affects the development of science. The selections included in this introductory section shed considerable light on this problem. Some of the papers included here focus on particular historical relationships between science and society. Others explore the kinds of questions which must be asked as well as the conceptual tools which might be used in trying to examine the interrelations of science and society, whether historically or at the present time. Fragmentary as our knowledge of these relations may be, it is clear that there have been many continuities as well as discontinuities in their historical development. Many facets of this interrelationship are entirely new; that is to say, they are no more than decades old. Many others whose development might be traced back for a century or more are so changed today that they may well be considered new and different relationships. The underlying story of the relations of science and society is indeed a dynamic and changing one.

The opening selection is a dramatic example of how recently, and how much, some of these relations have changed. The title—"The Sciences Were Never at War"—from the book by Sir Gavin de Beer, seems somewhat wistful and unreal in the world of today. Yet not so very many generations ago, scientists of a country at war with another were permitted to communicate with each other and even to exchange visits. Apparently the warring nations did not consider the information which might be exchanged as having any value or relevance for the conduct of the war. At the same time, because of the prestige of the scientists as well as for other reasons, governments were apparently willing to go out of their way, despite direct involvement in military operations, to facilitate and assure scientific communication. Whatever the reasons, scientists were apparently "above the battle" not so very long ago.

The fact that this is inconceivable today tells us something of the changing character of wars among nations. Even more important in the present context, it tells us something of the changing role of the scientists

9

in relation to military problems and to the society generally. We need hardly be reminded how intimate is the connection between science and military affairs today. Perhaps we do need to be reminded of the importance of facilitating communication among scientists today. In any case, the selection by Sir Gavin de Beer should serve to emphasize the importance of the changing relations of science and society as well as the value of studying these more closely than we have in the past.

The next selection by two Polish sociologists is an early outline of some of the problems to be studied in trying to understand the general relationships of science and society. It is essentially a programmatic statement of the need for a "science of science." It was first published in 1936 in a Polish journal. This in itself is of some interest inasmuch as the notion of studying about science in a scientific manner was not a widely held one at that time— in Poland or elsewhere.

Despite a proud tradition in scientific research, it could not be said that Poland was then at the forefront of scientific developments. Nor were there any special problems concerning the conduct of science in most of the other nations of the world. With the exception of the great debates (in Great Britain especially) about the "planning" of science versus the freedom of the individual scientist, and the recurring discussions about the scientist's responsibilities for the social uses to which his discoveries were being put (or not put), scientists and nonscientists alike were essentially oblivious to the need to study the social aspects of science. It is therefore all the more surprising that the Ossowskis should have chosen to write a paper on the science of science in the Poland of 1936.

Although the Ossowskis were themselves sociologists, they conceived of a science of science which was much broader than just the sociology of science. Sociology, to be sure, played an important role in the Ossowskis' conception of a science of science, but by no means was it restricted to this. With remarkable foresight and despite the paucity of empirical studies, the Ossowskis anticipated and laid out the lines of development for studies in a number of different disciplines. They suggested, for example, the need for psychologically oriented studies of the scientist and of the research process itself. Long before large-scale organizations for research were as prevalent as they are today, the Ossowskis called attention to the need for organizational studies in the conduct of research. Almost as if they anticipated the development and proliferation of national research councils, government ministries, and other agencies and the concern with the allocation of scientific resources which began to occur in earnest some twenty years after this paper was written, the Ossowskis called attention to the need for applied studies of the organization and support of different scientific activities in different contexts. Despite the new developments in the last decade or so, many of the suggestions put forward and the questions raised in the Ossowskis' paper have still to be recognized widely as worthwhile problems to be studied. Much of what they have suggested remains remarkably fresh and relevant today and still awaits a more complete implementation.

Much has been written about the emergence of modern science in the seventeenth century, but, until recently, little attention has been paid to the emergence of applied science. As we shall see in the next section, it is not always easy to distinguish between applied and basic science today. It was only a little more than a century ago, when applied science first began to develop in its own right, that such a problem even became relevant. For the moment, it may be sufficient to note that applied science refers to the application of scientific findings especially to industrial technology. It has often been associated with the emergence of industrial research laboratories.

Applied science did not just "happen." In fact, one of the more puzzling questions concerns the lateness of its development in England. With England pioneering the development of the Industrial Revolution on the one hand, and modern science on the other, one might have expected that applied science would develop first there as well. Instead, Germany pioneered in applied science and England lagged. In both cases, the origins can be traced back to the last century. And, even more important, the development of applied science can be traced to a number of social factors. Here, then, is yet another example of the way in which society has influenced the development of science generally.

The next selection is taken from a book by D. S. L. Cardwell which inquires into the conditions affecting the emergence of applied science in England in the nineteenth century. In doing this, Cardwell also traces its development in Germany and in both countries finds that a key role was played by a variety of social factors. To cope with these questions, Cardwell attempts to synthesize some of the more promising theoretical approaches suggested by social scientists in the study of the interrelations of science and society. It is this section of the book which is included here. It complements, and extends in a substantive fashion, certain portions of the programmatic statement formulated by the Ossowskis.

Cardwell found that the educational system generally and the universities in particular played a crucial, if somewhat indirect, role in the development of applied science. They played a far more direct role in the development of science itself. Yet it was not until the nineteenth century that we saw the beginning of a fuller acceptance of science and research within the universities, first in Europe and, in the latter part of the century, in the United States. During this period there were marked differences in scientific productivity among the leading scientific nations. It is certainly not easy to measure a nation's scientific productivity, but rough indices can be obtained by analyzing such things as the number of papers published or the number of classifiable scientific "discoveries." This is what Joseph Ben-David tries to do for several European countries as well as the United States.

Ben-David first describes and then tries to account for observed empirical differences in the productivity patterns of medical science in France, Germany, Britain, and the United States during the nineteenth century. The differences in the patterns found between these nations as well as the wide cyclical fluctuations within any particular nation's history are accounted for in part by the nature of the academic systems in each country. Each of these nations had a share of first-rank scientists, and each could be justly proud of its contributions to science. But in some countries, these scientific "greats" were able to thrive in spite of the system, and in others, they were supported and apparently helped by it. Above all, the total effort seems very much to have been related to two aspects of the university system. These were the degree of centralization within a particular country and the extent of the competitiveness among the universities. Ben-David shows, for example, how the decentralized academic system in the Germany of the early nineteenth century gave rise to considerable competition among the universities which in turn led to the establishment of many new chairs in the emerging scientific discipline. A high rate of scientific productivity is correlated with a more decentralized and more competitive university system.

Having established a case for the importance of academic systems in affecting the development of science during the nineteenth century, Joseph Ben-David and a colleague, Awraham Zloczower, proceed to investigate how and why the universities became what they are today in a companion paper which is our next selection. Again, the crucial variable examined is the degree of centralization or decentralization of the academic system. In addition, there is a systematic attempt to relate this and other characteristics of the academic system to facets of the society at large, especially the nature of the class system. In this manner, Ben-David and Zloczower seek to account for the particular nature of the development of the universities in a number of the leading scientific nations in the nineteenth and early twentieth centuries.

Further to emphasize the crucial role of changes in the universities and in the society for the development of science during the nineteenth century, our next selection by Cardwell takes us back to the question of the rise of applied science. Cardwell discusses the often accepted explanation that it was industrial demand which precipitated the rise of applied industrial research. He argues rather convincingly that it was changes in the educational system which were a necessary and prior condition for the rise of applied science and the emergence of industrial demand. The fact that these changes took place earlier in Germany set the stage for the earlier development of industrial research there. The new chemical industries, especially in the aniline dyes, were a direct outgrowth of scientific research. An English chemist, Perkins, discovered the first one, but England "missed the boat" and the Germans very soon achieved a marked superiority in this field, because, according to Cardwell, they had developed a core of trained professional scientists. This core was developed in the first instance to serve as teachers of science and technology in the various levels of the educational system. But when industry sought to establish its own research laboratories, these trained scientists were available to staff them. Even if the English industrialists had, by some chance, seen the light earlier and had wished to establish industrial laboratories, they would have found it most difficult to do so, because, in fact, England did not yet have a core of trained scientific professionals. And the reason for this can be traced to the nature of the educational system and to certain related factors in the larger society generally.

It would perhaps have been more accurate to label this section merely "an Introduction" to the Prologue. Certainly, the selections quoted here barely scratch the surface of the problems involved in the development of the relations between science and society. The objective here was a more modest one. The selections included here are illustrations, and quite crucial ones in the editor's opinion, of the ways in which society has affected the development of science. They illustrate the kinds of substantive knowledge as well as theoretical questions which would appear to be most helpful in trying to understand the contemporary situation.

The Sciences Were Never at War

SIR GAVIN DE BEER

F.R.S., F.S.A.

The modern world is become so accustomed to the notion of total war and its implications of maximal effort by whole populations, that it is difficult to realise that during the lifetime of our own grandfathers a very different system prevailed. From the time when the Royal Society of London and the Academy of Sciences in Paris were founded in the 1660s, until the last shot was fired between British and French soldiers and sailors on the downfall of Napoleon, Britain and France were at war for an aggregate of nearly sixty years. These prolonged periods of hostility naturally severed the normal means of communication, travel and conveyance for persons, letters, and scientific instruments and materials, but the men of science on both sides of the Channel never ceased to communicate with one another. They exchanged information on the results of their scientific work, they sent their publications, they travelled in each other's countries, asked for one another's good offices in securing the release of captured objects of scientific interest and of persons detained as prisoners of war, and elected one another to membership of the Royal Society of London and the French Academy of Sciences, war or no war.

From the days of Sir Hans Sloane in the seventeenth century to those of Sir Joseph Banks in the nineteenth, these principles were constantly upheld by men of science on both sides, without any suggestion that such action was reprehensible or derogatory to their sense of patriotism; and this good feeling is all the more remarkable because in general there was little love lost between the ordinary people of the two nations.

It is true that in 1667 Henry Oldenburg, Secretary of the Royal Society, was arrested and imprisoned in the Tower of London 'for dangerous designes and practises,' and it was supposed by Pepys that the reasons for his detention were 'for writing news to a virtuoso in France, with whom he

Pages ix–xiv of the Introduction in: Sir Gavin de Beer. *The Sciences Were Never At War*. (London: Thomas Nelson & Sons Ltd., 1960). Reprinted with the permission of the author and publisher. Sir Gavin de Beer is a Fellow of the Royal Society and a Corresponding Member of L'Academie des Sciences de l'Institut de France. He has published numerous works in zoology, embryology and the history of science.

constantly corresponds in philosophical matters.' If this had been so, then all the leading men of science for a hundred and fifty years would have deserved to be sent to the Tower or to the Bastille.

Actually, as Professor Douglas McKie[1] has shown, the probable reason for Oldenburg's arrest was that he had criticised the manner in which Charles II was conducting the war. London had just endured the Plague and the Great Fire, and the Dutch fleet had sailed up the Medway. Twenty years before the Declaration of Rights, that was clearly no time for an autocratic government to tolerate criticism; and there is nothing to suggest that Oldenburg's imprisonment was due to his imparting scientific information to his colleagues abroad. Before the institution of regular publications and scientific journals, personal correspondence was the only method whereby men of science could keep abreast of scientific progress in other countries, and this fact is reflected in the official appointment of correspondents and corresponding members by the learned societies. Oldenburg was released and no further sanctions were taken against him.

It was often with the specific approval and the direct help of ministers on both sides of the Channel that scientific publications were sent to and fro between the Royal Society and the French Academy of Sciences. In particular, astronomical tables, the results of the latest observations by the Royal Observatory at Greenwich and the Observatory in Paris were freely exchanged. It so came about that in 1804 Sir Joseph Banks sent the *Nautical Almanac* to *Citoyen* Delambre, and thereby provided France with the best instrument for accurate navigation in the year of Napoleon's threatened invasion of England, the year before the Battle of Trafalgar. In return, Banks received the French astronomical tables.

The modern concept of security was slow in developing, and it was almost apologetically that in 1760, at the height of the Seven Years War, the Duc de Choiseul wrote to Voltaire to say that he gladly gave a passport to John Craufurd of Auchenames to return from Geneva to England through France, but that he must not pass through a French naval port. The condition of the French navy was too serious for a British subject to have the chance of seeing the poverty of its establishments.

On the other hand, in response to Sir Humphry Davy's desire to visit the extinct volcanoes in Auvergne in 1813, when France's back was against the wall, Napoleon had no hesitation in granting him every facility. Not only that, but when in Paris, Davy attended meetings of the *Institut* where the latest scientific discoveries were reported, and himself performed experiments in his hotel with a portable chemical cabinet which he had been allowed to bring into France with him.

[1] D. McKie, "The arrest and imprisonment of Henry Oldenburg," *Notes and Records of the Royal Society,* vol. 6, 1949, p. 28.

If Napoleon's generosity on this as on many other occasions was re-markable, it is equally extraordinary that the British Government should have allowed Davy to go. He was the greatest living British chemist, and it must reluctantly be concluded that whereas Napoleon realised the impor-tance of science, the British Government did not. Things have changed since then, and in order to point the moral it is only necessary to remember how inconceivable it would have been for a British Government to allow Sir William Ramsay to go to Berlin in 1916, or Sir Robert Robinson in 1943.

When Edward Jenner wrote to the *Institut* saying that 'the sciences are never at war,' he was speaking a language understood and accepted on both sides of the Channel and throughout the civilised world. It was the language which inspired Benjamin Franklin to secure freedom from molestation for Captain Cook on his last voyage, should forces of the nascent United States make contact with his ships. It also inspired the British Government to grant safe-conducts to the French expeditions to the South Seas, and the French Government to give passports to Gregory Watt and Humphry Davy. It sponsored Woodville's visit to Paris to demonstrate the technique of vaccina-tion. It reflected the acceptance of the principle under which Edward Jenner was able to issue safe-conducts of no less validity than those issued by governments. The letters of Sir Joseph Banks and of the leading French scientists while the armies and navies were fighting echo the same sentiments again and again.

These letters reveal a degree of civilisation compared with which pres-ent conditions appear barbarous, but such a comparison must take into account the fact that, in several fundamental respects, the accepted stan-dards of thought and behaviour were then very different from what they have become under present conditions. In the first place, it must be remem-bered that the language of Franklin, Banks, and Jenner was spoken in an atmosphere of complete confidence in the security of European civilisation. This can be illustrated by reference to Gibbon's comparison between the conditions of his day and of those when the Roman Empire succumbed to the barbarians. Before such a fate could befall his Europe, said Gibbon, the barbarians must cease to be barbarous. That comforting reflection was equivalent to the postponement of nemesis to the Greek kalends.

The unity of European ideals and culture was such that France and Britain subscribed to identical principles of respect for truth and indepen-dence of learning. Scientists enjoyed complete freedom in their work and were above the battle.

Finally, there was the fact that war was only a specialist event, involv-ing governments and professional soldiers and sailors, but without liabilities imposed on civilians, least of all on men of science. The immunity enjoyed by medicine from the exigencies of war is well shown by the application of the Barber-Surgeons of London to the Lord Mayor in 1491 for exemption from an order to keep watch and ward. For the following information I am indebted to the late Dr. John Keevil.[2] Basing themselves on the medieval laws of arms, the Barber-Surgeons claimed to 'ben exempt and Discharged from alle offices and besynesse wherein they shuld use or bere any manner of armure or Wepyn.' They described how on battlefields 'as other places,' they had always enjoyed the same immunity as heralds, 'to stonde unharnessed and unwepened According to the lawe of Arms,' and insisted that they could not be employed in any manner 'whereby they shuld use or occupie Any Armure or defensible geere of warre,' since this would interfere with their professional duties and the exercise of their art and skill. The Lord Mayor and Aldermen approved the petition and framed an ordinance granting the Barber-Surgeons the exemption for which they asked.

Before the outbreak of war with France in 1514 the privileged status of the Fellowship of Surgeons was confirmed by Henry VIII (5 Henry VIII, c. vi). They were to be 'as Herawdes of Armes aswell in battelles and feldes as other places, ther for to stond unharnessed and unwappenned according to the law of armes, because they be persones that never used feates of warre nor ought to use but onely the besynes and exercise of their science to the helpe and comfort of the Kinges liege people in the tyme of their nede.'

It was as a revival of this tradition that Sir John Pringle succeeded in bringing about a convention according immunity to military hospitals in battle in 1743, and that the Geneva Red Cross Convention was enacted in 1864.

Since those days, the progress of science itself and the material power which it can confer on those nations most advanced in its pursuit, have resulted in science becoming involved to an increasing extent in national policy. This is a natural result of scientific progress, for even in the eighteenth century, some of the successes of the Royal Navy were in part due to the superiority and reliability of British chronometers as instruments of navigation, and of British practices of dietetics and hygiene in maintaining the health of ships' companies, just as the unexpected successes of the French revolutionary armies owed much to the chemical genius of Lavoisier in improving the effectiveness of French gunpowder.

At all events, it is now generally accepted that secrecy in scientific progress may be a necessary part of national security for survival. There is nothing more intrinsically barbarous in this than in war itself, nor is it anything new in principle. From time immemorial, trade secrets involving methods of application of science have been jealously guarded even in times of peace, and have played an ever increasing part in the development and maintenance of national prosperity in the face of international competition.

[2] City of London Archives, Letter Book L, f. 293.

There is nothing new except in degree in the suspicion which has led some very security-minded nations to invent the new crime of economic espionage expressly for guarding against this danger. When Baron Stein visited Cornwall in 1787, the most stringent orders were issued by Boulton and Watt to prevent him from inspecting the new steam engines which had just been installed.

What is sinister, however, is that in recent times some political systems have invaded the domain of science itself and distorted truth in order to control thought, on the principles which the Inquisition practised against Galileo. Thereby they have infringed the sacred freedom of science to pursue the truth wherever it may lead. When France was at war with Britain, from the point of view of the future progress and welfare of science, it would not have mattered at all which side was victorious, particularly as victory in those days did not imply total destruction, nor the imposition of dogmatic ideologies. If the consequences of the defeat of a nation now include the exposure of science to the danger of such interference for political or religious ends, the freedom of science must be defended if need be by men of science if they are to remain true to their subject. It is hardly too much to claim that in the late war it was scientific superiority which saved Britain and her allies and science itself.

The fact is that since science has achieved so vast an importance in the affairs of men, in times of national danger science now belongs to Caesar. In tracing the history of its use by nations even for the legitimate purpose of defence, the origin of the practice must paradoxically be ascribed to that great patron of science Napoleon, for he was responsible for the introduction of the principle of nationwide conscription. This began by involving only men; but enterprises, industries, and knowledge itself have now been brought under the yoke. Since the days of Napoleon, the breach and successive abandonment of conventions and restrictions, previously regarded as sacred, have accelerated the debasement of the currency of civilisation. The re-establishment of its credit cannot be achieved by further breaches of contracts by individuals. Professor A. V. Hill[3] has pointed out that the freedom with which science claims to pursue truth unmolested does not confer on anyone the right to give away other people's property, including Caesar's, either of goods or of knowledge. As the French statesman Portalis remarked, no man can aspire to become a good citizen of the world if he be not first a good citizen of his own country. Whether the past tense of the verb in the title of this book can be changed to the present is a question in which all men of science must be interested, but which they are not, by themselves, competent to solve, since its solution will depend on nothing less than the abolition not only of war but of its possibility.

[3] A. V. Hill, "The ethical dilemma of science," *Advancement of Science*, 1952, p. 1.

The Science of Science

MARIA OSSOWSKA AND STANISLAW OSSOWSKI[1]

TWO POINTS OF VIEW IN THE INVESTIGATIONS WHICH TAKE SCIENCE AS THEIR SUBJECT

For a number of years Science[2] itself has become the subject of scientific investigation, both Science in its functional sense (the whole of research activities), and in its static sense (the whole of the products of these activities, i. e. the whole of the scientific truths).[3] How vivid the interest taken in this research is, is eloquently proved by the bibliography published in vols. XIII and XIX of *Nauka Polska (Science and Letters in Poland)*.

In the first, as well as in the second sense, Science may become a subject of research in different ways. It seems, however, that two chief points of view may be established to which all investigations into the science of Science can be subordinated: the investigator is interested in Science either as a way to the knowledge of the world, or as a field of human culture. Let us call this first attitude the *epistemological point of view,* remembering, however, that we are concerned here with a wider range of problems than the one embraced by traditional epistemology. And let us call the second attitude *the anthropological point of view,* bearing in mind anthropology in that wide sense in which it is understood in the English-speaking countries (the science of man and his culture).

The distinction of these two points of view is not a division of the problems: besides problems specially connected with the cognitive functions of Science, and besides problems specially connected with that second attitude, there exist problems which may be approached from both sides. For

Reprinted with the permission of Professor Ossowska from *Organon* (Warsaw) 1936, Vol. I, pp. 1–12. By coincidence, this paper was also reprinted in *Minerva,* Autumn 1964, Vol. III, No. 1, pp. 72–82. Professor Stanislaw Ossowski, recently deceased, was one of the most distinguished and respected sociologists in Poland whose work was widely known and acclaimed all over the world. Professor Maria Ossowska, of the University of Warsaw, has achieved eminence in her own right through her contributions to sociology and philosophy.

[1] Ph. D., Lecturers at the University of Warsaw.

[2] The meaning in which we use the word "Science" with a capital has been pointed out in the Foreword.

[3] For this distinction see T. Kotarbinski: The Elements of the Theory of Knowledge, of Formal Logic, and of the Methodology of the Sciences. Lwów, Ossolineum 1927 pp 367 (in Polish).

example, the psychology of scientists may interest both those who study the connection of Science with man's creativeness and the development of culture, as well as those who study the question of a scientific cognition of the world (what qualifications he who is to discover or prove new scientific truths has to possess?).

The interest taken in cognitive functions is very old. The history of investigations of this kind goes as far back as the times of Xenophanes. The interest taken in Science as a field of human culture is something new. It was partly derived from historical research, partly called forth by the development of modern sociology, and partly by practical needs (the question of the encouragement and organization of Science). Research in this field is much younger than the science of religion, than the science of economic production, than the science of art.

Those interested in Science from the epistemological point of view treat the existing scientific works and research methods applied by scientists only as examples and as material for conceptual analyses, for classifications, for considerations of the cognitive value of various possible activities and theses. The degree of importance, attributed from this point of view to the separate cognitive activities and fields of Science, does not depend on its proper rôle in the development of human culture: the criteria of importance are established on the basis of the general postulates of the theory of knowledge and of methodology.

The theory of scientific cognition, treating its subject *sub specie aeterni,* may be in fact cultivated without a closer contact with the life of Science.

In investigations about Science, resulting from the interest taken in man and his culture, we have before us a concrete reality: the life of Science with its triumphs and errors. And though we look forward to general formulations we must study this life of Science in the fullness of historical circumstances.

PROBLEMS OF THE SCIENCE OF SCIENCE

The problems concerning Science in its manifold forms—both those already found in studies devoted to the science of Science and those which have not yet been voiced—could be grouped according to various principles. They could, for example, be divided in three groups: the one taking into consideration all problems connected with the *personality* of the creative worker in Science, the second pursuing all problems connected with the *activities* leading to the formation of Science, the third concerned with the problems relating to Science as a completed human *product.* This is one of the numerous possibilities. According to another, the same problems could be put under three other headings, analysing under the first all problems which answer the question what Science is, under the second how Science originates, and under the third—what effects it has.

While the principles of classifying the problems quoted above only as examples—must lead to the separation of problems which hitherto were usually considered jointly,[4] the grouping given below takes into account the hitherto prevailing division of labour among the scientists. According to this proposition the problems concerning Science would be grouped under five different headings, three of which would form the backbone of our new branch of science.

a. Among the first of these three fundamental groups we would propose to count all those problems which hitherto have been usually treated by philosophers and which could be called the *philosophy of Science*. Here would be placed such problems as that of the conception of Science and the numerous controversies connected with this question, as to what is still, and what is no longer Science. Here the classification of the different branches of Science would find a place. Here would be included a large group of general methodological problems: the analysis of the way of proving various kinds of statements, the analysis of the rôle of "as if" in scientific cognition,[5] analyses of such conceptions as that of scientific law, hypothesis and such like. In this group the epistemological point of view, spoken of at the beginning, would be dominant.

b. The second division of research about the science of Science could be called the *psychology of Science*. Here will belong such problems as, for example, the problem concerning the psychic development of a scientific worker, the distinguishing of certain types of investigators, the psychological analysis of various types of research activities and of various stages of scientific activity, the question of capacities necessary for the cultivation of certain branches of learning etc.

c. In the third group Science does not appear as in the first one, detached from any historical background, but against the background of social life and of the whole of cultural life in general. This division, in which the point of view, called by us anthropological, predominates, could be given the name of *the sociology of Science*.

Here will be included such problems as that of the relations between Science and other products of culture, like art or religion. Here will be voiced the dependence of the development of Science on economic conditions, on the structure of a given society, on the organization of education.

[4] So, for example, according to the first proposition the problems which we include in psychology, would be found both in the group of problems connected with the personality of the scientist and in that connected with the activities leading to the formation of Science.

[5] We refer to the book of Hans Vaihinger, translated into English by C. K. Ogden under the title "The Philosophy of 'As if.' "

Here not only the factors by which Science is influenced, but also its effects on cultural life, its influence on the economic conditions, on law, morality etc. will be examined.

One group of these problems is at present being discussed by German sociologists in the so called Wissenssoziologie.[6] These sociologists are in vigorous opposition to the widely spread treatment of the evolution of Science as if in this evolution only immanent factors played a decisive rôle.[7] Science like all other human products is in their opinion "sozialbedingt," and "the problem of knowledge being socially conditioned in its various forms" is one of the central focuses of their interests.[8] In accordance with the meaning of the word "Wissenssoziologie" their investigations do not only embrace Science. They are interested in knowledge in general. They are interested in the formation of public opinion, the arising of certain popular conceptions of life, characterising a given epoch, the shaping of certain ideologies. Related to these studies was the article by F. Znaniecki, entitled "The Subject and the Tasks of the Science of Knowledge" published in vol. IV of *Nauka Polska* (*Science and Letters in Poland,* 1923). Like the works mentioned before it had a rather programme-like character. As this is a new field of research it contains, of course, more plans than realisations.

d. In close contact with the group of sociological problems, singled out by us a moment ago, remains a large group of problems of a *practical and organizing character*. These problems have been hitherto chiefly undertaken by institutions carrying on the promotion of Science and using for certain practical ends the theoretical results of the former groups. Here belong such questions as the general problems of the organization of Science, social and state policy in relation to Science, the organization of higher institutions of learning, of research institutes and of scientific expeditions, protection of scientific workers etc. etc. These problems deserve to be singled out from the sociological group on account of their practical character and on account of the fact that in the hitherto prevailing division of labour they were allotted to somebody else.

e. Finally the fifth and the last of all the groups of problems enumerated by us, consists of *historical problems*. The history of the conception of Science, the history of the conception of the scientist, the history of the

[6] See: K. Dunkman, Die soziologische Begründung der Wissenschaft, *Arch. f. system. Philos. u. Soziologie,* XXX Bd. Hft. 1 & 2.—F. Grunwald, Das Problem der Soziologie des Wissens, Wien-Leipzig, Verl. von W. Braumüller 1934.—K. Mannheim, Wissenssoziologie, Handwörterbuch der Soziologie, A. Vierkandt 1931. F. Enke, Stuttgart.—M. Scheler, Versuche zu einer Soziologie des Wissens. München u. Leipzig 1924.—Al. v. Schelting, Zum Streit um die Wissenssoziologie, *Archiv für Sozialwissenschaft u. Sozialpolitik,* Bd. 62, Tübingen 1929.—K. A. Wittfogel, Wissen u. Gesellschaft, *Unter dem Bahnen des Marxismus.* Jahrg. V, Hft. 1.

[7] See the quoted article by Mannheim.

[8] See the quoted article by Wittfogel.

separate disciplines and of learning in general, these are materials which can be used by all the groups of problems, which have been mentioned above.

Undoubtedly these groups overlap in various ways, but perhaps there are in them fewer problems of a doubtful character than in other attempts at a classification of this diverse material. This attempt is of course only a provisional arrangement at which it would be difficult to stop. Looking at the question more closely, a further differentiation within the groups would prove indispensable, for the time being, however, we disregard this, sacrificing the accuracy of our presentation for its greater lucidity.

The set of problems proposed by us does not cover the same ground as those that have been previously classed by some under the name of science of Science. The history of German philosophy has for a long time made us familiar with the name "Wissenschaftslehre," but those who used it did so in a different sense from that in which it has been employed here.

Leaving aside Fichte who called his whole philosophical speculation by that name, this term was used in Germany chiefly to denote logic with general methodology, or logic with general methodology and the problems usually included in epistemology. In almost the same sense the term "Wissenschaftslehre" was used in the work of Bernard Bolzano, the subtitle of which explained "Versuch einer ausführlichen und grössentheils neuen Darstellung der Logik." It was logic understood in a very wide sense, with which we were later made familiar by German textbooks of the end of the XIX century and the beginning of ours.

Limiting philosophy to problems of logic, methodology and epistemology, Prof. Kotarbinski in the quoted "Elements" proposes to call philosophy the science of Science. It is clear that the territory of the science of Science, as spoken about in our article, does not correspond with the area marked out in these propositions. It is too wide an area in relation to ours, and at the same time too narrow. Only a part of the problems of logic and epistemology will go into our first division of the science of Science, while all the remaining divisions singled out by us will be in relation to that "science of Science" something new. Closer to our problems is W. Schingnitz in his article entitled "Scientiologie" (*Minerva-Zeitschrift* 1931, Hft. 5/6 and 7/8. Jahrg. 7), but his remarks, though frequently valuable, are fragmentary and do not compose a distinct whole. Problems related to those singled out by us in our psychological and sociological group, are also enumerated by E. Radl in an article entitled "Zur Philosophie der Wissenschaftsgeschichte" (*Scientia* 1933, vol. LIV, N. CCLIX-11). They are allotted by him—with which it is hard to agree—to the historian of Science. This research, according to him, should be conducted from the point of view, which we have called anthropological in the present article.

Schingnitz in the article just quoted did not only enumerate various possible types of research in the science of Science, but also proposed a name for it: he wished to include them under the term of *scientiology*. Those who wish to replace the expression "science of Science" by a one-word term sounding international, in the belief that only after receiving such a name a given group of problems becomes officially dubbed an autonomous discipline, could be reminded of the name *mathesiology,* proposed long ago for similar purposes.[9] This term might satisfy those purists who in the term "scientiology" may feel offended by its combined Latin and Greek origin.

QUESTION OF THE AUTONOMY OF THE SCIENCE OF SCIENCE

The conception of a new branch of science usually becomes finally crystallized only when this discipline has gained admission to the university curricula. Before this takes place it has to overcome the doubts as to whether there are sufficient reasons to recognize in it a separate, autonomous branch. These doubts were raised also in relation to the "science of Science."

From the theoretical point of view this is an insignificant matter. To a large extent it is a matter of convention whether we shall recognize a certain system of problems as a separate branch of learning, or whether we shall subordinate it to a more general science or assign it to several various branches. But as certain practical consequences are involved here, we shall for a moment consider whether in relation to the science of Science there are more reasons for such doubts than in other fields.

Against the autonomy of the science of Science the argument is raised that its problems already have their places in other formerly separated fields (psychology, sociology, logic with methodology, the theories of the separate sciences) ; the science of Science would be therefore a discipline without any such problems which would be peculiar to itself. Let us, however, consider that the areas of the separate sciences are not in general marked out like political or administrative territories; within their confines condominia cannot be avoided. These condominia are usually widest in the recently separated branches of learning, because usually, before a new discipline can emerge, the problems which are to form its foundation already exist, but up till now have been assigned to other divisions. Therefore it seems quite natural, that in the first stages of the history of a new science the whole repertory of its problems can be taken from other fields. It is only in the course of time, when we have already become sufficiently familiar with the

[9] This term was proposed by Ampère (see Eisler's Dictionary, article "Wissenschaftslehre").

new frames, and when from the borrowed problems new ones arise, that we begin to treat the problems of the new branch as peculiar to itself. What matters, is whether these various problems possess a sufficient internal unity.

This very internal unity of the science of Science was also frequently questioned. The scope of research in "science of Science" comprises investigations concerning widely different subjects; in some cases these will be into psychic phenomena, from which scientific works arise, or into the physiological conditions of scientific creativeness; then again certain social institutions are the subject of research, and still again the relations between scientific assertions, or between scientific assertions and reality etc. These various problems are solved by various methods. But also in this respect the science of Science is in a similar position to many officially recognized disciplines. A complete uniformity of subject and a uniformity of methods can probably be found only in the aprioristic sciences. The link between the problems of one branch of science does not necessarily consist of the unity of methods and points of view. Such a link can be formed by the subject which is the centre of interest; and this certainly does not mean that this subject should be the only subject of research of the given branch; we are also right in speaking of the unity of a subject when heterogeneous objects are being investigated, so long as they are objects of research on account of their connections with that common centre of interest. Let us take general linguistics as an example. The student of general linguistics is concerned with psychic as well as with acoustic and physiological phenomena and also with the field of meanings. He is concerned both with the processes which take place in the mind and body of the speaker, hearer and reader, and with morphological and semasiological changes in the history of language, with the mutual interdependence of different languages and the peculiarities of various dialects of the same language. He applies extrospection as well as introspection, historical methods as well as those used by natural science. But the autonomy of general linguistics is never questioned, because all heterogeneous subjects which come into the scope of linguistic research remain in definite relations to *human speech* and therefore interest the student of linguistics.

The case is the same with the science of Science. Here Science is the centre of interest (it doesn't matter, whether we have in mind Science as a product, or as certain activities). All other never entering the scope of research in science of Science remain in this or that relation to Science, and it is for this very reason that they are here the subject of research.

Another argument advanced against the autonomy of the science of Science, is the lack, not so much of objective, as of personal unity. We have here in mind the doubt whether one man may successfully carry on research so manifold and requiring such a manysided preparation; can there exist a specialist of the science of Science, a specialist who would have to be experienced in general methodology, to be familiar with the achievements of psychology, theory and history of culture etc.?

If we wish to decide whether these doubts hit at the autonomy of the science of Science, we can again refer to the above mentioned science of linguistics. The qualifications required to investigate thoroughly a given language are extremely manifold: phonetics, semantics or dialectology of a language are fields of research requiring a very diverse preparation. And what shall we say of one who wishes to become a specialist in general linguistics, where, besides the preparation in logic and psychology, besides historical and ethnological knowledge, it is indispensable to possess a knowledge of various languages which would make comparative studies possible.

The decision whether a certain group of problems can form a separate discipline, is not in fact dependent on whether one person is able to embrace all these problems. The scientific unities singled out in the traditional division of labour continue to live as unities, though, due to their growth, they have become impossible for a single individual to master. Such a principle of grouping the problems would take into account extremely casual factors: what one individual is able to master today, may be impossible for one to-morrow.

The contemporary life of Science makes us more and more familiar with group research, which, though it is done collectively, does not violate the unity of the discipline to which it is alloted. Such research is forced upon us especially where the same subject is to be investigated from various points of view i. e. in situations in which our science of Science is found. Its future will have to be entrusted to groups of people rather than to individuals.

Apart from this whole discussion we think that the legitimization of a new science should be brought about not by aprioristic considerations but by empirical ones. Only the pragmatic point of view should be decisive: is the given group of problems sufficiently vital for its importance to be emphasized by giving it a separate name? are there any concrete didactical considerations in its favour? have we any reason to expect fruitful consequences by grouping these problems in a common separate frame?

For if the question of the singling out of a certain group of problems into a separate discipline be insignificant from the theoretical point of view, it is not so from the practical one. A new grouping of problems lends additional importance to the original problems and gives rise to new ones and new ideas. The new grouping marks out the direction of new investigations; moreover, it may exercise an influence on university studies, the foundation of chairs, periodicals and societies.

ACTUALITY OF THE SCIENCE OF SCIENCE

Studies in culture, classed under the name of social or cultural anthropology are in general not concerned with Science in the present sense of this term, because Science in this sense is not a component of all the heterogeneous cultures with which the student of anthropology or ethnology is concerned. Almost every culture is characterized by some religion, some magic, art, technology, morals, but Science in the perspective of time and space is a rather exceptional phenomenon. It plays, however, an extremely important rôle in one culture which is of special importance for us: in modern European culture.

The majority of contemporary sociologists think that it is owing to Science that modern culture is a completely new type in history, quite incomparable with all pre-scientific cultures. It has no more than three centuries behind it, and the gulf which divides it from all former cultures grows with every year as the influence of Science on all spheres of life becomes more powerful.

The history of Science goes back, of course, to earlier times. Certain characteristic features of our "scientific culture" had already had their precedents in history, be it in the Hellenistic or the Chinese or even the medieval cultures. There is, however, something entirely new in this uninterrupted development of Science in the course of the last three centuries.

The realization of this fact will facilitate the proper appreciation of the science of Science. Therefore without entering upon an analysis of the conception "scientific culture" or "culture based on Science" it may be worth while to glance at some of its features which are most significant and which have been much written about in publications of recent years.

1. Pre-scientific cultures had to be stable in their foundations. Whatever had claims to complete stabilization met in them with highest approval. When, for example, religion was changed, it was either done in such a way that nobody distinctly realized it (slow transformation of religious tradition) or by means of a revolution when, instead of one "unchangeable" religion there was introduced another religion with claims to the same unchangeability. On the contrary, modern scientific culture is not only in a stage of constant changes, but this dynamic quality is accepted as a postulate by those who create it.

2. An equally new feature of the scientific culture is its universality. There is only one scientific culture, absorbing all scientific achievements, wherever and by whomever they are attained. There are no competing scientific cultures, there are no competing sciences as there are competing religions or codes of law. All incongruity between various scientific theories is considered a provisional stage which has to be overcome in this or that

direction. Our culture becomes also universal in the geographical sense: it has encircled the globe from pole to pole, on the waves of the wireless it penetrates the widest thickets of the jungle, it reaches the most isolated islands of the Pacific.

3. Modern culture enables man in an ever growing degree to transform his environment according to his own aims instead of adjusting himself to it. In relation to former cultures this is a rather quantitative difference, but in such a powerful degree, that it is impossible not to see in it a qualitative difference as well. Not limiting itself to ruling over an extrahuman environment, Science endeavours to assume control over human instincts, over social and economic forces. In the last few decades scientific plans have been forming for the organization of human life on a world scale. This was unknown to any pre-scientific culture.

4. Changes in the conception of life, caused by modern Science, are incomparably more far-reaching than the changes occurring at the transition from one pre-scientific culture into another. We have in mind here not only changes, directly called forth by certain new scientific discoveries, as, for example, the widening of the limits of time and space due to astronomical and geological discoveries, or the change of man's position in the world of living creatures, brought about by the discoveries of biology. Here are also involved certain general tendencies of thought. On the one hand the dynamic conception of human culture, which has been already mentioned, and on the other, rationalism. On the basis of scientific culture a conflict has arisen between Science and the spheres of culture which have survived from the pre-scientific era. This conflict is presented in various ways: intellect and subconsciousness, rationalism and the traditional mental habits, Science and Religion. The future will show whether this conflict is only something transitional, or whether it will be a permanent characteristic of our new type of culture.

Scientific culture is only in a stage of formation. The speed of its development is growing, but its most characteristic features have not yet been wholly attained. At any rate the changes, brought about by Science in social life and in human minds, suffice to lead us to the belief that the science of Science will have to occupy a special place in the rank of the sciences of man and his products. It was brought into existence not only by new interests, but above all by the *new reality*. As the discovery of electricity brought with it the creation of new divisions of physics, so the development of Science in modern society will bring about the rise of the science of Science.

PRACTICAL APPLICATION OF THE SCIENCE OF SCIENCE

Besides theoretical interests in Science, and besides its more and more powerful influence on the whole system of human life, *practical needs* also come into play. The growth of Science requires an extremely wide and many-sided supplementary apparatus and the building of this apparatus requires theoretical studies. Practical needs, as we have mentioned, played an important rôle in the genesis of the science of Science (cf. preface to the present volume and the table of contents of the 20 volumes of *Nauka Polska*).

The practical applications of science of Science do not require an explanation; the organization of scientific work, individual and collective, the organization of institutions, the protection of Science by the state and by social organizations, the education of the scientist, all this—if it is to be fruitful—cannot to-day do without studies just as specialized and complicated as those which are required for the construction of large industrial establishments.

But the investigations of which we speak play yet another rôle, though not such a conspicuous and direct one: teaching what Science is, contributing to form in the minds of scientific workers this or that conception of Science, they at the same time influence their further creativeness; for Science, like all other fields of culture, is a part of that particular sphere of reality whose history depends on what we think of it.

Science and Society

D. S. L. CARDWELL

The nature of natural science is frequently discussed by philosophers and their conclusions are usually given in terms of methodology and epistemology. They are concerned, that is, with the methods which the scientist uses to obtain his results and with the status and significance of the theories and concepts of science in the scheme of rational knowledge. While such investigations are of the greatest importance, especially in view of the specialisation characteristic of modern science, they do not, of themselves, exhaust the question; for science, the development of knowledge and thought, is essentially a social phenomenon. [1] From asking the question "What is science?" it is a short and natural step to ask "How did it arise?" or "Under what circumstances can we expect it to be actively pursued?" and it is at once apparent that, since scientists are not logical machines operating independently of their environment, these questions involve social factors. Indeed, we can say without further consideration that science is a variable of society and a very complicated one too; for, while many different societies have evolved advanced systems of law and philosophy and refined forms of art, only one society—our own—has possessed those vital elements which made possible the systematic and widespread development of the advanced sciences, and has succeeded, moreover, in utilising science in the solution of problems in industry and the arts.

The grandchild of ancient learning, this unique method of interrogating and interpreting nature, was born during the intellectual ferments of the Middle Ages and, aided by initial contributions from the Arabs and Indians, advanced slowly and painfully to the time when the masterly Galileo set the pattern for its full development. During and after this period it was in intimate relationship with the current philosophical and religious ideas, with the advance of technology and with the practices of the fine arts and medicine; drawing its inspirations and conceptions quite impartially

Chapter I, pp. 1–9 in: *The Organisation of Science in England: A Retrospect.* London: William Heinemann, Ltd., 1957. Reprinted with the permission of the author and publisher. Dr. D. S. L. Cardwell is a Reader in the History of Science and Technology at the Manchester College of Science and Technology where he continues his research on the development of scientific research in the universities in relation to the changing nature of science and society.

from all these distinct activities and, in return, making its contributions, material and intellectual, to the development of society. To elaborate this theme would be, in itself, to attempt a work of major scholarship; but one point can, I think, be made: to talk of the "impact of science on society" is surely to oversimplify the issue. Science is not an alien, external force like famine, pestilence or conquest; it is a characteristic of our society. It is made by men in that society and the relationship between their work and the social whole is both subtle and complex.

In the most general terms we can presume that the successful prosecution of science depends upon a number of "internal" factors, the chief among which are: the cultural heritage of abstract knowledge and practical techniques, the free circulation of ideas and constructive criticism, freedom of research, the adequate endowment of research and the state of the ancillary educational machinery. We should, therefore, expect to find that at all times, past and present, the predominantly important social institutions will play their parts in determining the conditions of the "internal" factors and hence the level of scientific activity. In particular, religious and philosophical ideas and economic and political institutions may all have a bearing on science although their effects will not, of course, be uniform and of equal importance in different periods. Also we may expect to find that the state of science will be correlated with the social institutions of different peoples at different stages of development. But here a peculiarity of science should be noticed: it is, of all human activities, the most truly international, for it is only in a trivial sense that we can speak of "English science." *Per contra,* when we speak of "English law," "French literature," "Italian art," etc. we may well be noting, indeed emphasising, significant differences from the practices of other countries and peoples. But the language in which a scientific memoir is written is of no importance—it loses nothing in translation. Therefore, to a greater extent than in the cases of other intellectual activities, the scientific achievements of any one country are a function of those of its neighbours. While this view rejects scientific chauvinism of the type: "Chemistry is a French science. It was created by Lavoisier ..." (Würtz), it does not prevent a reasoned use of comparative methods.

Science, then, is a European endeavour and any claim by one people, or nation, to pre-eminence or to be the founders of any particular science cannot be accepted. This odyssey of the European mind has survived the difficulties and dangers of the profound social, political and religious changes of the last four centuries. On the other hand, although we have a most inadequate understanding of the factors which favour the development of science in a given society, it does not seem overbold to maintain that, had the terms of trade changed against science at any time during that period, the scientific enterprise would have been snuffed out as effectually and finally as the Divine Right of Kings or the Rule of the Saints.

If these preliminary generalisations are accepted, as I think they must be, we are faced with the question as to which is the most profitable way of studying the social aspects of science. Here, the field is so wide and the possibilities so varied that choice is almost entirely a personal matter—the relations between scientific achievement, in the material sense, and scientific thought, in the philosophical, with other leading social activities are so profound and many-sided. However, it is reasonable to argue that as science is made by men in society the best way is to begin, continue and end with that group of men who practise science, and to try to elucidate those factors which have either advanced or retarded their work. This seems to me preferable to attempting to study the variation of scientific activity with economic changes or with the development of philosophical ideas, for until we have some clear idea as to what the scientist is, as a man in society rather than as an impersonal producer of information, such studies may lead to unwarranted correlations.

A BRIEF CONSIDERATION OF SOME THEORIES

To expand this point of view and, at the same time, to illustrate the difficulties of the theme, I should like briefly to consider certain theories put forward to account for the varying levels of scientific activity at different times and in different societies.

In his stimulating little volumes on Greek science, Professor Farrington arrives at the conclusion that ancient science perished through the social consequences of slavery which, by degrading labour and technics, necessarily cut science off from one of its most important sources of inspiration. It should be remembered, however, that the theory is not original. For example, as long ago as 1867 it was explicitly propounded by Justus von Liebig [2] and, in 1870, Lyon Playfair, referring to Greek science, remarked: "A citizen with slaves crushed invention lest it should interfere with their value on the market. . . ." [3] A popular writer of the same period, Winwood Reade, made much the same observation in his celebrated *Martyrdom of Man* (pp. 404–5). To put the opposite point of view: the theory has recently been criticised by Bernard Barber on the grounds that Greek science had a long career in an epoch when slavery was always a dominant social institution, [4] and another modern writer doubts whether "even in Classical antiquity the separation of technics and science was as complete as has sometimes been supposed." [5] It is quite sufficient, in this context, to do no more than mention the great civil engineering achievements of the Romans to see the force of these arguments.

Although it does not strain credulity to believe that a society which chose to regard many of its members as "living tools" could not have provided a healthy stimulus for technical innovation and invention, and might well have inhibited the development of science (apart from prestige occupations like mathematics and astronomy), it would surely be unreasonable to suppose that the institution of slavery is alone sufficient to account for the decline of ancient science. But if we suspect that a unicausal theory is an oversimplification, if we admit that other factors may well have been effective in determining the level of scientific activity, we must at once concede that the reverse proposition is, at least, feasible: that inability to forward science and scientific technology contributed to the protracted existence of the obnoxious and inhibiting social institution of slavery.

Among the additional factors which we presumed might govern the development of science were the leading religious, philosophical and cosmological beliefs current in society. This would suggest that it was no accident that the rebirth of science, together with the recovery of ancient learning in the twelfth century, occurred at a period of history well characterised as the Age of Faith. The significance of this coincidence has been commented on by Whitehead who, in a famous passage, relates the rebirth of science to Medieval insistence on a rational Deity and on a correlative rational Creation; it being argued that, without prior conviction that the universe is rationally ordered and susceptible, therefore, of rational interpretation, the scientist would never commence laborious and difficult researches. Against this theory Professor Dingle has maintained that the scientist does not assume a rational order; he sets out to determine whether, and to what extent, he can discover rational relationships between phenomena. This, it may be said, does not dispose of the argument that, although the scientist may be agnostic in metaphysical matters, his general inspiration comes from the seed-bed of ideas—the cosmological theories—of his time. But those who hold this latter view must then account for Professor Ginsberg's point that, *a priori,* it seems probable that the Buddhist metaphysic is more "scientific" than the Christian. [6]

On the other hand the universal acceptance of Christianity in Europe implied—from the scientific point of view—more than an adjustment of philosophies; it meant the emergence of entirely new social organisations. The Graeco-Roman world had been widely tolerant of different religions and different philosophies: ranging from the "scientific" determinism of the atomists to various kinds of mysticism. Under these conditions it is very difficult to see how such institutions as universities could come into being, for these imply some generally accepted corpus of philosophical knowledge which it is their duty to augment and to transmit to following generations. As opposed to schools of favoured philosophers (as, e.g. at Alexandria) the development of universities seems to be an almost exclusively European achievement. The learned monastic orders, Franciscans and Dominicans, the open universities—"Cosmopolite Corporations" as Sir William Hamilton called them—with their Regent Doctors, Masters of Arts and the scholars wandering from teacher to teacher, from university to university, were all conspicuous features of the Medieval scene. Couple these with a developing technology and you have a powerful fertilising influence irrespective of the inner content of the religion and the associated metaphysic.

Another study of the relationship between religion and science, this time in seventeenth-century England, forms part of a very interesting paper by R. K. Merton. [7] Following a suggestion of Max Weber's, Merton examines in great detail the connexions between Puritanism and science; and, after careful analysis reaches the conclusion that the Calvinist cosmology coupled with the characteristic "ethic" as expounded in sermons and religious writings provided strong stimuli for the development of science. This, he claims, is validated by the very large number of Puritans active in seventeenth-century science and associated with such enterprises as the foundation of the Royal Society. It is important to notice that Merton does not maintain that religion is the independent and science the dependent variable; nor does he suggest that a set of religious beliefs is sufficient to account for the emergence of great scientists, the Newtons and Boyles of this world. On the contrary, he says quite explicitly that the relationship between religion and science was one of reciprocal reaction.

Perhaps this very interesting theory can be summed up by saying that Calvinism induced a serious frame of mind and set a high value on diligent studies, while, at the same time, it commended natural philosophy, the study of the physical world, the work of the Creator, to the attention of the student. Calvinism, therefore, provides strong grounds, psychological, metaphysical and social for the pursuit of science. To this it should be added that the theory is, of course, of limited application; the role of Calvinism in inspiring scientific work should not be generalised. Scientific academies, which are, after all, indices of public interest in science, were founded in many countries: Lutheran, Catholic and Calvinist, contemporaneously with the Royal Society; and the magnificent French achievements in science in the seventeenth and eighteenth centuries owed little to Calvinism.

On the need for further comparative studies of religion and science, Merton refers to the suggestion that Protestantism is generally more favourable towards science than is Catholicism. In support of this, Protestant Scotland, with her long line of famous scientists, is compared with Catholic Ireland who, Anglo-Irishmen apart, can claim only one: John Tyndall. However, this generalisation seems unfair to Ireland's turbulent history, and the Irishman may be tempted to return a *tu quoque* in that Calvinist Wales has yet to produce a world famous scientist. If the histrionic arts, quoted as commonly repugnant to Calvinists, are characteristic of the Irish, do not the Welsh also possess a great measure of these gifts? It may be inferred that, in these cases, factors other than religious ones operated to determine the course of intellectual development.

Other social institutions: industry and commerce have clearly influenced the rise of science. The relationships between mining and the metallurgical arts on the one hand, and mechanics and chemistry on the other, are obvious *a priori*, and are abundantly confirmed by the facts of history. The industrial and economic factors in the growth of science, indeed the industrial origins of science and the correlative importance of the artisan and technician in contributing to scientific progress, were repeatedly stressed by Victorian writers like Whewell, Playfair, Lockyer and others. That theories of the social motivation of science[1] should become widespread in a utilitarian age is not, perhaps, surprising; especially in a society becoming increasingly aware of the industrial and social importance of science and, at the same time, moving towards the liberal democratic state. Accordingly, Playfair was voicing a fairly general opinion when, eighty-five years ago, he asserted that the springs of action in science were located in the industrious classes, while, on the other hand, an aristocratic society was not—and never had been—one which would be favourable for the advance of science.

There is some danger that theories of this nature become unduly extrapolated and the advance of science reduced to the status of a dependent variable of what are alleged to be large-scale social or economic movements. In these cases science is regarded largely, or entirely, from a utilitarian point of view; it is held to be the "cutting edge" of engineering and technology and, as such, entirely subordinate to, and dependent on, social needs. In brief, it is said that science is no more than the means to the end of extending mastery over nature. Sometimes a moral imperative is added: Comte, it will be remembered, applied the test of fecundity to science and would, as a result, have prohibited such "useless" studies as astrophysics. But criteria of this kind cannot be used: on what conceivable grounds can we justify the assumption that a science which is "useless" today will be equally "useless" tomorrow? Is it not possible that it might prove to be of the greatest practical benefit? Science deals with the at-present unknown; how can current "social needs" determine which of a number of unknowns will prove of the greatest fruitfulness in the future?

With regard to theories of the social determination of science, let us consider, for example, a proposition of the kind that the advance of science, either generally or during certain historical periods, can be understood in terms of the economic and technical requirements of certain social classes.

---

[1] Theories of this nature can be traced back to the Middle Ages.

If major scientific developments take place in response to socio-economic needs, then, *ex hypothesi,* an examination of the history of science should reveal a pattern of development of the various sciences which can be interpreted accurately by reference to the economic history of the appropriate social classes. Now even if we grant for the sake of argument that such parallels can, in fact, be found, before the interpretation can be valid it is necessary to prove that the problems in every science, at any given time, are all equally capable of solution, requiring only a "biassed" social stimulus for one group of problems, rather than another, to be solved. (In other words: we must be quite sure that the agent governing scientific development is the external, social, one. Specifically this means that you must prove that, in the seventeenth century for example, chemical, biological, geological etc., revolutions were all possible, equally with the Newtonian revolution, and could, therefore, have taken place had the appropriate social stimulus occurred.) It is, however, impossible to see how this proposition can be proved: yet without it we cannot even begin to justify the above interpretation, and the theory falls to the ground. And, for that matter, any theory which would explain the advances of science in terms of generalised social institutions must either fail, or be tautological, despite the plausibility with which correlations of this kind can sometimes be established. In fact, we do not usually require theoretical analysis in order to refute such theories; we find, for example, that the doctrine of utility breaks down when we attempt to apply it to such important sciences as electricity and sidereal astronomy, both of which were pursued with zeal and ability for several hundred years while remaining of little or no practical use at all. To take another, and very familiar, example, it has been said that the expansion of sea-borne trade was the great incentive to that work which culminated in Newton's *Principia.* An incentive no doubt it was, but it is very far from clear just what interests Copernicus, Kepler, Descartes and Galileo had in maritime affairs, nor, indeed, what common economic motive can be detected in their works.[2]

The great advances in mathematics, mechanics and astronomy from the time of Copernicus onwards owed much to fruitful cross-fertilisation between these sciences as well as to certain technical innovations such as the invention and development of the telescope. The process of discovery and inference culminated in the realisation that the solar system could be regarded as a working physical model, the details and movements of which could be accurately described. What was required was an interpretation and this Newton was able to provide. On the other hand the non-Newtonian sciences, while not without many devotees of genius, were not able to make

[2] Sir G. N. Clarke deals very judiciously with this aspect in his *Science and Social Welfare in the Age of Newton.*

such revolutionary progress: in chemistry, biology etc., the phenomena were complex and there did not exist any form of "working model." The great correlations in these sciences were yet to come.

This brief argument suggests that, apart from those social institutions which, at different times, provide mental and material incentives for the pursuit of science, two further factors governed scientific development. These were, firstly, the existing structure of knowledge together with what may be called the "inherent opportunities" of the situation and, secondly, the quite unpredictable emergence of men of genius and their response, in terms of rational creative thought, to the opportunities presented.

While these, and possibly other, factors determined the level of scientific activity there was virtually no formal organisation of science: there were no structures of authority and subordination, no limitations of function, no professional associations etc. Science was conducted by amateurs and even research of admitted national importance was left to individual goodwill: John Flamsteed, the first Astronomer Royal, had to equip the observatory at his own expense.

Even the universities, the patrons of learning, failed to achieve any notable organisation of science. In the early years university education was based on the study of the seven liberal arts followed, after graduation, by continued study in the great faculties of Divinity, Law and Medicine. The liberal arts and one of the professional faculties were, judged by contemporary standards, of a scientific nature; a fact reflected in the men of science to be found at medieval universities: early Oxford had a famous school of astronomers besides individual pioneers like Robert Grosseteste and Roger Bacon. Unfortunately these institutions did not prove sufficiently adaptable and, in later years, rigidity crept in; studies became formal, philosophies dogmatic and unalterable. The reaction, when it came, took the form of a protest by the humanists against what had become the dry pedantry of the scholastics and the reform, which the humanists achieved, was the incorporation of the study of classical literature in the arts faculty. This form of liberal education became increasingly important in the universities and professional training was gradually abandoned to such extra-mural colleges as the Inns of Court.

The decline of endowment of educational foundations during the seventeenth and eighteenth centuries coupled with the triumph of Aristotelean educational theory at the universities indicates that university education was becoming increasingly the prerogative of the upper classes: a literary education is an upper class education. This was hardly a favourable conjunction for university science.

During the years of decline, therefore, the brilliant assembly of scientists at the universities over the period of the Newtonian revolution stand out as a defiance of circumstance. They did not mark the beginning of the modern universities, conceived as centres of research and active scholarship; rather they represented the last and greatest efflorescence of the Medieval Schools. (Was it not symbolic that Newton himself entered college as a Sizar: as a "poor scholar"?)

REFERENCES

[*1*] L. T. Hobhouse, "Evolution and Progress," *Social Evolution.*
[*2*] J. von Liebig, *The Development of Science among the Nations,* 1867.
[*3*] Lyon Playfair, "The Inosculation of the Arts and Sciences." Address at Birmingham, 29th September, 1870.
[*4*] B. Barber, *Science and the Social Order,* 1953.
[*5*] A. C. Crombie, *From Augustine to Galileo: The History of Science A.D. 400–1650,* p. 143.
[*6*] M. Ginsberg, "The Scope of Sociology," *Studies in Sociology.*
[*7*] R. K. Merton, "Science, Technology and Society in 17th Century England," *Osiris,* Vol. 4, 1938, pp. 360–632. Also Max Weber, *The Protestant Ethic and the Spirit of Capitalism,* Chap. 4, note 145, p. 249.

Scientific Productivity and Academic Organization in Nineteenth Century Medicine

JOSEPH BEN-DAVID

The purpose of this paper is to describe and explain differences as well as fluctuations in the productivity of the medical sciences in Germany, France, Britain, and the United States, from 1800 to about the time of World War I. Scientific productivity as defined here does not comprise any evaluation of the greatness or depth of various scientific ideas, or of the "efficiency" of scientific production as measured by some input-output ratio. It refers only to two gross quantities: the number of scientific discoveries (including scientifically important technical inventions), and the numbers of people making such discoveries. Provided that these numbers are not a fixed proportion of the general population or some other general quantity, they are a measure of the active interest in science existing in a society at a certain point of time.

The two suggested indexes of productivity—the numbers of discoveries and of discoverers—have not precisely the same meaning and there are obvious objections to both. It can be argued that since scientific discoveries are disparate units of unequal significance, it is meaningless to count them.[1]

Reprinted from the *American Sociological Review,* Vol. XXV, No. 6, December 1960, pp. 828–843, with the permission of the author and the American Sociological Association. Dr. Joseph Ben-David is in the Department of Sociology of the Eliezer Kaplan School of Economics and Social Sciences of the Hebrew University in Jerusalem. He was a Visiting Professor of Sociology at the University of California, Berkeley, in 1964–65.

A preliminary draft of this paper was written while the author was a fellow at the Center for Advanced Study in the Behavioral Sciences, Stanford, California, in 1957–58. He is indebted to Harry Alpert, S. N. Eisenstadt, Jacob Katz, Morris Janowitz, Robert K. Merton, D. Patinkin, Dr. George G. Reader, and the late Dr. J. Seide for comments on the manuscript or discussion of its subject matter, and to A. Zloczower for his help with the research.

[1] The method is applied and discussed by T. J. Rainoff, "Wave-like Fluctuations of Creative Productivity in the Development of West-European Physics in the Eighteenth and Nineteenth Centuries." *Isis,* 12 (1929), pp. 291–292. See also S. C. Gilfillan, *The Sociology of Invention,* Chicago: Follet, 1935, pp. 29–32; Joseph Schneider, "The Cultural Situation as a Condition for the Achievement of Fame," *American Sociological Review,* 2 (August, 1937), pp. 480–491; Frank R. Cowell, *History, Civilization and Culture: An Introduction to the Historical and Social Philosophy of Pitirim A. Sorokin,* London: Black, 1952, pp. 90–106; and especially the

The first part of the claim is true, but not the deduction from it. It has been shown time and again that "great" discoveries had been preceded by intensive activity manifested in numerous "small" discoveries, often leading to the simultaneous finding of the final solution by more than one person.[2] Similarly, one of the signs of a great discovery is that it leads to a greater number of smaller discoveries based on the newly discovered principle.[3] Therefore, viewing science as a flow of constant activity, great discoveries appear as waves built up gradually by the ant-like work of predecessors, leading first to an upsurge of activity by followers and disciples and then diminishing into routine when the potentialities of the great idea have been (or seem to be) exhausted. Thus there is no need to weight the individual discoveries. The weighting is done automatically by the clustering of discoveries around the significant event. This is not to deny that there are lone discoveries, neither expected beforehand nor understood after they are made. For the historian who sits in judgment of individual greatness and stupidity, these are important events that prove the absurdity of our method of counting. But if one's purpose is to gauge the extent to which various social systems induce people to scientific productivity, then the relatively negligible weight accorded to the lone discovery is a good index of the relative lack of inducement to engage in research in that society.

The use of the number of discoverers (not students or graduates) as an index of scientific activity can be justified by similar reasoning. Such men as Newton, Lavoisier, and Einstein did not spring up in scientific deserts but in environments of intensive scientific interest, and their work inspired disciples and followers. So we can expect a general correspondence between this index and the previous one. Yet, there are numerous problems involved in the use of this index. In principle, the same numbers of discoveries can be made by quite different numbers of people, so that there may be no relationship between the two counts. In fact, however, the variation is quite limited, because the accomplishment of even a single scientific discovery demands as a rule considerable investment of time and training: one can assume that discoveries will be made by persons with special characteristics ("discoverers") and not randomly either by them or others. Thus we take this figure too as a good index of the social inducement to engage in research. No more than general correspondence between the two sets of data is expected, however, because, first, there may be variations due to institutional circumstances in the length of the creative period of discoverers, and in the chances of "outsiders" for making discoveries; and, second, even if these

---

methodological comments of Robert K. Merton, "Fluctuations in the Rate of Industrial Invention," *The Quarterly Journal of Economics,* 59 (May, 1935), p. 456.

[2] *Cf.* William F. Ogburn, *Social Change,* New York: Huebsch, 1922, pp. 90–122; Bernhard J. Stern, *Society and Medical Progress,* Princeton: Princeton University Press, 1941, pp. 41–44.

[3] Merton, *op. cit.,* pp. 464–465.

things were constant, the shape of the two curves would still differ because each discovery is a single event counted only once, at the time of its occurrence, while discoverers must be counted over a period of time or at an arbitrarily fixed point of time (such as their age at the beginning of the professional career). For these reasons we expect this second index to correspond with the first only in registering relatively long-term and gross changes. But in such details as the exact time of the changes and short-term fluctuations no correspondence between the two indices can be expected.

A second problem requiring preliminary clarification is the definition of medical sciences. We have adopted the criteria of our sources, which include discoveries that eventually became part of the medical tradition. Undoubtedly this implies the inclusion of some non-medical discoveries and discoverers; therefore, from the viewpoint of the history of scientific ideas, this may not be too meaningful a category. However, in a study of scientific activity one needs data reflecting activity in more or less homogeneous institutional frameworks, irrespective of whether they do or do not relate to a logically coherent system of ideas. On this score, medicine in the nineteenth century seems to be a good choice. Through most of the century it was closely interwoven with the natural sciences. It had been the first profession based on the study of natural sciences, and medical faculties were the first university departments to teach them. For many years the only large-scale and permanent organizations where research was systematically conducted were the teaching hospitals. Also, the art of the apothecary and the science of chemistry were often connected until the early nineteenth century. Thus the sciences associated with medicine have formed a complex of scientific activity which has been related to well defined social structures since the eighteenth century, whereas most of the basic sciences were the professional concern of only a few individuals in any country well into the second half of the nineteenth century. The medical sciences, therefore, appear to be well suited for discerning the effect of structural changes upon scientific creativity during the period under consideration.

THE QUESTIONS TO BE EXPLAINED

Table 1 is based on a count of medical discoveries made in the countries here surveyed from 1800 to 1926, according to a "Chronology of Medicine and Public Hygiene." [4] The data reveal two different trends.

First, between 1810 and 1819 a rise in the number of discoveries in France and Britain begins, followed in Germany in the next decade. By 1840, the rise has passed its peak in France and Britain and a decline sets in lasting until the 1870s. Second, an upsurge starts simultaneously in all

---

[4] Published in F. H. Garrison, *An Introduction to the History of Medicine,* 4th edition, Philadelphia and London: Saunders, 1929.

TABLE 1.
Number of Discoveries in the Medical Sciences by Nations, 1800–1926

Year	U.S.A.	England	France	Germany	Other	Unknown	Total
1800–09	2	8	9	5	2	1	27
1810–19	3	14	19	6	2	3	47
1820–29	1	12	26	12	5	1	57
1830–39	4	20	18	25	3	1	71
1840–49	6	14	13	28	7	—	68
1850–59	7	12	11	32	4	3	69
1860–69	5	5	10	33	7	2	62
1870–79	5	7	7	37	6	1	63
1880–89	18	12	19	74	19	5	147
1890–99	26	13	18	44	24	11	136
1900–09	28	18	13	61	20	8	148
1910–19	40	13	8	20	11	7	99
1920–26	27	3	3	7	2	2	44

Source: see footnote 4.

these three nations and in the United States in 1880. These parallel movements reflect the story of the convergence of chemical, anatomical, physiological, and pathological discoveries in the first half of the nineteenth century, and the spate of bacteriological and surgical innovations which followed the work of Pasteur, Lister, and Koch in the last quarter of the century. Both waves show only that certain fruitful ideas had been simultaneously, or nearly simultaneously, exploited in Western European countries beginning from the early nineteenth century, and in the United States as well from the end of the century. Apart from indicating that scientific communication among these countries was well established by that time and that therefore the phenomena reflect the course of scientific ideas, they call for no sociological explanation. What needs to be explained is the conspicuous change in the relative shares of the countries during this period. French supremacy in the beginning of the century with Britain a close second gave way to an overwhelming preponderance of German discoveries through the second half of the last century. The American share was rapidly increasing from the 1880s and became the largest by 1910–1919. Since this was the time of World War I, comparison with the European countries may seem of doubtful validity; but the relative decline of the European countries started prior to the war and lasted well into the twenties, so that it should not be attributed entirely to the war. Figure 1 shows the proportion of the total discoveries made in each nation during each period as a proportion of the country's relative share over the whole period

$$\left(y = 100 \; \frac{\text{country's share in decade } (\%)}{\text{country's share over whole period } (\%)} \right)$$

A significant aspect of this change of relative positions is that it is connected with an atypical growth in the curve of discoveries in the country which is gaining the largest share. Thus the number of German discoveries continually increases through the middle of the nineteenth century in a period of decline in France and Britain. A similar deviation marks the change in the relative position of the United States at the beginning of the twentieth century.

A similar pattern marks the number of discoverers. Table 2 shows the "productivity" of the various countries in terms of scientists.[5] France and Britain, with the largest numbers at the beginning of the century, fall behind Germany starting about 1835. While the number of German scientists entering upon their careers increases regularly, with only one considerable drop until 1885–1890, there are fluctuations and a generally downward slope in France and England through the middle of the century. The American trend, like the German, shows much less fluctuation. Thus, with respect to major trends, the two indexes validate each other.[6]

Two questions emerge: What explains the change of scientific leadership from France to Germany to the United States? And what explains the "deviant" nature of the development in Germany during the middle and in the United States toward the end of the nineteenth century, as manifested in (1) the continuous rise in the number of discoveries during periods of relatively low creativity in the other countries; and (2) the relatively smaller fluctuations in the number of people embarking upon scientific careers in these two countries compared with the others?

[5] Based on W. A. Newman Dorland, *The American Illustrated Medical Dictionary*, 20th edition, Philadelphia and London: Saunders, 1946.

[6] The pattern which emerges from these indexes parallels the qualitative descriptions of up-to-date histories of medicine and science. See, e.g., Arturo Castiglioni, *A History of Medicine*, New York: Knopf, 1947; Richard H. Shryock, *The Development of Modern Medicine*, New York: Knopf, 1947; H. T. Pledge, *Science Since 1500*, London: Philosophical Library, 1940. Rather than simply referring to such sources, I prefer to present the numerical indexes in detail for two reasons: (1) They contain some information not sufficiently emphasized—or even blurred—in those sources. Thus the small amount of medical research in Britain is blurred in the qualitative descriptions by the dazzling brilliance of England's few scientist-intellectuals and by the glamor of the British medical profession. Also, the different patterns of growth of scientific personnel (discoverers) is a subject not sufficiently emphasized in the histories of medical science. (2) What is called here scientific productivity is only one aspect of the development of science; in terms of the interrelationships of scientific ideas it is perhaps a peripheral one. Since traditionally the history of science is an history of ideas, even the few historians interested in such sociological phenomena as differences in the scientific development of various countries are not very explicit about the bases of their judgments, nor do they sufficiently differentiate between the various aspects of science as a social activity. It is important, therefore, to present explicitly the quantitative basis of the historians' judgment and clearly delimit the particular aspect of scientific activity dealt with here from others.

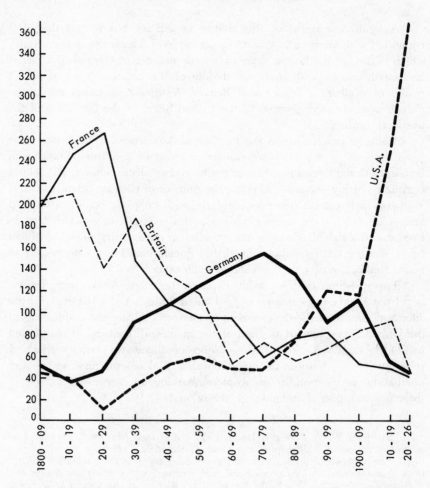

Figure 1. Changes in the relative share of medical discoveries by selected countries, 1800–1926.

HYPOTHESIS: THE ORGANIZATIONAL FACTOR

Neither the changes in scientific leadership nor the deviant nature of the German and American developments can be manifestations of differences in the scientific ideas in the various countries. This could be the case only if international communication had been deficient, so that new ideas in one country would have no effect upon the work of scientists in the others. This was by no means the case, as demonstrated by the parallel upward movements of the curves of discoveries in all the countries in periods of crucial scientific advance. Independently from this fact, whatever barriers to scien-

TABLE 2. Discoverers in the Medical Sciences at the Age of Entering Their Professions (Age 25) in Various Countries, 1800–1910

Year	U.S.A.	England	France	Germany	Other
1800	1	7	8	7	4
1805	1	8	5	8	2
1810	3	11	6	6	2
1815	2	12	12	7	3
1820	3	11	23	18	2
1825	2	17	15	18	6
1830	8	12	25	10	6
1835	11	13	26	29	7
1840	5	24	22	35	12
1845	5	14	13	33	5
1850	10	18	21	37	10
1855	15	16	20	49	27
1860	16	23	13	61	23
1865	25	15	36	71	26
1870	25	15	31	83	41
1875	40	31	23	84	46
1880	48	17	40	75	50
1885	52	16	34	97	52
1890	43	11	23	74	41
1895	47	9	27	78	29
1900	32	9	17	53	30
1905	28	4	4	34	25
1910	23	6	7	23	18

Source: Dorland's Medical Dictionary (20th ed.).

tific communication had existed between France and Germany during the first decades of the nineteenth century had disappeared by the beginning of the fourth decade. By about the same time, the British too established contacts with continental science, from which they had become isolated with decreasing splendor during the eighteenth century, as did the Americans.[7] Therefore nothing immanent to science as a body of ideas explains the observed differences and changes. The explanation has to be sought in external circumstances.

Among the possible external causes there are some general and obvious ones, such as population growth and the growth of national income. A few unrefined attempts to assess the population factor suggested that this is not a promising line of approach. The introduction of this factor does flatten

---

[7] Cf. Shryock, op. cit., pp. 193–196; Paul Diepgen, Geschichte der Medizin, Berlin: Gruyter, 1955, Vol. II/1, pp. 204–207.; Charles Newman, The Evolution of Medical Education in the Nineteenth Century, London: Oxford University Press, 1957, pp. 265–269.

out the curves somewhat, but does not eliminate the characteristic waves of development, and it hardly affects the changes in the relative position of the nations.[8]

Nor do differences in national or personal income seem to be relevant. The indexes of national income in all the countries here surveyed show a fairly gradual and constant rise through the whole period without such ups and downs and such extensive changes in the relative positions of the countries as indicated by our data. Moreover, the United States and Britain were the richest of these countries, at least since the middle of the nineteenth century (and no doubt earlier in the case of Britain). Yet, as to medical discoveries, these countries were relatively backward during much of the period.[9] None of these factors, therefore, seems to be directly and consistently related to the differences in the growth of discoveries in the various nations.

Thus, it is assumed that the conditions determining the differences are to be sought in the *organization* of science. But this is a complex phenomenon: we still must seek the particular organizational factor which reasonably answers our questions. It is proposed to isolate this factor by comparing the main aspects of the organization of science in France and Germany during the first half of the middle of the nineteenth century and those same aspects in Britain and the United States during the three decades preceding World War I. This particular pairing is selected because France and Germany maintained a publicly supported network of scientific instruction and research from the early nineteenth century, while Britain and the United States did not begin to develop their systems until the second half of the century. There were short-lived experiments in Britain during the first half of the century, but these were overshadowed by the archaic nature of the most important universities. If it is possible to isolate a theoretically relevant condition common to the organization of science in Germany and the United States, but absent in France and Britain, that condition may reasonably be taken as the cause of the observed differences.

FRANCE AND GERMANY

Three conditions are mentioned in the literature in explanation of German scientific superiority in the nineteenth century: (1) the relative excellence

---

[8] The sources used for population data were *La Population Française: Rapport du Haut Comité Consultatif de la Population et de la Famille,* Paris: Presses Universitaires de France, 1955, p. 19; Michel Huber, Henri Bunle, et Fernand Boverat, *La Population de la France,* Paris: Librairie Hachette, 1943, p. 19; W. S. and E. S. Woytinsky, *World Population and Production,* New York: Twentieth Century Fund, 1953.

[9] For national income data, see, e.g., Colin Clark, *The Conditions of Economic Progress,* 2nd edition, London: Macmillan, 1951.

of laboratory and hospital facilities for research and the faster recognition of the importance of new fields of research, especially physiology; (2) the clear recognition of the aim of the university as a seat of original research, and efficient organizational devices to achieve that aim, such as far-reaching academic self-government, the freedom of the teacher regarding the content of his courses, the freedom of the student in the choice of his courses and his teachers (including easy transfer from one university to another), the requirement of submitting theses based on research for attainment of academic degrees, and, above all, the institution of *Habilitation,* that is, the submission of a high level scientific work based on original research as a precondition of academic appointment; (3) the existence of a large number of academic institutions which made possible the mobility of teachers and students, and resulted in an atmosphere of scientific competition that did not exist elsewhere.[10] The superiority of the German scientific facilities from about the middle of the century is an undeniable fact. But instead of explaining the differences in creativity, it is itself a phenomenon that needs explanation.

The pioneering country in the establishment of modern scientific facilities was France. Founded in 1794, the Polytechnique had been the model academic organization in the natural sciences. Among other new features, it possessed the first academic research laboratories (in chemistry). The physiological laboratory at the Collège de France, where Magendie and Claude Bernard conducted their studies, was considered most inadequate by the middle of the nineteenth century. Yet it was there that modern experimental physiology began. The idea of studying illness as a natural phenomenon, not necessarily for the sake of cure, was first conceived in Paris, and the beginnings of systematic clinical research in medicine were made in the hospitals of that city.[11]

Until the 1830s German medical research and natural science research in general was backward compared with the French, and probably with the British too. The famous network of modern German universities already existed from the time when, following tentative beginnings at Halle, Goettingen and Jena, the University of Berlin was established in 1809.[12] But the universities, rather than promoting, retarded the development of empirical

[10] *Cf.* Abraham Flexner, *Universities: American, English, German,* Oxford: Oxford University Press, 1930, pp. 317–327; Donald S. L. Cardwell, *The Organization of Science in England,* London: Heinemann, 1957, pp. 22–25; H. E. Guerlac, "Science and French National Strength" in E. M. Earle, editor, *Modern France,* Princeton: Princeton University Press, 1951, pp. 85–88.

[11] *Cf.* Shryock, *op. cit.,* pp. 70–71, 151–169; Newman, *op. cit.,* p. 48; Guerlac, *op. cit.,* pp. 81–105.

[12] *Cf.* Flexner, *op. cit.,* pp. 311–315; R. H. Samuel and R. Hinton Thomas, *Education and Society in Modern Germany,* London: Routledge & Kegan Paul, 1949, pp. 111–113; Jacob Barion, *Universitas und Universitaet,* Bonn: Rörscheid, 1954, pp. 14–20.

science. They regarded philosophy as the queen of sciences, and usually disparaged empirical research. The biological sciences in particular were under the sway of *Naturphilosophie,* which stimulated much imaginative writing but little research.[13]

Only around 1830 did this atmosphere change under foreign influence. Liebig, who had studied in Paris, established in 1825 the first chemical laboratory at the small university of Giessen. A few years later Johannes Mueller, the central figure of German physiology, abandoned his early attachment to *Naturphilosophie* and became converted to the empirical method by studying the works of the Swedish chemist, Berzelius. Abut the same time the Vienna school of clinicians adopted the methods of investigation initiated by the Paris clinicians, and various learned journals began to propagate the new scientific approach in the medical sciences.[14]

Thus the French showed at least as much understanding of the value and the needs of scientific research as the Germans. It should not be assumed that this understanding suddenly declined around the middle of the century. The influentials of French science at that time, such as Dumas, and later Pasteur, Claude Bernard, and Victor Duruy, were certainly not less enlightened and brilliant than their German counterparts. In fact, they may have been more sympathetic to the needs of scientific research than German academic policy makers, since obscurantism was rather prevalent within both the faculties of the German universities and the governmental offices in charge of higher education.[15] The greater expansion of German scientific facilities and the prompter recognition of new fields are therefore as much in need of explanation as the continuous growth in German discoveries.

The second condition—the presumably peculiar values and organization of the German university—is also a very doubtful explanation. The idea of academic freedom notwithstanding, atheists, Jews, and socialists were often kept out of academic careers in Germany. Academic self-government was not necessarily enlightened: liberal scientists in the 1840s regarded it as an essentially retrograde arrangement. In fact, some of the most beneficial academic decisions—with relation to the growth of science—were taken by civil servants, most notably Friedrich Althoff, who interfered with academic self-government. Even the *Habilitationsschriften* were often rather mediocre

[13] Cf. Shryock, *op. cit.,* pp. 192–201; Diepgen, *op. cit.,* Vol. II/1, pp. 23–28.

[14] Cf. Cardwell, *op. cit.,* pp. 22–25; Shryock, *op. cit.,* pp. 188, 195; Garrison, *op. cit.,* pp. 451–452.

[15] See Guerlac, *op. cit.,* pp. 85–88 on France. On the relative backwardness of German academic administration, see Ervin H. Ackerknecht, *Rudolph Virchow: Doctor, Statesman, Anthropologist,* Madison: University of Wisconsin Press, 1953, pp. 139–140; Samuel and Thomas, *op. cit.,* pp. 114–130; Max Weber, *Jugendbriefe,* Tübingen: Mohr, n.d., pp. 151–52. In order to realize the amount of obscurantism and intolerance in German universities at the time it is useful to read the otherwise shallow work of Richard Graf du Moulin Eckart, *Geschichte der deutschen Universitaeten,* Stuttgart: Enke, 1929.

pieces of research, and there was nothing in the constitution of the universities efficiently to prevent mediocre professors from confirming inferior theses.[16]

At the same time, the ideas as well as some of the arrangements said to be characteristic of the German universities also existed in France. Freedom of teaching already formed the core of the tradition at the Collège de France before the Revolution and was carried further than in the German universities. The ideals of pure research were formulated in French scientific ideology at least as clearly as in German and they were practiced and encouraged in a great many ways.[17] There is no proof that the lack of the paraphernalia of academic self-government interfered with the research of French scientists more than in Germany. It is true that, compared with the *Habilitation,* the French *aggrégation* and the system of open examinations seem to be inefficient ways of selecting people for academic careers. But there is little evidence that this irrelevant hurdle actually prevented potentially creative people from entering scientific careers. Moreover, there were other means, such as numerous prizes and public honors, which encouraged original research in France.[18]

Decentralization has been written about much less than the first two conditions, partly because it was an unintended circumstance, and partly because its effect upon research is less immediately evident. The decentralization of the German academic system was the result of the political dismemberment of the German-speaking people. There were 19 independent universities in Germany proper, maintained by the princes of the numerous small states constituting Germany in the eighteenth and early nineteenth centuries, as well as German language universities in Switzerland, Austria (including the Czech provinces), and Dorpat in the Baltic Sea Provinces of Russia.[19] At the same time the French boasted a unified academic system, most of it situated in Paris. Although some of the features of this centraliza-

---

[16] *Cf.* Flexner, *op. cit.,* pp. 317–327; Samuel and Thomas, *loc. cit.*

[17] See Claude Bernard, *Morceaux Choisis,* dirigé et préfacé par Jean Rostand, Paris: Gallimard, 1938, pp. 16–18, for one of the most beautiful descriptions of the traditions of the freedom of teaching and research as it was practiced at the Collège de France. See also Ernest Lavissé, *Histoire de France,* Paris: Librairie Hachette, n.d., Vol. IX/1, p. 301, on the pioneering beginnings of the teaching of pure sciences in the same institution in the 1770s and 1780s.

[18] For a good description of how the French system of examinations actually worked, see René Leriche, *Am Ende meines Lebens,* Bern und Stuttgart: Huber, 1957, pp. 53–55. Leriche, like others, attributes the lack of originality of French medicine to the examinations. But his own account shows that the problem was rather the lack of career opportunities for young medical scientists (*ibid.,* p. 34).

[19] With the addition of Strassburg in 1872 there were 20 universities in Germany. *Cf.* Christian v. Ferber, *Die Entwicklung des Lehrkörpers der deutschen Universitaeten und Hochschulen 1864–1954,* Vol. III of Helmuth Plessner, editor, *Untersuchungen zur Lage der deutschen Hochschullehrer,* Göttingen: Vandenhoeck & Ruprecht, 1956, pp. 37–38. The German-language universities of Switzerland were Zürich, Bern, and Basel; and of Austria, Vienna, Prague, Graz, and Innsbruck.

tion introduced by Napoleon were deplored, the central administration of science and academic institutions generally was considered to be desirable by French politicians of science.[20]

Nevertheless, decentralization seems to have been the decisive factor in determining the differences in the scientific creativity of the two countries. It gave rise to academic competition, and competition forced upon the individual institutions decisions which would not have been made otherwise, or at least not made at that time. In all areas crucial to the development of the medical sciences German policies turned out to be in the long run more farsighted and bold than French policies, although the first initiative was often taken by the French.—What, then, was the actual competition and how did it influence the decisions about the crucial problems of academic policy?

THE CRUCIAL DECISIONS

Given the situation of the medical sciences (and perhaps of the sciences in general) at the beginning of the last century, the problem faced by the French and the German systems (and not confronted by Britain and the United States until later) was to find adequate criteria for the evaluation and support of science. The governments, and increasingly the people too (especially in France), believed in the value and usefulness of science. Academies, universities, and other institutions were set up everywhere, or rejuvenated where they existed before, in order to promote research and to disseminate knowledge. One of the aims of these institutions was to enable a selected few scientists, who had already proved their greatness, to devote all of their time to financially supported scientific research. But it was not intended to create in these institutions academic careers which one entered as in any other profession. The large majority of the scientists had independent means or a lucrative profession (very often medical practice, even in sciences not connected with medicine), and pursued their scientific interest in their free time, often at a considerable personal cost. This idealistic pattern seemed to fit perfectly that sacred pursuit of truth which was science. Academic appointments therefore were regarded as honors rather than careers, and turning science into an occupation would have seemed something like a sacrilege.

A corollary, in this amateur stage of science, was the absence of specialization. The great names of the early nineteenth century were those of generalists who were creative in more than one field. And the new scientific disciplines developed from their work. While it was increasingly believed

---

[20] *Cf.* Guerlac, *op. cit.,* pp. 87–88.

that the new disciplines required specialists, the fact that they were opened up by generalists seemed to indicate that specialization was not really necessary. Moreover, there persisted the reluctance to abandon the conception of general science which explains to the adept all the secrets of nature. Thus there was considerable disinclination to substitute for the *savant* such narrow specialists as chemists, physiologists, and the like. And there was even more reluctance to redefine such a traditionally unified field as medicine into a number of subspecialties.

The second problem was the development of criteria for the support of research. Today it is still difficult of course to decide what constitutes adequate and sufficient support of research, but at least budgets can be drawn for determined purposes. At that time even this was impossible, since research was an unpredictable, erratic process, and important discoveries were made as often outside as inside the laboratories.

Finally, there was the question of training scientists. Until the second half and particularly the last quarter of the nineteenth century, science had few practical applications. Most of it was pure science benefitting no practice. Under these circumstances, to train every medical student, would-be chemist, and engineer in scientific research was about as justified as it would be today to teach every concertgoer advanced musical composition.[21]

These problems existed in both countries and were approached in France and Germany with the same concepts. Yet, to repeat, the long-term decisions made in France concerning all three problems were the opposite of those made in Germany.

SCIENTIFIC CAREERS AND SPECIALIZATION

The creation of regular careers in science and the recognition of specialized disciplines were closely connected problems. Both may be illustrated with the case of physiology, the most decisive science for the development of medicine in the nineteenth century.

As a systematic discipline, physiology emerged at the beginning of that century. François Magendie, considered to be the founder of experimental physiology, was professor of medicine. He established the new specialty and could follow it undisturbed (though practically unsupported) at the Collège de France, because of the full degree of academic freedom prevailing in that institution. But his disciple, Claude Bernard, who became the most outstanding representative of the new field around the middle of the century,

[21] On the state of science in the early nineteenth century, see Pledge, *op. cit.*, pp. 115–151. On scientists in the same period, see Elie Halévy, *History of England in 1815*, London: Pelican, 1938, Vol. 2, pp. 187–200; René J. Dubos, *Louis Pasteur: Franctireur de la science*, Paris: Presses Universitaires de France, 1955, pp. 3–4; and Diepgen, *op. cit.*, Vol. II/1, pp. 2–5, 66–69, 152–153.

for many years had to use his private laboratory and private means to pursue his research. At last, against the opposition of those who regarded the new discipline as merely a branch of anatomy, a special chair was created for Bernard at the Sorbonne in 1854. Soon thereafter he also fell heir to Magendie's chair at the Collège de France and held both appointments until 1868; he then transferred his work to the Museum of Natural History, relinquishing the post at the Sorbonne to his disciple, Paul Bert.

The recognition of the discipline of physiology, however, did not create opportunities for purely scientific careers in the traditional field of medicine. In this connection, the only change was that after the retirement of the chair's incumbent a single successor would have to be found. This was not a prospect on the basis of which one could realistically take up research as a career. Therefore, potential scientists first had to build up a practice, and engaged in research as a part-time activity.[22]

Thus, the academic career changed very little in France through the nineteenth century. Appointments were made from an undifferentiated group of practitioners—amateur scientists—and usually at a fairly advanced age. Even academically successful persons did not become full-time scientists before they reached their forties or fifties, and since the chair to be vacated was not known they had to maintain as broad interests and activities as possible. But in the second half of the century there was increasingly less chance for non-specialists to make important discoveries. French scientific productivity therefore declined even in fields pioneered by Frenchmen. Whenever a discipline reached the stage of development where its efficient pursuit required specialists, there was little chance that the French system would produce such scientists.[23]

Physiology as a science was received with more sympathy in Germany than in France, but its recognition as an academic specialty there also ran into difficulties. The man who did most for the introduction of the discipline to Germany, Johannes Mueller, was a generalist who taught, in addition to physiology, anatomy, opthalmology, and surgery.[24] His eventual successor in Berlin, Du Bois-Reymond, had been refused one professorial chair after another because he was considered a mere specialist.[25] The early creation of

[22] *Cf.* Bernard, *op. cit.*, pp. 154–157, 263–285; J. M. D. Olmsted, *Claude Bernard: Physiologist,* New York: Harper, 1938, pp. 51–89. For the situation at the beginning of the twentieth century, see Edouard Rist, *25 Portraits des médicins français,* 1900–1950, Paris: Masson, 1955, pp. 29–40.

[23] See Rist, *op. cit.*, pp. 97–104, on the career of S. A. Sicard, who seems to have been a relatively lucky and successful scientist. When at the age of 51 he was appointed as professor he had to abandon his life-long interest and research in neurology because the vacant chair was designated for internal pathology, and course preparation in the new field required a great effort.

[24] *Cf.* K. E. Rothschuh, *Geschichte der Physiologie,* Berlin-Göttingen-Heidelberg: Springer, 1953, pp. 93, 112–118.

a separate chair in physiology (for Purkinje in Breslau, 1839) had no general effect, and for some years physiology and anatomy continued to be taught by the same person in all other German universities. But pressure for the separation of the disciplines by the younger generation of scientists continued, and those with some bargaining power raised the demand when they were offered university chairs. Thus, when Carl Ludwig was offered a professorship at Zürich in 1849, he accepted it only on the condition that a separate teacher be appointed for anatomy;[26] thereafter the recognition of the new discipline proceeded rapidly. No university could afford to neglect the new field, so that by 1864 there were already 15 full professors of physiology in Germany and several others in the wider system of German-language universities.[27] The separation of physiology from anatomy at this stage became the official policy of university administration. In some cases, where traditionally-minded incumbents were reluctant to abandon one of the disciplines, the separation was forced upon them by administrative pressure.[28]

All of this led to a complete transformation of the scientific career in Germany. In spite of the strictures against narrowness and of the continuing lip-service paid to the image of the scientist who works because of devotion, science became a specialized and regularized occupation. As we have seen, success, fame, or even sheer enterprise had a good chance for reward. Once a new and fruitful field was recognized in one university, strong pressures led other universities to follow suit, thereby creating more opportunities for those willing to work in the new field. Therefore, it was possible—and for the very able also worthwhile—to concentrate after graduation on one well defined and promising field of research with the definite aim of a scientific career. Not only was it unnecessary first to build up a practice and to

[25] George Rosen and Beate Caspari-Rosen, *400 Years of a Doctor's Life*, New York: Schuman, 1947, pp. 248–250; Ernst Gagliardi, Hans Nabholz and Jean Strohl, *Die Universitaet Zürich und ihre Vorlaeufer 1833–1933*, Zürich: Erziehungsdirektion, 1938, pp. 548–549.

[26] *Ibid.*, 539–548. Virchow, who was also offered the chair, refused to accept it on the ground that he wished a chair for pathological anatomy exclusively (without teaching responsibilities in either surgical anatomy or physiology). In Ludwig's time the nominal unity of physiology and anatomy was still maintained; the separate teacher in anatomy was only an extraordinary professor. But when Ludwig left Zürich in 1855 and the position was offered to Koelliker, the chairs were finally separated upon the latter's suggestion (although Koelliker himself refused the job). For similar instances of creating new specialties at the same university in order to attract or retain teachers, see *ibid.*, pp. 562, 879.

[27] *Cf.* Von Ferber, *op. cit.*, p. 204.

[28] For example, Valentin in Bern, in 1865; see Bruno Kisch, *Forgotten Leaders in Modern Medicine*, Philadelphia: American Philosophical Society, 1954, pp. 174–175.

retain as general interest as possible, but if one had taken such a course his academic prospects would have been negligible in competition with the full-time specialists. Thus specialized science became a career, and the amateur general scientist disappeared in Germany.[29] This difference in career possibilities, not the distinction between *Habilitation* and *aggrégation,* explains the greater research orientation of German than of French science.

The same mechanisms which explain the development of scientific roles also explain the development of facilities for research, and the introduction of scientific methods into the training of physicians. The creation of new facilities was part and parcel of the bargaining between universities and scientists. Facilities (laboratories, assistants, and so on) were offered to attract desirable candidates or to prevent scientists from moving elsewhere. The extension of facilities made possible, and to some extent made necessary, the training of a growing number of persons capable of doing research. Since not all such individuals could be given academic appointments in the basic medical sciences or otherwise, they used their research skills and interests to transform clinical medicine into an exact science. These processes and their results may be briefly illustrated.

RESEARCH FACILITIES

As has been pointed out, the French were the first to establish modern institutions for scientific training and research. But the facilities and arrangements established in France about 1800, considered to be ideal for their time, were hardly extended or changed until World War I or later. The Pasteur Institute, established in 1888, was the first independent research institute of the world. Again, it remained the only one in its field in France at least until World War I.[30]

---

[29] Max Weber, writing in 1918, regarded science as a most risky career; see his "Science as a Vocation," in H. H. Gerth and C. Wright Mills, *From Max Weber: Essays in Sociology,* London: Oxford University Press, 1947, pp. 132–134. But, it should be realized that Weber was referring to a crisis situation in an already established discipline; the circumstances were much more hopeful in the middle of the nineteenth century. Of those who took their *Habilitation* between 1850 and 1859, 85 per cent received full-time academic appointments, while for those who received their *Habilitation* between 1900 and 1909 only 62 per cent received such posts. The corresponding proportions in medicine are 84 and 48 per cent, respectively. (This does not necessarily mean a relatively greater decline of research in medicine, because there were good opportunities outside the universities in public hospitals.) See Von Ferber, *op. cit.,* pp. 81–82, for the statistical data; and Adolf Struempell, *Aus dem Leben eines deutschen Klinikers,* Leipzig: Vogel, 1925, on the *Habilitation* as a preparation for a hospital career.

[30] The ideal arrangements of French medical schools in 1798 are noted in Newman, *op. cit.,* p. 48. Concerning the quite different picture presented by French academic medicine early in this century, see Abraham Flexner, *Medical Education in Europe,* New York: The Carnegie Foundation for the Advancement of Teaching, 1912, pp. 221–223; and Leriche, *op. cit.,* p. 34. On the Pasteur Institute, see Guerlac, *op. cit.,* p. 88.

Thus in France a new type of organization was apt to remain a single show-piece for 50 years, while in Germany such novelties became routine features of the organization of research in a much shorter time. By the 1840s there were apparently more and better chemical laboratories in Germany than in France, and by the sixties the contrast was extreme. At a time when it was an achievement for Pasteur to obtain any (and most inadequate) laboratory facilities, the Prussian government built new laboratories at Bonn and Berlin (the Bonn laboratory, for example, could accommodate more than 60 students) equipped with the most up-to-date facilities, and the older ones probably were also more adequate than anything that existed elsewhere. And there were good laboratories at other universities in Germany.[31]

There were similar differences between Germany and France in the development of facilities for medical research and of specialized research institutions. The New Vienna School of clinical research began in the thirties, and its facilities seem to have been modest even until midcentury. But there were gradual improvements in one place after another, and by the sixties there evolved fairly uniform standards which made it possible to conduct clinical research with the aid of adequate laboratory facilities in a number of places.[32] Finally, the establishment of specialized research institutions became a matter of routine in Germany soon after the beginnings made in France. They became a tool regularly used by the universities' administrations, the governments, and local bodies to encourage and develop the work of famous scientists.[33]

SCIENTIFIC TRAINING

The differences in the development of medical training were no less conspicuous. The fact that until about the 1880s all the great advances in the basic medical sciences contributed little to the cure of illness largely explains the persistent and overwhelming emphasis on the practical art of medicine rather than on its few scientific bases in the training of the student-physician. Indeed, apprenticeship and bedside demonstrations were the most important parts of medical training in France, England, and the United States.[34]

Only in Germany did the training of the doctor become a privilege of scientists. By the 1860s even clinical chairs were given exclusively to people

[31] Cf. Cardwell, op. cit., p. 80; and Dubos, op. cit., pp. 34, 78–79.
[32] Cf. Diepgen, op. cit., Vol. II/1, 207–209; on the situation in the 1860s, see Theodor Billroth, The Medical Sciences in the German Universities, New York: Macmillan, 1924, p. 27; and at the turn of the century, Flexner, op. cit., 145–166.
[33] Cf. Flexner, op. cit., 1930, pp. 31–35.
[34] Cf. Diepgen, op. cit., Vol. II/1, pp. 212–214; Vol. II/2, pp. 154–155, 286–288; Abraham Flexner, Medical Education: A Comparative Study, New York: Macmillan, 1925, pp. 211–212, 241, 248.

with attainment in research rather than to outstanding practitioners. And from the middle of the century, even public hospitals were increasingly staffed by doctors both interested and trained in research. Thus much earlier than elsewhere (possibly prematurely), medicine in Germany became an applied science.[35] As a result, when the great opportunities for clinical research arose, following the discovery of the bacteriological causation of illness and the perfection of anesthesia and aseptic surgery, there were in Germany enough doctors trained in research to take full advantage of the opportunity, and to transform public (even non-teaching) hospitals into veritable institutions of applied medical science.[36]

DECENTRALIZATION AND COMPETITION

Thus, regarding all three crucial decisions—developing scientific facilities, creating scientific roles, and training larger numbers of research personnel than were justified by existing practical needs—the German system "behaved" with uncanny foresight. It has been shown that this foresight was not the result of greater individual wisdom. It was the result of competition due to the unintended decentralization of the German system.

"Competition" in this paper refers to the general condition underlying all the processes described above: it is a situation in which no single institution is able to lay down standards for the system of institutions within which people (in this case students and teachers) are relatively free to move from one place to another. Under such circumstances, university administrators required neither exceptional boldness nor foresight for continually expanding facilities and training, and for creating new scientific jobs. There was little if any need for fateful individual decisions. Improvements and innovations had to be made from time to time in order to attract famous men or keep them from leaving. In this way, laboratories and institutions were founded, assistantships provided, new disciplines recognized, and scientific jobs created. These innovations were repeated throughout the system because of pressure from scientists and students in general, irrespective of practical needs and of what a few scientific influentials thought.

If competition inevitably brought about the adoption of fruitful innovations in the universities, it also forced them to correct mistakes and to

[35] Diepgen, op. cit., Vol. II/1, pp. 152–153. See also Theodor Billroth, loc. cit.; Bernhard Naunyn, Erinnerungen, Gedanken und Meinungen, Munich: Bergmann, 1925, pp. 375–376.

[36] There was a parallel development in chemistry. There too the availability of relatively large numbers of trained chemists afforded Germany the opportunity to build up within a short time a chemical industry based on applied science, after the discovery of the aniline dyes made the practical application of science a permanent possibility; cf. Cardwell, op. cit., pp. 134–137, 186–187.

eliminate traditions which retarded scientific development. This process has been shown in the case of the separation of physiology from anatomy and the introduction of scientific criteria in clinical training in Germany.

BRITAIN AND THE UNITED STATES

The similarities, differences, and differential effects observed in the cases of France and Germany were, in essentials, repeated in the cases of Britain and the United States.

From the middle of the nineteenth century, British—and soon after, American educators—scientists, and administrators displayed increasing interest in the organization of science in Germany. Scientists and intellectuals who visited Germany returned home enthusiastic about German academic life, and soon German university training became a standard preparation for scientific careers among British scientists.[37]

Consequently British universities, though retaining certain traditions, introduced measures to bring themselves in line with German standards and practices. Oxford and Cambridge, which until the 1860s were training centers primarily for the rich and the clergy, began to emerge as institutions of empirical science and positive scholarship pursued in an atmosphere of academic freedom and autonomy. The newer University of London and the universities in the provinces imitated the German pattern even more closely and were imbued, from the beginning, with the spirit of empirical science.

The rapid growth of the modern academic system also began in the United States in the 1860s. The Land Grant Act passed in 1862 and other circumstances brought about a large increase in the number of American colleges and universities between the sixties and the eighties.[38] In the present context, the most important events were the rise of the graduate schools in the seventies, and in the following decade the establishment of Johns Hopkins Medical School which was directly influenced by the German example.[39] Eventually older institutions such as Harvard also abandoned certain traditions derived from pre-nineteenth century England and adopted new methods in imitation of the German.[40]

In this development of a system of up-to-date institutions for medical research and training Britain had most of the advantages over the United States, similar to those possessed by France over Germany at the beginning

---

[37] *Ibid.,* p. 50.

[38] *Ibid.,* p. 80.

[39] *Cf.* Flexner, *Universities...*, *op. cit.,* p. 73; and Abraham Flexner, *I Remember,* New York: Simon and Schuster, 1940, pp. 63–64.

[40] *Cf.* Edward D. Churchill, *To Work in the Vineyards of Surgery: The Reminiscences of J. Collins Warren (1842–1927),* Cambridge: Harvard University Press, pp. 193–197, 257–271.

of the century. The British began the adoption of the German patterns earlier, and they began from a higher level than did the Americans.[41] Nevertheless, while the effect of the academic reform on British science was slow and partial, in America it produced a conspicuous rise in scientific creativity.

That the social mechanisms at work in these cases were similar to those involved in our first pair of comparisons can be illustrated best by the organization of clinical research and the creation of clinical chairs. Attempts to copy the Germans by making hospital departments into virtual research establishments and filling the clinical chairs according to criteria of scientific achievement ran into serious opposition in both countries. They seemed like an infringement on the rights of the profession, whose members had run the teaching hospitals independently of the universities, and it also seemed to be endangering the charitable purpose of the hospitals. Therefore, when Oxford and Cambridge decided to overhaul their medical training programs along German lines, they confined themselves to the basic departments and sent their students to continue their clinical studies in the hospital medical schools of London. This division was a decision in favor of preserving the traditions of the professional fraternities attached to the various public hospitals and of the philanthropic bodies which governed these hospitals. Of course, it could also have been justified by the aim to keep apart pure research and professional practice.[42] However, *a priori* reasons for incorporating the teaching hospitals in the universities and staffing them on the basis of attainments in research might have been advanced. As shown above, this was one of the problems which could not at that time be decided on *a priori* logical grounds; only future experience could indicate the effective choice.

The conditions for acquiring the needed experience existed in England, since there were approximations of a proper university hospital and university clinical departments in the London University College Medical School (founded as early as 1836), and similar opportunities arose when the provincial universities were established.[43] Yet, instead of representing competing alternatives, none of these departments ventured further than the model established by the Oxford-Cambridge-London triangle; that is, their clinical departments were run by local practitioners as practical training centers

[41] *Cf.* Newman, *op. cit.,* pp. 269, 276; Cardwell, *op. cit.,* pp. 46–51, 80, 103–107, 110–114, 118–119, 134–137, and *passim.* Flexner, *Universities. . . , op. cit.,* pp. 46–65; Richard H. Shryock, *American Medical Research: Past and Present,* New York: New York Academy of Medicine, 1947, pp. 106–108, 118–119.

[42] *Cf.* "The First Hundred Years: Notes on the History of the Association," extracts from Ernest M. Little, "History of the Association," *British Medical Journal,* 1932, 1, pp. 672–676; A. M. Carr-Saunders and P. A. Wilson, *The Professions,* Oxford: Clarendon Press, 1933, p. 87; Flexner, *Medical Education. . . , op. cit.,* p. 28; Newman, op. cit., pp. 49–50, 133 ff.

[43] *Cf.* Flexner, *Universities. . . , op. cit.,* pp. 242–244.

rather than being organized as university departments engaged in research and staffed by persons selected on the basis of scientific eminence. This was quite different from the situation in Germany, where, for example, the little University of Giessen successfully pioneered in establishing its chemical laboratory, imitated later by universities of much greater prestige. It also differed from the innovation of the Johns Hopkins Medical School, where a full-scale medical faculty that included basic as well as clinical departments was established—a pattern that was followed by other universities and led to a rapid transformation of American medicine reminiscent of German, notwithstanding the strength of a professional and philanthropic tradition similar to that of Britain.[44]

All this shows unequivocally that the British system was not competitive. Yet seemingly it was decentralized, since universities and public hospitals were private institutions financed and governed in a variety of ways, as in the United States. In fact, however, Britain also had a centralized system, though centralized in a somewhat different way than that of the French. The provincial universities did not begin to confer degrees until 1880 (with the exception of Durham, established in 1831) and their status, as well as the status of London University, never reached that of the two ancient universities. The system was totally overshadowed by the Oxford-Cambridge duopoly, which, in spite of differences in matters of religion and politics, represented basically similar educational philosophies and academic policies.[45] The special position of these two institutions was maintained in large part by their unwritten exclusive right of educating the political, administrative, ecclesiastical, and professional elite of the nation. In the case of medicine, the two universities were, as we have seen, connected with the leading medical corporations of London, whose members traditionally received their pre-professional education in "Oxbridge." Thus the centralization of academic life, which in France was the result of administrative design, was achieved in England through the more subtle functions of a class system, in which academic institutions like people "were kept in their place" through internalized traditions and networks of semi-formalized bonds among persons, groups, and independent organizations.

[44] *Cf.* Donald H. Fleming, *William Welch and the Rise of Modern Medicine*, Boston: Little, Brown, 1954, pp. 173 ff. On competition in American academic life in general, see Logan Wilson, *The Academic Man*, London: Oxford University Press, 1942, pp. 157–174, 186–191, 195–214; and Theodore Caplow and Reece J. McGee, *The Academic Marketplace*, New York: Basic Books, 1958.
[45] *Cf.* Flexner, *Universities...*, *op. cit.*, p. 249; Bruce Truscot, *Red Brick University*, Harmondsworth: Penguin Books, 1951, pp. 19–29. See also R. K. Kelsall, *Higher Civil Servants in Britain*, London: Routledge & Kegan Paul, 1956, p. 137, on the preservation of the educational duopoly in another field; as late as 1950, 47.3 per cent of British civil servants in the ranks of Assistant Secretary and above had attended Oxford or Cambridge.

The United States, then, provides a case similar to the German, where competition within a decentralized system encouraged the establishment of specialized research roles and facilities. The usefulness and the necessity of such roles and facilities in the clinical field were not yet generally recognized at the turn of the twentieth century (in spite of the already existent German examples), and there was strong resistance against them in Britain as well as in the United States. At this time, like medical scientists (or natural scientists) in general, clinicians were still conceived as primarily practitioners and only secondarily as scientists. Thus the problem of transforming the practitioner-amateur scientist role into a scientific career in the clinical field was similar to the earlier problem of the creation of scientific roles in general. At this stage as in the previous one, competition was the decisive factor in the emergence of the new career.

CONCLUSION

The continuous growth in the curves of German discoveries during the middle decades of the nineteenth century and in the American curves starting from the 1880s is thus attributed to the extent to which these societies exploited, through enterprise and organizational measures, the possibilities inherent in the state of science. They were quicker than France and Britain in the recognition of new disciplines, the creation of specialized scientific jobs and facilities for research, and the introduction of large-scale systematic training for research. They were also quicker to abandon traditional notions which had lost their usefulness. None of these conditions alone could have sustained scientific growth for a long period of time. It was no coincidence, however, that they went together, since a common underlying factor, competition, determined the crucial decisions concerning all of these conditions in the two decentralized systems. Successful scientists were rewarded with university chairs and facilities. Their success encouraged others to take up science and, incidentally, transformed the pursuit of science into a regular professional career; it created pressure for further expansion of facilities and training, and exposed the inadequacies of out-of-date traditions.

This interpretation of the curve of scientific discoveries, according to which their growth was due to increased opportunities for entering research careers (and not, for example, to better selection of scientists), is also consistent with the differences between the countries shown in the second index based on the numbers of discoverers. As pointed out earlier, beginning in 1835 in Germany and in 1860 in the United States, the growth in the numbers of those entering upon scientific careers became continuous, while in France and Britain there were fluctuations over the whole period. Continuous growth represents a situation in which research becomes a regular career; fluctuations, a situation in which research to a large extent is a spontaneous activity engaged in by people as the spirit moves them.

In conclusion, some of the implications and problems raised by the existence of a positive relationship between scientific productivity and academic competition may be noted. According to the present explanation, this relationship is due to the impetus provided by competition for entering promising but undeveloped fields of research. This, however, suggests that the growth of discoveries in any field may be limited by the capacity for expansion of the institutional framework (jobs and facilities), a suggestion which seems to be worth further exploration.[46]

Another question concerns the *quality* of the impetus given to science by competition. The present hypothesis suggests that competition increases the gross amount of discoveries of all kinds through the thorough exploitation of potentially fruitful fields of research. It says nothing about the conditions conducive to the creation of fundamentally new ideas, and it is quite possible that the social conditions that stimulate basic innovations differ from those that facilitate the exploitation of fruitful ideas already discovered.[47]

Finally, nothing has been said about the conditions that maintain scientific competition. Political decentralization gave rise to competition in Germany, and political decentralization enhanced by private financing and administration of higher education led to competition in the United States. It is not argued, however, that competition is the only possible outcome of any state of decentralization, or that competition, once established, is self-maintaining. Decentralization may lead to collusion or mutual isolation as well as to competition; and competition may be replaced by either of these alternatives. Determination of the general conditions that ensure competition, therefore, is another problem which needs further study.

[46] This is the subject matter of A. Zloczower, "Career Opportunities and Scientific Growth in 19th Century Germany with Special Reference to the Development of Physiology," unpublished M.A. thesis, Hebrew University, Jerusalem, Israel, 1960.

[47] *Cf.* Joseph Ben-David, "Roles and Innovations in Medicine," *American Journal of Sociology*, 65 (May, 1960), pp. 557–568.

Universities and Academic Systems
in Modern Societies

JOSEPH BEN-DAVID AND AWRAHAM ZLOCZOWER

Universities engage in teaching and research. They prepare students to become men of action in practical politics, the civil service, the practice of law, medicine, surgery etc. Others studying at universities want to become scholars and scientists whose style of work is far removed from the on-the-spot decision-making which is so important among the former category. The professions and disciplines taught and developed at universities require a great variety of manpower and organization of entirely different kinds. Universities nevertheless insist on comprising all of them, in the name of an idea stemming from a time when one person was really able to master all the arts and sciences. They, furthermore, attempt to perform all these complex tasks within the framework of corporate self-government reminiscent of medieval guilds. Indeed there have been serious doubts about the efficiency of the university since the 18th century. Reformers of the "Enlightenment" advocated the abolition of the universities as useless remnants of past tradition and established in their stead specialized schools for the training of professional people and academies for the advancement of science and learning. This program was actually put into effect by the Revolution and the subsequent reorganization of higher education by Napoleon in France. The present day organization of higher education in the Soviet Union still reflects the belief in the efficiency of specialized professional schools as well as specialized academic research institutions.

Even in countries where universities are the typical institutions of higher education and research there are constant doubts about the ways universities are actually going about their tasks.[1] Some accuse them of undue tradi-

Selected excerpts from the *European Journal of Sociology*, Vol. III, No. 1, 1962, pp. 45–84, with the permission of the authors and publisher. Limitations of space have necessitated the omission of a much more detailed analysis of universities in England, as well as the section which dealt with universities in France and the U.S.S.R. Joseph Ben-David and Awraham Zloczower are colleagues in the Sociology Department at the Hebrew University in Jerusalem, Israel, who have made a number of collaborative, as well as independent, contributions to the sociology of science.

[1] Most of the discussion about the subject has been influenced by Abraham FLEXNER, *Universities: American, English, German* (New York, Oxford University Press, 1930). For some of the more recent discussion of the problems of universities,

tionalism and advocate the setting up of technological universities, training for a much larger variety of practical callings than most universities (at least in Europe) actually do. Others, on the other hand, accuse some of the universities (mainly in America) of having abandoned the true standards of science and scholarship by the introduction of courses of study which are really vocational in their nature. Universities are often criticized for their inefficient methods of teaching, resulting from the overwhelming interest of their staff in research. At the same time it is deplored that some universities pay too much attention to teaching, neglecting research which should be the principal task of the university. There is general agreement that teaching and research should be complementary rather than competing with each other, although it is well known that the two functions are not always compatible. The ability for teaching does not always go together with the ability for doing research, and research requires a different organization than teaching.

There is, finally, the question of the "unity of science" which the university is supposed to represent. The more successful universities are in promoting research, the greater becomes the gap in communication between the various branches of learning. There has been a constant demand for bridging this gap by means of some sort of general studies. The gap however does not seem to have diminished. Increased specialization also seems to counteract another cherished purpose of the university, namely, the formation of moral character. It becomes more and more difficult to see how and which part of university studies are suited for the accomplishment of this purpose. Finally, there seem to be great inefficiencies in university self-government. The autonomy of the academic body is defended by all. But professors constantly complain that their administrative duties encroach upon their time. Yet, in spite of all these inconsistencies and contradictions, the university has been a successful institution. Everywhere in the world universities have expanded rapidly. New countries, which had not possessed universities before, regard the establishment of a university as one

---

cf. Logan WILSON, *The Academic Man* (New York, Oxford University Press, 1942); H. E. GUERLAC, "Science and French National Strength," *in* E. M. EARLE ed., *Modern France* (Princeton, Princeton University Press, 1951), pp. 81–105; Helmuth PLESSNER ed., *Untersuchungen zur Lage der deutschen Hochschullehrer* (Göttingen, Vandenhoeck and Ruprecht, 1953), 3 vols.; Jacques BARZUN, *Teacher in America* (New York, Doubleday, 1954); Dael WOLFLE, *America's Resources of Specialized Talent* (New York, Harper, 1954); W. H. G. ARMYTAGE, *Civic Universities* (London, Ernest Benn, 1955); George F. KNELLER, *Higher Learning in Britain* (London, Cambridge University Press, 1955); Theodore CAPLOW and Reece J. McGEE, *The Academic Marketplace* (New York, Basic Books, 1958); David RIESMAN, *Constraint and Variety in American Education* (New York, Doubleday, 1958); John J. CORSON, *Governance of Colleges and Universities* (New York, McGraw Hill, 1960); Hans ANGER, *Probleme der deutschen Universität* (Tübingen, Mohr, 1960).

of their first priorities. Universities have also been markedly successful in research. The overwhelming majority of Nobel prizes and other scientific distinctions have gone to university professors, and their output of scholarly work has not been less impressive.[2] Universities, therefore, present a baffling problem for the sociologist. They have apparently chronic and irremediable problems of internal organization, yet they manage to be in some important ways extremely efficient in accomplishing their tasks; and in spite of the constant flow of criticism directed against them, there is a general belief in their necessity even among their critics.

It is not the purpose of this essay to take a stand for or against this widespread belief in the idea of the university or to suggest a solution for its problems. We shall rather ask the question how and why universities became what they are today. Instead of trying to arrive at some concept about the essence or the idea of the university, we shall try to find out under what conditions universities assumed their great variety of functions, and to what extent have they been able to cope with them.

GERMAN UNIVERSITIES AND THE IDEA OF THE MODERN UNIVERSITY

For about a hundred years, between the early nineteenth century and the advent of Nazism, German universities served as model academic institutions. The education of an American or British scientist was not considered complete until he had spent some time in Germany, studying with one of the renowned professors, far more of whom had won acclaim and scientific distinction than the scientists of any other country.[3] The still prevalent conception or 'idea' of the university, as well as the definition of the professor's role, originated in Germany during the 19th century. It was, furthermore, in the German universities, more than anywhere else, that the main fields of scientific enquiry developed into 'disciplines' possessing specialized methodologies and systematically determined contents.[4] Students who wanted to know what a discipline really was had to read German textbooks and those who wanted to keep abreast of scientific research had to read German journals.

The outside world, which became aware of the excellence of German achievements, connected these achievements with the internal structure and organization of the German universities. It came to be widely believed that what a university should be and how a university should be run was dis-

    [2] Cf. Bernard BARBER, *Science and the Social Order* (Glencoe, the Free Press, 1952), pp. 139–169.
    [3] Cf. D. S. L. CARDWELL, *The Organisation of Science in England* (London, Heinemann, 1957).
    [4] Cf. F. PAULSEN, *The German Universities* (New York, Longmans Green, 1906), p. 56; PLESSNER, *op. cit.* vol. I., pp. 23–24.

covered in Germany. The discovery was—and still is—often attributed to the ideas of German philosophers from Kant to Hegel who conceived of the university as a seat of original secular learning pursued as an end in itself, and who imparted to it supreme dignity.[5] During the 19th century reforms were introduced following the German example in Britain, France and the U.S., leading invariably to a rising standard of scientific work and a growing volume of production.[6] This confirmed the belief that the peculiar ideas and arrangements of German universities accounted for their excellence.

We shall attempt to show that these ideas and arrangements were not the cause but rather the result of the circumstances which had historically shaped the German university; that it was not the idea of the university which explains the success of the German university system, nor the diffusion of this idea abroad which explains the impetus to science in those countries introducing organizational reforms under its impact. In order to do this we shall have to examine the circumstances which determined the strength as well as the weaknesses of the German university system.

The pioneering period of the German universities, marked by the rapid development of the different academic fields and their differentiation into systematic and specific disciplines lasted until about the end of the 19th century. By about 1860 the original four faculties of theology, philosophy, law and medicine, comprising just about all higher knowledge existing at the beginning of the century had been transformed beyond all recognition. A host of new disciplines had found their place within the loose frame of the faculties, none of which—with the exception of theology—seems to have been averse to incorporating new fields. Commencing with the third quarter of the century this process of expansion and differentiation slowed down. Neither the emerging social sciences nor the various fields of engineering attained proper academic status at the universities. The latter was banished to the *Technische Hochschulen,* which only over the strenuous opposition of the universities attained the right of confering the title 'doctor.' [7] The universities not only began to offer increasing resistance to the introduction of

[5] The main protagonist of this idea was FLEXNER, *op. cit.* p. 326; cf. also Paul FARMER, "Nineteenth Century Ideas of the University," *in* Margaret CLAPP ed., *The Modern University* (Ithaca, Cornell University Press, 1950), pp. 16–17.

[6] Cf. about England Élie HALÉVY, *History of the English People,* Epilogue: 1895–1905, Book 2 (London, Penguin Books, 1939), p. 24; about France, GUERLAC, *op. cit.,* and about the U.S.A., Abraham FLEXNER, *I Remember* (New York, Simon and Schuster, 1940), pp. 63–64. About the fluctuations of scientific productivity in different countries, cf. T. J. RAINOFF, Wave-like Fluctuations in Creative Productivity in the Development of West European Physics in the 18th and 19th centuries, *Isis,* XII (1922), 287–319; and Joseph BEN-DAVID, Scientific Productivity and Academic Organisation in Nineteenth Century Medicine, *American Sociological Review,* XXV (1960), 828–843.

[7] CARDWELL, *op. cit.* pp. 184–185; FLEXNER, *Universities, op. cit.* pp. 331–332. There were however some who were sympathetic to the introduction of engineering studies at universities, cf. PAULSEN, *op. cit.* pp. 112–113.

new sciences which had mushroomed outside their walls, they also placed often insurmountable obstacles on the path of disciplines which had begun to develop organically within the established disciplines. Where previously it had been relatively easy to carve out new disciplines from the broad fields and gain recognition through the establishment of separate chairs for them, new specialities were increasingly condemned to permanent subordinate status under the pretext of being too narrow or shallow, and, therefore, '*nicht ordinierbar.*' The division of labor which arose in the *Instituten* (research laboratories usually attached to a university chair but not properly integrated within the university) raced far ahead of the increasingly out-of-date academic division of labor. The unity of teaching and research broke down when the academic scientist was forced to specialize in the *Institut* in research that threatened to isolate him from the main discipline which he had to teach if he wanted to become a full professor. The usual rule that each discipline was represented by only one professor contributed much in the previous decades to the establishment of new chairs, because the expansion of the academic staff could take place only in this manner. After the development of the institutes, however, the same rule became a veritable strangling-noose: research could be conducted only in the *Institut* but only one person, the director, could be professor.[8]

Thus gradually a fence was drawn around the existing academic fields, excluding an increasing part of scientific and scholarly enquiry from the universities. Originally the university was meant to embrace all intellectual enquiry.[9] It absorbed all existing disciplines, theoretical and practical. Even its philosophical founding fathers, like Fichte, Schleiermacher, and Schelling, were as much publicists as 'academic' philosophers. In the middle of the century the university became more strictly academic, but it created new disciplines and enlarged its scope, so that practically all the important scientific activity of that time originated at the university. Towards the end of the century both processes of extending the scope of the university came to a standstill.

This growing resistance to differentiation within, and to intellectual (or practical) influence from without, was accompanied by inflexibility of the organizational structure. The professorial role, and the career pattern *Privatdozent-Professor*, so well suited to the needs of research and teaching at the beginning and in the middle of the nineteenth century, when tech-

---

[8] Christian v. FERBER, *Die Entwicklung des Lehrkörpers der deutschen Hochschulen 1864–1954,* vol. III of PLESSNER, *op. cit.* pp. 67–71; for particular cases, cf. e. g. F. v. MÜLLER, *Lebenserinnerungen* (München 1953), pp. 150–151; H. FRIEDENWALD, A *Chronique Scandaleuse* in the Vienna School, *in* Emmanuel BERGHOFF, *Festschrift zum 80. Geburtstag Max Neuburgers* (Wien 1948).

[9] Cf. René KÖNIG, *Vom Wesen der deutschen Universität* (Berlin, Verlag Die Runde, 1935), pp. 134 sqq.

niques and organization of research were simple, became unable to carry any more the whole burden of research and teaching. *Privatdozentur* in particular became an anomaly in fields where the most necessary research facilities were open only to assistants in the *Institut,* so that a *Privatdozent* without a position in an *Institut* had no opportunity for doing scientific work. The main career-line became, therefore, the assistantship. Yet the constitution of the university and its official structure of roles has hardly taken note of the change. Officially, even today the institutes are only appendages facilitating the professor's research.[10] Even if in some cases this arrangement works well (depending on the personality of the professors and the nature of the discipline) it shows extreme traditionalism and ritualistic clinging to organizational forms which no longer reflect the changed functions of the university.

The explanation of this contradiction between the innovative vitality of the early years of the German university and its subsequent rigidity lies mainly in two circumstances[11]: the fact that the German cultural area extending over the major part of Central Europe has always exceeded the limits of any German state, and the position of the university in Germany's class system.[12] Due to the first factor there did not arise in Germany central national universities, like Paris in France, or Oxford-Cambridge in England. The university system was decentralized and competitive. Universities tried to outdo each other, or, at any rate, had to keep pace with each other. As a result innovations were introduced in Germany more easily and accepted more widely than elsewhere. The second factor, namely the position of the university in the class system, accounts for the inflexibility of its organizational structure which became manifest late in the 19th century. As it will be shown later, the status and the freedom of the university, seemingly so well established and secure, were as a matter of fact precarious, engendering fear of and resistance to any organizational change.

This interpretation of the developments is not in accordance with the usually accepted view which relates the rise of the German universities to the reforms introduced early in the century under the influence of the then current philosophical ideas, especially the establishment of the University of Berlin. We have to see, therefore, what was the share of ideas, and of competition and class structure, in the process. Indeed, Berlin was the

---

[10] PLESSNER, *op. cit.* vol. I., pp. 37–49, 192, 223; VON FERBER, *op. cit.* pp. 87–88; FLEXNER, *Universities, op. cit.* p. 332.

[11] This *Erstarrung* of the German university was observed by Troeltsch; cf. SAMUEL and THOMAS, *Education and Society in Modern Germany* (London, Routledge and Kegan Paul, 1949), p. 123.

[12] The importance of these circumstances in the development of scientific research has been treated in Joseph BEN-DAVID, *op. cit.,* and in "Roles and Innovations in Medicine," *American Journal of Sociology,* LXV (1960), 557–568.

first university in which the philosophical faculty (including arts and sciences) obtained a status formally equivalent, but in influence superior, to the old faculties of law, medicine and theology. There is no doubt that the granting of academic status to the new arts and sciences was a decisive step, and that philosophers had a great part in this innovation. There was a growing class of intellectuals in Germany towards the end of the 18th century who would not enter any more into the clergy as people like them had done before, and who interested themselves in the broad field of learning and methodical thinking which was called at that time philosophy.

* * *

During the first twenty to thirty years after the reform of the universities, the general intellectual approach which hardly distinguished between philosophy, history, literature and even natural sciences was broken down into specialized disciplines: history, linguistics, philology etc. All these were closely connected with the ideological bias of German philosophy which identified culture mainly with the humanities.[13] But the breaking down of 'philosophy' into specialized disciplines was in itself a departure from the ideological bias, and it occurred as the result of a simple mechanism; whenever the demand for professors in a certain field was saturated, there was a tendency among the more enterprising students to enter new fields regarded until then as mere sub-specialties of an established discipline, and to develop the specialty into a new discipline. Thus when the humanities were saturated around 1830-40, there occurred a shift of interest towards empirical natural sciences, and the interest in speculative philosophy at the universities abated.

This process has been traced in the development of physiology.[14] Lectures in the subject were held already during the first decades of the 19th century at German universities, but work was sporadic and haphazard. In 1828 physiology as an experimental discipline was represented in only six German universities by seven lecturers.[15] It was a side-line of anatomy which was beginning to separate from surgery, staking out the entire field of theoretical medicine as its domain. This process took place during the 30's and 40's and by the end of that period anatomy had become the main discipline of scientific medicine, the nucleus from which medicine was turned into a natural science. This new anatomy was taught at almost all German universities in connexion with physiology. Competence in physiology, rather than in surgery, became a necessary qualification for attaining the chairs for anatomy. It was however not always possible to implement this requirement. Vacant chairs for anatomy could be staffed with scholars

---

[13] Cf. PAULSEN, *op. cit.* pp. 55–63.

[14] Awraham ZLOCZOWER, *Career Opportunities and the Growth of Scientific Discovery in 19th Century Germany, with special reference to physiology*, M. A. Thesis, *Hebrew University*, Jerusalem 1960 (unpublished).

[15] K. E. ROTHSCHUH, *Geschichte der Physiologie* (Berlin, Springer, 1953), p. 93.

familiar with and competent in both fields, but what was one to do with the anatomists of the old school whose privilege to teach anatomy could not be revoked, who yet would not, and could not, teach the new subject? To establish separate chairs for physiology was easier than the creation of a second chair, part of whose function would be to duplicate work entrusted already to the incumbent of a recognized discipline.[16] The forties and fifties were thus periods when specialization in physiology was encouraged and scientific activity in this sphere stimulated. Scholars who hoped for calls to chairs in anatomy were encouraged to focus their research on physiological problems, since most universities still hoped to entrust the teaching of both physiology and anatomy to a single professor, while here and there separate chairs for physiology had already established the complete independence of the new discipline. The prospect of separate chairs stimulated those scientists with special aptitude to devote themselves entirely to the new discipline. Their concentrated work, partly, no doubt in response to the prospect of rapid advancement, soon disqualified the non-specialists from effective competition, and universities had to grant the demand of physiologists for the establishment of separate chairs.[17] The separation of physiology from anatomy, which had been a temporary 'emergency solution' to cope with obstacles to the modification of the role of 'anatomists,' thus became inevitable. This separation was implemented during the fifties and sixties of the 19th century. When in 1858 Johannes Müller died, and his chair was split into one for anatomy and one for physiology, this was not a pioneer innovation, but the rectification of an anachronism. Although the final separation in Giessen did not take place till 1891 the process of separation had been accomplished at almost all universities by 1870.[18]

Between 1855 and 1874 twenty-six scientists were given their first appointment to chairs of physiology (sometimes still combined with anatomy) Ten of these were appointed between 1855–59 alone. But therewith the discipline reached the limit of its expansion in the German university system (the number of chairs for physiology in German universities—excluding Austria and Switzerland—had reached 15 by 1864, 19 in 1873 and remained at 20 in 1880, 1890 and 1900).[19] Between 1875 and 1894 only nine scholars received appointments to chairs in physiology, stepping into chairs vacated by their incumbents.

That aspiration to a professorship in physiology during the seventies

---

[16] Bruno KISCH, *Forgotten Leaders in Modern Medicine* (Philadelphia, American Philosophical Society, 1954), p. 174. On the refusal of physiologists to accept chairs obliging them to teach anatomy as well, cf. E. GAGLIARDI *et al.*, *Die Universität Zürich 1833–1933 und ihre Vorläufer* (Zürich, Erziehungsdirektion, 1938), pp. 539–548.

[17] ZLOCZOWER, *op. cit.*

[18] ROTHSCHUH, *op. cit.* p. 108.

[19] v. FERBER, *op. cit.* pp. 204–205.

and eighties was all but hopeless, is shown by the tenure of chairs at various universities throughout that period by first-generation physiologists, the generation which had in a cohort-like manner conquered the chairs which the university system was capable of providing. Du Bois-Reymond monopolized the chair in Berlin from 1858–96; Brücke reigned in Vienna for four decades 1849–90; Eckhard held the chair in Giessen from 1855–91. Karl Ludwig, after more than fifteen years in the Josefinum in Vienna, Zürich and Marburg, managed to put in a further thirty (fruitful) years in Leipzig between 1865–95; Karl Vierordt remained in Tübingen from 1855 till his death in 1884; Göttingen, Breslau, Bonn and Munich were held during 1860–1905, 1859–97, 1859–1910 and 1863–1908 by Meissner, Heidenhain, Pflüger and Voit respectively, while Ecker and Rollett kept the chairs in Freiburg 1850–87 and Graz 1863–1903 out of circulation. Large and small universities alike had not a single vacancy in physiology for decades, and no prospect of such an occurrence was in sight during the seventies and eighties.[20] The result was that research in physiology lost momentum. A count of discoveries relevant to physiology in Germany shows that 321 such discoveries were made during the twenty years period of rapid expansion between 1855–1874 compared with 232 during the subsequent (and 168 during the preceding) twenty years.[21] Scientific idealism notwithstanding, young scholars sought greener pastures. The number of *Privatdozenten* and extraordinary professors which had been 12 in 1864 declined to 4 in 1873, 6 in 1880 and rose again only in 1890 to 13. There were better ways of becoming a professor than through the study of physiology: hygiene for instance had only one chair in 1873 and grew to 19 by 1900. Psychiatry grew from one chair to 16 and ophthalmology from 6 to 21 during the same period, while pathology, which had only 7 chairs in 1864 had reached 18 by 1880.[22] The enthusiasm for physiology cooled considerably.

This was the characteristic manner in which the German universities operated *as a system,* determining the life cycles of academic disciplines. It was the decentralized nature of the system and the competition among the individual units which brought about the rapid diffusion of innovations and not the internal structure of each unit, or the dominant philosophy of education. More than twenty first-rate full-time research positions in any one discipline was a huge market for early and mid-nineteenth century conditions, and an emerging discipline could attract considerable talent competing for those positions.

The same twenty positions, however, fell dismally short of the require-

---

[20] ZLOCZOWER, *op. cit.*

[21] Tabulated from K. E. ROTHSCHUH, *Entwicklungsgeschichte physiologischer Probleme in Tabellenform* (München und Berlin 1952).

[22] v. FERBER, *loc. cit.*

ments of sustained scientific research under modern conditions. But the internal structure of the individual universities, bolstered by the idea of the university, allowed the perpetuation of this archaic arrangement in the face of changing conditions, and obstructed the growth of research roles capable of meeting the demands of modern science. The structural limitations of the German university remained latent so long as role-differentiation permitted the continued expansion of the academic profession, but once the *Institut* blocked this path toward professorial chairs, the inadequacy of the structure became manifest.

The reason why at that stage the structure of the university was not modified lies, as pointed out, in the class structure of Germany. In order to understand the way this affected the universities, we have to go back again to the origins. Prussia's rulers, even when, heeding the propaganda of intellectuals, they established the University of Berlin, were no intellectuals themselves. For them the professional training of lawyers, civil servants, doctors and teachers was the main function of higher education. By inclination they would have preferred the Napoleonic type of separate professional schools, and indeed had established such schools themselves earlier. They were converted to the idea of the university, since, as shown above, under the circumstances philosophy served the political interests of the nation and because this was also a reasonable decision from the point of view of their absolutistic principles. By granting corporate freedom to the universities they not only showed themselves as enlightened rulers, sympathetic to the intellectual mood of the time, but also vindicated the principle of legitimacy; the corporate rights of the university had been, after all, a medieval tradition destroyed by the French Revolution.[23]

As a result, the newly founded University of Berlin, as well as the other universities following its example, have never been the institutions of which the philosophers had dreamt. The freedoms effectively granted to them were limited and the functions assigned to them were much more practical and trivial than desired.

First of all the influence of the state was always decisive, even where not visible. One of the simple ways through which state interference worked was the existence of government examinations for various professional titles. Formally, these examinations did not infringe the freedom of the universities to confer their own degrees, or establish their own courses of study. Since, however, the overwhelming majority of the students learnt for practical purposes, the curricula were greatly influenced by the wishes of the government. The influence was all the stronger, since the establishment of new chairs also depended on the government.[24]

[23] PAULSEN, *op. cit.* p. 51.
[24] SAMUEL and THOMAS, *op. cit.* pp. 114–115.

The curricula and in consequence the chairs and the faculties were, therefore, so constituted that the university was overwhelmingly a professional school. The freedom of the academic staff could only manifest itself within the framework established by the interest of the state. It manifested itself in the emphasis on basic subjects rather than practical training, and on theory rather than knowledge. This was the case even in the faculties of medicine and law, not to speak of the humanities and natural sciences.[25] In these latter, the fact that the overwhelming majority of students prepared for secondary school teaching was only recognized in the usual combinations of disciplines studied, but not at all in the contents of the teaching. This aimed only at imparting the systematic knowledge of the disciplines, but took no account of teaching methodology, educational psychology etc., all of great importance to the future teacher.

Academic freedom furthermore manifested itself in the criteria used for appointments or promotions. Achievements in original research were considered—at least in principle—the most important criteria, even in such supposedly practical fields as e.g. clinical medicine, and the expert judgement of the academic staff, supposedly the most competent to judge people according to this criterion, was always one of the important bases of appointments (made actually by the state).[26]

These circumstances then determined what was studied at the university and how it was studied. The philosophical or, later, the systematically scientific aspects were emphasized in courses, the contents of which were determined largely by professional requirements. And the dual role of the professor, officially paid for teaching a subject to would-be professionals, but actually appointed for outstanding research (not necessarily central to his subject of teaching), arose as a result of similar compromise. The idea of the university, according to which both arrangements were considered as the best ways of promoting university study as well as research, was but an ideological justification of this practical compromise. Like all ideologies, it was used in defense of a constantly threatened position. Universities had to be on their guard, lest by being used openly for practical purposes—for which they were used as a matter of fact under the guises and compromises here described—they lose their precarious freedom of engaging in pure research. Hence the resistance to the dilution of the charismatic role of the professor chosen from the ranks of free *Privatdozenten,* by fully institutionalizing the new research and training roles growing up in the institutes. These latter looked 'dangerously' like mere bureaucratic-technical careers. For

[25] Cf. DIEPGEN, *Geschichte der Medizin* (Berlin, Gruyter, 1955), vol. II-1, pp. 152–153; Theodor BILLROTH, *The Medical Sciences in the German Universities* (New York, Macmillan 1924), p. 27.
[26] PAULSEN, *op. cit.* pp. 83–86.

similar reasons the granting of academic standing to technology and new practical subjects was usually opposed. In brief, the freedom and the prestige of the German universities seemed to be safest when the university was kept isolated from the different classes and practical activities of society; it pursued, therefore, a policy aimed at the preservation of an esoteric and sacred image of itself.

Another important limitation of academic freedom was the fact that University professors were civil servants, and considered it a privilege to be part of this important corps. They were, therefore, expected to be loyal to the state, which under absolutist rule implied a great deal. As long as one genuinely agreed with the purposes of the rulers, this problem was not apparent. There was, therefore, a semblance of real freedom at the universities during the nationalist struggle and shortly thereafter, when on the one hand intellectuals often identified with Prussian politics, and on the other hand state-power was not very efficient. But after the middle of the century, when social problems and imperialism became the main political issues and the state increasingly efficient and powerful, the potential restraints on freedom became felt. Identification with the politics of the state often meant fanatical nationalism and obscurantism, a famous example of which was Treitschke, while opposition to it might have provoked interference by the state, as it happened in the case of social-democrats seeking academic appointments.[27]

Thus, again, freedom had to be sought within these given limits. It was clear that under the prevailing conditions the introduction of actualities, whether in the form of philosophical publicism, or in the form of politically relevant social science, would not have led to detached discussion and the emergence of objective criteria, but to the flooding of universities by anti-democratic demagogues and the suppression of the limited amount of liberalism which existed in them. Thoughtful liberals, such as Max Weber for example, chose, therefore, the doctrine of *Wertfreiheit* of scientific enquiry.[28] Declaring value judgements to be incompatible with true scientific enquiry and academic teaching seemed the most efficient way of ensuring freedom of discussion at the university. It was a morally respectable and logically justifiable principle which could be defended without recourse to the actual situation. But it was the actual situation which made this approach more or less the accepted doctrine of the university. It was the doctrine best suited to the maintenance of the delicate balance in a situation where free, non-

[27] SAMUEL and THOMAS, *op. cit.* pp. 116–118; PAULSEN, *op. cit.* pp. 105, 246–247; C. D. DARLINGTON, Freedom and Responsibility in Academic Life, *Bulletin of the Atomic Scientists*, XIII (1957), 131–134.

[28] Max WEBER, "Science as a Vocation," *in* H. H. GERTH and C. Wright MILLS, *From Max Weber: Essays in Sociology* (New York, Oxford University Press, 1947), pp. 129 sqq.; cf. SAMUEL and THOMAS, *op. cit.* pp. 121–123.

utilitarian enquiry was supported and given high status by an absolutist state; and where free-thinking intellectuals taught students usually sharing the autocratic views of the rulers of the state, and preparing for government careers as civil servants, judges, prosecutors and teachers.[29]

This doctrine of *Wertfreiheit,* most clearly formulated by Weber after the First World War, had been as a matter of fact an important guiding principle of academic thinking and action in the second half of the 19th century, i.e. as soon as the possible conflict between academic freedom and absolutism became acute.[30] It explains the extreme caution and wariness towards intellectual influences coming from outside the universities, especially if these influences had some ideological implications.[31]

The observed inflexibilities of the German university were, therefore, the results of its precarious position in the German class structure. Intellectual enquiry in Germany did not thrive as part and parcel of the way of life of a 'middle class' of well-to-do people, whose position was based not on privilege but on achievement in various fields. It started thriving as a hothouse flower mainly on the whimsical support of a few members of the ruling class, and desperately attempted to establish wider roots in society. The universities created under the—from the point of view of the intellectuals—particularly favourable conditions of the struggle against Napoleon, were the only secure institutionalized framework for free intellectual activity in the country. The status and the privileges of the universities were granted to them by the military-aristocratic ruling class, and were not achieved as part of the growth of free human enterprise. It was, therefore, a precarious status based on a compromise whereby the rulers regarded the universities and their personnel as means for the training of certain types of professionals, but allowed them to do this in their own way and use their position for the pursuit of pure scholarship and science (which the rulers did not understand, but were usually willing to respect). The universities had to be, therefore, constantly on the defensive, lest by becoming suspected of subversion, they lose the élite position which ensured their freedom.

The idea of the German university evolved as a result of these conditions. It stressed the pursuit of pure science and scholarship as the principal function of the university, divided learning into disciplines with specialized methodologies, extolled *Wertfreiheit* in scholarly teaching and writing, was wary of applied subjects, as well as non-academic influence (including

[29] *Ibid.* pp. 116–121, 128, about the delicate balance of the status of the *Gelehrtenstand,* and the spirit prevailing among students.

[30] *Ibid.* p. 118 about the reaction in the spirit of *Wertfreiheit* of the first Congress of German Historians in 1893 to the imperial decree of 1889, directing education to the task of combating revolutionary political doctrines.

[31] E.g. the social sciences; about their limited development, only somewhat modified after the first world war, cf. FLEXNER, *Universities, op. cit.* pp. 328, 332–333.

non-academic intellectual influence), and refused to grant institutional recognition to any teaching or research roles besides those of the *Privatdozent* and Professor. As it has been shown here, these ideas were not originally conceived as a means to an end. They were rather the description made into an ideology of the tactics actually employed by the universities in their struggle for maintaining their freedom and privileges.

It is true that the German universities had been highly successful in the development of the so-called pure scientific and scholarly fields. This success, however, was not due to any deliberate design or purpose on their part (according to the original idea there should have been a single German university devoted mainly to speculations in idealist philosophy), but to the unintended mechanism of competition which exploited rapidly all the possibilities for intellectual development open to the universities. That this development was largely limited to the basic fields was the result of the factors here described, as were the other aspects of growing inflexibility; the slowing down of the differentiation of existing disciplines into their unfolding specialties, as well as the ossification of university organisation refusing to take proper notice of the transformation of scientific work.

THE ENGLISH UNIVERSITIES:
HIGHER EDUCATION FOR THE "CLASSES"

If Germany was the first country to develop a system of modern universities, England was the first major country to be influenced by it. From the 1830's to World War I German universities were held up as a challenge, and/or a model to the English ones, and all the numerous new foundations and reforms of higher education and research were influenced by the German example.[32] Nevertheless, there never developed in England a German type of university. What emerged was something rather baffling to observers accustomed to use the German "idea of the university" as a yardstick for measuring academic accomplishment.

They admired English universities for the quality of their graduates; criticized them for their mediocre performance in many fields and their seeming indifference toward the active promotion of research; and were mystified by the nevertheless brilliant work of some English scientists.

This lack of success of the English universities in matching the German —or more recently the American—ones in the systematic development of research as well as their success as institutions of higher training and education has been the result of the social conditions of their growth. The same conditions used in the explanation of the German case, namely the extent

[32] CARDWELL, *op. cit.*

of centralization and the relationship of the universities to the different classes of society, seem to have been also the main determinants of university development in England. But the English university system has been centralized to a much greater extent than the German, while the class structure of England was much more open than that of Germany.

*   *   *

The core of the English university system has always been Oxford and Cambridge. Until the middle of the last century they had educated the sons of the nobility, and future clergymen.[33] They were educational institutions of the élite. Their scholarly standards were low, according to some even extremely low, but scholarship or science were irrelevant for the majority of élite positions. The few students who subsequently became physicians, surgeons or lawyers, could comfortably learn their professions as apprentices in their respective professional corporations, and all the erudition required by a clergyman could be acquired by private study. Intimate knowledge of the ways of the gentry was certainly more important for the ecclesiastical career than theological sophistication.

While Oxford and Cambridge served the gentry and the clergy, a new type of intellectual, interested in science and secular philosophy, grew up in the cities. Under their influence, and with the support of a liberal upper middle class, there arose different institutions, such as the Royal Institution, mechanics institutes, philosophical societies, colleges etc., providing some facilities for research and a platform for the dissemination of modern science. University College, London was the first university to emerge from these various popular efforts. It was meant to be a utilitarian institution designed for the acquisition of knowledge useful in practical life (about half of the students prepared for medicine).[34] This utilitarian tendency was enhanced in the University of London, chartered in 1836, which became an examining body, granting recognized degrees to students of an increasing variety of London colleges, provincial and colonial institutions, and later even to students preparing for the examination privately. This arrangement had incidentally introduced a great deal of uniformity to a great variety of provincial institutions.[35]

The modern English university arose . . . out of two traditions: aristocratic élite education designed to mould the character and impart a peculiar way of life on the one hand, and utilitarian training and teaching for pro-

---

[33] Cf. C. Arnold ANDERSON and Miriam SCHNAPER, *School and Society in England; Social Background of Oxford and Cambridge Students* (Washington, Public Affairs Press, 1952).

[34] ARMYTAGE, *op. cit.* pp. 173–174.

[35] *Ibid.* p. 216; CARDWELL, *op. cit.* pp. 36–37, 72.

fessional and industrial middle class careers on the other hand. Universities were not—as in Germany—preserves of privileged intellectuals, isolated from providing training for the diffuse positions of the élite, or for specific middle class careers, and enjoying the freedom of doing, as a matter of fact, a great many other things (especially research). They were educational institutions providing training for the diffuse positions of the élite, or for specific middle class careers, in both instances for a practical purpose.

Until the middle of the nineteenth century the two kinds of universities existed side by side without the one affecting the other. The reform of Oxford and Cambridge after 1850 was not the result of these universities attempting to change their function of élite education, but of apprehensions about the loss of their élite function. The new scientific and professional class acquired an increasingly important position in society and exercised a growing influence on the conduct of public affairs. Some of them were rising into the élite, others became the "new clerisy" replacing the influence of the clergy on the minds of men as writers, philosophers, advisers, experts and last but not least teachers.[36] Had Oxford and Cambridge not accepted the new learning, then inevitably they would have lost their central place in the so-called Establishment.

* * *

The English university system has . . . never become competitive. Universities, like so much else in that society, arranged themselves in a relatively neat hierarchy. Authority in academic matters has been centrally wielded by groups of people, most of whom were related one way or another to the two ancient universities. There has been no incentive for academic innovations: the two leading universities did not need it, and the rest had limited chances of competing with them through the introduction of novelties. The way to academic prestige has been through imitation of the accepted disciplines, of the 'solidly established standards' and the habits of thinking of the most prestigeful universities rather than through innovation and experimentation.

This explains the way the English system has worked. The universities, unlike those in Germany, or as will be seen later, in America, did not create new disciplines, or professions, and did not develop research systematically. At the same time, however, they were much more open to outside influences than were the German universities. Both parts of the system served certain classes of the society: Oxford and Cambridge the élite, and the provincial universities the middle classes. They have responded with relative flexibility to demands arising in these classes. Thus the two old universities introduced,

[36] Cf. Armytage, *op. cit.* pp. 178, 206.

in addition to arts, empirical science and a limited amount of professional studies, while provincial universities admitted a much greater variety of professional subjects. Research was also introduced as a result of specific outside demands (e.g. in agriculture), or as a requirement of teaching certain subjects, mainly experimental natural sciences, at a university level. This is why its development has seemed haphazard; it followed the emergence of this variety of demands, rather than its own internal logic.

* * *

THE AMERICAN UNIVERSITY: THE LARGE-SCALE ACADEMIC ENTERPRISE

The transformation of the modern university into a system serving a variety of purposes and adjusting itself to the needs of different classes of society began, as we have seen, in England. The transformation, however, was limited and with the passing of time lost momentum, due to the centralized hierarchic system of universities which turned the middle-class provincial universities into intellectual colonies of Oxford and Cambridge. The potentialities of the English beginnings were only realized in the United States. American universities grew out of the British tradition, and American class structure was even more open than the British: there was constant interchange and movement between the classes, and, in addition, there was no central hierarchy regulating these movements. The mobility of individuals, classes, and universities did not have to assume, therefore, the form of a gradual approach to the central model, but took place through competition, each unit exploiting its relative advantages.

During the first half of the 19th century the American academic scene was very similar to that of Britain. On the one hand there were the colleges, similar in their organization and scope of studies to the English or the Scottish universities, but their numbers were much greater, and none of them possessed a relative standing similar to Oxford and Cambridge. These were at that time institutions of modest intellectual calibre, usually of religious character. On the other hand there was a bewildering variety of professional schools in medicine, law and technology. There existed also numerous societies and colleges which advocated the cause of science but did very little about it. The reasons for this backwardness were the same as those which retarded academic development in England: scientific knowledge and research had few practical uses, and America was an even more utilitarian and pragmatic society than England. There were groups and individuals interested in science and scholarship as a hobby and quite a few who believed in its ultimate usefulness: but a great deal of conviction was needed to believe that one would go further by extending the frontiers of knowledge than by pushing back the frontier in the West.[37]

The transformation starting about 1860 was due to similar circumstances as in Britain, namely increasing conviction of the practical usefulness of science and higher education on the one hand, and the growth of scientific interest among a few rich and/or influential people on the other. As in England the first, utilitarian influence led to the establishment of vocationally oriented institutions, such as the M.I.T., the land-grant colleges, state universities etc., while the second led to the reform of Harvard and other older institutions, and the establishment of Johns Hopkins University aimed at fostering pure scholarship and science. In the U.S.A., therefore, as in England, the introduction of modern science and up-to-date specialized scholarship into existing universities, as well as the foundation of new types of colleges and universities, followed rather than created the emergence of social demand for such activity. Both were in these respects "open" educational systems, readily influenced by pressures arising at the same time in various classes of society.[38]

Here, however, the parallel ends. As indicated above, the U.S. has never possessed a representative university situated in the capital or near to it, with the intellectual élite of the country residing in the vicinity. This created the conditions necessary for competition, such as existed in Germany during most of the 19th century, but not in Britain. The old established universities could not, therefore, be content in the U.S. to stay out of the race for innovation, and even less could they inhibit by their example and the all-pervasive influence of their alumni the innovations made in the newer universities. They were rather compelled to follow suit, and to engage in innovations themselves, trying to preserve their pre-eminence through executing those innovations better than the others, or through different innovations of their own.

Thus when Gilman, the president of the newly founded university of Johns Hopkins, refused to follow the example of Harvard, and established a research university such as did not exist anywhere, Harvard and eventually all the important universities had to follow suit. A similar mechanism

[37] Cf. Richard HOFSTADTER and C. DeWITT HARDY, *The Development and Scope of Higher Education in the United States* (New York, Columbia University Press, 1952), p. 21; Richard J. STORR, *The Beginnings of Graduate Education in America* (Chicago, University of Chicago Press, 1953), pp. 1–6, 24, 52, 63, 79–80, 102, 107; Richard H. SHRYOCK, *Medicine and Society in America 1660–1860* (New York, New York University Press, 1960), pp. 138–143.

[38] Donald H. FLEMING, *William Welch and the Rise of Modern Medicine* (Boston, Little Brown, 1954), pp. 173 sqq., HOFSTADTER and HARDY, *op. cit.* pp. 26–28, 38, 60 sq.; Abraham FLEXNER, *Daniel Coit Gilman* (New York, Harcourt, Brace and Company, 1946), pp. 38 sq.

brought about the growth and diffusion of the practical professional training developed in the land-grant colleges.[39] As a result old colleges developed
graduate departments and professional schools, technological institutes and
state colleges introduced humanistic studies and social sciences, and all types
of schools—though not all individual schools—developed research in a
variety of basic and applied fields.

Thus have arisen the very large American universities within which
there is a clear differentiation of functions. Undergraduate teaching is separated from the research-oriented graduate school, and in addition there are
professional schools and often research institutions of one kind or another.

Another result of competition in this equalitarian system is the tendency
towards specialization. In spite of the constant addition of functions, universities may decide to do without certain departments or faculties altogether and concentrate their resources in fields where they have the greatest
chances of success. A good university may exist without a medical school,
or may deliberately neglect some of its basic science or humanities departments; some tend to concentrate on their graduate schools, others on undergraduate teaching. These are of course things which occur in England as
well. But (a) some of the differentiations hardly exist there at all (e.g.
undergraduate/graduate schools); and (b) the smaller universities specializing in certain selected fields never attain real excellence through specialization. In the U.S. there are specialized undergraduate colleges of very high
prestige, and first-rate law and medical schools in mediocre universities; and
small generally unimportant institutions may attain fame in a short time
through concentrating on one or two subjects. This possibility of establishing
the high standing of a university through developing a field neglected by
others has introduced into American universities departments of creative
writing, dramatic arts, music etc., i.e. cultural traditions—and such less
"cultural" ones as football and sports—which remained in Europe largely
outside the universities.

Thus in spite of the unprecedented comprehensiveness of the large
American university, there does not exist in America the conception that a
university has to consist of so many faculties and that each faculty has to
contain a certain well defined series of departments as a minimum. A number of relatively large universtiies would be considered by European standards
as only part institutions. The conception of the university has obviously
changed: it does not pretend to refer to some assumed organic whole of all
humanistic and scientific knowledge. The fact that the different faculties
and professional schools have entirely different requirements is more clearly

    FLEXNER, ibid. p. 108; Richard HOFSTADTER and Walter P. METZGER, The
Development of Academic Freedom in the United States (New York, Columbia University Press, 1955), pp. 378–383.

faced than in Europe. The question, therefore, of which faculties and schools should exist in a given university is not considered as a matter of principle but rather as one of expediency.

The same applies to the internal structure of the faculties. Here too the fiction that a faculty consists of professors, i.e. individuals rather than departments, has disappeared. The units within the faculty are departments which are not a one-man show, but an institution deliberately designed to provide an efficient and well rounded unit where experts in the different specialties complement each other. This is an entirely different organization from the German institute which exists to foster the research of its head, and where the representatives of other specialities than that of the head of the institute are invariably in a subordinate position. In an American department there may be, and in a good one there always are, several professors of equal rank, there is often a strong spirit of colleagueship, and the division of labor is functional rather than hierarchic.[40]

This provides a basis for teamwork and graduate training such as exists nowhere in Europe. Even in England where, as we have seen, there arose more differentiated departments than in Germany, the 'chairs' are severely limited and there are many invidious distinctions of status and power which prevent the development of an atmosphere of independence and self-confidence necessary for genuine co-operation.[41] It has to be repeated that the development of the departments into such self-contained and efficient units has been the result of competition. The distribution between universities of Ph. D. degrees in different subjects shows that only a relatively small number of institutions confer such degrees at all, and that the list of universities conferring Ph. D. degrees in each subject is constantly changing.[42] This shows that only efficient departments can compete at this level, so that universities have to concentrate constantly on building up their individual departments (and, as shown, quite often to make their choice among them). The existence of a growing number of industrial and governmental research units in a great many fields only enhances this tendency towards building up the departmental organization.

This variety of schools and departments each with its specialized function is reflected in the differentiation of academic roles which goes much further even than that existing in England. There are specialized academic educators and administrators; academic researchers who are hardly teaching at all, as well as advanced practitioners of professions and arts.

[40] Logan WILSON, *op. cit.* pp. 53–93; CAPLOW and McGEE, *op. cit.*
[41] Cf. J. M. ZIMAN, The American Scientist, *New Statesman*, LXII [No. 1591] (1961), 300–302.
[42] Cf. Office of Scientific Personnel, *The Baccalaureate Origins of the Science Doctorates Awarded in the United States* (Washington, National Academy of Sciences/National Research Council, Publication No. 382, 1955), p. 19.

This peculiar working of the system explains the often stated fact that the research function evolved in German universities and grafted on to both the English and the American ones took much better hold on the latter than on the former. But it is a mistake to assume simply that American universities took over and developed what they learnt from Germany. Research in America has developed in the departments which, as we have seen, are quite different organizations from German university institutes. It has thus become a regular university operation which, at times, may be of equal or superior importance to teaching. Universities, furthermore, fostered applied research of a kind which never developed in Germany.[43] One cannot, therefore, attribute these developments to beneficial European influence. They were rather the result of the same inherent characteristics of the American system which brought forth the much less admired proliferation of professional schools. This has been a system which placed a premium on innovations, and has been open to a great variety of social pressures. It adopted and developed, therefore, an ever increasing variety of functions in research, as well as professional and other types of education. Innovation became a pervasive tendency of the American university system, as in the similarly competitive German one during the 19th century, but in contrast to the German case this innovativeness has not been limited to pure non-utilitarian science and scholarship but has been extended to applied and professional fields too.

Comparing the three systems so far surveyed it can be said that while German universities were bent upon creating new science, and English universities intended to teach it to those using it (provided that they proved themselves 'respectable' enough for higher education), American universities have tried not only to teach and create new science but also new applications and professions catering for the élite as well as the masses. Thus universities assumed an important function in the growing professionalization of occupational life, and in making research an increasingly permanent aspect of business, industry, and administration.

For better or worse, the American university system, with its constantly expanding and heterogeneous functions, is now the most influential system of higher education and research. Most of the discussions about higher education and of the changes introduced in it since the end of the Second World War all over the world have been the result of American influence. This influence spreads partly through the increasing international contacts of academic workers which converge nowadays on America as they used to converge in the past on Germany, and partly through the emergence of new

[43] HOFSTADTER and METZGER, *op. cit.* pp. 380–383.

demands among development-minded government administrators, industrialists and businessmen for American-type professional training.

CONCLUSION

Universities only a hundred years ago were exclusive academies of scholars pursuing privately their learned interests and instructing a small number of highly selected students who prepared to enter the civil service or one of the traditional professions, and in exceptional cases became scholars themselves. Today universities educate—in some countries—as much as a fourth to a third of all the young people in the appropriate age groups, and conduct research of vital importance for the survival or destruction of human society.

This change of functions has been to a large extent the result of the work of the universities, though not everywhere and not at every time were universities equally active in creating new functions for themselves. As shown in this paper their eagerness to recognize and develop innovations into new disciplines depended on the existence of a decentralized competitive market for academic achievements; while their willingness to try and develop bits and pieces of practical insight and professional tradition into systematic theory depended on their direct, or government-mediated relationship to the different classes of society.

For reasons connected with their social structure the large countries of Western and Central Europe—England, France and Germany—have not kept pace with this evolution of the functions of higher education and research. They adhered to a conception of the university of a hundred years ago. This conception stems from an age when science had few practical uses, its fields seemed clearly mapped out, and significant research could be conducted in private libraries and laboratories. Today there seems to be no end to the potential uses of systematic research and knowledge; research in every field has become a co-operative enterprise where the lone worker becomes an increasingly rare phenomenon; specialization is so complex that most of the disciplines which about a hundred years ago still seemed narrow specializations are nowadays considered too broad fields for any one person to comprehend; and few people would dare to predict any more what will be the legitimate scope of science to-morrow. The European conception of the university is, therefore, woefully out-of-date. Incomparably more differentiated organization is needed to carry out all the greatly increased and increasingly varied functions of higher education and research.

Such complex academic organization has arisen in the United States and in the Soviet Union. In spite of the vast difference in the formal organization of their higher education and research, both countries have developed clearly differentiated functions of pure as well as applied research and purely scientific and scholarly education alongside highly practical professional training. And both countries managed to create a much greater variety of higher educational and research institutions—whether called universities or not—and, correspondingly, to institutionalize a greater variety of academic roles than the European countries.

European systems of higher education have, as a result, found themselves under pressure from a variety of sources urging them to adopt American academic forms and practices (the influence of the Soviet example is perhaps more felt in America than in Europe). These have resulted in considerable expansion of university education and research facilities and, to a more limited extent, in the establishment of new types of institutions (such as the establishment of technological universities in Britain). These reforms and the expansion which they involve will probably be beneficial to scientific work as such things always are. If, however, the present analysis is correct, the long term success of university reform in Europe will be dependent on the establishment of much less hierarchic and much more decentralized systems of higher education and research than those existing in England and France, and a much less authoritarian and much more flexible university structure than that existing in Germany.

This involves, besides concrete changes of organization, an important modification of the thinking about universities. It is feared that by consciously adapting to new functions academic systems may neglect the one function which, so far, no other organization has managed to foster efficiently: free research, unhampered by any practical consideration, aiming only at original and scientifically significant discovery. There is no doubt that in this respect American and Soviet work often fell below acceptable standards. The criticism levelled against their providing room for courses of doubtful academic standards, or research of no significance, may be justified; but not the conclusion drawn from it that these failures prove the correctness of the European approach, where academic institutions safeguard their standards by strict adherence to established academic forms placing the preservation of established standards before innovation and emphasizing the exclusive esoteric nature of scientific work. Such a conclusion is based on the same kind of fallacy which at the time of the industrial revolution led people to believe in the superiority of the old handicraft system over the new industries since the latter produced at times rather shoddy goods. It is simply not true that the expansion of scientific work lowered standards. The élite group of pure scientists working freely on their own problems has not disappeared in America and the Soviet Union, but has rather developed much beyond whatever exists in Europe. The exodus of European scientists and scholars to the United States has not only been motivated by higher income but often by better conditions for and greater freedom of research.[44] It is clear, therefore, that the irreverent uses made of higher education and research have not estranged science from its immanent standards and values. They have presented to it such dangers, but academic institutions are in a position to safeguard their own ideas where they form a huge and powerful system vitally involved in the affairs of society. There is, however, very little which is worth safeguarding where excessive fear of lowering established standards has led academic institutions to prefer the function of the critic to that of the active initiator of scientific and professional advance.*

[44] Cf. the interesting accounts of André WEIL, "Science française," in *La Nouvelle Revue Française*, III (1955), 97–109; ZIMAN, *op. cit.*, and for a French testimony about conditions at the beginning of the century, René LERICHE, *Am Ende meines Lebens* (Bern/Stuttgart, Huber, 1957), p. 34.

* The authors are indebted to Éric de Dampierre for his very useful suggestions and kind help in obtaining source material.

The Professional Society

D. S. L. CARDWELL

Up to the outbreak of the Great War the development of technology and applied science, as inferred from the supply of skilled labour and hence from the organisation of the training and educational facilities of the country, had been carried forward in response to certain important events. These can be enumerated as follows: the Great Exhibition, or rather the lessons allegedly learned from it, led directly to the South Kensington enterprise, to the Science section of the Department of Science and Art and also prepared the way for later developments in technical training. The alarms of the Paris Exhibition of 1867 fathered the great Technical Education Movement; a movement more concerned, generally speaking, with engineering than with applied science. This distinguishes it from the later movement in the 1890's and early 1900's which was stimulated by the much discussed German achievements in applied science, and which helped to produce increased State aid for the universities, as well as the foundation of Imperial College, the Manchester College of Technology, etc. During each of these times of panic a great deal was accomplished and much more was hoped for—we recall the persistent attempts to found an Industrial University—but, after a while, there came a period when the sense of urgency relaxed and things were allowed to drift until the next alarm; the process was one of fits and starts. There was, in fact, no kind of settled policy for orderly, evolutionary development; there were only a series of responses to awkward situations.

In the absence of such a policy it is not surprising that applied science did not, relatively speaking, play a major role in the first world war. This was not the case in the second world war, of course: science and technology were immensely important. Now the problems that were set and solved in the fields of physics and chemistry, are fascinating in themselves and in the talent and ingenuity needed to resolve them. But the social problems set and solved—the mobilisation of the abilities of a large number of pure and applied scientists—seems to have aroused little interest. This is all the more

Chapter 8, pp. 175–194 in: *The Organisation of Science in England: A Retrospect*. London: William Heinemann, Ltd., 1957. Reprinted with the permission of the author and publisher. Dr. Cardwell is a Reader in the History of Science and Technology at the Manchester College of Science and Technology.

strange when it is recalled that fifty years ago such an achievement, even on the relative scale, would have been quite impossible. It is therefore to the problem of the professional scientist, whether pure or applied, that we must now turn.

It is mainly with scientists of the second and third rank that we are concerned, but before we discuss them it is only correct to consider, briefly, those of the first rank. As we have seen, the machinery of high grade, specialised instruction had been assembled, by the universities and colleges, by 1881—just over the proverbial life-time age. We should naturally expect such a development sooner or later to affect even scientists of the first rank. It is unquestionable that the Royal Society represents the fountain-head of natural science in Britain; election to a Fellowship being regarded as the highest distinction for a scientist. That rationalisation has modified the composition of that Society in the direction of increased specialisation and correlative professionalism is clearly shown by the following brief analysis of Fellows in 1881, 1914 and 1953:

	1881	% Increase	1914	% Increase	1953
Distinguished Laymen	54		38		8
Sailors	13		6		2
Soldiers	26		6		3
Applied Scientists	62	27%	79	70%	134
Academic Scientists	134	116%	289	20%	348
Medical Men	55		11		6
Clergymen	14		4		0
Others	120		40		46

These figures do not require much explanation.[1] There has occurred, over the last seventy years, the virtual exclusion of all not engaged in the physical and biological sciences in a professional capacity—the excision of the amateur element has been surgical in its neatness. And not only the amateur element but those engaged in the sciences other than the "natural" ones have also been removed from the lists. In 1881 and in 1914 there were about six Fellows who were distinguished for their contributions to social science; today, there are about two. Incidentally, the complete absence of clergymen is also worth noticing: the last few years, since the death of Dr. Barnes, must be the first time since its foundation that the Society has been

[1] The clergymen and medical men in 1881, 1914 and the medical men in 1953 are those unassociated with any academic or applied science foundation. Many of the "others" in 1881 were distinguished amateurs—Darwin, Joule, Spottiswoode (P.R.S.), etc., etc. Today there are no amateurs.

without a clerical Fellow—how odd that would have seemed to the Fellows of a hundred years ago!

Limiting ourselves to the rigidly professional scientists, who are broadly grouped into applied and academic, the increases shown are very revealing. The percentage increase of academic Fellows between 1881 and 1914 is actually four times greater than the percentage increase of applied scientists. This does not surprise us when we reflect that that period was marked by the foundation of several new universities and university colleges, by increased State aid for higher education, by an increasing student population and by the foundation of new schools; in short, it was the period of the educational revolution and education was relatively much more important than applied science. On the other hand the period between 1914 and 1953 was marked by the converse process; the percentage of applied scientists increased three times as much as did the percentage of academic Fellows. This is explained by the simple, indeed obvious, fact that applied science has now been achieved in this country.

So much, then, for scientists of the first rank. For those of the second and third rank who in fact comprise the bulk of those in applied science, we shall have to consider industrial employments and secondary and technical school teaching. It would be very difficult to determine the exact number of industrial scientists in the country, but, limiting ourselves to chemists we find that in 1953 a section of the Chemical Industry—actually about one-third as defined by the Ministry of Labour—comprising[2] 234 firms with 151,349 employees, had a scientific staff of 7,406. There were 10,914 engaged on research and development and 3,267 of these were described as of scientific grade. [1] The inference here is that there must be some 9,000 research and development chemists engaged in the chemical industries of the country. But today the chemical industries are by no means the sole employers of chemists. The State, for one, employs very large numbers in places like Harwell and in the associated chemical factories of nuclear energy programmes as well as in the ordnance factories, the defence departments and in the many activities covered by the D.S.I.R. At the same time the physical and biological industries (the latter including agriculture and foodstuffs) are also large employers of research chemists. It would therefore be a plausible estimate that the number of research and development chemists in England is about 10,000 at the present day. In the case of physicists the number may well be somewhat lower but will still be of considerable magnitude.

As for the teaching profession, the Ministry of Education Report for

[2] Heavy chemicals, industrial gases, fertilisers, dye-stuffs, medicinal and other fine chemicals, explosives, plastics and synthetic resins; but not the compounding thereof to make paints, insecticides, etc.

1952 [2] gives the total of teachers holding degrees in the natural sciences and mathematics and engaged in primary, secondary and further education as 13,706. Assuming that one-third of these are chemists—a fraction that is probably a little too great—we get an estimated total of about 4,600 graduate chemistry teachers; adding the 500 or so chemists engaged in university teaching and not included in the Ministry's return, the grand total becomes about 5,100. Which is a number smaller than the combined total of those estimated to be engaged in industrial research and development and in the service of the State. These figures must not, of course, be treated as exact, they are only very approximate; but the trend they indicate is fairly clear: industry has replaced teaching as an occupation of the natural scientists.

Clearly we have made great progress since Dewar's address to the British Association in 1902 and the 200 or so graduate chemists in the chemical industries of that time. A large corps of professional applied scientists and scientific technologists has been created; science is being used systematically and on a national scale to minister to the needs of society, to extend mastery over the natural environment and—most important—to devise entirely new processes, materials and instruments for social use. What is so surprising is the extreme newness of the activity; it is at most some sixty years old. A group of men, numbering a few hundred at the beginning of the nineteenth century and a few thousand at the beginning of this, has been expanded to an unprecedented extent and used to create a series of entirely new technologies as well as to transform and rejuvenate the old established ones.

In his evidence before the Devonshire Commission, Edward Frankland estimated that, in 1845, about twenty persons a year received instruction in practical chemistry in England (none, of course, received instruction in practical physics). If his estimate was substantially correct, and we have no reason to doubt it, there cannot possibly have been more than a few hundred scientists of the second and third rank acting in a professional capacity in England a century ago. Such an estimate will include the staffs of observatories and museums, surveyors of the ordnance and geological offices, a small number connected with the defence forces (F. Abel, for example) and the scattered few in industry. We can illustrate this by comparing the social structure of science a century ago with a slender tower, almost as broad at the top as it was at the lower levels and ground floor. It was inferred that it was the absence of ground floor development that was the cause of the pessimism of those who, starting with Davy and Babbage lamented the decline of English science. Playfair recognised it and Huxley, as we have seen, summed it up accurately when he spoke of the absence of "rank and file." These two were by no means the only ones who understood the deficiency; and by 1916 it was officially admitted that we had still not yet learned to use "mediocre talent" (see above). Today, with our relatively tiny Royal Society and many thousands of second and third rank scientists the social structure of natural science can be correctly compared with a pyramid many times broader at the base than at the top.

Having outlined the establishment of professional science it is necessary to restate, in general terms, the difference between technology, which subsumes engineering, and applied science. The technologist uses the data and the established laws of science, relevant to the subject matter of the industry concerned, to achieve the most efficient production and/or the highest quality of product; to this end he uses both science and practical, i.e., industrial, experience. But the science he uses is established science and this must be so, for any attempt to forward a practical project, under the circumstances that the scientific laws governing the behaviour of the materials or processes involved are inadequately known, is to risk disaster. On the other hand the job of the applied scientist is complementary: it is to advance knowledge of those laws which are, or will be, of practical importance; his researches "feed" the technologist, concerned with practical application, and the sphere of his work is governed by the requirements of the industry which employs him. Of course it is not asserted that all technologists and all applied scientists can be neatly classified in this manner; the definitions are generalisations and there are many cases when it is impossible to say precisely whether a man is a technician or an applied scientist.

It may be argued that because an applied scientist is concerned with the investigation of laws of nature he warrants the title of scientist and the term applied scientist should be used—as it often is—to describe the work of the technologist. This, however, is unacceptable; the researches of the applied scientist are "guided" researches and they are directed, not by purely scientific considerations, but by the requirements of industry. The hallmark of the scientist is his absolute freedom of inquiry; he may wander at will from one field of knowledge to another as the nature of his researches and the impulses of his mind lead him. This freedom of research and its enormous importance for the advancement of science has been demonstrated many times in the history of science; to imagine that science can dispense with it and be unaffected thereby is a great illusion. But this does not mean that the applied scientist and the technologist are to be regarded as truncated scientists; their primary duty and loyalty are not to abstract knowledge but to the industrial welfare of the country.

Technology, judged on the basis of its scientific content, has, of course, existed for as long as the sciences with which it is concerned; and, although it merges imperceptibly into skilled craftsmanship it is, in one sense, antithetical to the latter. The aim of the great Technical Education movements was, above all, to increase the scientific element in technology at the expense of empirical, rule of thumb, or traditional skills. The technical colleges in England, the polytechnics in Germany and Switzerland were established for this very purpose, and with their expansion went the corresponding development of scientific technology and a reduction in the rule of old-fashioned craftsmanship, made necessary by the increasing number of industries founded on the results of contemporary scientific research. This raises a very important question. Is the practice of applied science merely a development or refinement, of technology? In other words, did the class of technologists evolve, in due course, the class of applied scientists?

So far as such a question admits of an answer, it must be in the negative. The evidence shows that the first professional applied scientists were usually trained as pure scientists and that the first industrial research laboratories—in Germany—were derived rather more from university practice—from Giessen and Heidelberg—than from the workshop or the plant. It is a straightforward deduction from this that, before industrial scientific research can be established on a notable scale, a number of conditions must be fulfilled. Respectively, they are: (1) A number of those concerned with the running of industry must have an adequate knowledge of science (this implies an efficient educational system). (2) It must have been shown that scientific research can be effectively carried out when deliberately restricted to certain problems (i.e., can be "guided") and that such researches can produce results which can be usefully applied within a reasonable time. (3) It must be appreciated that researches of this nature do not require first rate talent; quite moderate abilities suffice, and, (4) There must be an adequate supply of professional applied scientists available.

It is not immoderate to claim that, not until the closing years of the nineteenth century did any one of these conditions come near to being satisfied. Indeed, their fulfilment necessitated the abandonment or profound modification of certain well established English traditions and ideals; notably the ideal of the self-taught, self-made leader in industry, the long traditions of higher education and, not least, of learning and science. The meetings of the British Association ninety or a hundred years ago were patronised by a heterogeneous collection of clergymen, university professors, medical men, lawyers, engineers and amateurs, both wealthy and not so wealthy. The absence of a group of professional applied scientists meant that the relationship between science and technology was both loose and indirect, despite individual instances to the contrary. In fact, in the past, scientific revolutions have taken place, as in the seventeenth century, without technical changes and, as in the latter half of the eighteenth century, technical revolutions have been accomplished without effecting any marked changes in contemporary science. Today, science and technology are very closely linked; as the development of nuclear energy, for example, shows.

Sociologists and historians have pointed out that military discipline had to be invented before the use of firearms became effective in warfare. There is surely a marked parallel here with the development of applied science. We note that the professional scientist is, like the competent soldier, a thoroughly trained man and, again like the soldier, he is subjected to discipline; a discipline which, however, is economic and social rather than physical. The training of the professional scientist is generally in a "pure" science and is carried at least to the point at which he is competent to carry out his own researches; preferably research should have formed part of his training. The element of (social) discipline is provided by the fact that he depends on the practice of science for his livelihood.

The beginning of true applied science has been dated, with some precision, as occurring between 1858 and 1862, and in the first instance it appeared in the German dyeing industry. Surprisingly, for as we have seen, there was every incentive for England to render herself independent of foreign dyestuffs. An Englishman had made the actual discovery, the raw material—coal—was both abundant and cheap in England. The capital was available and it is inconceivable that there were no commercially enterprising Englishmen at that time. It may be argued that foreign "protection" and English patent laws were deterrents, but such excuses are special pleading. What is undeniably the case is that at the critical time there was no class of professional, highly trained chemists in England; no large group of men generally recognised as capable of carrying out research in chemistry and, at the same time, expecting to earn a livelihood by doing so.

The aniline dye industry was in one respect, nearly unique. It sprang solely from advance in science; in organic chemistry. The traditional animal and vegetable dyes were replaced by new, scientifically compounded, substances. Science was, we may say, the master key; it was not invoked merely to refine and improve methods or materials which were either immemorial or the result of rule-of-thumb development. At the same time it became clear that systematic research would yield more and even better dyestuffs from coal tar; and it was in this respect that Germany excelled. She had to import the raw coal tar from England, but, to "process" it, she had her large corps of professional research chemists on which her industrialists could draw. This was a point foreseen by Playfair: that the development of transportation would soon reduce local advantages in raw materials and skill would become a determining factor. Moreover, once the success of scientific research allied to industry had been demonstrated beyond doubt the rest followed quite naturally and we cannot be surprised by Germany's subsequent successes in the electrical engineering industries, etc. (This is no more than an assertion of the well known fact that the location and development of particular industries is governed by the available supply of skilled labour; it being assumed that industrial scientists can be regarded as skilled labour.)

We can now gather the threads together and conclude that the emergence of applied science depends on the "inherent opportunities" of the situation (see p. 37). The internal development of science produced a material of great social utility and, at the same time gave promise of even greater treasures along the same line of research. The issue, that is, was clear cut; a scientific challenge was posed. To respond to a challenge of this nature a society must have the services of a class of professional scientists. In the case of the "physical" industries the development of the thermionic valve, with its enormous possibilities for research and correlative utility, presented a challenge in some ways analogous to that of the aniline dyes. But, whatever the field in which the "challenge" occurs, it must be in a precise and easily grasped form; it would have been theoretically possible at any time, during the period examined, to have established research laboratories in connexion with the mining, metallurgical and engineering industries, and undoubtedly these would have led to great benefits. However, quite apart from the absence of professional scientists, the need for science in these industries was diffuse—it could not be brought home to the industrialist in a concise, inescapable form.

So far we have avoided the major issue. If there is no applied science how can a class of professional scientists be created? And if no class can be created how can there ever be applied science? This looks like a vicious circle and such, indeed *was* the case over most of the nineteenth century in England. But it overlooks the point that has been developed above: the professional scientist can also be a teacher, he need not be limited to industry. In fact, it is clear that, in principle, before you can have a class of professional scientists you must create the necessary educational machinery. This needs no proof whatsoever. But there is the additional factor: the very act of creating a suitable educational machinery also creates, *sui generis,* the professional scientist. This you cannot avoid doing unless by law, statute or custom you deliberately exclude science from the syllabuses. But then your educational system would be inefficient and retrograde as it was in England for so long.

We may pause for a moment to consider the significance of the Mathematics Tripos in the history of professional science. This justly famous course of training in mathematics and theoretical physics spans the whole period of this work, and during that time it underwent less modification than any other course of study; it implied, from the beginning, a highly specialised education and to this general form all other courses of study have gradually approximated. It is very natural to ask, therefore, why it was that the Tripos did not produce in England a class of professional scientists.

Quite apart from the technical reason that mathematics and theoretical physics are of more limited applicability than chemistry and experimental physics, two distinct answers can be given to this question. Firstly, the great majority of earlier candidates were young men of means and, as such, did not constitute the best human material for what is, from a certain point of view, the banausic art of applied science; moreover, tempting careers in Law, etc. were open to the young Wranglers. Secondly, when the opportunity occurred the Tripos course did, in fact, produce the professional scientist. It would be supererogatory to show that most public school mathematics masters were Tripos men; and when the development of university colleges and provincial universities began in earnest in the 1870's and '80's Cambridge found herself in the position of natural supplier of teachers and professors of mathematics and physics for those institutions.

The importance of teaching posts for the development of professional science had been foreseen by Lyon Playfair, James Hole, Henry Latham and T. H. Huxley before such posts were made available, and therefore before professional science began. It follows that this is not a question of wisdom *ex post facto*. We can see how, in practice, it works when we consider the case of a well-organised and smooth-running system of secondary and trade or technical schools together with effective universities, all of which require competent science teachers. Of course a good system of primary schools is also necessary and, at the same time, a very liberal scholarship ladder to accommodate the talented. Young men and women, educated at primary and secondary school, are vocationally trained at university to be returned to the former as teachers; they therefore perpetuate the principle. But some of these students—a small minority perhaps—will have talent above the ordinary and will want to do research at the university. A proportion of these will normally be retained as university teachers; but as supply generally exceeds demand in this case, those who do not become university teachers must either revert to school teaching, or abandon science, or become applied industrial scientists. From this point of view therefore the industrial scientist is to be regarded as an internal product of the educational system. Of course it is not asserted that applied science is in any way "inferior" as a vocation to university or school teaching; there are, today, those who undergo research training with the express intention of becoming industrial scientists.

The origin of the German achievement has been traced, as we have seen, to the foundation of the Giessen laboratory in 1826. But beyond that lay the educational policy laid down by von Humboldt in the first decade of the nineteenth century. In any case the Giessen venture began long before German industrial expansion, before German industries were in any way capitalist (Clapham) and before even the Zollverein was accomplished.

From a comparatively early date the integrated German educational system —the primary schools, the State secondary schools: the *Gymnasia,* the *Progymnasia* and the *Realgymnasia* which so aroused the admiration of Matthew Arnold and others, the trade schools and the polytechnics and universities all offered opportunities for the science teacher at different levels. We saw that Conrad ascribed the sharp increase in numbers of students in the philosophy faculty partly to the extension of this educational machinery; and Friederich Paulsen later commented that the Philosophy Faculty which in the eighteenth century provided preliminary training for the other Faculties (Divinity, Law and Medicine) added, in the course of the nineteenth century, the function of providing teacher training. Later on, according to Paulsen, the Faculty became conspicuous for scientific research and the training of advanced teachers. Such a system, which sent up young men well-prepared to the universities, could hardly fail to produce the professional scientist. There would always be those who would resolve on a career of learning, and those men would form the man-power potential of the new group. The ultimate deciding factor, therefore, must have been the educational machinery: the necessity of staffing the universities, polytechnics and schools. Indeed it is easy to believe that, in the 1850's, the number of professional scientists in German schools and universities must have exceeded those in German industries. Certainly the German Educational Revolution preceded the Applied Science Revolution by quite a few years; and it would be difficult to believe that this was carried out in the interests of, then *uninvented,* applied science. On the contrary the German academic can be very fairly charged with some degree of intellectual snobbery; Liebig, as we saw, thought that science in Germany was valued for its own sake and not, as in England, for what it produced. I gave a brief and, I hope, cogent reason for my belief that he was *wrong* with regard to England. One can accuse Liebig of ignorance of his own countrymen, but it is less easy to dismiss the professors' semicontemptuous phrase—"Brotstudien," and certainly the German universities strongly resisted the introduction of technology into the university syllabus. They were successful in this but it did not prevent them resisting, unsuccessfully this time, the raising of the polytechnics to university status—and this was long after Oxford, Cambridge and all other British universities had engineering faculties or departments.

It is apparent that the education system in England did not offer the same opportunities as did that of Germany. The universities adapted for the training of the English gentleman, were largely closed to research and the advancement of learning, as the nature of the degree system and examinations shows, to say nothing of the explicit statements of educationists. In the society of the time this did not seem anomalous (save to enthusiastic reformers and admirers of the German system) for science was, as we have seen, prosecuted with vigour and success by a brilliant group of semi-amateurs. The great public schools, in organic relationship with the universities, were naturally governed in accordance with the same educational aim, and the possibilities of science masterships were few until the "reform" movement became fully effective in the second half of the century. There remained the new university colleges but these were bedevilled by poverty and by the external degree system which made systematic study difficult to achieve; moreover even here the degree was liberal both in form and content.

For the rest little need be said. The Mechanics' Institutes relied, for many years, on part-time or voluntary lecturers and the standard must have been low and erratic. Also they were in decline due to bad primary education and other causes adduced above. Of the primary schools nothing need be said.

The first effective step was the foundation of the various university science examinations. But the pace of development was governed by the quality of the students coming up from school—and testimony is fairly complete that most were ill-prepared—and on the jobs available on graduation. As we saw from the Devonshire Commission and from the minutes of London University, it was only when the schools began to employ science masters that graduate science became a profession; and we saw, too, that the reorganisation of the South Kensington Colleges as a Normal School resulted in a flood of applicants that was greater than the available accommodation.

Such evidence is qualitative rather than quantitative. But there is one other aspect which must not be forgotten. The scientist must have had a practical training if he is to deserve the name. However, systematic practical classes did not become common until the later 1860's and practical examinations began later still. That is, many of the "science" men turned out before that date were merely book-learned; at best they might know about science, at worst they would know only how to pass science examinations. Thus, while this practice prevailed, the universities could not produce scientists, still less could the sterile State examination system—witness the boy who "passed" in 19 subjects.

The group of distinguished academics which met at the Freemasons Tavern in 1872 wanted to create a class of research men, which class, they said, did not exist at that time. It can hardly be supposed that these men did not know what they were talking about; that, in fact, there *was* such a class and they were unaware of its existence. Even if this is held to be inconclusive, that the professional scientist did not then exist was proved beyond question by the fact that the Department of Science and Art was forced to employ officers of the Royal Engineers as school inspectors, for the reason that they were, at that time, the only men in England with a professional training in science. From the 60's to the 90's England was unable to muster as many as 60 professional scientists to serve as part-time inspectors of her technical schools.

With the gradual reform of the secondary schools, the passing of the various Technical Instruction Acts and the founding of the university colleges, the opportunities for science teaching were greatly expanded. But the biggest factors seem to have been the elementary training colleges and, from 1902 onwards, the new State secondary schools. We have seen that the rapid expansion in numbers of degree students just before the war was linked first to primary and then to secondary educational developments rather than to any other factor. This meant the production of graduates who would be financially dependent on science teaching, and this implies the professional scientist. At the same time the old universities were being rapidly liberalised from within, which meant, of course, the admission of potentially professional students from poor homes. The numbers of successful candidates for Part II of the Natural Science Tripos, which had fallen steadily from 1881 to 1900 now began to rise steeply. . . .

To pursue this matter further would be to go into the general sociology of education and that would lead us away from the point. We have established, and I do not think it can be doubted, that the professional scientist is, in the first instance, the product of the educational system; to a much less extent is he the product of industrial practice and economic organisation. Or, to put the claim at its lowest, the applied science revolution cannot possibly be understood without reference to the reform of the educational system. Today there are frequent complaints of the shortage of teachers of science in schools, coupled with observations that industry has tempted too many graduates away from teaching. If these complaints are substantially true, then it looks as though scientific industry is devouring its own Alma Mater, and this would be very unfortunate. This forms part of the sociology of science today and, in the absence of further knowledge, any comment would be no better than speculation. None the less it would be very interesting and is important to know how the streams of natural science are divided among the various professions and what factors govern that distribution.

The old professions of law, medicine, etc., rested to a considerable extent on a personal relationship between the expert and the client; service was rendered to the community through the individual. [3] The professional scientist, on the other hand, must render his service to the individual through the community; an individualist relationship between the scientist and a client (or employer) is unthinkable. In this respect the professional scientist is more akin to the civil servant or the army officer than to the doctor or lawyer; indeed he transcends even the former pair in the impersonal nature of his services. Therefore it would follow that the level of professional science is a function of measures of public welfare, or of collective social action. Especially true is this of the initial stages, for the lengthy and expensive education of the natural scientist necessitates State aid on a substantial scale: that has been the universal experience of every country which has been able to develop applied science. The denial of State aid during the crucial period 1850–80 was the final reason why applied science was later in making its appearance in England than in Germany.

The theories of self-help and of individualism were given a full and fair trial in nineteenth-century England; whatever achievements are to their credit, and I do not doubt that they are many, they proved, when applied to science and education, quite incapable of producing the professional scientist. As the century progressed this fact was recognised by an increasing number of people; from the 1870's onward the doubters were in the majority, at least as far as science was concerned (see above, especially the Devonshire and Samuelson Commissions).

I am not here concerned with generalisations as to such large scale social institutions as "capitalism," etc. Such generalisations would not, in any case, teach us much, nor would they take us very far. In this context we should note that the free nature of American[3] and Swiss[4] political and economic institutions did not prevent them from liberally endowing their educational and scientific foundations while the rigid and highly differentiated class structure of Germany was likewise no obstacle to scientific progress in that country. But we are not concerned to discover ultimate causes, still less to pass moral judgment on men who, if they failed to see what the minority saw, were not therefore to be condemned. Here, we are concerned with the development of a certain small group of men and a certain mode of social action together with the conditions which governed the evolution of the group and its function. It needs to be emphasised, I think, that applied science is itself an invention and it is an invention which can only be effected in a certain type of society at a certain stage of development. The first scientist or industrialist to suggest the permanent employment of a research scientist, or group of scientists, was the person who invented applied science.

Even if we assume that industrial requirements on their own can break down an Iron Curtain of Latin and Greek, buttressed by class privilege and underpinned by the Established Church, we can hardly suppose that they could create a syllabus of studies and researches which is not understood by the educational authorities of the time. In whatever way industrial require-

[3] Universities, etc., the Lick, Yerkes Telescopes, etc.
[4] University and the famous Polytechnic.

ments express themselves, whether through the explicit demands of employers or otherwise, they cannot be wiser and see further than the received notions and ideas of those concerned with education. The point is that the utility of research, of laboratory practice, of applied science in the modern manner, is not at all obvious in the first instance. The properly trained scientist has been educated in a way and to a standard that would either be a luxury or useless when judged by the criteria of the day-to-day needs of industry; his employment cannot be justified after a week or a month or perhaps even a year's work.[5] What, the industrialist might have asked, is meant by "scientific research"? The question is a difficult one to answer; it exercises the wits of methodologists today. It cannot be expected therefore that an industrialist could understand the value of science *a priori*—he must see it in action before he can incorporate it in his industrial activities. If there is no way in which it can be brought to his attention and if there are no professional scientists available, it follows that he cannot utilise applied science.

I have already produced material evidence to suggest what I have argued in principle above—that until the universities were producing the professional specialist, industrialist demand could not make itself felt—did not, in fact, exist—and young men could not enter industrial research in large numbers. This is a reversal of that theory which explains professional scientific training by reference to industrial demand—it is an assertion of the opposite. The obverse of the professional coin is, of course, a form of specialism; but specialism, as I have shown, arose as a socially selected consequence of university examination, of Honours Schools and Triposes, and in such a manner that demand for professional applied scientists could not possibly have played any part in the process. Further, I went on to show that the first real professional scientists to be produced in any significant numbers were not would-be industrial researchers, but intending teachers; and it was only when those conditions were fulfilled that an industrial demand could, at last, arise. Industrial demand therefore played no more part in the specialisation of the various science degrees than it did in the specialisation of the Classics Tripos or the London B.A. Nor can industrial demand be credited (or blamed) for the form which specialisation has, generally speaking, taken.

Apart from universities, and university scholarship examinations, the specialisation of studies would be most congenial to schools. (The division of labour in the scholastic world was of long standing, and a good "Honours" man was an asset to the school.) But once the educational revolution was well under way and professional scientists were being trained in increas-

---

[5] Cases were quoted to early investigators (e.g. the 1884 Commissioners) of German applied scientists whose work had been fruitless for as long as two years. But it was added that such men justified themselves in the long run.

ing numbers, did it follow that the adoption of applied science by industry was inevitably and smoothly effected? To answer such a question, framed in the most general terms, would involve a study of the diffusion of ideas among the community and a wide study of the requirements and responses of different industries. The factors favouring the widespread adoption of science are, firstly, the diffusion of scientific culture through improved education; and, secondly, the incorporation of science courses in the various kinds of technical education. On the other hand, we have recorded many denunciations of the English manufacturer for his failure to appreciate science—and although many of these denunciations were unfair and even absurd (men like Mather, Samuelson, Swire Smith, Mundella, etc., were liberal and progressive employers and were well aware of the importance of science), it may be that for various reasons the English manufacturer was somewhat conservative in outlook, setting a higher value on practice than theory and experiment and reluctant to believe that anyone could teach him how to run even a part of his business. More material, possibly, was the small scale on which many British industries were organised, for, as H. A. L. Fisher put it, ". . . we are an old country of old and small traditional businesses. . . ." (British Science Guild, *Eleventh Annual Report,* 1917). Beneath these disincentives there may possibly have been additional psychological factors: a distaste for work in industry and factory on the part of men who might hold the intellectual qualifications for industrial research.

Whatever the shortcomings of the manufacturer—and these are conjectural—the marked deficiencies of the educational system must always be remembered in substantial mitigation. Up to 1902 this was quite obvious; as Mark Pattison had lamented: "The manufacturing and commercial interests of the country have outgrown us . . . they no longer regard us . . . they do not think we have got anything worth having. . . ." (1872). It is difficult to deny that the manufacturers were not without reason on their side.

Even after the great educational reforms the very small number of post-graduate science students (172) at the grant-aided colleges in 1914 does not argue much devotion to research. As long ago as 1884, the Samuelson Commission had stressed the value of research in industry and in training . . .; Dewar had stated that many of our examination scientists would be of little use in a research laboratory (1902) ; the Technical Education Board Sub-Committee had urged post-graduate research training and, more recently, J. J. Thomson's Committee and the Barlow Report [4] made exactly the same recommendations; the latter stating explicitly that three years' undergraduate study do not make a scientist. Therefore it is reasonable to suppose that even after the educational reforms were achieved (up to 1914) the development of applied science may well have been hindered by the unsatisfactory position of research training as opposed to the written examination system then widely practised. The large number of foreign graduates in industry tends to support this view: it would seem that the scientific industrialist placed more faith on the research examination (German) degree than on the written examination (English) degree.

Let us clarify this point. The action of written examinations is, we may say, collective rather than individual. Applied to a class of science students, some of whom will later abandon science, some of whom are intending teachers and some prospective research workers, etc., the final examination may well stimulate the maximum study on the part of the greatest number. It is quite possible that, in a vocationally ill-assorted class, there are many who are greatly benefited by this stimulus; but with regard to the would-be professional scientist the case is doubtful. We have seen that, up to 1914, most leading scientists did not approve of written examinations as the final arbiters of scientific education; not without reason, for surely it is obvious that research should form a substantial part of the training of the prospective research worker? Under these circumstances and from the point of view of the research scientist the value of exclusive written examinations can rightly be called in question. Yet wherever the truth lies in a debate between written examination and research degrees it is, at the very least, probable that had the Victorian industrialist enjoyed the benefit of a supply of trained professional scientists, even men without research training, the emergence of applied science in England would have occurred much sooner than it did and might very well have pre-dated the German achievement. Had it not done so, even then, the industrialist would certainly have deserved the strictures heaped upon him. But this is merely hypothetical.

To summarise the position reached, let us invoke (in imagination) a manufacturer of (say) 1880. Let us suppose that he is a progressively-minded man, a supporter of the Technical Education Movement and of the new local University College. This is quite justifiable, for we have seen that there were many such as he. He will favour extended education for all classes and may even have good ideas on secondary education. But if he is asked why he does not use science—research—and scientists in his industry he may well reply along the following lines: "The suggestion that scientists be employed in industry is absurd; as well ask Mme Schumann to teach my daughters to play the pianoforte. A man of science cannot be constrained to follow any prescribed path; he cannot produce discovery to order neither is it desirable that he should be expected to do so. He must, and all experience bears this out, be quite free to go where he will and research in whatever directions his genius prompts. Also we know that, although great benefits flow from science, it may take many years before such discoveries are of use, and even so we cannot predict just what use they will be. No industry could possibly afford such an enterprise even if men of science were prepared to serve it." Scientists, for our manufacturer, mean men like Dr. Joule, Mr. Darwin, the late Dr. Faraday. . . . And if it were pointed out that there were science graduates in the country—there were at most 1,000 by that time—he might be pardoned for taking a somewhat sceptical view of their potentialities. He could not afford to employ one on the offchance that he might be another Faraday, and, if one pointed out what was happening (on a very small scale) in Germany, he would reply that that was all right but he had little time for mere book-learning without experience that transcended the text-books.

Whatever the industrialists and scientists of the past achieved or failed to achieve, we must remember that we are, ourselves, in a situation similar to that which often confronted them. The present great national interest in applied science and technical education is stimulated, as before, by the threats of foreign competition; and many of the views now held, and the arguments being put forward, are, it will be agreed, very similar to those circulating during previous "technical education movements."

THE SPECIALISED SOCIETY

The growth of professionalism was one of the remarkable social changes of the nineteenth century. Not only did the long-established professions develop a number of subordinate and ancillary professions but wholly new and distinct ones were founded. As the century progressed the casual, sometimes non-existent, training requirements and the individualistic conditions of entry and practice gave place to carefully prescribed training together with rationalised conditions of entry and defined norms of conduct. The rise of professionalism was, perhaps, inevitable under the circumstances of developing political democracy on the one hand and the rapid advance of mechanical and scientific industry on the other. But, while it would be absurd to ascribe this radical change to the advances of pure and applied science, it would be equally unreal to suppose that science, as a social activity, could in any way avoid the ever-widening net of professionalism.

There are substantial areas of science where such factors as increased cost of research and great complexity of theoretical knowledge do not apply and cannot, therefore, satisfactorily explain the virtual disappearance of the amateur scientist. Nor can recent social levelling tendencies be held accountable, for lack of money has, in the past, proved no deterrent to scientists. Professionalism itself must therefore be invoked to complete the explanation of the decline in amateurism. The mechanism whereby the professional, publicly recognised and approved, must supplant the amateur requires no detailed explanation; it is enough to point out that even those whose means could guarantee them complete intellectual freedom are socially orientated towards admission to the professional circle, and so have little difficulty in accepting the norms of the profession.

Generally speaking the achievement of professional science is, of course, a great advance in social organisation. But certain aspects of specialisation, in one form or another an inevitable corollary of professionalism, are of less evident desirability. Specialisation, today, is frequently characterised by an education which, from the age of eighteen or so onwards, is limited to one branch of science, being increasingly directed to narrower sectors; a continued vocational structure which admits and canalises recognised specialists only, and a society which expects, when it does not demand, that specialists shall continue in their prescribed specialism.

Many leading thinkers deplore such specialisation on the grounds that its cultural effects are bad, that it does not accord with the ideal of a liberal education. While this is no doubt a valid criticism it can also be argued that specialisation, carried beyond a certain point, must hinder the advance of science. It is clear that what has happened must have profoundly changed the tone and temper of thought in general. Fields of study have become vertically stratified, one science is isolated from another, and that cross-fertilisation of the sciences which, in the past, was so fruitful is rendered more difficult. This is surely not a happy development? Talent, still more genius, has the essential quality that it is unpredictable. An original thinker is by definition one who finds a unity where previously none was suspected, and to do this he may well have to cross artificial frontiers between the sciences. If, for a long time, a man is effectively discouraged from seeking knowledge other than that approved, if he must choose either this discipline or that discipline, there is some danger that a creative talent may be frustrated. The maxim for craftsmanship—the cobbler must stick to his last—is not necessarily applicable to science.

Considerations of this kind were evidently in the mind of the German educationist Paulsen who, writing at a time when the German universities were riding the flood-tide of success and prestige, could still complain of over-specialisation, and demand a broader approach: "No scientific study can prosper in isolation. Every science is indissolubly related to others; they presuppose each other as auxiliaries." [5]

This leads to a brief consideration of the examination system, the present instrument of specialisation. It will be remembered that among the reasons for the adoption of examinations were the need to devise a means of selection for college office, the need to stimulate wealthy young men to do some systematic study, the desirability of having some way of easily classifying merit, etc. They were, that is, elaborated at a time when the universities did not conceive it their duty to advance knowledge but rather to provide a liberal education. Now the system has been taken over generally, although it is undeniable that the functions of the university and the organisation of society without have changed radically. That a system designed to stimulate liberal education in the nineteenth century is also the best method of producing professional scientists under modern conditions would seem to be a *non sequitur*. It is clear that, whatever the intrinsic merits of the examination system, it must be kept flexible in order to take into account changes in social organisation and the issues that these raise for science.

It is not to be supposed that a liberalisation of scientific education and —probably more important—of subsequent vocational opportunity would notably increase the number of first class scientists, nor is it claimed that the result would be the immediate solution of specific and intractible problems. All that is being asserted is that every allowance must be made for the occasional emergence of the unorthodox thinker, bearing in mind that unorthodox ideas may prove to be the most fruitful. In a certain sense the advance of science is marginal in that great advances often occur where and when they are least expected (certainly by the majority of people). It is also salutary to remember that there are fashions in science as in every other social activity. Thus nuclear physics is perhaps the fashionable science today: its practical importance and philosophical interest make its position in some ways analogous to that of geology a hundred years ago. But no one can, of course, predict what will be the significant and fashionable sciences in the years to come.

The argument is, then, that it is of paramount importance to ensure that the social environment of science is the most favourable for continued development that we can achieve. We must maintain, in the world of science, an "open society." It is not disputed that the great increase of knowledge and the importance of applied science together make some degree of specialisation inevitable. Indeed, the specialised society is now a condition of social advance in respect of the conquest of deficiencies, material shortages, diseases and the extension of mastery over nature. The problem, as it seems to me, is how to reconcile such very desirable activities with the full development of the potentialities of the individual. There are of course two aspects to this: the ethical, for we may assert that the development in freedom of all potentialities of the individual is a constituent of the good; and the utilitarian, for it is only when the individual can so develop that the full material benefits of science, pure and applied, can be realised in society. On this point the whole story of the development of science assures us.

REFERENCES

[1] *Nature,* Vol. 173, 19th June, 1954, p. 1175.
[2] *Annual Report of the Ministry of Education,* 1953.
[3] T. H. Marshall, *Citizenship and Social Class,* 1951, pp. 128–55.
[4] *Report on Scientific Man-Power* (Barlow), 1946, Cd. 6824.
[5] Friedrich Paulsen, *German Universities and University Study,* English Translation, 1908, p. 322.

PART II

Science as a Changing Institution

The term "institution" is used by sociologists to refer to a set of norms and social roles which cohere around important activities within a society. In effect, these are systems of behavior and organization evolved in societies for coping with certain basic problems. Thus, for example, we may speak of behavior systems for coping with human procreation, the care of the young, and the relationships of people to each other within such a system. This is referred to as the kinship institution, with the family the basic social unit.

In a similar vein, it is possible to identify a set of norms and social roles which cohere around activities identified as science. Underlying and supporting the purely technical activities of a scientist behaving as scientist, there are values and rules and social roles as well as a variety of organizations which make it possible for the scientist to engage in science. Sometimes these arrangements facilitate his technical activities as a scientist; at other times, these arrangements may impede or hamper these activities. Because the technical activities are so important and so visible, we are often inclined to forget about the underlying arrangements which affect these technical activities. The selections included in this section should help to overcome such a tendency. Here the emphasis is precisely on those institutional underpinnings of the activities identified as science.

Among the institutional aspects of science examined in this section are the social and cultural factors within the institution of science which influence the scientist's behavior and attitudes toward his work and the nature of, and the difficulties with, that portion of research which is often labeled "pure" or "basic." The interest in basic research is twofold. On the one hand, there are the problems connected with the attempt to provide adequate support for its maintenance and encouragement. On the other hand, there is the very closely related problem of how basic research is embedded in the institution of science.

Above all, the selections included here emphasize the dynamic character of the social institution of science. The opening selection by Robert K. Merton, for example, presents an analysis of the socially structured norms facing the scientist. Merton discusses some nine major pairs of conflicting norms to which the scientist is supposed to adhere. As a social institution, the rules of the game are not always as clear cut and unambiguous as the technical rules of science are (or are supposed to be). Yet these social norms exist, and the result is often a certain ambivalence and conflict.

For those who would study and try to understand the behavior and attitudes of the contemporary scientist, the Merton analysis presented here is an essential prerequisite. And as science and scientists come to play an increasingly important role in our society, it will become all the more necessary to seek this kind of understanding and discard outmoded and unrealistic stereotypes. Again, it should be emphasized, this ambivalence of scientists is not an idiosyncratic personality problem. It is rather a socially structured and socially determined phenomenon to which scientists (with or without personality problems) are forced to respond. The dynamic character of the social institution of science at any particular time is vividly illustrated and documented in this Merton analysis.

In the next selection, we turn to the observations of an astute working physicist concerning the world of the scientist. Although influenced by the technical nature of his work, the world of the scientist as described by F. Reif is in large measure a socially structured one. The picture Reif presents does not conform to most of our stereotypes of what it is like to be a scientist or, for that matter, what the scientific life is like. Whether or not the idealistic picture of the self-effacing scientist working away in his laboratory far removed from the basic motivations of the ordinary job in this society, seeking only after new knowledge and truth, has ever been true completely, the accelerating growth of science in recent decades has intensified competition for status and prestige among scientists. Indeed, some observers have argued that such competition has always been a part of the scientific life although the particular form of competition, its intensity, and other manifestations may have changed over time. In any case, it is important for both the scientist and the layman to try to understand science and scientists as they really are. In so doing, it becomes possible to understand some of the underlying social factors which are relevant and to identify the differential effects of social influences on science. This paper by Reif with the previous one by Merton provide a solid beginning for such an understanding. Both emphasize the importance of the social factors, as opposed either to the technical or to the individual and idiosyncratic factors which may also be important.

The intensified struggle for prestige and priority which Reif describes results in psychological strains for the scientist. The struggle for prestige reflects also the conflict between the traditional values of science and those of the market place involving especially personal gain and fame. According to Reif, reflection may be abandoned in favor of quick production. Minimal-risk projects are often deemed more attractive. Large-scale facilities are often used unimaginatively in the quest for a quick payoff. Slipshod work may be turned out. Secrecy instead of free communication is often the rule in the attempt to preserve one's own potential priority claims. But this new competitiveness has certain positive consequences as well. For example, work is more likely to be duplicated more rapidly, thus insuring the possibility of avoiding and not perpetuating errors. Higher standards may result since so many of the scientists are, so to speak, looking over each other's shoulder. The pace of exploration and exploitation of results may be increased.

This picture, it must be emphasized, is one of the pure scientist, and especially in one field of physics. Reif is not even considering the problems of the so-called applied scientist working in industry or government. It is also important to stress that Reif is not talking about isolated individual scientists responding to idiosyncratic motivations, but rather of scientists in general being affected by changes in the character of the organization of scientific activities and the nature of the scientific institution in itself.

The next two selections are concerned with a persistent and somewhat troublesome problem in science, namely, the nature of basic research. It is difficult to read very much about science without encountering some allusions to basic or pure research. Are we supporting too much of it, or is our support for it inadequate? Should it be confined to the universities, or should industrial and government laboratories also engage in the conduct of basic research? Above all, what is basic research and how does it differ from applied and developmental and other types of research? Often, it seems as if there are almost as many definitions as there are discussions of this phenomenon. Many of these are deceptively simple and frequently rely heavily on one rather nebulous factor which most "hard" scientists would reject out of hand in other circumstances as too fuzzy a notion. This key factor is said to be the motivation of the scientist doing the work, and the question is put in terms of whether the scientist is interested in the knowledge for its own sake *or* for the ultimate uses to which it might be put. If the research is motivated by a desire for knowledge for its own sake, it is labeled "basic." If it is motivated by desire for practical uses, whether for profit or for humanitarian purposes, it is often labeled "applied research." Yet no one seems to be happy with this kind of distinction, while all agree that some kind of distinction is absolutely essential.

Writing from the point of view of an administrator of a granting agency in the federal government who must often decide whether a research proposal for which financial support is being sought is basic or applied, Charles V. Kidd finds the usual definitions and approaches to the problem quite hopeless. Kidd classifies most definitions into two kinds: those which are centered on the investigator and those which are substance centered.

In the investigator-centered definition, the focus is on individual motives and questions of freedom enjoyed by the scientist—often difficult if not impossible to assess precisely. The substance-centered definition focuses on the end product of the research with the main question being whether the research product can be put to some useful end. This is, of course, most difficult to ascertain *before* the research is performed and, very often, even for some considerable time after the research is completed. Since no operational definition would appear to rescue us from such dilemmas, Kidd suggests a somewhat different approach. This is based on the assumption that most investigators in certain research environments have a higher probability than others of turning out basic work. To support such work effectively, then, Kidd suggests placing as few restrictions as possible on these investigators and at the same time strengthening the values and social system of science designed to promote basic research.

What kinds of research environments are most likely to promote basic work? The implicit assumption in Kidd's paper, and one which is widely shared in this country, is that the universities naturally provide the best environment. This assumption is probably a valid one in terms of the usual comparisons made with most industrial or government laboratories. However, there are alternative possibilities, for example, the independent research institute dedicated primarily to the encouragement of research for its own sake.

In the last selection of this section, Caryl P. Haskins, the President of one such organization—the Carnegie Institution of Washington—provides us with new perspectives on many of the problems raised throughout this volume. Dr. Haskins describes some of the institutional and organizational conditions which seem to provide the most effective encouragement for what might be labeled "basic" research. Whatever the term used, Dr. Haskins stresses a type of research where the investigator has no specific or precise objectives but is free to follow his scientific curiosity wherever it may take him which often leads to new scientific innovations. This is contrasted with equally necessary research undertaken to attain specific ends. In these instances the results which can be expected are generally known (although not necessarily in any detail) very near the outset.

As we have already seen, any such distinctions, viewed in the abstract, give rise to many difficulties. Dr. Haskins is the first to recognize this and very quickly moves on to a consideration of concrete cases. He discusses in some detail three examples of important recent scientific discoveries which are alike in that they have led to new directions in scientific thought. These cases provide Dr. Haskins with significant clues for the underlying conditions necessary for the encouragement of this kind of science.

While the internal nature of science is being transformed by the proliferation of large teams in massive research programs as well as large-scale research organizations, Dr. Haskins' essay reminds us that there are other kinds of science which require different institutional arrangements. We must, he contends, continue to reserve a place for the gifted individual, the small and mobile research group, and the small research institution. For it is here that we are most likely to achieve significant new scientific discoveries.

It is altogether appropriate that these observations and analyses should be found in a paper written on the occasion of the Sixtieth Anniversary of the Carnegie Institution of Washington. Dr. Haskins reviews the development of the Carnegie Institution in the light of the changing nature of science and the changing relations of science to society which have taken place since 1902.

The requirements for different kinds of scientific endeavors are not the same and a society which would promote the full flowering of science must recognize these differences. The question, as Dr. Haskins puts it, is "can small and mobile enclaves of thoughtful and imaginative men and women continue to maintain integrity and distinctive freedom within the greater society?" (p. 174). This is not to deny the importance and excitement of the applied and developmental work which does and will undoubtedly continue to occupy the vast majority of scientists. As Dr. Haskins notes, "In massive and compelling developmental undertakings opportunities will continue to be provided to great numbers of active minds to labor for ends not only dramatic, not only economically and socially adaptive, but as creative and as meaningful in our times as the tasks of the builders of Chartres or of the Parthenon must have been in theirs" (p. 174).

A deeper understanding of the institution of science and of its connections to the larger society is of fundamental significance not only for the scientist himself but for all of us in the larger society. We have much to learn still about the nature of these institutional requirements and of how they might best be translated into specific mechanisms and organizational structures. This is precisely the kind of question examined in the next section in particular as well as in the subsequent ones. But before these specific problems can be attacked, it is necessary to remind ourselves again of the importance of understanding science as an institution. If the society would create the social conditions which support and encourage science most effectively, then all of us must work much harder at understanding the underlying factors involved.

The Ambivalence of Scientists

ROBERT K. MERTON

AMBIVALENCES IN THE SOCIAL INSTITUTION OF SCIENCE

Science, and the men who create science, can be examined from different though connected points of view. There is the standpoint of the body of scientific knowledge itself. This requires little interest in men of science, centering only on the fruits of their work. What has been found out? how sound is the evidence? what are the implications for new knowledge? Beyond this is the perspective of the philosopher and logician of science who concerns himself with the assumptions underlying scientific ideas and the logic of inquiry. Still another angle of vision is that of the psychology of the scientist, focused on the processes of learning and of that special kind of learning that is creative investigation. These and other perspectives on science contribute each to our understanding of the life and work of scientists, but I shall say nothing about them here.

Instead, I shall stick to my last and examine a restricted set of questions in the sociology of science. From this perspective, science appears as one of the great social institutions, coordinate with the other major institutions of society: the economy, education and religion, the family and the polity. Like other institutions, science has its corpus of shared and transmitted ideas, values and standards designed to govern the behavior of men attached to the institution. The standards define the technically and morally allowable patterns of behavior, indicating what is prescribed, preferred, permitted or proscribed. The culture of science refers, then, to more than habitual behavior; its norms codify the values judged appropriate for men of science.

The third Daniel Coit Gilman Lecture printed in the *Bulletin of the Johns Hopkins Hospital*, Vol. CXII, No. 2, February 1963, pp. 77–97. Reprinted, with the exception of the brief introductory remarks, with the permission of the author, the editor and the publisher, The Johns Hopkins Press. Dr. Robert K. Merton is Professor and Chairman of the Department of Sociology at Columbia University. Professor Merton made his first major contribution to the sociology of science in 1938 with the publication of his pioneering study, *Science, Technology and Society in Seventeenth Century England*. The author of numerous books and papers in many fields of sociology, Professor Merton's recent contributions have again been almost exclusively in the sociology of science. The investigation providing the basis for this lecture was aided by a fellowship from the John Simon Guggenheim Memorial Foundation.

Now, one characteristic of social institutions is that they tend to be patterned in terms of potentially conflicting pairs of norms. This sets a task for those governed by the institution to blend these imposed inconsistencies into reasonably consistent action. This is what I mean by saying that sociological ambivalence is imbedded in social institutions generally and, in its distinctive fashion, in the institution of science as well. Consider only, in swift review, some institutionally defined pairs of norms and note the tension that can be generated by potential inconsistency within each pair.

1. The scientist must be ready to make his newfound knowledge available to his peers as soon as possible, BUT he must avoid an undue tendency to rush into print. (Compare Faraday's motto: "Work, Finish, Publish" with President Gilman's anticipation of Ehrlich's motto: "Viel arbeiten, wenig publizieren.")

2. The scientist should not allow himself to be victimized by intellectual fads, those modish ideas that rise for a time and are doomed to disappear, BUT he must remain flexible, receptive to the promising new idea and avoid becoming ossified under the guise of responsibly maintaining intellectual traditions.

3. New scientific knowledge should be greatly esteemed, BUT the scientist should work without regard for the esteem of others.

4. The scientist must not advance claims to new knowledge until they are beyond reasonable dispute, BUT he should defend his new ideas and findings, no matter how great the opposition. (Compare C. N. Yang on the scientific credo: "it will not do to jump to hasty conclusions" and Pasteur: "do not fear to defend new ideas, even the most revolutionary.")

5. The scientist should make every effort to know the work of predecessors and contemporaries in his field, BUT too much reading and erudition will only stultify creative work. (Compare Cayley's omnivorous reading of other mathematicians—that same Cayley who with Euler and Cauchy, is among the three most prolific mathematicians of all time—with the irritation of his collaborator, Sylvester, at being expected to master what others had done. And, of course, there is always Schopenhauer's sin against the Holy Ghost: "to put away one's original thoughts in order to take up a book.")

6. The scientist should pay scrupulous attention to detail, BUT he must avoid the excessive accuracy of the pedant, fastidious only when it comes to inconsequentials.

7. Scientific knowledge is universal, belonging to no nation, BUT each scientific discovery does honor to the nation that fostered it.

8. The scientist should recognize his prime obligation to train up new generations of scientists, BUT he must not allow teaching to preempt his energies at the expense of advancing knowledge. Of course, this reads just

as persuasively in reverse. (Remember the complaints about Faraday that he had never trained a successor as Davy had trained him and consider the frequent criticism of scientists who give up research for teaching.)

9. Young scientists can have no happier condition than being apprenticed to a master of the scientific art, BUT they must become their own men, questing for autonomy and not content to remain in the shadow of great men. (Remember Kepler's ambivalence toward Tycho Brahe; Sir Ronald Ross's ambivalence toward Manson, his devotion to the master pushing him to extravagant praise, his need for autonomy pushing him to excessive criticism; in psychiatry, Bouchard's ambivalence toward Charcot and the secessionists Jung and Adler displaying theirs toward Freud; Sir Everard Home's mixed feelings about John Hunter, and the rest in the long list of ambivalent apprentices in science.)

And so, on and on, with norms garnered from the literature of science which can be paired into actual contradictions, potential contradictions or near-contradictions. Before turning to one conspicuous kind of ambivalence experienced by scientists, I should first say a word about the spirit in which this inquiry is conducted. Embodying as they do some of the prime values of world civilization, scientists have been placed on pedestals where they have no wish to be perched—not, at least, the greatest among them. This is not the result of a conspiracy, not even a conspiracy of good will. It is only that men of science have been pictured, through collective acts of piety, as though they were more than human, being like gods in their creativity, and also as less than human, being deprived of the passions, attitudes and social ties given to ordinary men. As a result, scientists have been dehumanized by being idealized and, on occasion, idolized. Contributing greatly to this centuries-long process of distortion are the pious biographers who convert indubitably great men of science into what Augustus de Morgan once described as "monsters of perfection." Yet an honest appreciation would see them as men, not gods, and so subject to the pressures, passions and social relations in which men inevitably find themselves. Rather than deny their human qualities, we must examine them. As the historian of science, A. C. Crombie, observed for one of the most notable cases in point:

> We must completely misunderstand Newton the man and we run the risk of missing the essential processes of a mind so profoundly original and individual as his, if we exclude from our field of historical investigation all those influences and interests that may be distasteful to us, or seem to us odd in a scientist.

Did my time and your patience allow, it would be possible to consider, first, how potentially contradictory norms develop in every social institution;

next, how in the institution of science, conflicting norms generate marked ambivalence in the lives of scientists; and finally, how this ambivalence affects the actual, as distinct from the supposed, relations between men of science. Instead, I shall consider the socially patterned sources of only one kind of ambivalence—toward the claiming of priorities in cases of multiple scientific discovery. This one type is not necessarily typical of the rest. But by examining it in the needed detail, we can perhaps catch a glimpse of the ways in which ambivalence is socially generated by each of the other potentially opposed pairs of norms in the institution of science: erudition *vs.* originality, apprentice-emulation *vs.* personal autonomy, and so on.

AMBIVALENCE TOWARD PRIORITIES IN SCIENTIFIC DISCOVERY

As is well known, men of science typically experience multiple independent discoveries as one of their occupational hazards. These create occasions for acute stress. Few scientists indeed react with equanimity when they learn that one of their own best contributions to science—what they *know* to be the result of long hard work—is "only" (as the telling phrase has it) a rediscovery of what was found some time before or "just" another discovery of what others have found at about the same time. No one who systematically examines the disputes over priority can ever again accept as veridical the picture of the scientist as one who is exempt from affective involvement with *his* ideas and *his* discoveries of once unknown fact. The value of observing the behavior of men under stress in order to understand them better in all manner of other situations need not be emphasized here. By observing the behavior of scientists under what they experience as the stress of being forestalled in a discovery, we gain clues to ways in which the social institution of science shapes the motives, social relations and affect of men of science. I have tried to show elsewhere how the values and reward-system of science, with their pathogenic emphasis upon originality, help account for certain deviant behaviors of scientists: secretiveness during the early stages of inquiry lest they be forestalled, violent conflicts over priority, a flow of premature publications designed to establish later claims to having been first. These, I suggest, are normal responses to a badly integrated institution of science, such that we can better understand the report of a sample of American "starred men of science" that, next to "personal curiosity," "rivalry" is most often the spur to their work.

In saying that the social institution of science is malintegrated, I mean that it incorporates potentially incompatible values: among them, the value set upon originality, which leads scientists to want their priority to be recognized, and the value set upon humility, which leads them to insist on how little they have in fact been able to accomplish. These values are not real contradictories, of course—'tis a poor thing, but my own—but they do call for opposed kinds of behavior. To blend these potential incompatibles into a single orientation and to reconcile them in practice is no easy matter. Rather, the tension between these kindred values creates an inner conflict among men of science who have internalized both of them. Among other things, the tension generates a distinct resistance to the systematic study of multiple discoveries and associated conflicts over priority.

This resistance is expressed in various ways: by seeking to trivialize the subject, by regarding the conflicts over priority as rare or aberrant, by motivated misperceptions of the facts of the case or by an hiatus in recall and reporting. Such resistance often leads to those wish-fulfilling beliefs and false memories that we describe as illusions. And of such behavior the annals that treat of multiple discoveries and priorities are uncommonly full. So much so, that I have arrived at a rule-of-thumb that seems to work fairly well. The rule is this: whenever the biography or autobiography of a scientist announces that he had little or no concern with priority, there is a reasonably good chance that, not many pages later in the book, we shall find him deeply embroiled in one or another battle over priority. A few cases here must stand for many.

The authoritative biography of that great psychiatrist of the Salpêtrière, Charcot, states that, despite his many discoveries, he "never thought for a moment to claim priority or reward." Our rule of thumb leads us to expect what we find: some 30 pages later, there is a detailed account of Charcot insisting on having been first in recognizing exophthalmic goiter and a little later, emphatically affirming that he "would like to claim priority" [the language is his] for the idea of isolating patients suffering from hysteria.

Or again, Harvey Cushing writes of the brilliant Halsted that he was "overmodest about his work, indifferent to matters of priority . . ." Alerted by our rule-of-thumb, we find some 20 pages later in the book where this is cited, a letter by Halsted about his work on cocaine: "I anticipated all of Schleich's work by about six years (or five) . . . [In Vienna], I showed Wölfler how to use cocaine. He had declared that it was useless in surgery. But before I left Vienna he published an enthusiastic article in one of the daily papers on the subject. It did not, however, occur to him to mention my name."

But perhaps the most apt case of such denial of an accessible reality is provided by Ernest Jones, writing in his comprehensive biography that "Although Freud was never interested in questions of priority, which he found merely boring, he was fond of exploring the source of what appeared to be original ideas, particularly his own . . ." This is an extraordinarily illuminating statement. For, of course, no one could have known better than Jones— "known" in the narrowly cognitive sense—how very often Freud turned to matters of priority: in his own work, in the work of his colleagues (both friends and enemies) and in the history of psychology altogether. In point of fact, Freud expressed an interest in priority on more than 150 occasions. With characteristic self-awareness, he reports that he even dreamt about priority and the due allocation of credit for accomplishments in science. He oscillates between the poles of his ambivalence toward priority: occasionally taking multiple discoveries to be practically inescapable, as when he reports a fantasy in which "science would ignore me entirely during my lifetime; some decades later, someone else would infallibly come upon the same things—for which the time was not now ripe—, and would achieve recognition for them and bring me honour as a forerunner whose failure had been inevitable." At other times, he reluctantly or insistently acknowledges anticipations of his own ideas or reports his own anticipations of others; he "implores" his disciple Lou Andreas-Salomé to finish an essay in order "not to give me precedence in time"; he admonishes Adler for what he describes as his "uncontrolled craving for priority" just as he admonishes Georg Groddeck for being unable to conquer "that banal ambition which hankers after originality and priority"; over a span of 40 years, he repeatedly reassesses the distinctive roles of Breuer and himself in establishing psychoanalysis; he returns time and again to his priority-conflict with Janet, reporting that he had brought the recalcitrant Breuer to publish their joint monograph early because "in the meantime, Janet's work had anticipated some of his [Breuer's] results"; he writes nostalgically about the days of "my splendid isolation" when "there was nothing to hustle me . . . My publications, which I was able to place with a little trouble, could always lag far behind my knowledge and could be postponed as long as I pleased, since there was no doubtful 'priority' to be defended"; again and again, he allocates priorities among others (Le Bon, Ferenczi, Bleuler, Stekel being only a few among the many); he even credits Adler with priority for an error; and, to prolong the occasions no further, he repeatedly intervenes in priority-battles among his disciples and colleagues (for example, between Abraham and Jung), saying that he could not "stifle the disputes about priority for which there were so many opportunities under these conditions of work in common."

In view of even this small sampling of cases in point, it may not be audacious to interpret as a sign of resistance, Jones's remarkable statement that "Freud was never interested in questions of priority, which he found merely boring . . ." That Freud was ambivalent toward priority, true; that he was pained by conflicts over priority, indisputable; that he was concerned to establish the priority of others as of himself, beyond doubt; but to describe him as "never interested" in the question and as "bored" by it requires the extraordinary feat of denying, as though they had never oc-

curred, scores of occasions on which Freud exhibited profound interest in
the question, many of these being occasions which Jones himself has detailed
with the loving care of a genuine scholar. It is true that Freud appears to
have been no more concerned with this matter than were Newton or
Galileo, Laplace or Darwin, or any of the other giants of science about
whom biographers have announced an entire lack of interest in priority just
before, as careful scholars, they inundate us with a flood of evidence to the
contrary. This denial of the realities they report and segregate seems to be
an instance of that keeping of intellect and perception in abeyance which
so typically reflects deep-seated resistance.

Such resistance has obvious parallels with other occasions in the history
of thought, not least with psycho-analysis itself, when amply available facts
with far-reaching theoretical implications were regarded as unedifying or
unsavory, ignoble or trivial and so were conscientiously ignored. It is a little
like the psychologists who once ignored sexuality because it was a subject
not fit for polite society or regarded dreams, incomplete actions and slips of
the tongue as manifestly trivial and so undeserving of thorough inquiry.

Complicating the problem in the case of multiple discoveries and prior-
ity-conflicts is the fact that investigation requires the detached examination
of the behavior of scientists by other scientists. Even to assemble the facts
of the case is to be charged with blemishing the record of undeniably great
men of science, as though one were a raker of muck that a gentleman
would pass by in silence. Even more, to investigate the subject systematically
is to be regarded not merely as a muck-raker, but as a muck-maker.

The behavior of fellow-scientists involved in priority-disputes tends to
be condemned or applauded, rather than analyzed. It is morally judged,
not systematically investigated. The disputes are described as "unfortunate"
with the moral judgment being substituted for the effort to understand what
the disputes imply for the psychology of scientists and the sociology of
science as an institution. At least since Goethe, we find references to "all
those foolish quarrels about earlier and later discovery, plagiary, and quasi-
purloinings." We are free, of course, to find this behavior unfortunate or
foolish or comic or sad. But these affective responses to the behavior of our
ancestors- or brothers-in-science seem to have usurped the place that might
be given to analysis of this behavior and its implications for the ways in
which science develops. It is as though the physician were to respond only
evaluatively to illness, describe it as unfortunate or painful, and consider his
task done or as though the psychiatrist were to describe the behavior of
schizophrenics as absurd and to substitute this sentiment for the effort to
discover what brings that behavior about. The history of the sciences shows
that the provisional emancipation from sentiment in order to investigate
phenomena methodically has been a difficult task, that it has been achieved
at different times in the various sciences and at different times for selected

problems in each of the sciences. I suggest that only now are we beginning
to emancipate the study of the actual behavior of scientists from the human
tendency to respond to that behavior in terms of the sentiments and values
which we have made our own rather than to examine it in reasonably
detached fashion.

Contributing to the substitution of sentiment for analysis is the often
painful contrast between the actual behavior of scientists and the behavior
ideally prescribed for them. When confronted with the fact that their discovery is a rediscovery or, much worse, when confronted with the suggestion
that it is a plagiary, their behavior scarcely matches the image of the dis-
passionate man of science, exclusively absorbed by his scientific work. It is
often seen as ugly, harsh and greedy for fame. And in the bitter social
conflict that ensues, the standards governing behavior deteriorate. One or
another of the discoverers caught up in a multiple—or often a colleague or
fellow-national—suggests that he rather than his rival was really first and
that the independence of the rival is at least unproved. Grouping their
forces, the other side counters with the opinion that plagiary had indeed
occurred, that let him whom the shoe fits wear it and furthermore, to make
matters quite clear, the shoe is on the other foot. Reinforced by group
loyalties and sometimes by ethnocentrism, the controversy gains force,
mutual charges of plagiary abound, and there develops an atmosphere of
thoroughgoing hostility and mutual distrust.

This is not exactly in accord with the ideal image of scientists and
particularly, of the greatest among them. When we identify ourselves with
the role-models provided by great scientists of the past and by lesser as well
as outstanding ones of the present, we find it painful to observe their behavior in these situations of conflict. Regarded in terms of sentiment rather
than of understanding, it may seem a bit sordid for a Galileo to engage in
seemingly egotistic attacks on one Grassi who tried "to diminish whatever
praise there may be in this [invention of the telescope] which belongs to
me"; or to go on to assail another who "attempted to rob me of that glory
which was mine, pretending not to have seen my writings and trying to
represent themselves as the original discoverer of these marvels"; or finally,
to say of a third that he "had the gall to claim that he had observed the
Medicean planets ... before I had [and used] a sly way of attempting to
establish his priority."

For all of us who harbor the ideal image of the scientist it can be only
disconcerting to have Edmond Halley forthrightly described by the first
Astronomer Royal, John Flamsteed, as a "lazy and malicious thief" who
manages to be just as "lazy and slothful as he is corrupt." Or to have Flamsteed assert that he found Newton "always insidious, ambitious, and ex-
cessively covetous of praise."

Almost all those firmly placed in the pantheon of science—a Newton,

Descartes, Pascal, Leibniz or Huyghens; a Lister, Faraday, Laplace or Davy
—have at one time or another been caught up in these fierce disputes. As
we approach our own day, we hear an echo of these angry and agitated
words reverberating through the corridors of the peaceful temple of science.
Since these episodes involve our contemporaries and often our associates,
they become, we must suppose, even more painful to observe and more
difficult to analyze with detachment. Even the social scientists who may not
be directly involved, at least for the moment, feel acutely uncomfortable.
Uneasy and distressed, they can hardly bring themselves to study this behavior. For when sociological analysis is stripped bare of sentiment, it often
leaves the sociologist shivering in the cold. And to respond with detachment
to these hot conflicts of their associates becomes all the more difficult. The
study of multiple discoveries and priorities accordingly remains undeveloped.

The disputants themselves manifest ambivalence toward their own behavior. Even while he is assembling documents to prove his priority, for
example, Darwin registers his mixed feelings, writing Lyell: "My good dear
friend, forgive me. This is a trumpery letter, influenced by trumpery feelings." In a postscript he assures Lyell that "I will never trouble you or
Hooker on the subject again." The next day, he writes: "It seems hard on
me that I should lose my priority of many years' standing." Then, a few
days later, he writes again to say: "Do not waste much time [on this matter].
It is miserable in me to care at all about priority."

Freud recognizes his own ambivalence when he writes of his work on
the Moses of Michelangelo that, having come upon a little book published
in 1863 by an Englishman, Watkiss Lloyd, he read it

> with mixed feelings. I once more had occasion to experience in
> myself what unworthy and puerile motives enter into our thoughts
> and acts even in a serious cause. My first feeling was of regret that
> the author should have anticipated so much of my thought, which
> seemed precious to me because it was the result of my own efforts;
> and it was only in the second instance that I was able to get plea-
> sure from its unexpected confirmation of my opinion. Our views,
> however, diverge on one very important point.

This degree of self-awareness is a far cry from the ambivalence of a
Descartes who manages to write that he "does not boast of being the first
discoverer" and then proceeds to insist on his priority over Pascal or to beg
his friend Mersenne "to tell him [Hobbes] as little as possible about ... my
unpublished opinions, for if I'm not greatly mistaken, he is a man who is
seeking to acquire a reputation at my expense and through shady practices."

The ambivalence toward claims of priority means that scientists are contemptuous of the very attitudes they have acquired from the institution to which they subscribe. The sentiments they have derived from the institution of science, with its great premium upon originality, makes it difficult to give up a claim to a new idea or a new finding. Yet the same institution emphasizes the selfless dedication to the advancement of knowledge for its own sake. Concern with priority and ambivalence toward that concern together register in the individual what is generated by the value-system of science.

The self-contempt often expressed by scientists as they observe with dismay their own concern with having their originality recognized is evidently based upon the widespread though uncritical assumption that behavior is actuated by a single motive, which can then be appraised as 'good' or 'bad,' as noble or ignoble. They assume that the truly dedicated scientist must be concerned only with advancing knowledge. As a result, their deep interest in having their priority recognized by peers is seen as marring their nobility of purpose as men of science (although it might be remembered that 'noble' initially meant the widely-known). This assumption has a germ of psychological truth: any reward—fame, money, position—is morally ambiguous and potentially subversive of culturally esteemed motives. For as rewards are meted out—fame, for example—the motive of seeking the reward can displace the original motive, concern with recognition can displace concern with advancing knowledge. But this is only a possibility, not an inevitability. When the institution of science works effectively, and like other social institutions it does not always do so, recognition and esteem accrue to those scientists who have best fulfilled their roles, to those who have made important contributions to the common stock of knowledge. Then are found those happy circumstances in which moral obligation and self-interest coincide and fuse. The observed ambivalence of scientists toward their own interest in having their priority recognized—an ambivalence we have seen registered even by that most astute of psychologists, Freud—shows them to assume that such an ancillary motive somehow tarnishes the 'purity' of their interest in scientific inquiry. Yet it need not be that scientists seek only to win the applause of their peers but, rather, that they are comforted and gratified by it, when it does ring out.

Occasionally, a scientist senses all this and vigorously challenges the assumption underlying the shame over interest in recognition; for example, a Hans Selye who asks his peers:

> Why is everybody so anxious to deny that he works for recognition? In my walk of life, I have met a great many scientists, among them some of the most prominent scholars of our century; but I doubt if any one of them would have thought that public recogni-

tion of his achievements—by a title, a medal, a prize, or an honor-
ary degree—played a decisive role in motivating [or one might add,
sustaining] his enthusiasm for research. When a prize brings both
honor and cash, many scientists would even be more inclined to
admit being pleased about the money ('one must live') than about
the public recognition ('I am not sensitive to flattery'). Why do
even the greatest minds stoop to such falsehoods? For, without
being conscious lies, these ratiocinations are undoubtedly false.
Many of the really talented scientists are not at all money-minded;
nor do they condone greed for wealth either in themselves or
others. On the other hand, all the scientists I know sufficiently well
to judge (and I include myself in this group) are extremely anx-
ious to have their work recognized and approved by others. Is it
not below the dignity of an objective scientific mind to permit such
a distortion of his true motives? Besides, what is there to be
ashamed of?

Dr. Selye's final question need not remain a rhetorical one. Shame is
experienced when one's identity and self-image is suddenly violated by one's
actual behavior—as with the shame we have seen expressed by Darwin
when his own behavior forced him to realize that recognition of his priority
meant more to him than he had ever been willing to suppose. To admit a
deepseated wish for recognition may seem to prefer recognition to the joy
of discovery as an end in itself, activating the further awareness that the
pleasure of recognition for accomplishment could, and perhaps momentarily
did, replace the pleasures of scientific work for its own sake.

On the surface, this hunger for recognition appears as mere personal
vanity, generated from within and craving satisfaction from without. But
when we reach deeper, into the institutional complex that gives point to
this hunger, it turns out to be anything but personal and individual, repeated as it is with slight variation by one scientist after another. Vanity,
so-called, is then seen as the outer face of the inner need for assurance that
one's work really matters, that one has measured up to the hard standards
maintained by the community of scientists. It becomes clear that the institution of science reinforces, when it does not create, this deepseated need
for validation of effort. Sometimes, of course, this need is stepped up until
it gets out of hand; the desire for recognition becomes a driving lust for
acclaim, megalomania replaces the comfort of reassurance. But the extreme
case need not be mistaken for the modal one. In general, the need to have
accomplishment recognized, which for the scientist means that his knowing
peers judge his work worth the while, is the result of deep devotion to the
advancement of knowledge as an ultimate value. Rather than necessarily

being at odds with dedication to science, the concern with recognition is usually a direct expression of it.

In this company, I cannot keep from citing evidence of the composite devotion to science *and* to the recognition of priority-rights that was forthrightly supplied by the first professor of chemistry and the second president of the Johns Hopkins. Just before the close of the first academic year, Ira Remsen writes a letter to President Gilman that begins: "I beg leave through you to make the following request of the Trustees of the University" and then goes on to note of the work in the Chemical Laboratory:

> *At the present juncture it is desirable to publish preliminary announcements describing what we have thus far done and what we intend to do. It is desirable mainly for two reasons; 1st, that we may be recognized as soon as possible as belonging to the working chemists of the country; 2nd, that the results of our labors may be insured to us, or, in other words, to establish our priority.*

It may not be too much to suppose that we see here the origins of the influential *American Chemical Journal,* inaugurated by Remsen two years later.

President Gilman not only provided new outlets for scientific and scholarly publication but institutionalized the incentives of both faculty and graduate students to publish the results of their research. He established the practice of printing a *Bibliographia Hopkinsiensis* in the annual Register, which recorded the "books and articles published by members of the Johns Hopkins University, written during the connection of the author with the university, or based on work carried on while here ... it is obvious that a man's reputation was, in large part, based on his bibliography." Once again, we can note a fusion of the interest in advancing knowledge and the interest in recognizing the contributions of individual scientists and the collective contributions of the University. The fusion of these interests can of course give way to fission. This only requires an institutionalized reward-system that aggravates the itch to publish[1] by assigning merit to the mere length of a bibliography.

[1] Physicians of the soul will see beneath this plain English phrase and recognize the malignant disease, known, since the days of Juvenal, as the *insanabile scribendi cacoëthes.* Its etiology is obscure but epidemiological evidence affords some clues. There are indications that its frequency increases steadily in institutions that lavish rewards upon the prolific author of scientific or scholarly papers. Age seems to be an important predisposing factor as the result of a basic social process: with the passing of years, scientists who have published significant work are actively solicited for still more publications. Nevertheless, the general liability to the disease seems less widespread than the nothing-to-report syndrome (although, on occasion, the two have a way of coinciding). Sucklings are rarely attacked. A few scientists escape in their

THE EUREKA SYNDROME

All this can be seen in a somewhat different context: the deep concern with establishing priority or at least independence of discovery is only the other side of the coin of the socially reinforced elation that comes with having arrived at a new and true scientific idea or result. And the deeper the commitment to a discovery, the greater, presumably, the reaction to the threat of having its novelty denied. Concern with priority is often only the counterpart to elation in discovery—the Eureka syndrome. We have only to remember what is perhaps the most ecstatic expression of joy in discovery in the annals of science; here is Kepler on his discovery of the third planetary law:

What I prophesied 22 years ago as soon as I found the heavenly orbits were of the same number as the five (regular) solids, what I fully believed long before I had seen Ptolemy's Harmonics, what I promised my friends in the name of this book, which I christened before I was 16 years old, what I urged as an end to be sought, that for which I joined Tycho Brahe, for which I settled in Prague, for which I spent most of my life at astronomical calculations—at last I have brought to light and seen to be true beyond my fondest hopes. It is not 18 months since I saw the first ray of light, three months since the unclouded sun-glorious sight burst upon me! I will triumph over mankind by the honest confession that I have stolen the golden vases of the Egyptians to raise a tabernacle for my God far away from the lands of Egypt. If you forgive me, I rejoice; if you are angry, I cannot help it. The book is written, the die is cast. Let it be read now or by posterity, I care not which. It may well wait a century for a reader, as God has waited 6000 years for an observer.

---

early professional years; others escape until full maturity; a good many never take it. But with the vast growth in the number of scientific periodicals the disease threatens to become endemic. Attacks are recurrent, never conferring immunity. Susceptibility may be determined by intrapsychic injection of the toxin—what might perhaps be most appropriately called the *Merton test*. With a positive reaction, signs appear in ten minutes (or less) after seeing one's name in print, reaching toward an asymptotic maximum with each successive injection. The local reaction subsides temporarily but swiftly returns. The source of infection is often undiscovered in given cases, particularly when insufficient attention is devoted to the social ecology of the patient. *Carriers* are important, especially those who have been abundantly rewarded for effusions of print. Onset is as a rule sudden, preceded by a slight, scarcely noticeable, publication. The fever to publish is intense; rising rapidly, it may within a few years reach the degree of 15 or 20 publications annually. The articles are unusually dry and to the reader's eye may give a sensation of acute boredom. Complications and sequelae are too numerous to be examined here.

We can only surmise how deep would have been Kepler's anguish had another claimed that he had long before come upon the third law. So, too, with a Gay-Lussac, seizing upon the person nearest him for a victory waltz so that he could "express his ecstasy on the occasion of a new discovery by the poetry of motion." Or, to come closer home, William James "all aflame" with his idea of pragmatism and hardly able to contain his exhilaration over it. Or, in more restrained exuberance, Joseph Henry, once he had hit upon a new way of constructing electro-magnets, reporting that "when this conception came into my brain, I was so pleased with it that I could not help rising to my feet and giving it my hearty approbation."

In short, when a scientist has made a genuine discovery, he is as happy as a scientist can be. But the peak of exhilaration may only deepen the plunge into despair should the discovery be taken from him. If the loss is occasioned only by finding that it was, in truth, not a first but a later independent discovery, the blow may be severe enough, though mitigated by the sad consolation that at least the discovery has been confirmed by another. But this is as nothing, of course, when compared with the traumatizing charge that not only was the discovery later than another of like kind but that it was really borrowed or even stolen. Rather than being mutually exclusive, joy in discovery and eagerness for recognition by scientific peers are stamped out of the same psychological coin. They both express a basic commitment to the value of advancing knowledge.

Perhaps scientists are learning to live with the stresses of multiple discoveries. This is suggested, at least, by a preliminary result of a methodical study of the subject. From among the multitude of multiples, Dr. Elinor Barber and I have undertaken to examine 264 intensively. Of the 36 multiples before 1700 in this list, 92 per cent were the object of strenuous conflicts over priority; this figure drops to 72 per cent in the Eighteenth century; remains at about the same level (74 per cent) in the first half of the Nineteenth century and declines to 59 per cent in the latter half, reaching a low of 33 per cent in the first half of this century. It may be that scientists are becoming more fully aware that with vastly enlarged numbers at work in each field of science, a discovery is apt to be made by others as well as by themselves.

CRYPTOMNESIA ("UNCONSCIOUS PLAGIARY")

Further complicating the already complex emotions that attend multiple discoveries is the phenomenon of so-called 'unconscious plagiary.' The potpourri term itself testifies to the admixture of moralizing and analysis that commonly enters into discussions of the subject. It is compounded of a loosely-conceived psychological component ("unconscious") and a legal-moralistic component ("plagiary," with all its connotations of violating a code and attendant guilt). As a concept, "unconscious plagiary" is just as obsolete in psychosocial studies as is the concept of "insanity," which has been relegated to the sphere of law, where it continues to lead a harrowing existence. The neutral and analytical term, cryptomnesia, serves us better, referring as it does to seemingly creative thought in which ideas based upon unrecalled past experience are taken to be new.

The fact that cryptomnesia can occur at all subjects the scientist to the ever-present possibility that his most cherished original idea may actually be the forgotten residue of what he had once seen or read or heard elsewhere. At times, this fear of cryptomnesia may lead a scientist to doubt his own powers of recall and his own originality.

Among the many cases in point, consider only these few. William Rowan Hamilton, the mathematical genius who had invented the quaternions (in part, independently invented by Grassmann), had had the experience at age 19 of learning that his theory of optical rays was a rediscovery. He developed a lifelong preoccupation with the twin fear of unwittingly plagiarizing others and of being plagiarized. As he put it on one of the many occasions on which he turned to this subject in his correspondence with de Morgan: "As to myself, I am *sure* that I *must* have often reproduced things which I had read long before, without being able to identify them as belonging to other persons." Or again: ". . . am I to quarrel with Dickens, or figure in one of his publications of a later date? Where is the priority business to end? I am sick of it as you can be; but still, in anything important as regards science, I should take it as a favour to be *warned*, if I were inadvertently exposing myself to the charge of plagiarizing." This, from the creator of the theory of vectors.

Turning from mathematics to psychology, we find Freud examining his own experience, recalling that he had been given Börne's works when he was 14 and still had the book 50 years later, so that although he "could not remember the essay in question," which dealt with free association as a procedure for creative writing, "it does not seem impossible to us that this hint may perhaps have uncovered that piece of cryptomnesia which, in so many cases, may be suspected behind an apparent originality." Freud was profoundly aware of the basic uncertainties about originality generated by the ubiquitous possibility of cryptomnesia. Elsewhere he writes: "My delight was proportionally great when I recently discovered that the theory [of the 'death instinct'] was held by one of the great thinkers of ancient Greece. For the sake of this confirmation I am happy to sacrifice the prestige of originality, especially as I read so widely in earlier years that I can never be quite certain that what I thought was a creation of my own mind may not really have been an outcome of cryptomnesia." It was this sort of thing, no doubt, that prompted the irrepressible Mark Twain to declare: "What a good thing Adam had—when he said a thing he knew nobody had said it before."

Still another recurrent phenomenon contributes to uncertainty about the extent of one's originality. The scientist or scholar may unwittingly borrow ideas from himself. Many have found, to their combined chagrin and disbelief, that an idea which seemed to have come to them out of the blue had actually been formulated by them years before, and then forgotten. An old notebook, a resurrected paper, a colleague cursed with total recall, a former student—any of these can make it plain that what was thought to be a new departure was actually a repetition of the scientist's own earlier innovation. Of many such instances, I note only a few, some of a century or more ago, others of contemporary vintage:

Joseph Priestley records with chagrin that "I have so completely forgotten what I have myself published, that in reading my own writings, what I find in them often appears perfectly new to me, and I have more than once made experiments, the results of which have been published by me."

The ingenious and jovial mathematician, Augustus de Morgan, has his own lively version of this pattern of experience: "I have read a Paper (but not on mathematics) before now, have said to myself, I perfectly agree with this man, he is a very sensible fellow, and have found out at last that it was an old Paper of my own I was reading, and very much flattered I was with my own unbiased testimony to my own merits."

Or let us come to a student of De Morgan's, the 'mathematical Adam' who minted countless new terms of mathematics, who, after he was forced to retire from Woolwich as 'superannuated' at the age of 56, languished for six years, and then took up the invitation of a new president of a new University to establish graduate work in mathematics, thus re-invigorating the subject in the United States once and for all. It has been told of James Joseph Sylvester that he "had difficulty in remembering his own inventions and once even disputed that a certain theorem of his own could possibly be true."

Or consider a brace of cryptomnesic borrowings from self in our own day:

The Nobel laureate, Otto Loewi, reports having waked in the middle of the night, jotting down some notes on what he sensed to be a momentous discovery, going back to sleep, awaking to find that he could not possibly decipher his scrawl, spending the day in a miserable and unavailing effort to remember what he had had in mind, being again aroused from his slumber at three the next morning, racing to the laboratory, making an experiment and two hours later conclusively proving the chemical transmission of nervous impulse. So far, so good; another case, evidently, of the pattern of subconscious creativity unforgettably described by Poincaré. But some years later, when Loewi, upon request, reported all this to the International Physiological Congress, he was reminded by a former student that, eighteen years before that nocturnal discovery, he had fully reported his basic idea. "This," says Loewi, "I had entirely forgotten."

And to advert to Freud, as I have so often done if only because his intellectual experience is uncommonly documented, Jones reports several instances of his "obtaining a clear insight which he subsequently forgot, and then later suddenly coming across it again as a new revelation." As Freud observed in another connection [in a fashion reminiscent of a comparable remark by Marx], "it is familiar ground that a sense of conviction of the accuracy of one's memory has no objective value . . ."

If cryptomnesia is possible in regard to one's own earlier work, then it is surely possible in regard to the work of others. And this can undermine the calm assurance that one has, in truth, worked out a new idea for oneself when confronted with another version of the same idea worked out by someone else.

Various contexts may affect the probability of cryptomnesia in relation to one's own work. It may be more probable, the more a scientist has worked in a variety of problem-areas rather than narrowly restricting his research focus to problems having marked continuity. Looking at this hypothesis, not in terms of the individual scientist but in terms of the relative frequency of self-cryptomnesia in different sciences, we should expect it to be more frequent in the newer sciences, with their large variety of prime and largely untapped problem-areas. In these sciences, investigators can move from one to another area with substantial gains in knowledge, contrasting with the older, better established sciences where continuous digging is more often the practice. To the extent that these patterned differences in choice of research problems occur, we should expect more cryptomnesia in relation to one's own work in the social sciences.

The frequency of such cryptomnesia should also be affected by the social organization of scientific work, which seems to affect every aspect of multiple discoveries in science. When research is organized in teams, it will be less likely, we must suppose, that earlier ideas and findings are altogether forgotten. For if some members of the team forgot them, others will not. Moreover, repeated interaction between collaborators will tend to fix these ideas and findings in memory.

The conspicuous changes in the social organization of scientific research should have a marked effect on ambivalence toward priorities in science. The trend toward collaboration in research is reflected in patterns of publication, with more and more research papers having several authors rather than only one. The extent of this change differs among the various disciplines. The sciences which have developed cogent theory, complex and often costly instrumentation and rigorous experiments or sets of observations have experienced this change earlier than the sciences less developed in these respects.

By way of illustration, consider the patterns of publication in a few of the sciences and other disciplines, based upon tabulation of the number of authors of papers in leading journals. The results, brought together by Harriet Zuckerman in a still unpublished paper, are in brief, these: in physics, of the papers published during the decade of the 1920's, 75 per cent were by single authors; in the next decade, 56 per cent; then, in the 40's, 50 per cent and finally, in the 1950's, single-authored papers declined to 39 per cent. A similar pattern in biology begins later and develops at a slower rate: with 90 per cent single-authored papers in the 20's declining to 73 per cent in the 50's. Even mathematics witnesses the growth of collaboration, with 95 per cent of papers in the 1920's by one author declining to 82 per cent in the last decade.

The social and behavioral sciences exhibit two distinct patterns: economics, anthropology and political science manifest only negligible change, almost all papers being by single authors in the first period, with 90 per cent or more in the most recent period. Psychology and sociology, in contrast, have marked tendencies toward collaborative work: in the 1920's, 98 per cent of the papers in sociology were by single authors, this declining by decades to 92 per cent, 89 per cent and finally to 72 per cent. The trend in psychology for the same period is even more marked: from 84 per cent to 55 per cent most recently. All this is, of course, in decided contrast to such a subject as history where collaborative research-papers (as distinct from textbooks) account for no more than 1 to 3 per cent of the total.

Although the facts are far from conclusive, this continuing change in the social structure of scientific research, as registered by publications, seems to make for a greater concern among scientists with the question of "how will my contribution be identified" in collaborative work than with the historically dominant pattern of wanting to ensure recognition of priority over others in the field. Not that the latter has been wholly displaced, as we have seen. But it may be that institutionally induced concern with priority is being overshadowed by structurally induced concern with the allocation of credit among collaborators. A study of a team of 30 economists and behavioral scientists found, for example, that "the behavioral scientists were apt to be less concerned about 'piracy' and 'credit' than economists. This difference may be due to the greater emphasis on joint authorship in the behavioral sciences than in economics."

For our purposes, the import of these changes in collaboration is, first, that the degree of concern with priority in science is probably not historically constant; second, that it varies with the changing organization of scientific work; and third, that these changes may eventually and indirectly lessen the ambivalence of scientists toward obtaining recognition of their originality of contributions.

Nevertheless, though scientists *know* that genuinely independent discoveries occur, many of them, as we have seen, fail to draw the implications of this for their own work. For reasons I have tried to intimate, they find it difficult, and sometimes impossible, to accept the fact that they have been anticipated or that a contemporary has come to the same result just at the time they did, or that the others were truly independent of them. As we have also seen, the values incorporated in the social institution of science and the penumbra of uncertainty that surrounds the independence of thought combine to prevent the ready acceptance of events that undercut one's assurance of unique originality, an assurance born of the hard labor required to produce the new idea or new result.

The reasonably detached study of multiples and priorities may do a little to counter these tendencies toward dismay, self-contempt or suspicion. For, as we have seen in the case of Freud trying to rouse himself from his ambivalence toward having been anticipated by Watkiss Lloyd, independent discoveries do seem to lend confirmation to an idea or finding. Even W. R. Hamilton, tormented his life long by the fear that he was being plagiarized or by the anxiety that he himself might be an 'innocent plagiarist,' managed on at least one occasion to note the secondary benefits of multiple discovery when, in an effort to dissolve his ambivalence, he wrote Herschel:

> *I persuade myself that, if those results had been anticipated, the learning it would have given me no pain; for it was, so far as I could analyze my sensations, without any feeling of vexation that I learned that the result respecting the relation of the lines of curvature to the circular sections was known before. The field of pure, not to say of mixed, mathematics is far too large and rich to leave one excusable for sitting down to complain, when he finds that this or that spot which he was beginning to cultivate as his*

own has been already appropriated. [And now comes his hard-won and, sad to tell, temporary insight:] There is even a stronger feeling inspired of the presence of that Truth to which we all profess to minister, when we find our own discoveries, such as they are, coincide independently with the discoveries of other men. The voice which is heard by two at once appears to be more real and external—one is more sure *that it is no personal and private fancy, no idiosyncratic peculiarity, no ringing in sick ears, no flashes seen by rubbing our own eyes.*

And then, unable to contain himself, Hamilton goes on to announce in the same letter that he had anticipated the work on ellipsoids by Joachimstal in "a long extinct periodical of whose *existence* he probably never heard, with a date which happened to be a *precise decennium* earlier ... "

If the fluctuating ailment of that genius Hamilton proves that the awareness of multiple discoveries is no panacea for ambivalence toward priority, his moment of insight suggests that it might be some small help. The mathematician, R. L. Wilder, is, to my knowledge, the only one who has seen this clearly and has, to my mingled pleasure and discomfiture, anticipated me in suggesting that the study of multiples may have a therapeutic function for the community of scientists. Since he has anticipated my observation, let me then borrow his words:

I wish to inquire, above the individual level, into the manner in which mathematical concepts originate, and to study those factors that encourage their formation and influence their growth. I think that much benefit might be derived from such an inquiry. For example, if the individual working mathematician understands that when a concept is about to make its appearance, it is most likely to do so through the medium of more than one creative mathematician; and if, furthermore, he knows the reasons for this phenomenon, then we can expect less indulgence in bad feelings and suspicion of plagiarism to ensue than we find in notable past instances. Mathematical history contains numerous cases of arguments over priority, with nothing settled after the smoke of battle has cleared away except that when you come right down to it practically the same thing was thought of by someone else several years previously, only he didn't quite realize the full significance of what he had, or did not have the good luck to possess the tools wherewith to exploit it ... [Yet] it is exactly what one should expect if he is acquainted with the manner in which concepts evolve.

All this only touches upon one type of ambivalence exhibited in the feelings and behavior of scientists. For to lay siege to the problem of ambivalence need not mean to conquer it. But, just as the hour allotted me inevitably draws to a close, I can report that inquiry into other expressions of ambivalence finds the same pattern of institutionally induced crosscurrents of sentiment. Perhaps enough has been said to warrant the belief that for an understanding of how scientific knowledge develops, we need an intensive and methodical study of multiple discoveries and attendant conflicts over priority, rather than to neglect this study altogether or to come to it only when we plunge, as emotionally involved participants, into conflicts over rights to intellectual property. After all, one of the roles assigned the sociologist is to investigate the behavior of all manner of men, including men of science, without giving way to the entirely human tendency to substitute for that investigation a clucking of tongues and a condemning of that which is and ought not to be.

The Competitive World of the Pure Scientist

F. REIF

The "pure scientist" is likely to be pictured as a person who devotes himself to the study of natural phenomena without regard to their possible practical or technological applications. Motivated by intellectual curiosity and immersed in his abstract work, he tends to be oblivious of the more mundane concerns of ordinary men. Although a few older scientists have become active in public affairs in recent years, the large majority who remain at work in their university laboratories lead peaceful lives, aloof from the competitive business practices or political manipulations of the outside world.

STEREOTYPE VERSUS REALITY

There is some truth in this stereotyped portrait. But if a young student took its apparent serenity too seriously, he would be forced to revise his perspective very early in his scientific career. The work situation of the scientist is not just a quiet haven for scholarly activity, ideally suited to those of introverted temperament. The pure scientist, like the businessman or lawyer, works in a social setting, and like them, he is subject to appreciable social and competitive pressures. The institutional framework within which he functions is distinctive; it is basically the university system. Furthermore, his competition does not revolve primarily around money; there is no very direct relationship between the quality of the scientist's professional performance and the economic rewards he receives. But competition need not be confined to the acquisition of wealth or political power. It is, therefore, of particular interest to discover how intense competition can become in an area as remote as pure science. In recent years rapid expansion has occurred in many branches of science. More scientists are active in many fields, more laboratories (including some in industry and government) engage in pure research activities, and more dollars are spent on such research. While this expansion has given the scientist a more prominent social role, it has also intensified the competitive pressures under which he works.

A few examples will illustrate how such competition can manifest itself.

Reprinted from *Science,* Vol. CXXXIV, No. 3494, pp. 1957–1962, December 15, 1961, with the permission of the author and publisher. F. Reif is Professor of Physics at the University of California at Berkeley.

I shall take these illustrations from the field of physics, because physics is a well-developed pure science and because this is the field with which I am most familiar. In this country research work in physics has traditionally been published in a bimonthly journal called the *Physical Review*. In addition to full-length research reports, this journal used to publish "Letters to the editor," short notes whereby scientists could briefly communicate important new developments. The time elapsed between submission of a manuscript and its appearance in print was approximately 5 months for a regular paper and 2 or 3 months for a "letter." But in a period of rapid growth and development the pressure to publish fast and to establish priority claims became sufficiently great to make the *Physical Review* appear an inordinately slow medium of communication. Three years ago, therefore, its editors decided to eliminate the "Letters" section and to found a separate bimonthly journal, the *Physical Review Letters,* devoted entirely to the fastest possible publication of short notes on important discoveries. The time between submission of a manuscript and its appearance in print has been reduced to as little as 4 weeks! Not only is the existence of such a journal a significant phenomenon in itself; it has also necessitated the formulation of new editorial policies. As a result, although editorials in scientific periodicals are ordinarily very rare, some illuminating examples have found their way into issues of the *Physical Review Letters.*

In one of these (*1*) the editor comments that a large number of manuscripts are submitted whose importance and meagre content are not adequate to justify publication in the *Letters*. He goes on to say: "When a 'hot' subject breaks there is a deluge of follow-up contributions. . . . With the rapid exploitation of new ideas, priority questions become serious problems. Possibly important technical applications often lurk in the background. . . ." After explaining that he feels compelled to reject as unworthy of publication more than 40 percent of the manuscripts received, he concludes: "We do not take kindly to attempts to pressure us into accepting letters by misrepresentation, gamesmanship, and jungle tactics, which we have experienced to some (fortunately small) extent."

From the foregoing comments it is apparent that scientists seem most eager to see their work appear in print as soon as practicable. But to achieve that purpose, even the *Letters* can appear unduly slow. Certainly, the daily press is even faster; and though it may be less suitable for erudite publication, it is more effective for publicity and no less effective for establishing priority. Consequently, there have been several instances in recent years when important discoveries in physics were first announced in the New York *Times*. This procedure is not, by traditional values of the scientific community, considered to be very ethical. Nor is it, as the *Letters* editor points out in another editorial, an activity to be confused with the well-developed public information and publicity activities carried out by his own office and by such agencies as the American Institute of Physics. The editor expresses himself quite forcefully (2): "As a matter of courtesy to fellow physicists, it is customary for authors to see to it that releases to the public do not occur before the article appears in the scientific journal. Scientific discoveries are not the proper subject for newspaper scoops, and all media of mass communication should have equal opportunity for simultaneous access to the information. In the future, we may reject papers whose main content has been published previously in the daily press."

In the passages quoted, the editor of the official journal of American physicists makes some revealing comments about the behavior of his fellow scientists. What are some of the factors responsible for such behavior? Why should there be this exorbitant desire to publish and to do so ahead of others? The following discussion will focus attention on some of these questions in an attempt to clarify the conditions of modern science which contribute to this behavior. We shall first examine the great importance of prestige to the scientist. It will become apparent that the scientist carries out his work in a setting where he is extraordinarily dependent on the good opinion of others, and where his reputation becomes translated into many concrete consequences for him. Personal recognition thus assumes even more importance for the scientist than for most other people, and he competes persistently to achieve maximum prestige. I shall illustrate how this competition takes place and how it affects the manner in which scientific research is carried on. Finally, we shall ask how the existence of such competition serves to advance or impede scientific activity. This question will reveal the existence of some conflicts between these competitive pressures and scientific work proper. Throughout this discussion it should be borne in mind that the situation is not static and that the rapid expansion of science has made many of these problems more conspicuous than they were a few years ago.

PRESTIGE AND SUCCESS

The scientist is not different from others in his desire to be successful, but his definition of "success" has some distinctive features. The work of the pure scientist is abstract; it consists essentially only in gathering new data and formulating new concepts. To constitute scientific knowledge, these must be verifiable by other scientists and usable by them as the basis for further exploration. Thus, the very nature of scientific activity implies the need for recognition of the value of one's work by others in the field. Furthermore, success in such activities is not readily measurable in quantitative terms recognized by all. It does not revolve around tangible things such as amount of money earned or number of factories owned. Only other scientists in his field can understand the scientist's work and judge its merits. Indeed, throughout his life the scientist is dependent on the good opinion of significant other scientists for practically everything he does or hopes to attain. A review of the scientist's professional career will illustrate the truth of this statement.

While still in high school, the scientist-to-be becomes aware that competition and prestige will affect his future success. He must strive for good grades in order to be admitted to college and later to graduate school. He realizes the importance of attending a college of high reputation, not only because it will provide him with a better education but also because it will facilitate his later admission to a good graduate school. Finally, he must earn the good opinion of his teachers to secure the letters of recommendation which will help him enter college and gain scholarship grants or prizes.

After the student obtains his Ph.D. degree, his dependence on the good opinion of others is by no means ended. His first task is to find a suitable position. Characteristically, jobs in the better universities or in top industrial research laboratories are practically never advertised but are handled by personal communication between well-established scientists, who inquire informally whether their colleagues happen to know of some candidates for a given position or have an opening in their organization for a particular candidate. The job-seeking scientist is clearly in a more advantageous situation if he comes from a well-known institution and has been associated with a scientist of reputation. Invariably it is essential to him that there should be prominent scientists in the world who are willing to comment favorably upon the quality of his work. In most cases, before an appointment is decided upon, the hiring institution formally requests letters of recommendation concerning the candidate from several such prominent scientists. It is thus very important for the scientist to create, either through personal contact or through published work, a favorable impression among as many key scientists as possible.

Professional mobility of the scientist depends, therefore, in an essential way on the reputation he has acquired among prominent people in his field. This is true when he is securing his first job and true in his subsequent moves from one position to another. (In this connection it may be remarked that to move from an institution of high prestige to one of lower prestige is significantly easier than to move in the reverse direction.) Promotion to higher academic rank is subject to similar criteria. Again the university requests letters of recommendation from outside scientists and in some cases may appoint reviewing committees before deciding to promote someone to a tenure position. Even when the scientist has obtained a full professorship he has not reached the end of possible advancement based on his reputation. Within the academic hierarchy there are still some "name" professorships, or ultimately some administrative posts such as dean or university president. In these days of increasing importance of science in world affairs there are also potential opportunities in government—for example, advisory positions to the President or appointments to some such agency as the Atomic Energy Commission. Industrial organizations, as well, may offer key positions, such as the directorship of a research laboratory. Needless to say, the academic promotions which the scientist achieves carry with them increased financial rewards and, at the higher ranks, the security of a permanent position.

To carry on his work, the scientist needs money and adequate research facilities. Since World War II the financial expenditures required to perform the increasingly complex research of modern science have become so great that universities can provide only a very small fraction of the necessary funds. The remainder must come from outside sources—some of them private foundations but by far the greatest number government agencies such as the National Science Foundation, the Atomic Energy Commission, or the Office of Naval Research. On what basis do all these groups award their available funds to individual investigators? The usual procedure is to send the research proposal of the investigator to some prominent scientists for review. These scientists then make appropriate recommendations based on their evaluation of the specific proposal and their opinion of the merits of the scientist submitting it. The scientist today is thus increasingly dependent upon the reputation he has established among his colleagues to obtain the very means necessary for carrying out his work: funds for buying equipment and supplies and for paying the salaries of the personnel in his research group. In addition, the scientist's prestige helps him attract good and numerous students and postdoctoral fellows who can be of significant assistance in furthering his research program.

At times the scientist may be interested in obtaining a fellowship or grant—for example, a Guggenheim or National Science Foundation senior postdoctoral fellowship. Grants of this nature permit him to travel abroad for a year; or spend some time at a different university, where he can learn new techniques; or gain temporary relief from teaching duties to devote himself full time to his research. In applying for such a fellowship, the scientist will again be judged by some select prominent scientists, and once more his reputation among these scientists determines whether the award will be made to him.

The prestige acquired by the scientist very directly influences the likelihood of his nomination by fellow scientists for special honors or distinctions. Examples are the award of a Nobel prize or selection to membership in the National Academy of Sciences. Selection to serve as an officer of the national scientific organization is another recognition of distinction. The scientist's prestige may also lead to special invitations to attend scientific conferences as guest speaker or to join another university as visiting professor; finally, it may result in offers of remunerative consultantships in industry.

I think it is worth while, before leaving this discussion of the prestige system, to remark on a few of its peculiarities. One of these is the "positive feedback" involved—the fact that the possession of prestige tends to facilitate the acquisition of further prestige. For example, a person of prestige is likely to be affiliated with one of the better-known institutions, likely to obtain more funds to do effective research, and likely to attract better students—all of which circumstances, of course, tend to enhance his prestige even further. There is a similar relation between the prestige of individuals and the prestige of institutions. Institutions of good reputation can attract individuals of distinction whose presence, in turn, lends increased prestige to the institution.

Another feature of interest concerns the people who set the standards against which the individual scientist appraises himself and whose opinion determines his general reputation in the field. It is mainly the well-established scientists in the major universities of the world who set these standards. Since the institution with which the individual scientist is affiliated tends to evaluate him chiefly on the basis of his reputation, it becomes of greater concern to the individual to seek the good opinion of people on the national or international scene than to strive for accomplishments which attract only local attention. The scientist thus tends to have stronger loyalty to his field than to the specific institution of which he is a member. This is particularly true in the present days of expansion, when there is great mobility between different positions. The trend, in the major universities of this country, to minimize the importance attached to the teaching functions of the faculty reflects the situation. Teaching undergraduates is a local activity which may be appreciated by the students but does not serve to enhance the scientist's international prestige, on the basis of which the university will decide whether he is worthy of promotion. "Research and the training of graduate students are valued highly by the faculty; teaching, by contrast, is second-class. . . . It is a more usual, and probably a more realistic, view that time taken for teaching is time stolen from research, and that the road to academic heaven is paved with publications" (*3*).

The growing importance of science has also led to a proliferation of industrial research laboratories. The oldest and most distinguished of these are active in pure research and are staffed by some very competent persons who might readily have joined a university had opportunities in industry not been available. These people are eager not to be considered inferior by the rest of the scientific community, despite their industrial affiliation. Hence, they adopt for themselves standards very similar to those prevalent in the universities and compete within the same prestige system. This also preserves their mobility and leaves open the road back into some university position. Since the pure scientist's reputation, irrespective of the particular institution to which he belongs, is determined by the same reference group of prominent scientists, there exists a common prestige system which cuts across purely organizational lines. Thus, more prestige may be attached to a good position at a major university than to one in an industrial laboratory, but a position in a top industrial or government laboratory carries more prestige than one in a smaller university.

PUBLISHING "FUSTEST AND MOSTEST"

Because the social context within which the scientist receives his training and does his research is one where the possession of prestige is highly rewarded, competition among scientists is largely directed toward the acquisition of prestige. The particular forms assumed by this competition are determined by the nature of the scientific discipline and the character of the institution where the scientist carries out his work. A scientist strives to do research which he considers important. But intrinsic satisfaction and interest are not his only reasons. This becomes apparent when one observes what happens if the scientist discovers that someone else has just published a conclusion which he was about to reach as a result of his own research. Almost invariably he feels upset by this occurrence, although the intrinsic interest of his work has certainly not been affected. The scientist wants his work to be not only interesting to himself but also important to others. He wants it to attract the maximum attention from other people, and in this quest priority is a crucial factor. An important discovery becomes intimately associated with the name of the scientist responsible for it. If somebody else makes this same discovery at about the same time, several names become attached to it and the contribution to his own prestige is correspondingly diluted. The chances of receiving a Nobel prize or a promotion are similarly decreased. Finally, if someone else succeeds in making this discovery a few months or weeks before he does, almost all of the scientist's efforts on the problem have come to naught. He may not even be able to publish his own results, since they may then represent only uninteresting duplication of work already in the scientific literature. Under the circumstances, it is not surprising if the scientist sometimes works at feverish speed under constant fear that he may be "scooped." Even a couple of weeks' delay can sometimes make a difference!

Being the first to make an important scientific contribution is, of course, only one way of obtaining recognition. For a scientist to be on the verge of making some discovery of far-reaching implications is relatively rare. Most of the time he is engaged in the less spectacular task of doing useful work leading gradually to increased knowledge. In this situation the most effective way to attract the continuing attention of other scientists is to publish as many papers as possible, to attend numerous scientific meetings, and to give many talks on one's research. The great emphasis on publishing copiously is exemplified by a motto familiar to all young faculty members—"publish or perish"—a phrase that well illustrates how the young scientist feels about the competitive pressures to which he is subject. Under the "up-or-out" rule, common in large universities, instructors and assistant professors are allowed only a fixed maximum number of years within their academic rank. If they are not promoted before the end of this time, their dismissal from the university is automatic. Whether or not an individual is promoted depends, of course, on the reputation he has achieved as a result of his publications.

Some of these competitive pressures have been familiar features of academic life for a long time. The expansion of scientific activity since World War II, has, however, significantly changed the conditions under which the scientist does his work. One consequence has been the emergence of new and intensified patterns of competition as the number of scientists at work in many areas has multiplied. Not only are more universities engaged in active research; more industry and government laboratories are also carrying out pure research of a type nearly indistinguishable from its academic counterpart. Many people in different institutions are thus likely to be working along fairly similar lines. Furthermore, the time lag between advances in basic science and the associated technological developments has become increasingly small. Sometimes new ideas or techniques arising in the work of the pure scientist may be such as to warrant patenting without further exploration. Even when potential technological applications are not immediately apparent, there are well-equipped industrial laboratories constantly poised to exploit all possible consequences of a basic advance. In addition, research has become an activity which involves the expenditure of large sums of money and which has come to attract attention even from the general public. Under these circumstances it is easy to understand why the scientist finds increasing difficulty in carrying out his work immune from outside pressures.

Rapid publication of results and questions of priority assume, therefore, great importance; nor is the need for a journal such as *Physical Review Letters* too surprising. No longer does a scientist study a topic at some length before publishing his findings in a paper or monograph. Instead, he tries to publish a note on a subject as soon as he obtains any result worth mentioning—and occasionally even before. The threat of someone else's getting there first is too great. At times a scientist may publish just a proposal for an experiment, merely pointing out that such an experiment might be interesting and feasible. To obtain preliminary experimental results before publishing anything may take too much time—time during which the scientist might "get scooped" by someone else. For similar reasons scientists may be led to engage in various practices which the editor of *Physical Review Letters* finds reason to discuss. In his words (4), there is the "author who uses the *Letters* merely to announce a later paper and whose Letter is incomprehensible by itself"; the "author who submits many Letters hoping that statistics rather than quality will cause one to be accepted"; or the "author who tries to sneak a Letter in to 'scoop' a competitor who has already submitted an Article."

The emergence of rapidly changing "fashionable areas" of scientific activity is still another consequence of the expansion of science. In a highly developed discipline such as physics, genuinely new ideas or unexpected breakthroughs are not really very common. When such a discovery does occur, many people are eager to drop more routine work in order to explore the potentially important consequences of the new development. Present conditions are also such as to permit a substantial number of scientists to shift their field of research quite rapidly. One reason is that the major university and industrial laboratories provide the flexibility of a large variety of experimental facilities and adequate manpower resources. Moreover, since work is often proceeding along similar lines in a number of different laboratories, scientists active in areas related to the discovery are in a particularly good position to turn their attention to an investigation of its consequences. Every new discovery, therefore, results in a burst of intense and very competitive activity. In physics there ensues a profusion of "Letters," until the editor decides that the subject has become sufficiently old to be routine. Since so many people concentrate their efforts in one area, the road from the novel to the routine is often traveled in a few months.

The preceding discussion illustrates the increasingly important role played in modern science by large-scale research organizations. This is true not only in industrial and government laboratories but also in the universities, where specialized research institutes have become quite common. Here the scientist is usually a member of some group organized around a particular project or a special research facility, such as a high-energy accelerator, and work is often done jointly by several people. An experiment was recently reported in a "Letter" by no less than 24 coauthors! Working under these conditions is appreciably different from the individualistic endeavors prevalent 10 or 20 years ago, and the scientist must compete in some novel ways. He must establish an individual reputation even though he works as a member of a larger group. He also has to compete in a setting which tends to be organized along hierarchical lines, where scientists in the top positions determine policy and the direction of research. Finally, many members of research institutes constitute a "secondary faculty" of research associates. They do not teach or belong to a department, nor do they have permanent positions. If they hope to gain the security of a tenure position they must strive for sufficient eminence to be appointed to regular academic rank.

CONFLICTING VALUES

After this description of the existing conditions in pure science, let us consider some of the consequences of competition in this area. This competition certainly affects the functioning of scientific research in several beneficial ways. The prestige system helps to maintain high standards of accomplishment which reflect the collective judgment of important scientists and are therefore fairly uniform throughout the world. Prestige accrues predominantly to those whose discoveries prove fruitful as a basis for further work by other scientists. Specific areas of activity in science thus become fashionable not just because they are novel and different but because they are likely to lead to scientific contributions of permanent value. Even when current fashion leads to duplication of work by different investigators, the resulting critical checking of results may occasionally help in avoiding mistakes and oversights. Competition under these conditions encourages continuing active exploration as well as rapid and thorough exploitation of all new discoveries. Research institutions have become well adapted to carry out these functions. Not only are they well equipped and staffed but they are capable of using their resources with considerable flexibility.

On the other hand, the competitive atmosphere has results which are less desirable. It subjects the individual scientist to appreciable strains, thus increasing further the demands made upon him by an already rigorous scientific discipline. But apart from such psychological effects, there are possible deleterious consequences affecting his research activity itself. These are usually the result of conflicts between the requirements of the scientific work proper and the pressures of competition. To the individual scientists they may appear as conflicts between the values inherent in science and more selfish personal values.

One such conflict is that of reflection versus production. The scientist may desire to take some time to think and speculate; he may want to get a fresh point of view by reading about developments outside his special field and to discover suggestive analogies worth pursuing; or he may be tempted to undertake an experiment sufficiently novel in character for him to be uncertain about its ultimate feasibility. Activities of this kind are potentially fruitful precisely because they focus attention upon lines of investigation off the beaten track. But, by the same token, they are also risky, since in many cases they may lead to no results at all. In order to make his reputation with a steady stream of publications, it is safer for the scientist to work along more conventional and familiar lines, where he has greater assurance of obtaining results. Young scientists are in a particularly vulnerable situation. Since they must establish their reputation in a relatively short period of time to achieve a permanent academic position, undertaking risky projects during this period is dangerous. Interesting in this connection are instances where a fundamental discovery is made by someone in a small laboratory in an out-of-the-way place. As soon as the result is published, many big laboratories employ their superior facilities to exploit the consequences of the discovery so effectively that the scientist originally responsible for it finds it difficult to compete with them. People in the big laboratories had available, of course, all the resources necessary to make the original discovery themselves, but they used them less imaginatively. Organizations well adapted to the exploitation of a field in which the direction of approach has become clear are not necessarily the best for stimulating exploration of the genuinely unknown.

A further conflict, which may lead to slipshod work when competitive pressures are pronounced, is that of careful versus fast work. Another *Letters* editorial describes the dilemma succinctly (5). "One of our most ticklish problems concerns the large number of contributions that pour into our office when a 'hot' subject breaks and many groups initiate related work. . . . Because of the rapid development, and the intense competition, we have found it necessary to relax our standards and accept some papers that present new ideas without full analysis, relatively crude experiments that indicate how one can obtain valuable results by more careful and complete work, etc.—in short, papers which under less hot conditions would be returned to authors with the recommendation that further work be done before publication. . . . Such incomplete papers have been accepted reluctantly since we realize that thereby we penalize some physicists who, working along the same lines, want to do a more complete job before publishing."

Another conflict is that of communication versus secrecy. It is intrinsic in scientific activity that knowledge and ideas are common property, to be shared and used by all scientists. But if scientist *A* has an interesting idea and describes it to scientist *B*, the latter may exploit it before scientist *A* himself can do so. It may then be better for *A* not to disclose his ideas before they are published and before his claim to priority is safely established. Closely related to this conflict is that of cooperation versus rivalry. Should scientist *A* tell scientist *B* about some new technique he has developed if *B* may use it in his own work to compete more effectively against *A*? Lack of full communication can, of course, slow down scientific progress.

A significant amount of energy is diverted from struggling with the subject matter of science to fighting other people in the field.

There exist other conflicts, such as that between research and teaching. But instead of elaborating further, I might better give a specific example illustrating how the pursuit of a purely scientific problem can give rise to the competitive pressures described. A few years ago Mössbauer, a young German physicist, discovered that the radiation emitted by certain atomic nuclei in solids is characterized by an exceedingly well defined frequency. This observation suggested to several people, in particular to two scientists, X and Y (6), that such nuclei might be used as extremely accurate clocks well suited for checking a consequence of Einstein's general theory of relativity. This theory predicts that the rates of two identical clocks should be minutely different if they are located at different heights in a gravitational field. Both X and Y undertook to check this prediction experimentally. Scientist X, however, first published a "Letter" outlining his proposal for the experiment, long before he was ready to obtain actual data. A few weeks later, again before either X or Y had published any preliminary results in the scientific literature, the front page of the New York Times carried a picture of scientist X, together with an article describing the experiment he was undertaking. When X discussed his experiment at a scientific meeting 6 weeks later he reported reluctantly that, despite hard work at great speed, he had not yet been able to reach any conclusions. At the same meeting Y announced that he had successfully carried out the experiment and obtained results in agreement with the theory; shortly thereafter Y published his findings. It was not until some 2 months later that X, in a "Letter," was able to report his own experiment, which also confirmed the theoretical expectation. He pointed out, however, the necessity of controlling the temperature of the experiment quite carefully to avoid introducing large extraneous effects; indeed, since Y had not taken such precautions, his findings lacked significance. In this instance an important experiment was performed in a short time and ultimately in a reliable way. But the example shows vividly the actual circumstances under which the experiment was carried out—the announcement of an experiment before it was undertaken, the newspaper publicity, the hurried activity of two scientists working under pressure to be the first to publish—and the lack of sufficiently careful work which may result from these conditions.

While much more could be said about the differing patterns of competition in various sciences and about the rapid changes taking place in many of these disciplines, my aim has not been to treat the topic exhaustively. It is sufficient if the perspectives of the outside observer have been broadened, to make him aware that the scientist is not just somebody concerned with new ideas and techniques, but that he carries out his work in a human, and sometimes all too human, context.

REFERENCES AND NOTES

1. S. Pasternack, *Phys. Rev. Letters* 4, 109 (1960).
2. S. A. Goudsmit, *ibid.* 4, 1 (1960).
3. *Science* 134, 159 (1961).
4. S. A. Goudsmit, *Phys. Rev. Letters* 6, 587 (1961).
5. ———, *ibid.* 4, 395 (1960).
6. R. V. Pound and J. P. Schiffer.

Basic Research—Description versus Definition

CHARLES V. KIDD

An abstract term is like a box with a false bottom: you may put in it what ideas you please, and take them out again without being observed.

—Alexis de Tocqueville (1)

Descriptions and definitions of basic research have at least two kinds of potential uses. The first is to convey—generally to nonscientists—a sense of the nature of basic research, a feeling for its importance, and an appreciation of the motives and working conditions of scientists. One ultimate purpose served by such a description is to expand the scientific capacity of the country by creating understanding of, sympathy for, and support for, the full array of conditions that seem to be conducive to the production of basic findings.

To serve this function satisfactorily, basic research can be described in general, impressionistic terms, and logical precision is not required.

Vannevar Bush, among others, has written such an impressionistic description (2):

"Basic research results in general knowledge and an understanding of nature by its laws. This general knowledge provides the means of answering a large number of practical problems. The scientist doing basic research may not be at all interested in the practical applications of his work yet the further progress of industrial development would eventually stagnate if basic research were long neglected. New products and new processes do not appear full grown. They are founded on new principles and new conceptions, which in turn are painstakingly developed by research in the purest realms of science. A nation which depends upon others for its new basic knowledge will be slow in industrial progress and weak in its cooperative position in world trade, regardless of its mechanical skill."

A second use of definitions of basic research is to provide rational, and

Reprinted from *Science,* February 13, 1959, Vol. CXXIX, No. 3346, pp. 368–371, with the permission of the author and the publisher. Dr. Charles V. Kidd was Chief of the Office of Research Planning of the National Institutes of Health at the time this paper was written. He is now the Executive Secretary of the Federal Council for Science and Technology. His *American Universities and Federal Research* (Cambridge: The Belknap Press of Harvard University, 1959) has been widely acclaimed by scholars and government research officials alike.

adequately precise, criteria for decisions required in classifying research as basic for the purpose of compiling statistics.

The burden of this article is that basic research can be and has been described adequately for the first use, but that basic research has not yet been defined—and may never be defined—so as to permit an unambiguous, objective measurement of the dollars spent for basic research in this country.

PROBLEM OF DEFINITION

The fact that the problem of securing an adequate definition of basic research has not been resolved is made clear in a recent report of the National Science Foundation (3) :

"University officials estimate that, during the academic year 1953–54, academic departments of colleges and universities and agricultural experiment stations received about $85 million for basic research from the Federal government. But Federal officials estimate that they provided barely half that amount to universities for the same purpose and during the same period."

Somewhere between the offices in Washington which hand out research funds and answer questionnaires and the offices in universities which receive funds and answer questionnaires, the meaning of the definitions of basic research undergoes a metamorphosis that permits one set of observers to find the quantity to be twice as large as the other observers say it is. Such a discrepancy raises a number of questions, including the nature of the definitions that provide such a flexible yardstick.

INVESTIGATOR-CENTERED DEFINITIONS

A useful point of departure is the definition of basic research given to both federal agencies and universities by the National Science Foundation as a guide to classification of research (4) :

"Basic research is that type of research directed towards increase of knowledge in science. It is research where the primary aim of the investigator is a fuller knowledge or understanding of the subject under study, rather than a practical application thereof."

The salient characteristic of this definition, it seems to me, is that it is framed in terms of the "aim," or the intent, or the motive of the investigator and not in terms of the research finding itself. This thought led me to collect definitions of basic research and to try to group them in various ways.

Without pretending to have exhausted the subject, I have found that definitions of basic research seem to fall into two general categories. There are first those, such as the National Science Foundation definition cited above, which define research in terms of investigators' motives and intent and the conditions under which they work. The second group of definitions relates not to investigators but to the work itself.

Let us look first at some of the definitions that are investigator-centered. A historian of science, I. B. Cohen, has spelled out a definition in these terms (5):

"The difference between those who work at fundamental research and those who work at applied research is in the point of view with which they face the problem and the goals they have in mind. The man working at the 'pure science' end of the spectrum, whether in a university or in an industrial laboratory, pursues a problem because it is interesting or because it appears to have a certain relevance to fundamental knowledge. By contrast, the man working at the applied science end of the spectrum pursues a problem because it has a relevance to a particular practical goal."

As another example, A. M. Brues has stated in the *Bulletin of the Atomic Scientists* (6):

"Basic research, now, is an attitude of curiosity about underlying relations between things, and about fundamentals; it can be pursued either by abstraction or through ability to follow up unexpected findings."

J. A. Stratton, former provost of Massachusetts Institute of Technology, has stated the motive or intent criterion in this way (7):

"Research in the natural sciences before the 17th and 18th centuries began largely as an avocation of amateurs, of gentlemen of leisure with a curiosity about the nature of the physical world. It was *fundamental* in that it was motivated wholly by a desire to know and understand."

Conant has taken the same approach (8):

"One may consider science as an attempt to either lower the degree of empiricism or to extend the range of theory. . . . Almost all significant work of scientists today, I believe, comes under the heading of attempts to reduce the degree of empiricism; the distinction between one group and another is in the motivation. Those who are interested in the fabric of science as such are ready to follow any lead that gives promise of being fruitful in terms of extending theoretical knowledge."

A distinct subgroup of investigator-centered definitions distinguishes between basic and applied research in terms of conditions under which the investigator works, and particularly of the degree of freedom he enjoys. Thus, basic research is sometimes defined as research undertaken by the "uncommitted" investigator—that is, an investigator who is not bound by external forces to follow a predetermined line of study. Such a definition appears in *Basic Research, a National Resource,* a 1957 publication of the National Science Foundation (3):

"Basic research is systematic, but without direction save that which the investigator himself gives it to meet the challenge of the unknown. He is strictly on his own, guided primarily by his interest in learning more about the workings of nature."

There is a logical distinction between the motive and intent of investigators on the one hand and the degree of freedom with which they work on the other hand. However, the two are often considered together, as is the case in the quotation immediately above. In any event, both criteria are clearly centered around the scientist—his motives and intent and the degree of freedom with which he works.

SUBSTANCE-CENTERED DEFINITIONS

Let us turn now to definitions of basic research which center around the substance of research.

One category within this group distinguishes between basic and applied research in terms of the prospective utility of findings in meeting some practical need in the near future. Here the criterion is that the work, as described in advance, does not appear to have any immediate practical application. Such a definition, intended to indicate the kind of basic research the National Science Foundation and other federal agencies should support, appears in Executive Order 10521 (21 March 1954) : ". . . support by other Federal agencies of basic research in areas which are closely related to their missions is encouraged." Such research is designated as "special purpose" basic research, in contrast to "general purpose" basic research to be supported by the National Science Foundation. Unfortunately, this definition in practice does not provide a usable means of distinguishing between types of research because there is no inherent distinction, particularly before the work is initiated, between the substance of "special purpose" and that of "general purpose" basic research.

In the second category of substance-centered definitions, distinction is made between basic and applied research in terms of the scientific significance of findings.

There is a wide agreement among scientists that breadth of findings is the criterion for assessing the basic character of a discovery. For example, Poincaré has stated (9) :

"There is a hierarchy of facts. Some are without any positive bearing, and teach us nothing but themselves. There are, on the other hand, facts that give a large return, each of which teaches us a new law."

Hardy, the mathematician, has noted that (10) "mathematicians value ideas by their generality and depth."

Conant wrote (11) :

"Systemized or well ordered empirical inquiries are one element in the advancement of science; the other element is the use of new concepts, new conceptual schemes that serve as working hypotheses on a grand scale. Only by the use of new ideas of broad significance has science advanced. . . ."

This criterion of the generality, breadth, or significance of findings has been well summarized by Cohen (5):

"We thus naturally classify scientific work according to the degree whereby it affects scientific thought and procedures; according to the amount by which it changes the foundation or structure of science itself. We may call this the fundamental character of the research. Some work is of a more fundamental character than other work simply because it affects a broader area, or because within its narrow area of applicability it has a deep and penetrating effect."

CONTRADICTIONS AND INADEQUACIES

If each investigator-centered and substance-centered definition is taken literally as satisfactory and self-contained, as is often done, each of them is patently inadequate.

For example, the definition of the National Science Foundation—that basic research is research "where the primary aim of the investigator is full knowledge or understanding of the subject under study, rather than a practical application thereof"—invites the obvious rejoinder that persons aiming to solve a very practical problem have produced findings of general significance. This definition, drawn up for the foundation's statistical reports on the volume of basic research conducted in this country and fairly widely used for other purposes, suffers from the further deficiency that decisions as to who will or who will not receive a research grant cannot in practice be based on assessment of scientists' motives. Accordingly, as the deputy director of the National Science Foundation has stated in describing how the foundation selects research proposals for support, "There is really only one criterion, and that is the excellence of the particular research proposal which is made to the Foundation" (12). Implicit in this procedure, which is not literally followed in practice, is a definition of basic research which relies on the substance of proposed research rather than on an assessment of the man or of his motive, intent, or working conditions.

Those who define basic research solely as research conducted by investigators free to follow wherever their findings and curiosity lead are open to the observation that some research performed under these conditions is worthless. Furthermore, if basic research is defined solely as work with no foreseeable application, some trivial and irrelevant research will be admitted to the category of basic research.

Apart from the inadequacies of each definition, the group of investigator-centered and the group of substance-centered definitions of basic research are, if accepted literally as adequate self-contained definitions, mutually exclusive. Thus, if the breadth of findings is to be the criterion for defining basic research, such things as the investigator's motive and the freedom with which he works are irrelevant. Conversely, if the attitude and approach of the investigator and the degree of freedom which he enjoys are to be the exclusive criteria defining basic research, the nature of the findings has no bearing on whether research is basic or not.

Each of the criteria, when considered singly and literally, does lead to contradictions which have been unwisely invoked to ridicule the concept of basic research. Yet if the idea of basic research is critically important, as it certainly is, it is also important that a generally acceptable definition be worked out.

RECONCILIATION

Inadequate and mutually exclusive definitions of basic research are currently used without apparent concern by intelligent and experienced people. Such a situation leads to the suspicion that there may be some underlying problem forestalling a clear resolution of the contradictions pointed out above. I think that there is such a problem, arising from an unapparent confusion of ends and means.

To reconcile the various definitions of basic research in a way that is not only logical but operationally useful, it seems to me imperative to begin by drawing a distinction, pointed out by others, which may appear to be overly nice. "Basic findings" are fundamentally different from "basic research" because findings are an end product and research is a process. This distinction, seen clearly by Brues (6), is not always drawn, even though it is of central importance to a clear resolution of the problem of definition. Failure to draw the distinction generally leads to confusion. This is illustrated by Cohen's statement quoted above. The system of classification implied by his definition is ambiguous because one cannot tell whether the *work* referred to is the process of research or the findings. Literally, this *work* is a process, but the sense of the word *work* in the context of Cohen's description is "findings."

For the administrator, definitions in terms of the end product—basic science or basic findings—are not usable because decisions must be made before the research is completed and the findings are known. Administrators are forced to be prophets. They must support basic research before the returns are in. This can actually be done with an adequate degree of precision by observing the kinds of people, the kinds of motives, and the kinds of working conditions that have as a matter of probability tended to produce basic findings.

With this view of the problem of definition, the array of criteria used to describe the research process must be viewed not as literal descriptive definitions but as statements of the probability of producing a basic finding. Thus, a "definition" of basic research in terms of the investigator's freedom is simply the statement of an assumption that those whose thought is not restricted and narrowly channeled are more likely to come forth with scientific ideas of great breadth or depth than are those working with less freedom. Definitions in terms of the motive and intent of the investigator are essentially statements of a belief that those with wide-ranging native curiosity are more likely than others to produce basic findings.

When the criteria of basic research are viewed as statements of the probability that basic findings will be produced under certain conditions, rather than as a literal description of the process of basic research itself, apparent contradictions disappear. For example, the "no practical application" criterion would mean not that no one working on an applied problem can produce a basic finding but simply that the probability of producing a fundamental finding is greater among those whose thinking is not restricted by a search for application. Definition in terms of the freedom with which the investigator works would not mean that basic findings are produced by all of those who are free to do whatever they wish but that the probability of producing new ideas of broad significance is greater among investigators who are free.

PROBABILITY DEFINITION FOR COLLECTION OF STATISTICS

A definition of basic research in terms of the circumstances that appear as a matter of probability to lead to basic findings is inherently unsuitable for the purpose of collecting statistics. One reason for this is that a sound and usable definition of the conditions under which basic findings are, as a matter of probability, most likely to be produced must encompass all of the predisposing factors. Motives, intent, working conditions, and prospective applicability of findings must all be included. Other circumstances that appear to increase the probability of producing basic findings may be added to those already generally accepted. Just what circumstances should be included in a definition, and the weight to be given to each, are matters decided in large part by the exercise of subjective judgment.

Second, motives, attitudes, and working conditions cannot be measured precisely. How curious must a scientist be about fundamental phenomena before his work is viewed as basic research? How free must he be? And free from what, or for what? How remote from application must his findings be before his research is considered basic? These questions suggest that even if there were a firm consensus as to the criteria that are properly a part of a definition of basic research, it would be impossible to measure such factors quantitatively and comparably.

The criteria to be used in defining basic research and the weight to be given to each are both affected by such things as institutional goals, traditions, and personal experiences and predilections. This explains why, as shown in the first part of this article, people in universities have looked at a given universe of research and have decided that the proportion of this research belonging in the basic category is twice as large as the proportion placed in the basic category by federal administrators. As another example of the nature of this problem, if engineers and physicists had to classify each others' work as basic or applied, less engineering and more physics would be called basic than would be the case if each discipline classified the work that is done in its own fields.

It may be that these difficult problems of definition can be overcome in time. Magnitudes that were in earlier years the source of sharp debates are now measured by generally accepted techniques. For example, such things as the national income accounts—the gross national product, private investment, savings, and so forth—have evolved into standard statistical series only after years of sustained effort and critical discussion by a large group of economists.

Whether a comparable effort could produce a generally accepted set of statistics dealing with basic research is a matter of judgment. For the reasons set forth above, it seems to me that the problem is inherently unsolvable, and that efforts to secure adequately precise and comparable statistics by undertaking to improve the definition of basic research are therefore futile. But I could be wrong.

Even if statistics on basic research are inherently affected by subjective judgments, it may be better to collect and publish what can be collected than to make no effort to do so. The case for making the effort rests essentially upon our strong national predilection to rely upon statistics in reaching judgments. If one accepts the idea that the nation would be better off if greater attention were paid to basic research, and if statistics help to convince people of the validity of the idea, it may be worth while collecting and publishing the information even though the statistics are inherently allegorical.

PROBABILITY DEFINITION FOR ADMINISTRATIVE DECISIONS

Definitions of basic research in terms of such factors as the degree of freedom with which the investigator works and the prospective applicability of his findings are useful in making administrative decisions on the support of research. In practice, administrators do not decide to support work because it is basic or not basic. Indeed, the term *basic research* is used much less frequently in the day-to-day business of research administration than it is in communicating with the nonscientific world.

Administrators consider the man—his past performance as judged by his peers—even though the merit of the research project is ostensibly the basis for judgment. They consider the facilities available to him. They take into account the support available in his field—whether it is a "gap area" or one well financed. What those who make decisions cannot do and do not attempt to do is to judge the intentions and the motives of investigators. Definitions of basic research in terms of motive and intent are, in practice, used by administrators—those who participate in decisions on the distribution of research funds—neither in administering research nor in collecting statistics on research.

The criterion of freedom of the investigator as a condition conducive to the production of basic findings is also usable and used as a guide to research administration. More broadly, this criterion encompasses the total array of factors conducive to scientific research of high quality. H. A. Shepard, in an article in the *Journal of the Philosophy of Science* (*13*), came to this conclusion.

"Efforts to define basic research operationally are misleading and bring about neglect of the forces that produce it—the training, discipline, values, way of life and system of social control that motivate men to advance knowledge for its own sake. . . . Support for basic research means support of a social system which so motivates men."

I am suggesting, first, that it is not possible to define basic research operationally. Second, I think that basic research can be effectively promoted by concentrating on provision of funds under terms and conditions designed to strengthen the forces, values, and social system which appear as a matter of probability well designed to promote basic findings.

Administrators—federal, university, or industrial—do have it within their power either to give scientists a large degree of freedom or to hem them in with a wide array of well-known requirements and restrictions. Freedom means, here, broad definition of areas of research; easy, informal changes in the direction of the research; assured stability of support; and freedom from onerous and essentially unproductive reporting requirements. In administrative terms, the terms and conditions under which all federal funds are provided affect basic research as significantly as does provision of funds for work labeled as basic. To the extent that scientific freedom affects the character of findings, a plea that the Federal Government "support more basic research" is a plea for administration of a larger proportion of federal research funds in a manner which places few restrictions upon investigators.

REFERENCES AND NOTES

1. A. de Tocqueville, *Democracy in America,* vol. II, book I, chap. XVI.
2. V. Bush, *Science, the Endless Frontier. A Report to the President* (Washington, D.C., 1945), p. 13.
3. National Science Foundation, *Basic Research, A National Resource* (Washington, D.C., 1957), p. 25.
4. ———, "Federal Funds for Science, Fiscal Years 1956, 1957 and 1958" (Washington, D.C., 1958), p. 20.
5. I. B. Cohen, *Science, Servant of Man* (Little, Brown, Boston, Mass., 1948), pp. 303, 355.
6. A. M. Brues, *Bull. Atomic Scientists* 11, 344 (1955).
7. J. A. Stratton, *Chem. Eng. News* 31, 2581 (1953).
8. J. B. Conant, *Science and Common Sense* (Yale Univ. Press, New Haven, Conn., 1951), p. 58.
9. H. Poincaré, *Science and Method* (Dover Publications, Dover, Del., 1952), p. 284.
10. A. H. Hardy, *A Mathematician's Apology* (Cambridge Univ. Press, Cambridge, Mass., 1941), p. 17.
11. J. B. Conant, *Modern Science and Modern Man* (Doubleday, New York, 1953) p. 46.
12. Society of Sigma Xi at the Rensselaer Polytechnic Institute, *Changing Patterns of Academic Research* (Troy, N.Y., 1957), p. 55.
13. H. A. Shepard, *J. Phil. Sci.* 23, 57 (1956).

The Report of the President on the Sixtieth Anniversary of the Carnegie Institution for 1961–1962

CARYL P. HASKINS

This year marks the sixtieth anniversary of the Carnegie Institution of Washington. Sixty years ago, in 1902, Andrew Carnegie transmitted to a newly elected Board of Trustees a deed of trust conveying the sum of ten million dollars "to found, in the city of Washington, an Institution which with the cooperation of institutions now or hereafter established, there or elsewhere, shall in the broadest and most liberal manner encourage investigation, research, and discovery. . . ." At the end of January in that year, the Trustees elected Daniel Coit Gilman, fresh from the career for which he was already noted as president of The Johns Hopkins University, as first president of the Carnegie Institution, and resolved "to promote original research by systematically sustaining projects of broad scope that may lead to the discovery and utilization of new forces for the benefit of man . . . projects of minor scope that may fill in gaps of knowledge of particular things or restricted fields of research . . . administration of a definite or stated research under a single direction by competent individuals."

* * *

The establishment of the Carnegie Institution of Washington marked a new direction in the kinds of institutions made possible by Mr. Carnegie's gift. In fact, it established a new kind of institution for America—the first to be devoted wholly and completely, in intent and in philosophy, to the ideal of research scholarship over wide fronts of science in its broadest, most unfettered, most completely uncommitted aspect. This was a novel concept and, quite obviously, from some of the records of the time, one neither everywhere comprehensible nor even everywhere palatable in a youthful

Selected excerpts reprinted with the permission of the author from *Year Book 61*, Carnegie Institute of Washington (Baltimore, Md.: Garamond Press, 1961). Dr. Caryl P. Haskins is the President of the Carnegie Institution in Washington, D.C. His main scientific contributions have been in physiology and genetics and he has written extensively on the relations of science and society. His most recent book is *The Scientific Revolution and World Politics* (New York: Harper & Row, 1964).

nation with a strongly established pragmatic tradition. It represented, indeed, a notably original idea, which six following decades have shown to be both great and enduring.

*   *   *

But through all the years the major philosophies of the Institution and one major feature of its organizational pattern have stood constant, tested and retested in situation after situation and proved as fresh and relevant today as when they were conceived. The decision made at the outset that flexibility and effectiveness in the kind of research to which the Institution is dedicated can best be achieved through a series of rather small unit laboratories, each mobile and relatively independent, each able to seize the initiative in new and appropriate fields as they appear, yet all sufficiently connected so that they may be of mutual assistance as the needs arise, was a remarkable one, both for its uniqueness at the time and for the subtlety of the vision that dictated it. Over the decades, as research has burgeoned in the nation and groups devoted to research have multiplied, many other experiments in organizational form have been tried. But it is especially interesting that some of the most modern thinking and experimenting in organization for research, in this country as well as abroad, has returned to precisely this pattern as one of the most effective in exploring the dynamic frontiers of scientific knowledge.

Organization, however, is only a framework, vital but at last only supporting. Most significant—and most truly enduring—have been the elements of philosophy and purpose which inaugurated the Institution and which have remained unchanged through all the years: the philosophy that all its resources, all its deepest purposes, are centered in the creative individual, whatever be his field, that in the truest sense he is the uncommitted investigator, suitably endowed and suitably protected, whose time, quite literally, is bought by the Institution and then returned as unconstrained endowment. And with this goes the philosophy, equally deep-seated and equally important, that this freedom from fixed commitment applies to fields of endeavor as well as to men: that high mobility within specific fields, that the unfettered crossing of fields, that the fashioning of unconventionally wide-ranging programs, are subject only to the limitations imposed by Nature and by the judgment of gifted and discriminating investigators, and that making this mobility and this flexibility possible is a principal objective of the Institution.

*   *   *

In the seventh decade of the twentieth century, it is hard to recast the scientific and technical America in which the Carnegie Institution was founded in 1902. . . . By then, science and technology were already familiar concerns within the federal government. They were indeed concerns as old as the nation itself. It was Thomas Jefferson who as Secretary of State in 1790 submitted a "Report . . . on the Subject of Establishing the Uniformity of the Weights, Measures, and Coins of the United States," and who, upon recommendation of the American Philosophical Society, transmitted to the Congress a proposal for the establishment of a United States Coast Survey, which was set up within the Treasury Department seventeen years later. And it was John Quincy Adams, when he was Secretary of State, who personally prepared for the Congress a similar report upon weights and measures. It was Adams, too, who led the fight to accept the bequest from James Smithson, who had died in 1829, to found the organization that was to grow to the Smithsonian Institution of today. The establishment of the Department of Agriculture dated from Civil War days, contemporary with the passage of the Morrill Act. So also did the National Academy of Sciences, from whose recommendations, somewhat later, were to follow the Geological Survey and the Weather Bureau.

These early involvements of the federal government in science and technology, however, gave little hint of the massive and commanding role it would play on the national scene in little more than half a century. Even at the end of the fourth decade of the twentieth century the total federal research program is estimated to have cost annually only about one hundred million dollars—less than the annual budget for the National Science Foundation alone in 1962. Twenty years later, however, yearly federal expenditures for research and development had grown to over a billion dollars out of a total estimated national commitment of about three billion. By 1960 the national total had climbed to fourteen billion dollars or more, of which the federal government supplied some nine billion. Today it may have reached sixteen to eighteen billion. The budget of the National Science Foundation for scientific research and related activities as submitted to the Congress for 1963 will total one hundred and sixty-five million dollars, while the Department of Defense is expected to spend about seven billion dollars on research and development, the National Aeronautics and Space Administration about two and one-half billion, the Atomic Energy Commission approximately another one and one-half billion. The total government funds spent in research and development in 1963 are expected to reach almost twelve and one-half billion dollars, of which expenditures for research alone may attain to one and one-half billion dollars, as compared with approximately one billion for the present year.

It has been calculated that the total funds expended for research and development in the United States over the past decade have increased at approximately fifteen per cent per year, leading to a doubling of volume every five years. If the present rate of increase of our expenditures in the field were to continue, indeed, our projected monetary support of research and development in their current definition could formally exceed our total governmental budget before 1975, and could exceed our gross national product before the end of the century—a reflection, however hypothetical, that vividly illuminates the scientific and technical dynamism and the scientific and technical problems with which we live. How different is this scene from that upon which the Institution entered!

The implications of this astonishing vista are many. One is the degree to which, with almost explosive suddenness since World War II, science and technology have been universally recognized as of major national concern. Another, of course, reflects the depth and intensity of technological competition in the world and our own needs in national defense. A third mirrors both the rate of population growth and, most pointedly, the growth of wealth in the United States. And the climates in which these expenditures on both the private and the public fronts have taken place and the governmental patterns through which they are effected in the public sector—patterns at present in perhaps their most active phases of evolution and of adjustment—make a compelling chapter in the history of development both of American scientific enterprise and awareness and of American political institutions, and reveal much about their nature.

All these factors—the vast increase in the volume of our scientific and technical resources, in human and in monetary terms and in terms of scientific and technical facilities, the pressing demands of overriding national objectives, economic and military, the consequent larger and larger participation of federal resources in the total funding of the national research and more especially of the national technical effort—have, not unnaturally, had profound impacts on our thinking about science generally. Bit by bit they may have led to some subtle changes, perhaps well-nigh unconscious ones, in our conception of the ways in which, typically, the frontiers of truly new scientific knowledge are pushed back. This evolution could carry implications grave enough to warrant serious thought.

In all the years of American scientific research, from the times of Josiah Willard Gibbs to those of the second world war, we were accustomed to think of the great advances in scientific thought, of the initiation of its great new directions, as being predominantly the product of individual genius, working in environments which, however modest, and in part perhaps because of that very modesty, were especially adapted for flexibility, for absence of constraint, for a maximum of freedom in concept and in execution. We thought of the outstanding scientific conquest as typically an achievement of extraordinary brilliance, originality, and insight in individual innovation, giving significant new dimensions to its time, and ideally climaxing a career of unfettered scholarship. We did not particularly conceive research in this sense as the composite product of large numbers of men working in numerous and highly organized groups.

Since the second world war, however, following the spectacular demonstrations of technical conquest wrought by great organizations, of which the Manhattan Project was but the forerunner, we have sometimes been inclined by analogy to conceive of pioneering research for basically new ideas in rather similar terms—inclined, perhaps, to more than half believe that in the contemporary world it too may require such teams. It is then only logical to reason that if, at this stage of the world's scientific development, pioneering scientific research critically depends upon the large-scale efforts of highly organized and massively implemented teams, its effectiveness may be roughly proportionate to the material resources bestowed upon it—and that cost and magnitude themselves may provide an important index of scientific significance. We have even been tempted at times to imagine that the speed and effectiveness with which new scientific frontiers are breached may be a simple function of numbers of men and rates of expenditure, and to expect that the attainment of new scientific vision in an area of basic research may be accelerated in direct proportion to the size of teams and the amounts of money committed to the search.

This philosophy, so directly derived from the demonstrated course of practical achievement, appeals especially to that keen pragmatic instinct that has run like a golden thread through all the fabric of our development as a nation, and to the genius for organization which has so long been one of our most pronounced national characteristics. Nor is there lack of evidence that at first sight seems to confirm the idea. It is patent today that the physical equipment required on the frontiers of research in many of the sciences, especially those of the greatest conceptual maturity, is massive, complex, and expensive, and requires the collaboration of sizable teams in designing it, in manipulating it, and in gathering data with it if truly new information is to be obtained. The productiveness of research in many such fields since men and money have made possible the design of powerful new tools and massive teams have been assembled to operate them gives vivid testimony to how powerful, and indeed how indispensable, resources of this kind may be in some of the most highly developed fields of science.

Yet in a deeper sense this judgment may harbor a considerable, and sometimes a positively dangerous, misconception, especially when it is assumed that great teams and high costs are prerequisites for the setting of new *directions* in scientific thought. A part of that misconception doubtless stems from a failure to demark sufficiently two general approaches in research, which, though they are complementary and often intergrade, yet have certain characteristics and pose certain requirements that are quite distinct. In one the basic ends of the investigation are generally evident, if not wholly clear in detail, at or near its beginning. The preeminent challenge to the investigator is to chart the road toward his goal—mapping it, projecting it, building it, all that it may approach a citadel already at least dimly visible on the horizon. The other general kind of research may begin without specific ends or, indeed, without consciously conceived objectives of any kind. Its driving motive is likely to be pure curiosity, the winning from Nature of deeply new knowledge, of knowledge won wholly for its own sake. The talents and the training demanded by these two kinds of research, and the difficulty of the scientific challenges posed by each, are often much the same. At one end of a spectrum of research they intergrade, and any distinction attempted between them becomes formal and unreal. At their extremes, however, the challenges they present are undoubtedly quite different, often to be met in widely divergent ways. Above all, whereas research programs of the first kind can frequently be visualized in a general way ahead of time, and so planned intelligently, the same is rarely true in the second type of research. A very large share of the concerns of such a great team effort as was involved in the program of the Manhattan Project, for instance, fell into the former category. The deeply underlying theoretical knowledge, the unexpected and radically new ideas about Nature, on which the whole program of the Project was based and on which it turned, had been achieved by investigators like Meitner and Hahn and Strassmann in Europe in 1938, by such individuals as Rutherford and his colleagues at Cambridge in 1914. They had been won through research of the second kind, conducted by a very few gifted scientists working in the settings we have traditionally visualized as consonant with the finest of individual creative effort.

It is no accident that today we sometimes make these distinctions less clearly than we might. At a very deep level it may be a consequence of our peculiar history and circumstances. Throughout our earlier years as a technically developing nation we were able to rely on the older countries of Europe for basic ideas on which to build our applications as implicitly, and often as unconsciously, as we relied upon the British navy for the protection of our seas. It was both natural and adaptive that the kind of scientific and technical contributions at which we early became most adept and developed most highly, and to which perhaps we initially attached greatest attention and attributed greatest value, should have involved the brilliantly organized, the meticulously careful development, often undertaken on the boldest and most breathtaking scale, of basic ideas that had been conceived abroad. Today such ideas are much more often drawn from our own resources. But historically our first attachment was to their execution rather than to their generation. And so it is not surprising that we sometimes fail to distinguish innovation from execution, and have not always recognized the limitations within which we can extrapolate experience from one kind of activity to the other.

But there is more to the matter than this. For it is demonstrably true that gains in our knowledge of Nature as new and fundamental and unexpected as any in the world can come, unbidden, from the investigations of great teams for research and development in many areas. As our resources for team research grow in the coming years, we can properly expect the rate at which such new knowledge is revealed to increase also—if not proportionately, at least very substantially. And so we should not fail to ask an implied question of great importance. The philosophy that envisaged the environment of brilliant, original, unfettered individual research as the *milieu* in which the great new directions of scientific thought were born and nourished, the philosophy which has had such confirmation in recent scientific history, was itself developed in the days of scarcity in science—scarcity not only of material wealth, but especially scarcity of scientific workers. Now we live and work in a nation committed to an unparalleled rate of growth in the material resources for research, and in a world in which perhaps eighty per cent of all the scientists who have ever lived are our contemporaries. Is it possible that the philosophy itself was adjusted to the needs of other times; that it is not relevant to an era of plenty? May it actually be true today not only that major advances in new knowledge, the setting of radically new scientific directions, *can* be achieved in the environment of great and highly organized research teams, but also that, in practice, such environments are indeed *essential,* or, at any rate, the most favorable, to the process? Is it possible that we are witness to a profound revolution in the very character of research itself? Is it possible that the small and mobile groups to which we earlier looked for some of the most significant scientific innovations, the groups which in the past characteristically had an influence on scientific progress out of all proportion to their numbers or their social cost, can no longer in our day provide such significant approaches to the unknown?

Such a radical query, of course, bears profoundly on the whole philosophy of research. It is far more than a practical question. It touches some of the deepest wellsprings of scientific faith. It touches belief in the very nature and effectiveness of the individual search for truth in our time. In subtle ways it touches on the nature of scientific truth itself. It is an important question for the Carnegie Institution, deeply committed to the faith that the distinguished, unfettered individual can bring unique gifts to his society, and deeply committed, too, to belief in the uniqueness and the importance of the influence which a community of independent scholars can exercise on scientific progress.

For a question of such magnitude and gravity, abstract analysis will not suffice. Contemporary evidence alone can give convincing answers. Have the recent great advances in our knowledge of the universe and of our own more immediate environment, the original ideas of scientific stature achieved in the last few years which promise to open truly novel avenues of thought for the future—have these been necessarily, or even primarily, associated with the massive programs of great teams? Or do the basic contributions of small and mobile research groups continue in our day to have their old significance?

Such an abundance of evidence springs to mind, provided by striking advances no more than a half-dozen years old, in so many regions of scientific inquiry, that its very selection poses a problem and must necessarily be arbitrary. But three outstanding areas of recent investigation are particularly interesting to consider from this standpoint, because their environments and circumstances span such an extraordinary range of magnitude and character and form.

The first example may comprehend that immense complex of research and development dedicated to the placing of man in outer space and ultimately on the moon or on neighboring planets, its present great achievements in our country vividly symbolized by the voyages of Shepard and of Grissom, of Carpenter, Glenn, and Schirra. The second is of quite a different kind. It involves an achievement in astronomy of the year just past which in the staggering distances with which it deals emphasizes anew what a thin terrestrial shell is the outer space so far entered by man. It is the identification of what has proved to be by far the most remote celestial object ever discovered in the heavens—an object certainly billions of light years distant from us—and the measurement of the redshift of its spectrum. The third selected area of advance may in some ways be the most profound of all, though it is far from the best known. It includes the experimental evidence so brilliantly obtained in the last few years, and the reasoning directing the search for it, indicating beyond reasonable doubt that the information governing the inheritance of all the qualities of living things is structurally graven on the chromosomes within their germ cells in the form of a genuine code. It includes, as a climax, the demonstration of the general nature of that code, which the year just past has witnessed. These findings may well mark the greatest single advance in genetics since the demonstration five decades ago that the genes of heredity lie in the chromosomes in a linear array.

These three advances in natural knowledge bear much resemblance in certain fundamental qualities. All have won important and striking new knowledge. In all of them, the research for that knowledge has included a variety of scientific disciplines apparently far removed from the main concern—in the case of the third as far removed as crystallography seems to be from conventional genetics. Profoundly new directions of thought have resulted from all three. Possibly the third has produced the most thoroughly revolutionary new insights. The first has brought a sense of liberating conquest and a wealth of first-hand information about regions known hitherto only palely and at second hand.

But in many features of the modes and environments of research characterizing them, the three examples diverge about as much as scientific activities can differ. The contrast is particularly vivid when cast in terms of the parameters under special consideration: the relative size of the efforts, the sheer volume of human and material sources brought to bear, the kinds and degrees of organization. The enormous magnitude of the space program and the tremendous cooperative efforts currently involved in its prosecution and planned for the future need little emphasis. In this respect, indeed, Project Apollo is much in the tradition of a Manhattan Project, though yet bolder in both variety and scale. It is estimated that by the close of the budget for 1963 the National Aeronautics and Space Administration will have spent more than four thousand millions of dollars for the conduct of research and development. For research facilities alone it will have expended more than eight hundred and twenty millions. Behind the great individuals who have manned the space vehicles, and have recorded and analyzed the data of research, and who will do so in the future, lie the years of development on a scale of unprecedented magnitude and the immense organizations required for its successful prosecution. Behind the fashioning of the tools the final explorers command lie combinations of highly specialized disciplines and intricate techniques of the most varied kind—chemical, electronic, mechanical—ranging from the arts of propulsion engineering to those of miniaturization. It is interesting to notice in this connection that the cast of the effort at present is, as it perforce must be, importantly oriented about the design and use of *tools*. In considerable measure it is basically an engineering effort —perhaps the most exciting and compelling engineering effort of this century.

Shortly after the second world war, when instruments of radio detection were being put to a new use in the service of astronomy, several surveys of the skies were undertaken to detect and locate the positions of celestial bodies that were emitters of radio waves. The equipment then available, however, was relatively poor in both resolution and accuracy. It could not effectively complement the far more precise tools of optical astronomy. Resolution and precision were often too low to permit a reliable identification of radio sources with corresponding objects observed optically, though sometimes they were suspected to be the same. As the techniques of radio astronomy sharpened, however, as larger dishes were built and manned and put into use, both penetration and resolving power improved greatly. At the radio observatory of the Cavendish Laboratory in England and at the observatory of the California Institute of Technology at Bishop in the Owens Valley, instruments of outstanding capacity were built. During 1959 and 1960 two fresh surveys of the skies were undertaken with them: in Cambridge at 169 and 189 centimeters, in California at about a sixth that wavelength (31.2 cm). In the course of these surveys the celestial positions of certain emitters of radio waves were determined with a new precision. So precise was the location of one of these objects, indeed, that the two-hundred-inch Hale telescope could be brought to bear upon it. The peculiar color characteristics of the object suggested that it might include a pair of galaxies in collision, and so might be expected to have one or more emission lines in its spectrum. And so it happened that a prescient astronomer of the Mount Wilson and Palomar Observatories was able to obtain two spectra of the visible light from this source and to measure the degree of redshift in them. At the same time another observer, obtaining multicolor photometric observations of two of the fainter galaxies of the same cluster and constructing their curves of continuous emission, confirmed this measurement of redshift. It corresponded to a recession velocity of nearly half the speed of light. This heavenly body defines a new boundary for the universe comprehended within human ken. It marks by far the most searching probe into unplumbed reaches of space that the mind and hand of man have yet accomplished, ranging certainly to the order of several billion light years. When it is recalled that a single light year amounts to almost six million million miles—about sixty-three thousand times the distance of our own world from the sun—it makes the orbits of earth satellites, spectacular as they are, yet appear as comparatively near-neighborhood adventures.

Perhaps the greatest ultimate significance of this achievement will lie in the contribution it can make to our ideas about the basic nature of the universe. Indeed, this newly determined point of distance, so far beyond any other yet obtained, has already offered suggestive evidence on the great question of whether our universe is a continuously expanding one, or a universe in which the continuous creation and destruction of matter stand in equilibrium, or whether the universe in fact may experience alternate expansion and contraction extending over astronomic periods of time.

In sharp contrast to the first example, the planning of these observations, their confirmation, and the deductions from them were not the work of great teams of highly coordinated technical workers. These were the fruits of observations and calculations made by a few individuals laboring in relative solitude, the fruits of work of a relative handful of gifted astronomers. Perhaps never in science has the work of individuals been more clearly identifiable. The contrast with the first example is sharp.

Yet behind this classical achievement of gifted individuals lay many decades of research and engineering focused on the design of the powerful modern tools of optical and radio astronomy. Without them the achievement itself would have been quite impossible. These tools, like those involved in the space effort, were the products of hands and minds and toil in literally hundreds of specialized skills. And it was not skill and art that alone were brought to bear, but with them the magnificent resources of intellect and materials and time and research that gave them scope and effectiveness. The achievement itself dramatically underlines how significant and how essential the gifted and untrammeled individual investigator is today on some of the most advanced frontiers of the physical sciences. It was primarily focused on the gathering and the interpretation of information about nature, not on the design of tools. Yet its success depended in turn on a panoply of instruments brought to perfection in other times and other places, the development of which had required a structure of science and technology of whose cumulative magnitude and scope no scientist of an earlier generation could have had the faintest dream.

The third example embodies yet a different pattern. It would be hard to imagine a more fundamental or more sweeping discovery than one elucidating, at a deeper level than had hitherto been imagined, the manner in which the information governing all the qualities of inheritance may be recorded and stored in the chromosomes of plants and animals and men—stored with such extraordinary effectiveness and such enduring stability that there are organisms living today whose hereditary characteristics have been maintained more durably than the very rocks within whose strata the fossils of their remote ancestors are preserved. Yet in terms of magnitude the human and the material resources committed to that search, by comparison with the preceding illustrations, have been positively minuscule.

In 1953 Linus Pauling and Robert Brainard Corey at the California Institute of Technology suggested that the molecular structure of the unit of heredity, the "molecule" of deoxyribonucleic acid, might consist of chains of polynucleotides intertwined in the form of a helix, with four characteristic bases, the purines adenine and guanine and the pyrimidines thymine and cytosine, attached to them and projecting outward, while phosphate groups were oriented to the center. There were features of this model which conflicted with experimental evidence, notably that it was hard to reconcile the fact that DNA is an acid with the existence of bases lying, as it were, on the outside of the molecule. But the model involved one very great idea which, though it was not widely credible in terms of that particular construction, yet was to prove fundamental to all further thinking on the matter. It was the idea that the biological specificity of the unit of DNA, on which its power of determining inheritance must rest, must inhere in the sequence of occurrence of these bases along the molecular chain and the suggestion that the periodic distances at which these bases occur might be of the right order to permit them to order the sequence of amino acids in the construction of a protein. This was a most important foundation upon which to rear what would prove a truly extraordinary arch of reasoning. But for long even the idea that the nucleic acid structure could be locally specific was resisted. Until that idea had been widely accepted, its more detailed consequence could hardly gain effective credence. Both these developments were made possible by a second great idea, which might be likened to a keystone of the arch.

This critical idea was provided by J. D. Watson when, in a flash of insight reminiscent of Kekule's vision of the structure of the benzene molecule that came to him in a London bus almost a hundred years ago, he imagined the consequences of, in effect, turning the model inside out, pointing the bases inward, and pairing the purine molecules with the smaller pyrimidines. Highly significant correspondences with nature were achieved by this remarkable insight. The first and fundamental rule of the composition of deoxyribonucleic acid, namely that it incorporates purines and pyrimidines in equal ratio, was given a rational basis. And the contradiction between the acidic nature of DNA and its presumed outwardly pointing bases, which had plagued the model of Pauling and Corey, was resolved. But there were impressive difficulties to be met also. The idea that the bases were outward-pointing had not resulted simply from neglecting the alternative that they might point inward. That possibility, indeed, had been carefully examined in formulating the earlier model. But it had been concluded that such a structure was not possible. For the new model to be convincing, the physical possibility of such an arrangement had to be demonstrated, and the details of the linkages between the purines and pyrimidines had to be worked out— formidable tasks requiring concepts and techniques familiar to those dealing with the structure of crystals.

And so it was that, also in 1953, Watson and F. H. C. Crick, working in the Molecular Biology Unit of the British Medical Research Council adjacent to the Cavendish Laboratory at Cambridge, announced their brilliant hypothesis of the structure of the unit of heredity, of the "molecule" of deoxyribonucleic acid, as a pair of "ribbons" wound in the form of a double helix around a common axis and linked by the four bases, the purines adenine and guanine and the pyrimidines thymine and cytosine, paired in a highly specific fashion. The model of Pauling and Corey had suggested that the bases could not be packed in the center of the molecule. The new model proved that indeed they could, and from that demonstration came perhaps the most significant idea in the whole chain—the concept of base pairing itself, and with it the associated and important notion that a maximum of four kinds of base pairs could be involved. The beauty and credibility of the model gave firmness and emphasis to the earlier idea that the biological specificity of the unit of heredity must derive in large measure from the ordering of the pairs of bases along the chain of the deoxyribonucleic acid.

All together, three biological consequences stemmed directly from the model, which must rank among the most important advances of our age in the understanding of the fundamental nature of earthly life. First, the model allowed the extraordinary phenomenon of the replication of the genetic pattern which occurs at every division of every living cell—the mechanism fundamental to the very process of the growth and multiplication of life on earth—to be understood consistently for the first time. Second, the nature of the phenomenon of the sudden changes in inheritance which we call mutation, intensively studied since the days of de Vries but never understood in their fundamental molecular mechanisms, now for the first time became comprehensible at that level, in terms of known changes in bases which could result in alterations of their sequence to produce such changes. Third, and greatest of all, perhaps, was the full rationalization of the key concept that biological specificity in inheritance must in large part derive from the sequential ordering of the bases in the nucleic acids.

This third great consequence was to lead to a scientific vision of new and unexpected dimensions. That vista was provided by the idea that genetic information might in fact be *coded* in the DNA molecule in the form of a linear message for which the four permissible combinations of bases might serve as alphabet, in a manner, indeed, reminiscent of the coding of a message on the punched tape of a computer. This radical concept was first examined in detail by the astrophysicist Gamow in 1954. Although the precise form of the code suggested at that time has since proved incorrect, the basic idea has become established as one of the great theoretical advances in our view of the nature of the living world. And so was posed the pointed question: if such a code exists, what is its specific nature?

It is that question which theoretical and experimental work of the past two years has done much to answer. An important share of the answer, like the original question, has come once again from the laboratory of the Unit for Molecular Biology at Cambridge; other critical parts have followed from several American university laboratories, from the National Institutes of Health, from the Carnegie Institution of Washington. Suffice it to say that preponderant evidence suggests that the code employs words containing very few "letters," probably not more than three.

A virus may include within its single chromosome something of the order of a hundred thousand base pairs. A billion pairs of bases may be included within the total store of information of our own chromosomes. It is a startling concept that if the DNA strands from all the cells in a single human body were uncoiled their total length might well span the solar system. There is ample opportunity for diversity in the ways that the elements of the code can be combined.

With this conceptual advance, carrying the implication that one of the basic challenges offered by the problem of heredity might lie, in effect, in the decoding of a script, progress in meeting that challenge has come with remarkable speed. What may well prove to be a Rosetta stone has been provided by the development of methods of accomplishing protein synthesis in cell-free systems under the influence of artificial ribonucleic acids composed of only two bases in known ratios and therefore containing specified code words in known frequencies. The composition of the resulting protein should yield the key to code "letters" in terms of the ratios of specific amino acids corresponding to them. Another highly promising approach involves techniques for investigating the coupling between the base-pair patterns of the deoxyribonucleic acid of an organism and the "messenger RNA" of related forms, which may differ in their coding only in relatively minor, but specific and determinable, particulars. The current year sees work of this kind at a peak of activity. With wing-swift speed, a whole new area in our understanding of the basic mechanisms of heredity at the molecular level is being exploited.

Here, then, are three .genuinely great advances marking the technical and scientific progress of the last three years. In a profound sense all three are typical of their age, and, for a variety of reasons, could not have occurred at any earlier time. Obviously neither space exploration nor the astronomical investigations of the new "edge of the universe" now within our ken could have been achieved with the tools of any other era. The peculiar modernity of the third example involves especially a yet different circumstance. For the very idea that the information of inheritance may be recorded as a code is peculiarly consonant with our age—perhaps so characteristic that it should be treated with a caution doubled by this very fact. In the nascence of primitive biological thought fire was a living thing, dangerous and bright, and the expression "vital fires within us" remains to remind us how much we once thought of life as the "inhabiting property" of something that was obviously dynamically alive. In an age when the frontiers of engineering exploration concerned pumps and hydraulics the mechanism of the circulation of the blood was a fascinating and fertile subject of physiological speculation and of physiological research. For the age of Descartes, strings and pulleys provided compelling images for the mechanisms of life, and images of clockwork for the mind. In the early nineteenth century, dominated by the vision of steam power engineering, energy transformations seemed among the most important aspects of life, and the rise of large-scale electrical power engineering in the latter part of the nineteenth and the early twentieth century reinforced the vision. Then, in our own era, with its emphasis on small-current engineering and the modulated control of gigantic mechanical and electrical processes, the aspects of living processes included under the rubric of Cybernetics have occupied a center of the stage. Studies of those fascinating properties of living systems involving, in all their varied and exquisitely elaborate mechanisms, the maintenance of homeostasis, the preservation of balance in dynamic systems, have held a special attraction for our time. And in our immediate day, when communication of new orders of content and of speed, and with it the massive processing of information, so dominates our lives, when we are inevitably so much concerned with the coding of information and the unraveling of such codes, it is scarcely surprising that a natural process operating upon those principles, which has evidently been central to the evolution of all life, as no doubt it was also in its origin, should only now have so powerfully focused our attention as to be on the threshold of solution. It follows, too, that, just as each of the earlier interpretations of living processes subsequently gave central place to its successor but left the residue of its own unalterable truth to contribute permanently to our basic understanding, we must be prepared to accept—and indeed to welcome—the same fate for the concept of genetic coding.

The likenesses uniting these three examples, then, lie deep. It would be hard to select the most significant among them, though in the achievement of particular new insights the second and especially the third may predominate. What now of the parameters of scale, of magnitude of the resources committed, of the extent of organization of the work, as criteria of its significance? Here it would be difficult to imagine wider contrasts.

At every point in the extraordinary conceptual development that marks the third example, the commitment to it in terms of numbers of workers, in terms of material resources, was extraordinarily modest. The Unit for Molecular Biology of the Medical Research Council at Cambridge began with two crystallographers. Ten years later, when its revolutionary discoveries were well launched, it numbered perhaps a dozen workers and was housed in a temporary building behind the Cavendish Laboratory and in various University rooms—a very minimum of space. It was, indeed, superbly instrumented for its task. But such instrumentation was incredibly modest in both mass and cost compared with that required in either of the other fields. In that free and flexible atmosphere, built about the largely unfettered efforts of a few gifted individuals working within a minimum of formal organization, have been made some of the most important advances in man's concept of his world and of himself possible to the twentieth century. It is striking to compare this situation with that in which the exploration of space must go forward.

This, then, is the character of the contemporary evidence. Such contrasts of size and structure and organization in the modes of some of the most significant assaults on the frontiers of natural knowledge in this decade strongly suggest that these parameters, broadly considered, bear little direct relation to their scientific significance. They inspire compelling reflections about the continuing effectiveness, in our own day, of the scale and the pattern and the philosophy of research to which the Carnegie Institution is so deeply committed. It seems abundantly clear that the essential qualities and requirements of inquiry at the very frontiers of man's knowledge of his universe do not now, and in all probability will not in the foreseeable future, differ significantly from those of our classical scientific past. Such inquiry will surely continue to bear the unmistakable stamp of the gifted and un-trammeled individual, whatever may be the scale of resources, in knowledge, in tools, in human and material support, which he may require.

Bronowski has pointed out that perhaps the most fundamental discovery of the scientific age was that Nature was to be approached and won, not by attempting to outwit her by magic, as many a medieval alchemist had imagined reflecting a prevailing climate of his time, but rather by discover-ing the true quality of natural laws and taking care to work within them. It is easy to forget how tremendous was that change of view, how much of trial and vision was comprehended within Newton's simple admonition that "science must be kept free from occult influences." The atmosphere of true research is still as it was when that great advance of philosophy was made, still the atmosphere in which, as Lionel Trilling has recalled, Faraday re-fused to be called *physicist,* holding the term too narrowly imprisoning a chamber for his life's commitment. These are the dimensions, whatever be the nature of the structures in which they are embedded, which still evoke the great advances of today.

In the central context of discovery, it seems clear that the magnitude and organization of a research effort may be the least meaningful of param-eters in any fundamental or enduring sense. One may indeed think of the large and the small research enterprises in our society as essentially symbi-otic, each fulfilling its specific role—one more example of the rich diversity by which we live.

The relation, however, is actually more subtle. The responsibility that devolves upon small and mobile groups dedicated to the exploration of new frontiers is clearly greater in our own day than merely that of one compo-nent in a many-hued panoply of research. At least one aspect of the relation is far more serious, and wears a significance which must inevitably sharpen further in the coming years. It is not only important that the small and mobile research group be maintained and strengthened to ensure continuing advance along those remote boundaries of natural knowledge so vital to our spiritual as well as to our material well-being. It is not only important be-cause, in such a massive and highly advanced technical and engineering society as our own is today and must even more become tomorrow, the scientific "leverage" of such pioneering groups must inevitably increase. It is a further and a significant truth that, while climates that foster innovation can be maintained in the midst of complex and highly organized technical undertakings, preserving them intact is no common or easy achievement. It requires a particular determination, an extraordinary persistence of vision and pertinacity of will, an unusual sensitivity and skill, to sustain conditions favorable to original, exploratory research on remote and far-flung frontiers of the mind in massive working environments over considerable periods of time, undeflected by all the immediate demands that architecting to known ends in those environments inevitably imposes, in some multiple proportion of intensity to scale. Without the sustaining view that small and mobile groups attaining great discoveries can offer, without their inspiration, the task must become doubly difficult. These circumstances may define for the small and mobile group the most demanding and important of all its functions—the heavy responsibility of the keeper of a vision—the vision of the creating individual.

In the future that responsibility may well become not only wider but yet more challenging. For it is abundantly evident that science and technology, in the world as a whole as well as in our own nation, have entered phases of development in our day so different in scale and complexity from their beginnings—or from what, incidentally, the newly developing nations of the world may confront or may require in their own immediate futures—as to differ essentially in kind. As Pierre Teilhard de Chardin has written with sensitive perception, "The Earth is covering itself not merely by myriads of thinking units, but by a single continuum of thought, and finally forming a functionally single Unit of Thought of planetary dimensions." An important aspect of the qualitative growth of contemporary science, of course, inheres in its essentially additive nature, in the formidable integration of knowledge and of thought characteristic of a pursuit where discoveries in one field may in the span of a few months alter the entire basis against which thinking in very different areas must be projected. Another concerns almost the opposite situation. The significance of great research is largely measured by the impact of its results over a wide range of frontiers of inquiry, demanding the widest and swiftest communication possible and challenging human intellectual capacities for assimilation and generalization to their limits. But the *processes* of research bring heavy demands on quite opposite qualities—on extraordinarily detailed knowledge of a single field, on that supreme mastery of all its coordinates down to the most minute, developed over long periods of years, which so often is prerequisite to significant and sustained advance. In the past, science has been able to reconcile these two quite opposite requirements in tolerable fashion. With increase of scale the problem takes on new dimensions.

Science in the last decades has responded to the challenge with enormously increased sophistication, with vastly expanded organization and integration of knowledge, with, indeed, quite a new development of recent years, the field of research on research itself. But as science has matured in its modes of cultivating the whole vast field of its thought, as its power has grown to enter and occupy new areas of research in force so soon as the first hint of them appears, these very qualities have brought novel and troubling consequences for the gifted individual, particularly for the gifted young research student just entering upon his life's work, upon whom so much of the future depends. As A. B. Pippard, among others, has pointed out dramatically, the legions of investigators can now be mobilized with such speed and effectiveness at a new and attractive breach in the frontier of knowledge that, particularly if the area offers a promise of practical benefit, a green and fertile intellectual valley can be reduced to aridity for the innovator within less than the working life of a generation of young scientists. The consequences incident to such swift and locustlike invasions, however effective and profitable they may be for a technical society in the large, can be discouraging to vulnerable individuals, and they bear at precisely the points of talent and dedication most precious to us. There can be no more urgent imperative than the creation of opportunity for individuals faced with this dilemma to address themselves once again to wholly new fields of inquiry. This too lies peculiarly in the domain of small and mobile and basically highly uncommitted research groups.

What, in final essence, is the deepest meaning of the scientific way? In the profoundest sense, what is the meaning of the individual human life dedicated to it? Within the scientific context, as well as outside it, what, at last, are people *for*? A generation, perhaps even a decade, ago such a question was all but unasked by most Americans. Certainly it was all but unasked in 1902. Even if put, in that day, it would have appeared to many not only irrelevant but quite possibly sinister. But in a world with a population estimated at nearly three billion and predicted by conservative demographers to reach almost four billion by 1980 and to attain nearly seven billion by the turn of the century, the question wears quite a different aspect. In our own nation, with a population now over one hundred and seventy million and destined perhaps to reach two hundred and twenty million by 1975, the revolutionary consequences of this flood tide upon every facet of the world we know demand no emphasis. It must profoundly affect every circumstance of our society, of its organization and its function. It must affect the individual's inner view of himself and his conception of his relation to his universe, his understanding and his reach in his own physical world, and much else besides.

The rate of growth of the scientific effort today considerably exceeds that of the population as a whole. Inevitably, it would seem, it must change after two or three more periods of doubling. But in absolute terms it would seem beyond reasonable doubt that the legions of technically trained people in the future will vastly exceed in numbers those now active, even as these in turn so vastly exceed the numbers of only a few decades ago. Great technical and engineering efforts will be ready and available to confer rich meaning on the lives of many. In massive and compelling developmental undertakings opportunities will continue to be provided to great numbers of active minds to labor for ends not only dramatic, not only economically and socially adaptive, but as creative and as meaningful in our times as the tasks of the builders of Chartres or of the Parthenon must have been in theirs. Pippard has presciently pointed out that, if the field of technology is to prove sufficiently magnetic to attract first-class intellects to it, opportunities for the dramatic and the spectacular, outlets for the moral impulse to share in socially significant undertakings, the sheer intellectual quality of the undertakings themselves, must provide the motivations. Among the great and challenging technical and engineering undertakings of our time, all three motivations are presented on a scale the world may never have experienced before.

But there will be other scientific workers, too, of other and less specially identifiable tastes and talents, hostages to a more distant future. For them the requirements will be quite different. Perhaps the deepest question the times can pose for them, and as well the most poignant for all man's spiritual welfare, will be this. In a society as densely packed, as intricately organized, as highly urbanized, as our own must inevitably become in future years, can small and mobile enclaves of thoughtful and imaginative men and women continue to maintain integrity and distinctive freedom within the greater society? On their ability to do so in the broadest context will depend in no small measure the fate of the individual and of those goals and motivations through which in the past we have lived and taken our national being. In a very real sense their persistence alone can effectively preserve the priceless jewel of the opportunity for quietness and temporary solitude which in our past has been so vital a nursery for individual American greatness as well as for that of our society as a whole. For it is the gifted, unorthodox individual in the laboratory or the study or the walk by the river at twilight who has always brought to us, and must continue to bring to us, all the basic resources by which we live. His position must be guarded and honored and implemented with every resource that we can muster, now and in the future, for he is irreplaceable. This matter too, and all the circumstances attendant upon it, must be a central and abiding concern through all the coming years for the Carnegie Institution of Washington. As Chaucer said six hundred years ago, so may we today: "Out of the old fields cometh the new corn."

PART III

Scientific Research and Laboratory Organization

Of the specific problems connected with science, the subject of this section has received more attention than others. The internal organization of the research laboratory, the administration of laboratories, the optimum size of research units, problems of teamwork and individual effort, the evaluation of research results, the assessment of individual as well as organizational productivity, optimum organizational atmospheres or climates for research—these are but a few of the many problem areas within the broader one of internal laboratory organization which have been the subject of numerous studies.

The wealth of literature in this area presents special problems in selection for a volume such as this. Because much of this literature is quite specific, technical, and specialized and because several collections of papers on these problems already exist, it was decided deliberately to omit most such selections from this volume. A sampling of these may be found in the bibliography. Instead, the selections included here are addressed to the more general discussions which outline and raise questions about the broader aspects of the problems of laboratory organization. The papers included here should be of value and interest to the technical experts who are actually doing research in this field. But these technical experts will have to go well beyond these papers to learn more about specific research techniques which have been employed as well as specific findings from a large variety of studies. For the informed layman, as well as for the physical scientist, who, although involved in the process, does not actually and actively study the process himself, the papers included here should provide a reasonably adequate introduction to the kinds of perspectives which have been employed and to the state of knowledge at this time. The questions focused on here are those concerned with the growth and proliferation of large-scale research organization, the internal structure and processes within the laboratory, the effects on the working scientist of different organizational patterns, and the emergence of new roles and new types of organizational structures and processes.

At first glance the introductory selection in this section seems to be at odds with the criteria just mentioned. It is specifically focused on the

175

emergence of brain research institutes, certainly a highly specialized type of institute. However, it is included here because it provides us with some historical perspective on the development of such research institutes and the problems faced a half-century or more ago when the first attempts to establish such institutes were made. Incidently, it also indicates the awakening interest of the scientists who are themselves involved in the process, in the evolution of their present-day working arrangements. This essay originally appeared in a volume otherwise devoted entirely to the purely scientific and technical advances on the frontiers of the brain research field. The fact that this essay on the historical evolution of brain research institutes was included in such a volume and that it was the only nontechnical paper supports our contention of an awakening interest among the natural scientists in this field.

Many of the problems mentioned in this essay by Horace Magoun are as relevant today as they were when they first arose more than a half-century ago. In fact, for reasons which have yet to be investigated, many of the early problems mentioned anticipate trends which did not become noticeable in most other fields of science for many decades afterwards. It would be tempting to speculate about why these early pioneers in the brain research field were "ahead of their time" with respect to the institutional arrangements they were trying to introduce.

As a consequence of discussions at an international gathering of scientists, an international brain research commission was established after the turn of the century which spawned and encouraged a number of brain research institutes all around the world. There were many problems, of course, and many of these early attempts floundered and even failed. And, as is apparent from Magoun's description, more often than not it was a variety of social rather than technical considerations which led to the early successes as well as failures. In retrospect, for example, the failure of Dr. Cushing (one of the world's foremost brain surgeons of his or any other time) to secure support for his plans to develop a large-scale institute after the end of World War I can be seen as a concrete example of being ahead of one's time—much more in sociological than in technical terms.

At about the same time as these brain research institutes were being founded, the idea of establishing research units within an industrial company was slowly beginning to be recognized. The number of industrial research organizations has increased many times over during this past half-century or so, but there is still considerable discomfort and disagreement about the proper organization of a research laboratory. In the next selection, Charles Orth is particularly concerned with the optimum kind of research organization appropriate for industry. He presents a forceful case for a particular strategy involving attempts to transplant a university type of organization and its "atmosphere" into the industrial compound. In so doing, he raises many questions about many types of research organizations and the effects of their characteristic climates.

Orth suggests, among other things, that there be specific recognition of the special status of the scientist who should not be treated as just another employee, especially in relation to lay administrators. The importance of research, and especially that this is basically the creativity of the scientists involved, should be recognized and stressed overtly by management. Clues to an optimum working atmosphere or climate for research are to be found in the university, and this, plus a change in attitude among management executives toward research, can yield the "best" research organization.

Of course, there are those who hold a diametrically opposing view. Research activities in an industrial organization should, in this view, be treated much like any other activity. Research itself, as far as industry is concerned, is only qualitatively different from any of a number of other high-level activities requiring considerable advanced training. In between such polar positions are those who believe that certain modifications must be made, both on the part of the scientists as well as on the part of management in the organization of research within industry. On the basis of the evidence available to date, it is not easy to reconcile these differing positions. It is not even clear that we have found the right questions which must first be asked, and while Orth's essay certainly goes a long way toward fulfilling that goal, there are undoubtedly many others which will be uncovered as our knowledge increases.

Even before the answers can be ascertained, it is important to recognize that different patterns of research organization are possible even within the same institutional context and society. Further, these different patterns presumably affect the conduct and the results of the research. They may also affect the rate and quality of the scientific effort which is possible. The experiences and the research-on-research organization in the next decades should yield an even more solid foundation for the creation of optimum climates for different research efforts not only in industry but in all other contexts as well.

In the next two companion pieces, Norman Kaplan focuses on the newly emerging role of the research administrator in an attempt to illuminate some of the more general problems of research organization. The first of these papers describes and analyzes the role as it appears in a number of industrial and other types of research organizations in the United States. This new role gives rise to and emphasizes distinctions between the goals of science and those related to the maintenance of the organization in which the research is conducted.

In the second paper, the American version of the research administrator is compared and contrasted with the one found in similar types of research organizations in the U.S.S.R. The Soviet research administrator has a far less important role with fewer responsibilities which impinge upon the conduct of research. There is even the suggestion that there may well be less red tape in the Soviet research organizations. Certain aspects of the larger social structure in both countries are suggested as possibly contributing to the differences observed.

In addition to stressing the importance of the larger society for any studies of internal laboratory organization, these papers indicate the importance of comparative studies for a better understanding of any single organization within a particular country.

The last paper in this section was written by a physicist who works in the European Center for Nuclear Research (CERN), one of the world's foremost international physics laboratories. While it appears to be based largely on his own experiences and observations at CERN it highlights and touches upon many crucial aspects of research organization today. Even more important perhaps is that this particular discussion, in no small part because it does stem from experiences at CERN, raises many questions about the organization of research which are likely to become increasingly important in the years ahead as more and more such international organizations are formed. In this sense it goes beyond some of the previous papers which have concentrated on organizational patterns more typical of the organizations which are still so prevalent today.

In the brief interval between the original publication of the Kowarski paper and its reappearance here, the dynamic qualities of "big science" are amply illustrated by the changes in Dr. Kowarski's own organization. When he wrote his article, CERN had a total staff of 1,150; it numbers 1,675 today. From 200 scientists and engineers a few years ago, the number has risen to 325. From 1,700 Fellows, visiting scientists, and supernumeraries, together with experimental teams from various universities, the number has now gone up to about 2,300.

The large-scale international organizations of tomorrow emphasize teamwork and introduce new styles of research. These in turn affect the scientific communications process, the conferral of individual rewards and prestige, and the nurturing of individual creativity. Insofar as L. Kowarski concentrates on the effects of such organizations on individual scientists, the reader may wish to compare this treatment with that of another physicist, Reif, which appears in the previous section.

All of the papers included in this section illuminate some aspect of the internal laboratory organization. They provide us with some insights into the kinds of organizations and the kinds of problems faced by those responsible for organizing a research unit as well as for those who work in them at the laboratory bench. Sometimes explicitly, and more often implicitly, all of these papers call attention to the importance of external social factors, and of the larger society generally, in influencing the internal development of a research organization. Insofar as this is so, these papers illustrate yet another facet of the underlying theme of this volume concerned with the ways in which society affects the conduct of science.

Development of Brain Research Institutes

HORACE W. MAGOUN

The establishment of research institutes has been a significant feature of current growth of scientific endeavor in many fields. Prior to their founding, the long-time encouragement of science came chiefly from two sources: the universities and the scientific academies. The universities, dating from the medieval period, were traditionally concerned with the preservation of knowledge and its transmission in education, but they supported investigation as well. The scientific academies, appearing with the Enlightenment of the seventeenth and eighteenth centuries, were primarily committed to the acquisition of knowledge and therefore naturally played an influential role in promoting research. The first widespread appearance of research institutes toward the end of the nineteenth century was largely attributable, however, to practical advances in immunotherapy and to other contributions to public health.

In Germany, the discoveries of Robert Koch were recognized by the establishment, in 1880, in Berlin, of an Institute for Infectious Diseases. Pasteur's discoveries and especially his demonstration of a preventive treatment for rabies led the French Academy to open an international subscription for the establishment of a Pasteur Institute, ceremoniously inaugurated in Paris in 1888. Other centers established in this pattern included the Institute for Experimental Medicine, founded in St. Petersburg in 1890; the Institute of Preventive Medicine, founded in London in 1891, with Lister as its first chairman; and the Rockefeller Institute for Medical Research, founded in New York in 1901, as the first large-scale research institute to be established in the United States (4).

By the turn of the century, these developments had brought the concept of research institutes to widespread public attention and had demonstrated the great benefit to investigative activity which their establishment made possible. With infectious disease and immunology obviously well provided for, it was natural that succeeding efforts should be devoted to comparable

Reprinted from *Frontiers in Brain Research* (edited by J. D. French), New York: Columbia University Press, 1962, with permission of the author and publisher. Dr. Howard W. Magoun, a Professor of Anatomy and member of the Brain Research Institute at the University of California at Los Angeles, is now the Dean of the Graduate Division of that institution.

developments in other fields. It was at this point that institutes for brain research, a number of which had been developing locally through the initiative of individual investigators, first received general recognition and support.

At an inaugural assembly of the International Association of Academies held in Paris in 1901, the Royal Academy of Sciences of Saxony formally moved to encourage increased research upon the brain. This action was initiated by Wilhelm His, Professor of Anatomy at Leipzig, who had become impressed by the advantages of research institutes on a visit to the zoological station in Naples in 1886 (16). The Association sanctioned the establishment of an International Brain Research Commission dedicated to promoting study of the structure and function of the central nervous system. This Brain Commission hoped, through the influence of the academies, to convince the various governments of the importance of increasing international activities in this field, primarily by establishing central institutes for brain research where special collections of investigative material could be accumulated and facilities made available for their study.

The members of this International Brain Research Commission were chosen by nomination from learned societies of the different countries, with the Royal Society of London acting as "teller." A small central committee consisting of His, Waldeyer, Ehlers, Munk, Flechsig, Golgi and Obersteiner was formed to facilitate action. His (17) had planned the committee but died before its first meeting, and Waldeyer succeeded him as chairman. By 1907, sixteen different countries were represented in the Brain Commission, whose membership then numbered forty (33).[1] Seven special committees with heavy anatomical emphasis were formed to coordinate aspects of brain research dealing with descriptive anatomy (Waldeyer, chairman), comparative anatomy (Ehlers), histology (Golgi), embryology (Retzius), pathological anatomy (Obersteiner), physiology (Munk) and clinical neurology (Flechsig). By 1908, seven already existing research institutes had been made associates of the International Brain Research Commission (34) and later some of them were designated as Central Institutes: the Neurological Institute of the University of Vienna (Obersteiner), the Neurohistological Institute of Madrid (Cajal), the Senckenberg Neurological Institute of Frankfurt am Main (Edinger), the Institute of the Neurological-Psychiatric

---

[1] Elliot Smith, Cairo; Gehucten, Louvain; Hansen, Copenhagen; Edinger, Frankfurt am Main; Ehlers, Göttingen; Flechsig, Leipzig; Munk and Waldeyer, Berlin; Langley, Cambridge; Sherrington, Liverpool; Horsley and Ferrier, London; Cunningham, Edinburgh; Dejerine, Raymond, Girard, Lannelongue and Manouvier, Paris; Kure, Tokyo; Golgi, Pavia; Luciana and Mingazzini, Rome; Romiti, Pisa; Mosso and Lugaro, Turin; Winkler, Amsterdam; Guldberg, Christiania; Exner, Obersteiner and Zuckerkandl, Vienna; Lenhossek, Budapest; Bechterev and Dogiel, St. Petersburg; Henschen and Retzius, Stockholm; Monakow, Zurich; Cajal, Madrid; Mall, Baltimore; Minot, Boston; and Donaldson, Philadelphia.

Clinic at Leipzig (Flechsig), the Neurological Institute at Zurich (von Monakow), the Psycho-Neurological Institute at St. Petersburg (Bechterev) and the Wistar Institute of Anatomy and Biology at Philadelphia (Donaldson and Greenman). In 1909, an eighth, the Netherlands Central Institute for Brain Research (Kappers), was newly established at Amsterdam. These remarkable achievements of the Brain Commission ceased with World War I.

As a background for consideration of each of these centers, it may be pointed out that with the development of sectioning and staining procedures in the later nineteenth century, it first became possible to explore the internal organization of man's brain, so important both for understanding its function and for diagnosis and therapy in clinical neurology and psychiatry. With little more than the previous foundation in descriptive external anatomy and gross dissection, the laboratories and investigators of the turn of the century pursued the study of the internal structure of the central nervous system by a variety of methods. Because the brain of the normal adult man was so bewilderingly complex, attention was directed to individuals with special endowments, to clinical cases with focal injury or special pathology, to instances of teratology, as well as to simpler embryological stages, comparative anatomical specimens and animal brains with regional degeneration following experimental procedures. When stained with differential methods, these provided a range of material for ubiquitous microscopic examination. With this growth of multidisciplinary study, it became difficult for single departments to support laboratories with adequate resources.

A few zealous and enterprising individuals had earlier developed centers, however, in which more or less the whole scope of investigative approach was represented. Among these were the laboratories of Obersteiner in Vienna, of Edinger in Frankfurt, of von Monakow in Zurich, of the Vogts in Berlin and of Flechsig in Leipzig. All were established privately and for a long time were supported chiefly or entirely by income from the neuro-psychiatric practice of each director. With the advent of the International Brain Research Commission and its plan for associated institutes, the status of these laboratories was much improved. While previously occupying crowded and often borrowed space, they were accorded more extensive facilities and were usually assigned a supporting budget and university affiliation as well. The interest and support of the International Brain Research Commission thus led to great improvement in the resources and programs of the institutes, each of which may now be considered briefly.

The first neurological institute was established in Vienna in 1882 by Heinrich Obersteiner, who had graduated in medicine there and had undertaken research in von Brücke's laboratory while still an undergraduate (20, 21, 24). Beginning in two rooms in the old Physiological Institute, his laboratory gradually increased, became a part of the University of Vienna in

1905 and, in 1907, on being designated the Central Institute for Brain Research in Austria, moved into newly constructed quarters. At this time its library contained 60,000 items, of which Obersteiner, a great bibliophile, had contributed more than half. His versatile mind encompassed nearly every aspect of neurology and psychiatry, but the research activity of the Institute was centered chiefly on neuroanatomy and pathology. Contributions to these fields were published in the *Arbeiten aus dem Neurologische Institut am Universität Wien,* begun in 1892. In 1938, the Institute was revived by Hans Hoff and Franz Seitelberger; the latter is currently its director. As a measure of its tenure, it may be noted that the 75th Anniversary of the Vienna Institute was celebrated in 1957.

During the 1880's a Brain Research Institute was established by Paul Flechsig in relation to the Neurological-Psychiatric Clinic at the University of Leipzig, where he was Professor of Psychiatry (*31, 14*). Flechsig contributed importantly to the understanding of the organization of the cerebral cortex through myelogenetic and other studies, in which he was joined by such students as Beevor, Bechterev, Darkschevitsch, Schutz, Vogt and Held. Both for his own contributions and as an associate of His at Leipzig, Flechsig was made an initial member of the Central Committee of the Brain Commission. Upon the designation of his laboratory as one of its associate institutes (*34*), he reported in 1908 that it had

> *begun a collection of brains from persons known during life, from which suitable cases will be described. In addition, there is a large pathological-anatomical collection of the brains of persons suffering from speech defects, and also brains of anthropoids, among which are two gorilla brains; also a collection of 60,000 brain sections. Finally there is a department for experimental psychology and one for chemical work.*

Activities of the Brain-Anatomical Institute in Zurich began in 1886, when Constantin von Monakow was joined by a young American zoologist, Henry Donaldson. In a room borrowed from the Pathological Institute, they cut and studied sections of the brain of a dog from which Hermann Munk, in Berlin, had extirpated both occipital lobes with resulting cortical blindness (*22, 23, 32*). As in the case of Vienna, where the work of Turck and Meynert preceded the establishment of a neurological institute by Obersteiner, so in Zurich Goll had described the posterior column bundle which bears his name; while von Gudden, Hitzig and Forel succeeded one another at the Psychiatric University Clinic before von Monakow established a brain anatomy institute.

From 1905 to 1916, the *Arbeiten aus dem Hirnanatomischen Institut*

Zurich reported the numerous contributions of von Monakow and his students, Fuse, Tsuchida and others. Initial studies were concerned with organization of the visual and acoustic pathways and with thalamocortical relations. Subsequently, von Monakow introduced dynamic concepts of diaschisis to account for functional impairment following injury to the brain, and in the last part of his career, he attempted to relate ethical and philosophical values to his earlier neurobiological work. His Institute became part of the University of Zurich in 1910 and, in 1928, von Monakow was succeeded as director by M. Minkowski, whose research interests lay in the maturation of motor function systematically compared with the development of the fetal central nervous system. In 1961, Konrad Akert was appointed director of the Institute of Brain Research in which anatomical studies are related to programs of neurophysiology, initiated at Zurich in the 1930's and 40's by W. R. Hess and his students.

In 1901, a considerable time after these programs of brain research had been established in Vienna, Leipzig and Zurich, the Spanish government recognized the achievements of Santiago Ramón y Cajal, Professor of Anatomy at the University of Madrid, by creating a Laboratory of Biological Research, called the Instituto Cajal (*4, 28*). It occupied the third floor of a small building next to the university museum, but the expanded facilities provided great impetus to Cajal, who, in 1888, identified the nerve cell as the unit of neural structure and provided a monumental amount of novel information concerning the histological organization of the brain. In 1906 Cajal shared the Nobel Prize with Golgi, whose reduced silver stain he had put to such profitable use. Upon Cajal's retirement at the age of 70 from the University of Madrid, the Spanish government established a large new Instituto Cajal, completed in 1932, whose research programs, interrupted by the Spanish Civil War, are currently being restored under the directorship of Julian Sanz Ibanez.

The Senckenberg Neurological Institute at Frankfurt am Main was established by Ludwig Edinger (*1, 7, 9, 18, 19*). In addition to practicing clinical neurology in Frankfurt, Edinger pursued myelogenetic and other neuroanatomical studies, first in a laboratory in his mother's home and, from 1902, in a borrowed room in Weigert's pathological laboratory. Following Weigert's death in 1904, the Senckenberg Foundation constructed a neurological institute on the upper floor of a new building and appointed Edinger director of its programs in comparative neurology and neuropathology. Its financial support was derived from Edinger's clinical practice, and he contributed also a library of 6,000 volumes on neuroanatomy and extensive collections of brain sections from amphioxus to man. In 1914 this neurological institute was made part of the newly founded University of Frankfurt.

With an interest in evolution carried over from his early education,

Edinger sought an understanding of the functional organization of the human brain in terms of comparative neuroanatomy. Already in 1886 he had formed the idea that "perhaps the brain consisted of two different parts, one for elementary functions and another which develops along with the evolution of the animal series." His later work confirmed this view and permitted differentiation of the paleoencephalon, or stem of the brain—which does not change greatly in evolution—from neoencephalic structures, consisting of the cerebral and cerebellar hemispheres—which grow in substance with vertebrate evolution and achieve highest development in man.

The Psycho-Neurological Institute at St. Petersburg was established and directed by V. Bechterev who, following graduation from its Military Medical Academy, spent a period in Europe working with Flechsig and Wundt in Leipzig (35). Returning to Russia in 1886 as Professor of Psychiatry at the University of Kazan, Bechterev "organized a psychiatric clinic, the first psycho-physiological laboratory in Russia, and the first 'Brain Institute' in which the anatomy and physiology of the nervous system were investigated in relevant connection with clinical experience."

In 1893 Bechterev was awarded the Chair of Nervous and Mental Diseases at the Military Medical Academy of St. Petersburg, which was then the foremost academic center in Russia. "In 1907, with the help of private funds, he founded and became Director of the Psycho-Neurological Institute at St. Petersburg. According to his scale of plans, the Institute was to embody his ideas of liberal education in medicine, psychology and sociology, and to serve as a research center for the study of behavior in the broadest sense of this broad term—neuroanatomical, physiological, psychological and sociological, with the essential qualification—objectively." After 1920, this Psycho-Neurological Institute became the State Institute of Brain Research in Leningrad.

In addition to improving the status of existing institutes, the influence of the International Brain Research Commission was instrumental in establishing, in 1909, a completely new Central Institute for Brain Research in Amsterdam (2, 5). Its director, C. U. Ariëns-Kappers, was attracted from Edinger's Institute in Frankfurt where he was already directing the program in comparative neuroanatomy. In an inaugural address, Ariëns-Kappers outlined the search for general principles of neural organization, which was to characterize the chief interest of the Dutch Institute, as it did that of all the others of the time. Advantage was to be taken of the gradual development of the brain with emphasis upon ontogenetic and comparative studies. "More and more," Kappers pointed out, "the idea will urge itself upon us that there is no nerve cell whose place is not determined by fixed law, no dendrite growing in a certain direction and no tract whose origin and ending are not prescribed by fixed rules." To Kappers, the concept of neurobiotaxis accounted best for the basic determinism in brain organization, which he pursued through early work on phylogenetic displacement of the motor ganglia of the oblongata, which he rather lyrically described as the "quadrille of the nuclei," to later preoccupation with endocranial casts of Peking man and racial migrations in near-Eastern prehistory, cultivated during visiting appointments at Peking and Beirut in the latter part of his career. The fiftieth anniversary of the Netherlands Central Institute for Brain Research was celebrated in 1959, with an International Symposium on "The Structure and Function of the Cerebral Cortex" which marks the direction of its current investigative program under the directorship of S. T. Bok.

During the period when the plans of the Brain Commission were being formulated, an independent development in Berlin led ultimately to the establishment of another major institute for brain research (*12, 13, 25*). The responsible individuals were Oskar Vogt and his wife, Cécile, who had met in Paris during their study of clinical neurology. Returning to Berlin in 1898, they opened the Neurological Central Station which, in 1902, became the Neurobiological Laboratory of the University of Berlin. So great was the Vogts' progress that, in 1931, the Kaiser Wilhelm Institute for Brain Research was opened in Buch, a suburb of Berlin, with support from governmental, municipal and private sources. The Institute was organized into departments for each investigative discipline, and the large staff included Brodmann and Bielschowsky in histology and Kornmüller and Tönnies in electrophysiology.

From an initial interest in brain-mind relationships, the research program of the Vogts and their colleagues became predominantly concerned with increasingly sharply defined localization of function in the central nervous system. Topistic units were identified both in cyto- and myeloarchitectural study, as well as in responses to stimulation of excitable cortical areas. Focal patterns were similarly recognized in the electroencephalogram, and topistic vulnerability, called "pathoclisis," involving glial and vascular as well as neuronal susceptibility, was proposed in brain injury and disease. A large number of specific fields were ultimately differentiated in the cerebral cortex, and studies were extended to the basal ganglia and thalamus, as well as to the limbic and reticular parts of the brain by the Vogts themselves and by Maximilian Rose, Lorente de Nó, and Olszewski, who were among their many students. In 1937 the Vogts were forced to leave Berlin and, moving to Neustadt in the Schwarzwald, they established another Institute for Brain Research, where work was continued on their extensive neurological collections. Cécile's 75th and Oskar's 80th birthdays were celebrated widely in 1950.

A clear-cut tendency for brain research institutes to reproduce themselves, already attested by derivation of the Dutch institute from that of

Edinger at Frankfurt, is even more strikingly illustrated by the multiple off-spring of the Vogts' Institute. In Germany, the Max Planck Society is currently establishing a multidepartmental Institut für Hirnforschung, sections of which will be located in different cities. In addition to the Institute at Neustadt, comparative anatomical studies are proceeding in Giessen and behavioral research is under way at Seewiesen. Sections for neurophysiology are being established in Göttingen and in Munich, for genetics and neurochemistry in Marburg and for tumors and general neurology at Köln. Most interestingly, because of its relation to the old Edinger Institute, still another section of the Max Planck Institut für Hirnforschung, to be opened soon at Frankfurt, will devote itself similarly to neuroanatomy and pathology.

An earlier offspring of the Berlin-Buch Institute was the Brain Research Institute in Moscow, established under Vogt's direction following the death of Lenin in 1924. When Vogt was called to the USSR and commissioned to arrange facilities for studying the Soviet leader's brain, the mansion of a former industrialist was adapted, a group of Soviet scientists was trained and, in the course of two and one-half years, Lenin's brain was cut in complete serial section. In a preliminary report of the study, Vogt (32) called attention to the hypertrophy of pyramidal cells in the association cortex and, drawing analogy to the muscular hypertrophy resulting from repeated physical exercise, suggested that Lenin might be considered an "association-athlete."

The Moscow Brain Institute gained independent status in 1929 and today includes a number of research departments, as well as a museum where dissections of all stages of animal life provide an impressive display of neural evolution. An atlas of cortical cytoarchitecture of the human brain has recently been published by its director, S. A. Sarkisov; electrophysiological work is exploring the activity of individual cortical laminae; and electron microscopical study is currently being introduced.

The manner in which the participation of the United States developed in the programs of the International Brain Research Commission is of considerable interest. As one of His' most distinguished students, Franklin P. Mall, Professor of Anatomy at Johns Hopkins, was appointed an initial member of the Brain Commission (29). In 1904, when Charles Minot, Professor of Anatomy at Harvard, was asked to join, Mall wrote to him:

> Don't for a moment hesitate to join the Hirnforschung Institut. It gives you a great opportunity. 1. It will be easier for you to get human embryos and workers; 2. It gives the best possible backing abroad to get funds in America; 3. It puts us in closer touch with foreign workers.

A year later, in 1905, Mall was consulted by Piersol, Professor of Anatomy at Pennsylvania, about the reorganization of the Wistar Institute for Anatomy and Biology in Philadelphia (*10, 11*). This had originated from the activities of Caspar Wistar, who occupied the Chair of Anatomy at the University of Pennsylvania early in the nineteenth century. Following his death, a quantity of his anatomical preparations was presented to the University and ultimately gained the status of a museum. In 1892 the University of Pennsylvania succeeded in interesting a descendent, General Isaac Wistar, in the incorporation of this museum as a Wistar Institute of Anatomy and Biology. The pursuit of research and the support of publications were introduced in 1905, a step plainly supported by the General, who wrote: "I fully agree that the Wistar Institute should be designed for the use of investigators, rather than a mere gaping public."

It was at this point that Mall, consulted by Piersol, immediately seized the opportunity to promote the plans of the International Brain Commission, which had requested the National Academy to establish a special institute for study of the brain. Mall wrote:

> *It seems to me that it would be natural and proper that the Wistar Institute should be designated. Through it, all the work in neurology in America could be enlarged and correlated with the work abroad. . . . What I have just written shows, it appears to me, the brilliant opportunity before the Wistar Institute . . . it would be almost criminal if the Wistar Institute did not take part in it.*

As a consequence, the Wistar Institute did at that time initiate a neurological program and, on Mall's recommendation, appointed Henry H. Donaldson as its head. Donaldson gathered a large quantity of data relating to the growth of the nervous system, and his interest in the establishment of biological norms also found expression in standardization of the Wistar albino rat as a common laboratory animal. His successor, E. G. Coghill, later introduced research correlating the development of behavior of the salamander with the maturation of its nervous system, but increasingly strained administrative relations led finally to the termination of Coghill's appointment (*15*).

In 1919 a second effort to establish a major institute for brain research in the United States met with even less success (*8*). In an address at the opening ceremonies of the Montreal Neurological Institute in 1934, Harvey Cushing (*6*) recalled:

> *As World War I drew to a close, a small group of overseas medical officers, whose official positions had thrown them close together,*

found themselves disinclined to return to their former humdrum professorial tasks. In talking the matter over, they conceived the idea of founding a National Institute of Neurology, whose primary purpose was to aid the government in supervising the further treatment of the disorders and injuries of the nervous system sustained by our soldiers. . . . We looked forward, not only to having suitable wards for organic, psychopathic, infectious and neurosurgical disorders, but also a well-equipped operating suite, proper laboratories for neuropathological investigation and experimentation, a working library and a new organ of publication. . . . It was our ambition to have the organization grow into a postgraduate school for those whose interests pointed toward neurology or any one of its many bypaths. . . . Were such an institute to be put in operation and kept out of politics, we on our part, as whole-time servants, freed from the distractions of private practice, agreed to devote the remainder of our working lives in the effort to make it a success. . . . Neurosurgery was to be my province, and Lewis H. Weed, who had been in charge of an experimental laboratory for the study of nervous diseases under Army auspices, had agreed to become Director of Laboratories.

In retrospect, the government might have been saved some of the hundreds of millions of dollars that have since been expended largely on the care of these very patients, but when it was suggested that the erection and maintenance of such a supervising institute as we had in mind might cost ten million dollars, this was looked upon as fantastic. We then appealed to the Rockefeller Foundation, where we had a warmer reception, and for a time it seemed that the program might be put through. Unhappily, to make the story short, we met with opposition from certain influential quarters; the undertaking finally was abandoned, and we one and all drifted back to our former academic positions. Disappointed as we were, I like to think the seed did not fall on wholly barren ground, and that our long forgotten project may have eased the way for McGill to establish this unit which, let us hope, will set an example to be emulated by large university centers elsewhere.

With support from the Rockefeller Foundation, this Montreal Neurological Institute was formally opened in 1934, six years after its director, Wilder Penfield, had joined McGill University to introduce clinical neurosurgery and neurological research at its medical school (26, 27). At the opening ceremony Penfield stated, "We have carved in stone on the outside of this building a simple declaration of our cause in the words, 'Dedicated to the relief of sickness and to the study of neurology.' " In 1953, at the opening of the McConnel Wing, doubling the institute's facilities, he remarked, "From the day of the First Foundation of 19 years ago, this building has housed two activities: 1) a neurological hospital; and 2) a scientific unit, each supported by a separate budget. This is what a clinical institute is—a place of treating patients and a place nearby for the study of the human and scientific problems thus presented."

High motivation contributed importantly to the accomplishments of the Montreal Neurological Institute. In Penfield's words: "The task to which this institute is dedicated in all humbleness of spirit is the achievement of greater understanding of the neurological ills to which man is heir, so that physicians may come to the bedside with healing in their hands." The provision of research laboratories was also significant, for, as Penfield remarked:

> *No one could become familiar with neurological problems and with the handicaps imposed upon the workers in this field without concluding that adequate laboratories . . . were essential to further progress. For any constructive ideas that I may have contributed I have to thank the guiding influence of the men under whom it has been my good fortune to work. Most important was the initial influence of Sir Charles Sherrington. In his laboratory at Oxford, to search for the hidden truths of neurology became a habit of mind, a coloring to all one's thought.*

Additionally, provision was made for research fellows, of whom Penfield said:

> *The important work of research is carried on by men who have finished all preliminary training and who have not yet undertaken positions of responsibility. Some of them are voluntary laboratory assistants, others are on a research stipend. These men may be wandering students from any part of the world. If well chosen, the research fellows are the most important part of the staff of an institute of this sort.*

At the Montreal Neurological Institute investigative activity has flourished—in neuropathology with Cone, in neurochemistry with Elliott and in neurophysiology with Jasper. In Penfield's hands, the neurosurgical operating room was additionally a laboratory and indeed the Institute's program, which over the years contributed so productively to knowledge of the brain, was undertaken jointly in the operating room and laboratories in the search for mechanisms related to epilepsy. In discussing the future Penfield concluded, "Permanence requires that there shall be transmission, through a succession of native sons, of contagious scientific enthusiasm." Appropriately, Theodore C. Rasmussen was recently called back to the Institute's direction as Penfield's successor.

More recently, Cushing's earlier plan to form a national neurological institute has again borne fruit, this time in his own country and with federal support. Following World War II, the United States Public Health Service established the National Institutes of Health in Bethesda, outside Washington, D.C. A multidisciplinary program of neurological research was established jointly by the National Institutes of Mental Health and National Institute of Neurological Diseases and Blindness, under the research directorship of Seymour Kety and his successor, Robert Livingston. Among its extensive activities have been those in physiology with Marshall, Tasaki, Frank, Lilly and MacLean; in psychology with Rosvold; in pharmacology with Cantoni; in anatomy with Windle; and in biochemistry with Tower and Axelrod; to name but a part of its large program.

More recently, institutes for brain research have developed in this country in university settings as well. An Institute of Neurology was established at Northwestern University Medical School in 1928, with Stephen W. Ranson as director. With limited support, a productive investigative program was maintained until Ranson's death in 1942, with the subsequent closure of the Institute. At this time, another institute was opened in Chicago as the Neuropsychiatric Institute of the University of Illinois Medical School. In it, sections housing neurology, neurosurgery and psychiatry were connected by a basement laboratory, in which similarly productive programs of research were developed by Warren McCulloch, Percival Bailey, Gerhardt Von Bonin and their associates.

This account, which is essentially devoted to pioneer developments, primarily discusses such activities in other countries. I have made reference to only two American Institutes—one at Northwestern University, the other at the University of Illinois—because, through the association of John D. French and myself with them, they form in a sense the parent organizations from which has stemmed the currently opening Brain Research Institute of the University of California, Los Angeles. Its heritage is an exceedingly rich one; may its accomplishments come to occupy a place of merit among those of such a distinguished past.

REFERENCES

1. Ariëns-Kappers, C. U., Ludwig Edinger (1855–1915), Folia Neurobiologica, 9:343–66, 1915.
2. ———, Dutch Central Institute for Brain Research at Amsterdam, in *Methods*

and Problems of Medical Education, 10th series, pp. 1–6. New York, Rockefeller Foundation, 1928.

3. Blake, J. B., Scientific institutions since the Renaissance: their role in medical research, Proc. Am. Philos. Soc., 101:31–62, 1957.

4. Cannon, D. F., *Explorer of the Human Brain; the Life of Santiago Ramón y Cajal (1852–1934).* New York, Schuman, 1949.

5. Crosby, E. C., Address in memory of Cornelius Ubbo Ariëns-Kappers, in Tower, D. B., and J. P. Schadé, eds., *Structure and Function of the Cerebral Cortex,* pp. 1–6. Amsterdam, Elsevier, 1960.

6. Cushing, H., Psychiatrists, neurologists and the neurosurgeon, in *Neurological Biographies and Addresses,* pp. 17–36. London, Oxford Univ. Press, 1936.

7. Edinger, L., Bericht über das Dr. Senckenbergische Neurologische Institute 1902–1906, Frank. Zeit. f. Path., 1:200–04, 1907.

8. Fulton, J. F., *Harvey Cushing, a Biography.* Springfield, Thomas, 1946.

9. Goldstein, K., Ludwig Edinger (1855–1918), Zeit. f. d. ges. Neurol. u. Psych., 44:114–49, 1918.

10. Greenman, M. J., Concerning the Wistar Institute of Anatomy, Anat. Rec., 1:119–24, 1907.

11. ———, The Wistar Institute of Anatomy and Biology, appendix in *Autobiography of Isaac Jones Wistar.* New York, Harpers, 1914.

12. Hassler, R., Cécile und Oskar Vogt, in Kolle, K., ed., *Grosse Nervenärzte,* Bd. 2, pp. 45–64. Stuttgart, Thieme, 1959.

13. Haymaker, W., Cécile and Oskar Vogt, on the occasion of her 75th and his 80th birthday, Neurology, 1:179–204, 1951.

14. ———, ed., *The Founders of Neurology.* Springfield, Thomas, 1953.

15. Herrick, C. J., *George Ellett Coghill, Naturalist and Philosopher.* Chicago, Univ. of Chicago Press, 1949.

16. His, W., Über wissenschaftliche Centralanstalten und speciell über Centralanstalten zur Förderung der Gehirnkenntniss. *K. Sächsische Gesellschaft der Wissenschaften, Leipzig.* Math. Phys. Klasse, 53:413–36, 1901.

17. ———, Protokoll der von der internationalen Association der Akademien ixeder gesetzen Centralkommission für Gehirnforschung. *K. Sächsische Gesellschaft der Wissenschaften, Leipzig.* Math. Phys. Klasse, 56:2–4, 1904.

18. Krücke, W., Ludwig Edinger (1855–1918), in Scholz, W., ed., *50 Jahre Neuropathologie in Deutschland,* pp. 20–33. Stuttgart, Thieme, 1961.

19. Krücke, W., and H. Spatz, Aus den "Erinnerungen" von Ludwig Edinger, in *Ludwig Edinger (1855–1918),* Schrift. Wissensch. Gesellsch. University of Frankfurt, Naturwisschensh., pp. 1–25. Wiesbaden, Steiner, 1959.

20. Marburg, O., Zur Geschichte des Wiener Neurologischen Institutes (Festschrift zum Feier des 25 Jährigen Bestandes des Neurologischen Institutes an der Wiener Universität), Arb. a. d. Neurol. Inst. a. d. Wiener Univ., 15: VII–XXIII, 1907.

21. ———, Heinrich Obersteiner, Arb. a. d. Neurol. Inst. a. d. Univ. Wien., 24:V–XXXII, 1923.

22. Minkowski, M., Die Poliklinik für Nervenkranke und das Hirnanatomische Institut, Zürcher Spitalgeschichte von Regierungsrat des Kantons Zurich, pp. 427–73, 1951.

23. ———, Constantin von Monakows Beiträge und impulse zur Entwicklung der neurologischen Grundprobleme des Aufbaus, der Lokalisation und des Abbaus der nervösen Funktionen, Schweiz. Arch. f. Neurol. u. Psych., 74:27–59, 1954.

24. Obersteiner, H., Die internationale Gehirnforschung, Deutsche Revue, 33:77–82, 1908.
25. Olszewski, J., Cécile und Oskar Vogt, Arch. Neurol. and Psychiat., 64:812–22, 1950.
26. Penfield, W., The significance of the Montreal Neurological Institute, in *Neurological Biographies and Addresses*, pp. 37–54. London, Oxford Univ. Press, 1936.
27. ———, The second foundation of the Montreal Neurological Institute, in *Prospect and Retrospect in Neurology*, pp. 23–42. Boston, Little, Brown, 1955.
28. Ramón y Cajal, S., *Recollections of My Life*, trans. by Craigie, E. H., Memoirs Am. Philos. Soc., Vol. 8, Parts 1 and 2, 1937.
29. Sabin, F. R., *Franklin Paine Mall, the Story of a Mind*. Baltimore, Johns Hopkins Press, 1934.
30. Vogt, O., Bericht über die Arbeiten des Moskower Staats Instituts für Hirnforschung, J. f. Psychol. u. Neurol., 40:108–18, 1929.
31. Von Bonin, G., *Some Papers on the Cerebral Cortex*. Springfield, Thomas, 1960.
32. Von Monakow, C., Über Hirnforschungsinstitute und Hirnmuseen, Arb. a. d. Hirnanatomischen Inst. in Zurich., 6:1–27, 1912.
33. Waldeyer, W., Document 1 of the report of the President of the Brain Commission (Br. C), Anat. Rec., 1:181–86, 1907.
34. ———, Report on the present status of the academic institutes for brain study, together with a report of the meetings of the Executive Committee of the Brain Commission held at Berlin, March 14, 1908, Anat. Rec., 2:428–31, 1908.
35. Yakolev, P. J., Bechterev, in Brazier, M. A. B., ed., *The Central Nervous System and Behavior*. New York, Josiah Macy, Jr. Foundation, 1959.

The Optimum Climate for Industrial Research

CHARLES D. ORTH, 3RD

Why is the research laboratory unique and why are the scientists who work in it "different"?

What are the five basic components of a creative industrial research climate, and what can the manager do to develop them?

What management attitudes need altering for the sake of healthy relationships with the scientist?

Why is it that the manager must adapt his understanding more than the scientist does?

These are some of the questions I want to discuss in this article. My thesis can be stated simply, although its implications for management are not so simple and may even impress some executives as being radical. The idea is: *the creative work of research personnel is the basic product of the research laboratory.* And the degree of productivity evidenced by laboratory personnel will depend on the degree to which the optimum climate for professional research work has been developed and maintained by research management. Effective recruiting depends on such a climate; and problems of evaluation and compensation of technical personnel are simplified where this climate exists.

KINDS OF PEOPLE

It is difficult for a layman to get the feel of the working climate required, by research personnel unless he understands the kind of people who work in the world of science and the influence on their values of the special training which made them scientists. There are many differences between the ideal working atmosphere of a research laboratory and that expected, or

Reprinted from *Harvard Business Review*, March-April 1959, pp. 55–64, with the permission of the author and the publisher. Professor Charles D. Orth, 3rd, is Assistant Dean of the Graduate School of Business Administration at Harvard University. Together with Joseph C. Bailey and Francis W. Wolek, he has recently published *Administering Research and Development* (Homewood, Ill.: Richard D. Irwin & The Dorsey Press, 1964).

even desirable, in the other parts of an industrial organization. The particular values about themselves and their work that researchers bring to their jobs are atypical, in the sense that they are by and large strange to the business world.

In seeking an understanding of these differences, an important clue can be found in the universities, where most research people work for a number of years while earning advanced degrees in their special fields. Indeed, it is fair to state that, though individual researchers are frequently hired from the laboratory of another company, the environment that has had most to do with their way of thinking about themselves and their work is the university laboratory in which they learned about science and scientific methodology.

HEAD IN THE CLOUDS?

The industrial community tends to look on the academic environment and the academicians who inhabit it with a curious mixture of suspicious derision and amused tolerance for "absent-minded professors" and "head-in-the-clouds thinking." Even though the men concerned may be renowned in their special fields and, in the case of scientists, often paid considerable sums as consultants by industry, it is a commonplace to hear industrial managers say something like, "These boys are fine if they stay in their own back yard where they're carefully sheltered from the realities of life. But they're pretty helpless when they get into business—they just don't understand what goes on."

Considering this assumption, it is not hard to understand why industrial managers find it difficult to deal with the people who work in their research laboratories. Yet a sophisticated understanding of these people and their values is a necessity if the optimum climate for creative research is to exist in a nonacademic laboratory.

What is it about the academic laboratory that makes it a unique institution? What is it the scientist finds there that influences him throughout the rest of his life?

THE UNIVERSITY LAB

The atmosphere of the university laboratory is a curious mixture. On the one hand, we have the permissiveness, lack of pressure, and concentration on the ideas and knowledge characteristic of academic life, and, on the other hand, the rigorous discipline of scientific methodology. And though laboratories vary in many ways—their reputation, their particular areas of interest, their ability to attract financial support, the equipment and facilities available, and so forth—they always have certain characteristics in common:

1. Perhaps the single most important characteristic of the university laboratory as implied above is the *emphasis on basic research and on the discipline of scientific methodology.* This implies the pursuit of knowledge according to a rigorously defined methodology which demands acute observation, separation of facts from opinions, meticulous recording of results, and the reporting of verifiable conclusions.

It is no accident that most of the basic research done in this country, with the exception of a few laboratories supported by our largest industrial companies, is done in universities. The requirements for a Ph.D. degree in the basic sciences include original research in the special field of the investigator. Furthermore, the goal of any university is the pursuit of knowledge without reference to the practicability of its application. As a result, the chemist, physicist, or metallurgist seeking his degree usually chooses a thesis subject which will contribute a small slice to the sum of basic knowledge in this field and which will demonstrate, as he seeks this knowledge, his expert use of the scientific methodology which graduate programs in the sciences are designed to teach him.

2. A second fundamental characteristic is evidenced by the *permissive, low-pressure atmosphere* which is found in the university laboratory in common with other academic units. Within this atmosphere individuals make many decisions for themselves about their work and the direction it will take, while at the same time always having the counsel and direction of the faculty group available to them. Within such a climate graduate students learn to think for themselves and necessarily become accustomed to an independence of thought and action which is difficult to eradicate once it becomes a part of their professional life.

3. Another characteristic of the university laboratory is found in the *opportunity for constant interaction with colleagues and faculty who are interested in the student's own and related fields of investigation.* The student becomes used to being able to talk about his problems with sympathetic and interested co-workers who have enough knowledge of his field to ask stimulating questions and suggest interesting alternatives. He discovers that his own ideas are often sparked by such conversations and soon learns to depend on the availability of interested and informed colleagues.

4. A further characteristic concerns the basic motivation of faculty and students alike. This motivation can best be described as *a desire for intellectual development and achievement.* The heroes of the scientific world are men who have made great discoveries, men who have added significantly to the world's knowledge in various fields. The graduate student of science, no matter what his future career may be, never quite gives up the hope that he too will someday record significant additions to our store of fundamental knowledge.

5. A final important characteristic is suggested by those already stated,

and it concerns the way scientifically oriented people evaluate themselves and their colleagues. *Scientists are evaluated according to their knowledge of their field, the degree of expert methodology they display in their work, and the originality of thought and method evidenced in reports of their work.* For the rest of their careers they will always be evaluated in these terms, and, since no one else knows enough about their work to evaluate it accurately, the judgment of their colleagues in the scientific world will always be more important to them than judgments made by persons outside this area.

SCIENTISTS AS INDIVIDUALS

Now let us consider research-oriented personnel as individuals. The scientist who emerges from the environment of the university laboratory thinks and behaves as he does because of the influence of this environment, or maybe he entered the academic world in the first place because he thinks and behaves as he does; it hardly matters. Whether you believe the chicken or the egg came first, the resultant personality matrix of the scientist is familiar to anyone who has associated at all closely with these men. Men of science differ as individuals from each other, of course, but they differ even more significantly—typically and in general—from other people.

Starting out with a high degree of intelligence, they have been subjected to an intensive and lengthy education from which they have emerged as specialists and professionals in highly complex fields. Perhaps because of the demands made on men intellectually in learning all there is to know about a particular area of technical knowledge, their field of interest tends to be highly concentrated. In thinking about things, people, and events, they tend to be logical, opinionated, impatient, intense, thorough, meticulous, reserved, and clannish.

More often than not, their independent ways of thinking and expressing their thoughts, along with their impatience with abstractions and intuition tend to separate them from other people and to inhibit the outgoing characteristics of their personality. They normally regard conformity as a cardinal sin, and in their efforts to avoid it they often behave in unexpected ways or become interested in the bizarre and unusual.

SPECIAL WORK PATTERN

Careers in the world of science tend to follow a pattern in the years immediately after the scientists have earned their doctorates and as they gain experience and confidence and delve deeply into the intricacies of their special fields. These years and those until they are about 45 are their best creative years.

Few men of science who have not made their reputations by the age of 40 will ever be regarded as at the top of their field. In their late 40's and 50's they begin to slow down, lose their fine edge, and fall behind the advances made in their field. They often retain an intensity and dogged curiosity plus a wealth of experience which enables them to spark and teach younger men, and of course there are those who are able to maintain a high degree of creative effort throughout their working lives. But the average scientist is like the rest of us. He slows down as he grows older. He knows too many things that will not work to be really creative.

The combination of the unusual personal characteristics of most scientists and their knowledge that their golden years careerwise are relatively few often results in behavior which is misunderstood outside the environment which produced it. When they move from the academic to the industrial world, the fact that they think and behave differently makes life difficult for practically everyone in an industrial organization who must deal with them. Businessmen find it hard to understand almost everything such men say and do. They do not understand why scientists who have chosen to work in nonuniversity laboratories cannot conform to the traditional ways of doing things which are built into the organizations supporting such laboratories. They cry, "These men are not at the university any more. They are in business."

Managers expect the demands of the organization to be met by the people working in the research laboratory to the same measure and in the same way these demands are met by other departments of their company. They do not believe that such demands are unreasonable, but they do believe that the counterdemands made by scientists trying to do research in the industrial environment reflect the desire of these men to be coddled, protected, and set apart from the rest of the organization.

Lacking understanding of the research process and the research mind and personality, industrial managers are inclined to meet these demands half-way or not at all—and the climate for research in their organization suffers accordingly.

BALKING AT ORGANIZATION

While what I have said applies most specifically to the research scientist, there is much in common between these men and all professionally trained technical people. Professional training in itself, whether it be in medicine, chemistry, or engineering, appears to predispose those who go through it to unhappiness or rebellion when faced with the administrative process as it exists in most organizations. Scientists and engineers *cannot* or *will not* (and is there any practical difference?) operate at the peak of their creative potential in an atmosphere that puts pressures on them to conform to organizational requirements which they do not understand or believe necessary.

The tendency has been for industrial managers to insist that the scientists working in their laboratories recognize as a truism the often quoted "When in Rome. . . ." They point out that a laboratory supported by the funds of a profit-making organization exists for different reasons and must be run differently than a university laboratory. I have known of industrial research organizations where this belief is carried so far that all workers, including senior scientists, are required to punch a time clock on entering and leaving the laboratory!

This practice is an almost ludicrous example of the extent to which lack of understanding can wreck morale. Even more devastating, however, because they are less obvious, are the subtler attempts of industrial managers to run their laboratories in the same way they run a factory which produces automobiles or soap.

CLIMATE FOR CREATIVITY

Since the dawn of history the professional in any field has been used to and expects a certain deference based on his advanced knowledge and skill. The man of ideas, be he artist, philosopher, or scientist, has always insisted on creating for himself a climate where ideas flow freely or, at the very least, where he can find independence within a group effort dedicated to similar pursuits.

Creative activity cannot be forced. The creative people of this world have always been the free, unchanneled minds, the nonconformists, the individualists, the uninhibited. It is perhaps worth noting that throughout history the greatest additions to our cultural heritage have been made where and when the artist has been revered. It is perhaps even more to the point to note that in Russia, where the scientist is placed on a pedestal, scientific and technical progress is racing ahead today at a pace we are finding difficult to match.

In the Western world the tendency has been to defer to the scientist only, as it were, after the fact—after he has become great, after he has made important contributions—rather than while he is struggling to make them. This is, of course, not always so, but the exceptions are illuminating. Thus:

We can recall the amusing, touching, and fascinating story of Irving Langmuir, who, in the early years of the General Electric Laboratory, almost helpless in affairs of everyday life, was surrounded and supported by people whose major responsibility was

*to smooth the way for him and to see to it that he wanted for
nothing, either personally or professionally. At the end of his
career, speaking at a testimonial banquet in his honor and trying to
explain his productive life at the laboratory, he said, "You know,
I never had to worry about budgets."*

LITTLE TIN GODS?

We do not, of course, want the scientists and other professional technical people working in industrial laboratories to become little tin gods of the
industrial world. But it is highly desirable that we learn to create a climate
which will provide such men, while they are young and relatively unsung,
with the basic atmosphere necessary for the fullest emergence of their creative potential.

If we assume, as we must, that the basic product of the research laboratory is the creativity of research personnel, then the problem seems hardly
different from that facing the plant manager who attempts to produce as
much of that plant's product as possible with the men, materials, and money
available to him. The plant manager knows that he must try to understand
the motivations of his work force if he is going to stimulate productivity
successfully. It appears obvious that those responsible for the management of
research must do the same thing. They must learn to understand the professional researcher and, having succeeded in this, must then work to create
the best possible climate for creative research work.

The optimum climate for creative research can be thought of as being
made up of several separate elements which blend together to form an
atmosphere within which professional workers can discharge their creative
potential with a minimum of distraction or irritation. Most of these elements
follow naturally from the facts previously mentioned about the kinds of
people working in research and the values they prize as a result of academic
training. Yet the makeup of a good climate is always an elusive thing;
certainly it has perplexed many businessmen thus far in our history. Accordingly, I have singled out what might be considered the five most basic
elements of the climate for creative research. Let us look at them in some
detail.

RECOGNITION OF STATUS

As mentioned previously, few companies in the industrial world have found
it easy to assimilate their professional technical employees. Generally speaking, they have tended to assume that the research, engineering, or other
technical components of their organizations should be organized and administered in the same fashion as the rest of the company. In acting on such

assumptions industrial management has failed to recognize the importance to research workers of their professional status. They have chosen to ignore or to find "queer" or "unrealistic" the needs expressed by research workers for *different* organizational structures and *new ways* of administering research organizations.

While most research workers are unusually intelligent and highly individualistic people who would prefer to work for and by themselves, they actually are about the only professional people who cannot practice their profession without some kind of institutional support. When they decide to come to work in industry, they do so, not because they like the idea of working for an industrial organization, but because:

They need the facilities, equipment, and project opportunities that they cannot finance for themselves.

They do not want to have to worry about running a business.

They need the stimulation of colleagues active in the same or allied fields.

They desire or need the somewhat larger salaries obtainable in industry in comparison with those typical of academic institutions.

No wonder many industrial managers feel that in return for the facilities, service, equipment, and larger salaries provided by industry, any scientist should be willing to conform to the requirements of the industrial organization. They cannot help resenting the fact that he appears to want to have his cake and eat it too. One can certainly sympathize with such feelings, but I have found that action *based* on them is almost guaranteed to destroy or seriously limit the creative potential of a research group.

Assuming that the manager recognizes the dangers of insisting on conformance from research personnel and wishes to signal his recognition of their professional status, how exactly can he translate thought into practice? Four policies or rules of action impress me as being especially helpful.

1. *The manager should refuse to impose rules and regulations on the professional staff which imply their lack of intelligence, maturity, or understanding.*

Most industrial organizations have found it necessary to promulgate such rules and regulations as a way of controlling the activities of the *rest* of their work force. A typical example concerns hours of work:

Most companies specify reporting and quitting times, strictly enforce overtime regulations, and, as noted previously, make use of time clocks for both manual and clerical workers. Even where companies have insisted that research personnel punch time clocks just like every one else, managers of other company departments often protest the fact that scientists insist on coming to work at noon and working until midnight whenever they feel like it, instead of working normal hours. They are particularly apt to protest (and with some justification) if the research organization is housed within or close to company plants or offices where employees who observe more traditional hours of work can observe the goings on at the research laboratory.

Recognizing the ill grace with which professional workers take to organizational discipline, many companies have decided that the only way to handle the situation is to remove the research activity physically from the rest of the company, and certainly this is often a workable solution to the problem. If it is not workable, for financial or other reasons, then management must balance the disadvantage of annoying manual and clerical workers against the disadvantage of annoying scientists. Somewhere along the line a cost must be paid.

2. *The manager should insist on consulting with professional workers about plans or proposals which will affect them and/or their work before decisions are made.*

The highly skilled professional worker does not want to be bothered with the details of administration, but he does want to have a chance to express himself concerning policies, plans, or proposals which will directly affect him.

There are numerous ways of doing this, and the desired result will be accomplished if the manager's willingness to consult is sincere and based on real understanding of the need for it. It is rarely necessary to communicate explicitly with every member of the technical staff concerning matters of this sort. Usually formal or informal communication with senior members who can represent the rest of the technical staff is sufficient. Depending on the size and structure of the laboratory organization, communication on these matters may be through formal meetings or informal individual conversations.

No matter how such communication is accomplished, it is important to remember that the manager should never consult with the attitude that plans are fixed and that he is merely letting the men in the organization know about them before they become operative. On the contrary, his assumption is that the ideas of men at the bench could and often do cause him to change or at least modify his own ideas about how things need to be done.

It should be pointed out that if the research manager is as closely in touch with the scientists as he should be, he will already know how they will react to various proposals involving them, and he will be able to act accordingly without specific consultation. He ought to be very sure of his ground before attempting this, however. Even if he thinks he knows, it never hurts to ask a few questions.

3. *Within reasonable limits imposed by the business situation, the man-*

ager should allow researchers considerable freedom to plan their own work. This is perhaps the most controversial suggestion made so far. In many ways it goes against all of the logic of management and impinges on prerogatives which industrial managers usually insist are theirs as managers.

Certainly the need to control expenditures, to budget, and to plan for optimum results from money spent have always been management functions. I am not suggesting that managers of research, or top management, should turn these functions over to scientists at the bench. I *am* saying that scientists at the bench know better than anyone else the areas of technical activity which, if worked on, would produce the desired results. Particularly in regard to basic research, they know best how much work should be done to bring projects to a conclusion.

If a company is not willing to support effort in a researcher's field of interest, the researcher should not be working in the company's laboratory. If a man is hired to do certain work, he is presumably the best man who can be found in his field. This being so, the company should be willing to support him and his work to a degree which has been agreed on in substance before he comes to work in the laboratory.

Needless to say, conditions change—competitively, financially, or in some other way—and long-term projects may have to be revised downward in accordance with these changes. Also, a company cannot always support all the work in a particular field it would like to, and it is unreasonable to expect unlimited support for any but the most vital projects. Limits do have to be imposed—limits which are a product of the total funds available, the caliber of personnel in various fields working at a particular laboratory, the time available for completion of important projects, and other less important factors. The manager cannot and should not expect bench scientists to make final decisions in the planning and control areas. But he can and should give considerable weight while making these decisions to the ideas expressed by his men concerning the work which should be done in their fields.

In this respect a research organization differs considerably from the other parts of a company. The manager of a production organization is supposed to know more about the operation of that organization than anyone else; that is one of the reasons he was made a manager. In research laboratories this is not true. A manager cannot possibly know as much about several complex technical fields as the men who specialize in these fields. Necessarily, therefore, he has to trust them to make realistic proposals concerning future requirements within the budgetary limits imposed on the laboratory as a whole. To this end he can make things easier for himself if he consciously makes a practice of keeping the men at the bench informed about the company situation.

4. *The manager should encourage (but not press) scientific personnel to keep up with their fields and to add to their professional stature by attending meetings of professional societies and writing and delivering technical papers.*

The important distinction here is between encouraging and exerting pressure. Because the over-all standing of a laboratory in the eyes of the scientific world increases in almost direct relation to the number of technical papers presented by laboratory personnel, research managers often are under a natural temptation to prod their personnel to write up and publish the results of their research activities. Certainly it is important both from the point of view of individual scientists and from the point of view of the laboratory itself that these papers find their way into scientific journals. But the need for publication often preoccupies a research manager to such an extent that he places undue emphasis on it.

Certainly, as in the academic world, the ability to do work worthy of publication and the ability to write up results in publishable form is a prerequisite if a scientist is to gain respect and the financial and other benefits which go with an increase in professional stature. The manager of research should make it clear to scientific personnel that this is so. Having made this clear, however, he should tread delicately. There is a difference between making the time available for men to write up their results and insisting that these results be written up when a scientist is preoccupied with furthering subsequent projects.

FACILITIES & ASSIGNMENTS

The second basic element of the climate for creative research involves the need for:

1. First-class facilities for whatever work is to be done in the laboratory.
2. Colleagues of high professional stature.
3. Work assignments of real interest to scientists on the professional staff.

The need for these things necessarily imposes on research management the requirement of careful planning. Many research projects have floundered and died because men were hired to work on them when funds were not immediately available to provide the equipment and facilities required. Many projects have been slowed considerably because the scientists involved were unable to interact with colleagues who could spark their imagination and ask the questions which so often lead to breakthroughs on apparently insoluble problems. Many laboratories have lost good men who were not provided with assignments of real interest to them in their special fields.

I realize, of course, that the realities of industrial life do not make it easy for the research manager to provide in full measure the requisites mentioned above. Given a critical problem in an isolated field of technical work, he often has to hire a good man, put him in a corner with the minimum of facilities, and hope for the best. Given good men in a variety of fields, he often finds it impossible to keep them continuously supplied with critical problems that are of real interest to them. Nonetheless, constant effort should be maintained to give the scientists what they need. If a company is not prepared to do this, it should reappraise the situation *before* it goes about hiring researchers.

RELATION TO ADMINISTRATORS

No scientist wants to be regarded as just "an employee" (even a high-class one). As mentioned earlier, he typically does not really want to work for an organization. The fact that scientists, generally speaking, *must* work for an organization does not make them any the less conscious of their status as professional people. They regard themselves as "entrepreneurs of ideas" —as creative people who require a very special environment if their creativity is to emerge. As such, they believe that they should be served by the organization for which they work, rather than be regulated by it.

More specifically, scientists do not like to think of those men who have chosen to pursue administrative careers in research as their superiors. Regardless of the fact that in an industrial society managers are regarded as superior to the operator or worker, scientific personnel would prefer to regard these men simply as individuals who have chosen to pursue a career in the administration of research rather than a career at the bench.

TROUBLESOME ASSUMPTION

It is in this area of relationships that the atmosphere or climate for creative research may be most easily solidified or destroyed. If the manager of research chooses to regard himself as a manager with all the prerogatives of management, and as a superior with all the ways of behaving implied by superiority, he will find it difficult to create the climate I speak of, no matter how carefully he works to provide the other vital elements of it.

On the other hand, he will find it very difficult to regard himself *as a superior* if his attitude toward his operating colleagues is such that he is able to provide in full measure the other elements of the creative climate. To feel superior, one must believe that he is better at what he is doing than anyone else involved in the activity. While the manager of research may be better at getting things done through people than some of his colleagues at the bench, he cannot realistically assume that he knows enough to be better than most of them at the work they are doing.

Just as a doctor's income is usually considerably higher than the income of the man who administers the affairs of a hospital, the income of a creative scientist may, and often should be, higher than that of the man who manages the laboratory where he works. It is very difficult for men who have been brought up in industrial organizations to understand this radically different point of view. They are steeped in the assumption of our industrial society that the function of management is more important than, and should be compensated more highly than, any work done which does not involve responsibility, authority, and the supervision of the work of others.

The fact remains: the point of view of the scientist, influenced by his years in the university laboratory, is a stubborn reality which, if ignored, will invariably result in a loss of creative potential for the laboratory as a whole.

OPPORTUNITY FOR MOBILITY

If we think of research work as involving a spectrum with basic research at one end and product development at the other, we find it important to organize our laboratories and plan work along the spectrum in such a way that research personnel can move from basic research through applied research to development work as and if their orientation and interests change.

Usually, a young scientist coming to work in industry for the first time would like to continue working in the basic research area which engrossed him while he was at the university. Having already had to reorient his thinking when making the shift from academic to industrial life, he finds it far easier to make the shift if the initial projects on which he is to work are closely allied to the work he was doing before this change in environment.

Unfortunately, many industrial laboratories do not support work at this end of the spectrum. At best, the research they are doing may be termed "applied." This being so, it is of course impossible to assign new men to fundamental research. But in those industrial laboratories large enough to support fundamental research, it has been found very helpful to assign new men to work at the fundamental end of the spectrum so as to give them time to look around and acquaint themselves with the other work being done in the laboratory. This gives the man an opportunity to decide in his own good time and with reference to his performance in comparison with his colleagues whether or not he would like to remain in fundamental research or move along the spectrum to applied research, or even to development work.

It often happens that a man will be doing work in the fundamental area which results in some sort of application. Such men often decide they would like to follow this work into the applied area rather than turn to other projects of a fundamental nature. This follow-up possibility is one great advantage which industry has to offer.

CHOICE OF WORK

There appear to be two major factors which influence a man's decision about the kind of work he wants to do:

1. He is constantly evaluating himself as a scientist in comparison with his colleagues. If he finds that his performance in the fundamental area does not stack up with that of other men at the laboratory, he will often consider work at other points along the spectrum.

2. The other factor involves his personality. If he finds that he enjoys dealing with people in connection with projects on which he may be working, he will be more inclined to move along the spectrum toward development work, where interaction with people from other parts of the company is an important element in the successful completion of work.

The main point to be remembered is that the graduate scientist is unfamiliar with the rewards offered at various points along the spectrum until he has had a chance to accumulate some insights concerning the advantages and disadvantages of particular kinds of work in the industrial environment. Many people concerned with research in industry decry the fact that all young scientists seem to want to do fundamental research. This is heard most often in laboratories where no basic research is done. Managers of such laboratories must recognize the realities of their situation and understand that it is hardly unusual for anyone to want to do the kind of work he has been doing rather than to shift suddenly from one kind to another.

Where no fundamental research is done, this should be made quite plain during the recruiting conversations. It is not unknown for recruiters to dangle the carrot of fundamental research before the noses of graduates, and hope that the new men will quickly adjust to the level of work actually being done in their laboratories. This recruiting technique is not apt to improve the climate for research and often results in such disillusionment that the new man is never able to integrate his preconceptions with the facts, and he soon departs for greener pastures.

A laboratory can be organized and work can be planned so that men can shift jobs quite easily as their interests change and as they become more familiar with the kinds of work being done. In many cases such changes of interest will be obvious to all concerned, and appropriate transfers can be made. In other cases a man may not be aware of his potential in other areas until the possibilities are suggested to him. It should be emphasized, however, that there is a fine line to be drawn between such suggestions and attempts to force men to make such changes because it is more convenient for management.

IMPORTANCE OF RESEARCH

It seems hardly necessary to mention that the final factor in an optimum climate for creative research is management's recognition of the importance of the research effort. But since there are so many companies where this recognition is not apparent, its importance must be stressed.

Certainly it is difficult for top management of companies whose research effort is relatively new to have complete faith in that effort until results are forthcoming, but unfortunately results are often a long time coming and companies that have decided to support a research effort have made a relatively expensive decision. It is perhaps unfortunate that early management reviews of such decisions sometimes take on the aspect of criticism and lack of faith in research management and personnel, with consequent loss of morale. That this is so merely underlines the necessity for quickly establishing and maintaining over the long run an atmosphere of confidence. Once this atmosphere is established, periodic reviews of research policies and financial commitments may be undertaken as necessary without endangering the creative climate.

OTHER PROBLEMS

I have left until last—and for quite brief treatment, at that—any discussion of the problems of recruiting, evaluation, and compensation. These problems are the subject of much attention and worry, yet the most important things I can say about them I have already said. Almost everything depends, it seems to me, on the climate in the laboratory. If the climate is right, the problems either disappear or become much easier to handle; but if the climate is wrong, the problems loom up despite the most carefully devised methods and techniques for alleviating them.

RECRUITING

Take recruiting, for example. It is considered to be one of the most widespread problems in industrial research, yet recruiting practices *as such* are not, in my opinion, the issue at all. The real clue to the trouble would seem to lie in the fact that the list of industrial laboratories where a favorable climate for creative research is known to exist is discouragingly small.

I would venture a guess that a survey of graduate students who are about to take their advanced degrees asking them to name the industrial laboratory they would prefer would result in first choices being limited to four or five laboratories in 90% of the responses. Each year these laboratories get the cream of the crop from the universities. Starting salaries are no higher; in fact, they are often lower than those paid by laboratories that do not have such enviable reputations. The word gets around, and the judgments about various laboratories fed into the scientific grapevine can have devastating effect on a particular company's recruiting problems.

There is, of course, some public relations involved in establishing a good reputation for a particular laboratory, but in the scientific and engineering world public relations will not help a company for long if the creative climate does not exist. Furthermore, public relations for a laboratory cannot be laid on whenever you start a recruiting drive. It is a continuing effort backed up by the ability to tell the story scientists want to hear. If management wants to go to the expense of inviting prospective recruits to visit the laboratory, or if it is eager to maintain close relationships with the university professors who know the prospects as students, that is fine and good; these are very worthwhile practices indeed. But they can only help. They cannot do the main job.

MAKING APPRAISALS

Much the same thing can be said about the problems of evaluating, compensating, and developing the competence of research people. In a poor climate, all kinds of disagreements, failures in communication, and bad feelings arise. They can frustrate all management methods. Yet the same methods will be successful, and frustration will rarely occur, in a good climate. This is so mainly because the members of the technical staff know that their past, present, and future are being evaluated and rewarded by their colleagues in the world of science—not by "management." The setting is therefore a conducive one for efforts to:

Establish criteria that discriminate realistically between men who are merely satisfactory in their technical fields and men who are known (by their colleagues) to be outstanding.

Make performance appraisals that reflect not only the section head's judgment but also the judgment of other technical men who know the researcher well.

Set salary ranges that reflect current market practice.

Emphasize a man's future possibilities and development in periodic discussions with him of his performance.

CONCLUSION

The problems of status, security, and discipline which plague those laboratories lacking an atmosphere of confidence and mutual respect between scientists and management simply do not exist in laboratories where this climate is present. The issue is largely a management one. The essential element for creation of a good climate is a belief on the part of management that the basic product of a research laboratory is the creativity of research personnel, plus a willingness among managers to revise their traditional attitudes so that their behavior while interacting with scientists will reflect this belief.

Does such a conclusion place too much weight on the need for changes in traditional management attitudes? Is it based too much on the assumption that the scientist should be allowed to maintain his values without change? Essentially, I *am* suggesting that management attitudes should change if they are not based on understanding of and respect for the values of scientific personnel. All of my own experience underlines the often stated fact that you cannot try to change professionals into "organization men" if you expect them to be creative. William H. Whyte, Jr. has made this point in no uncertain terms in an important chapter of *The Organization Man*. Among other things, he has this to say:

> *"Management has tried to adjust the scientist to the organization rather than the organization to the scientist. It can do this with the mediocre and still have a harmonious group. It cannot do it with the brilliant; only freedom will make them harmonious."* [1]

At another point Whyte observes:

> *"A company cannot bring in young men and spend several years trying to make them into one kind of person and then expect them, on signal, to be another kind. Cram courses in 'brainstorming' and applied creativity won't change them. If the company indoctrinates them in the bureaucratic skills and asks them to keep their minds on the practical, it cannot suddenly stage a sort of creative play period and then, on signal, expect them to be like somebody else."* [2]

So the point of view implied by my concept of the optimum climate for research is heavily weighted on the side of a need for basic changes in management attitudes. I believe strongly that managers must learn to think about and behave toward the professional employee "differently." If they seek the maximum return of their investment in research, these changes in attitude are also in their own self-interest.

[1] New York, Simon and Schuster, Inc., 1956, p. 213.
[2] Ibid., p. 215.

The Role of the Research Administrator

NORMAN KAPLAN

As research organizations have grown in size and complexity, a new organizational role has tended to emerge—the role of the research administrator. This role is still so new that there has been very little systematic research concerning it.[1] Yet it seems clear that this role is of crucial importance for an understanding of many aspects of large-scale research organizations. This paper is a preliminary report on some of the key definitions and expectations of the role. In the process, some basic conflicts and dissatisfactions which appear to be structural features of the role are discussed. Finally, this analysis offers tentative hypotheses indicating how this developing role is affecting the character and policies of the research organization.

This report is based on a series of empirical studies of research organizations in the physical and natural sciences conducted over the past two years.[2] Formal visits were made to seventeen research organizations in universities, industry, and government, as well as to several independent nonprofit institutes. Although some of these have been in operation for several decades, most were either established after, or have been expanded considerably since World War II. The organizations studied employed from several hundred to several thousand persons, but typically about 600 persons were involved in the research operation.

Reprinted from the *Administrative Science Quarterly,* June 1959, Vol. IV, No. 1, pp. 20–42, with permission of the publisher, the Graduate School of Business and Public Administration at Cornell University. This is one of a series of reports growing out of long-term studies of research organization. Support for this research was given by the United States Public Health Service, National Institutes of Health, Division of Research Grants (RG 5050 and RG 5289).

[1] This statement is made despite the extensive literature in the field of research administration; cf. especially George P. Bush, *Bibliography on Research Administration—Annotated* (Washington, D.C., 1954), which contains over 1,100 references. There has, however, been relatively little emphasis on the emerging role of the top-level research administrator discussed in this paper, as opposed to the research director who may still carry administrative burdens or to administrative roles at the laboratory, section, or division level within a research organization. With rare exceptions, moreover, the literature is anecdotal or polemical, and though illuminating for many purposes does not represent any systematic research effort.

[2] I am indebted to the many research directors, administrators, scientists, and others whose interest and co-operation made these studies possible. A fuller description of the study as a whole will appear in a forthcoming monograph.

An intensive case study was conducted in one organization for over four months; much shorter periods were spent at the other organizations. Data were obtained primarily through interviews, organizational documents, and observations. At most organizations detailed open-ended interviews were conducted with the research director (typically the vice-president for research in industry), the administrator (sometimes called business manager), and other top staff officials, as well as with research scientists. Detailed references and illustrative quotations from specific individual interviews have been kept to a minimum; the emphasis in this paper has been rather on analysis and the implications of the data as a whole.

Before we proceed, one possible source of confusion in terminology concerning the term "administrator" should be noted. The discussion will center around the *role* of the administrator and not on the specific individual occupying the position in any concrete organization. Reference is to the job description, the norms defining the duties, responsibilities, and relationships of the *highest* position in a research organization which is formally concerned with the nonscientific aspects of maintaining the organization. The highest position within the research unit concerned with the scientific aspects will be referred to as the research director or scientific director, regardless of his specific title in any given organization. The key distinction is between responsibility for the direction of the scientific program per se and responsibilities which focus on the nonscientific aspects of the program. While this distinction was recognized in the organizations included in our study, the exact location of the position in the organizational hierarchy as well as the particular definition of the job of research administrator varied from one organization to another.

This paper is divided into three sections. The first discusses varying definitions of the job of the research administrator, sources of recruitment for the position, and the place of the administrator in the formal hierarchy. The second section discusses the role of the administrator in the context of the goals of the research organization and of the scientists who work in it. The third section deals with selected aspects of the role which seem to be of special importance in understanding some of the inconsistent expectations in the role as well as some of the problems which emerge for the organization as a whole.

THE JOB OF THE RESEARCH ADMINISTRATOR

Although the title of research *administrator* (as opposed to director) existed in practically every research organization visited, the actual duties and responsibilities of the research administrator varied from one organization to another. Probably the most restricted definition of the research administrator is that of business manager. In such organizations the research administrator may be responsible for purchasing, payrolls, personnel matters, and maintenance of building, equipment, and service operations (glass washing, construction and maintenance of laboratory equipment and so on). At the other extreme is the least restricted definition, and by far the most difficult to work with, the treatment of the job as a residual category. In addition to all the business aspects already mentioned, the research administrator may be responsible wholly or in part for the allocation of laboratory space within the organization, for relations of a nonscientific nature with the scientific staff, such as arrangements for travel, as well as numerous other activities. Much more will be said in the subsequent discussion concerning the specific duties and responsibilities of the research administrator. For the moment it may be sufficient to note that the range of duties of the research administrator is very wide not only within a given organization but also between organizations.

From one point of view it would appear that insofar as most of the duties of the research administrator resemble those of administrators in other types of organizations, there would be little difference between administrators in research organizations and in other organizations. Contradicting this is the widely held assumption that there is something very different about the administration of a research organization. This difference is sometimes put in terms of the peculiar character and personality of the scientist: he is supposed to be temperamental and to have an inherent dislike for administrators. This, however, is merely a surface manifestation of an attitude toward scientific research organizations which is basically different from the attitude toward other types of organizations. This difference lies in the fact that in a nonresearch organization the administrator is as qualified (or is supposed to be as qualified) as the men whom he directs in his administrative capacity. In a research organization, however, the scientist knows more about his job than the administrator does. This is a fundamental difference and an ever-present source of conflict in a research organization. The first encounter with this conflict is in the recruitment patterns for research administrators.

THE RECRUITMENT OF RESEARCH ADMINISTRATORS

Since the role is such a new one, there are no standard sources for recruiting persons to fill it. Few educational institutions can claim to offer intensive programs of study to train students as research administrators.[3] Probably one of the reasons for the lack of such training is the fact that the

---

[3] American University is one of the few known examples of a nonengineering school that has offered courses in research administration for some time. Schools of industrial engineering, notably Columbia and M.I.T., have also been strong in this area. Most others including the business schools may have an occasional course but no intensive program of study and research in research administration specifically.

job is still not very well defined, nor very well standardized, among organizations. Furthermore, there is little agreement on the extent to which there is a carry-over from general administrative theory and practice to the administration of research.

The first question to be answered before canvassing recruitment sources is whether the administrator has to be a scientist or not. On this question there is a good deal of conflict and heated opinion. Scientists in general tend to argue that the administrator must know what it is that he is administering, that administration is very simple, involving only logic, common sense, and a desire to do things systematically (which a scientist does by definition in scientific research anyway), and that consequently a scientist is pre-eminently fitted for this job. But even among the scientists who argue in this fashion, there is likely to be some contradictory feeling about the use of a scientist in this capacity, i.e., they believe that it is a waste of good scientific talent to use a scientist for administration. So in effect they frequently seem to argue for the use of "poor" scientists for administrative duties.

Since many others share the view that it is wasteful to have a scientist in a full-time administrative position, and since in addition there are many administrators who feel that there is a body of knowledge and practices which must be learned in order to be a good administrator, the argument is put forward that the administrator should be chosen from the ranks of administrators. In actual practice one finds administrators drawn from very diverse sources. Some have come directly from the business schools or the industrial engineering schools, with some smattering of course work in the area of research administration, and have to be trained in the practices of a specific organization. Others have moved from scientific research to research administration, usually from within the same organization. In still other cases administrators have been drawn from other business organizations.

The diverse attitudes expressed toward the administration of research tend to depend on previous experience. For example, it is usually the men who come from business organizations who feel that there is little, if any, difference between the administration of a research organization and the administration of any other department of the company. Usually the differences that are apparent and recognized are clothed in personality terms— that is, scientists are said to have peculiar personalities and consequently one must handle the interpersonal relations more delicately and with somewhat more imagination. From the point of view of the scientist, the more business-oriented the research administrator, the less likely is he to merit the full confidence and co-operation of the scientist. It appears that the scientist likes to think that administration of a research organization involves some special problems which are not the same as those in other industrial operations.

One thing is clear, however, and that is that the sources of recruitment as well as the specific training, attitudes, and values of the research administrator influence the development of certain aspects of the research atmosphere in a particular organization substantially.[4] This is so partly because of the position of the administrator in the hierarchy of the research organization. According to the formal organizational chart, the research administrator helps to run the organization, but from the point of view of many scientists, he hinders the operation of the research organization and should, if he must be included at all, be somewhere down near the bottom.

THE PLACE OF THE RESEARCH ADMINISTRATOR IN THE ORGANIZATIONAL HIERARCHY

The research administrator is hardly ever at the very top but almost always very near the top. Rarely if ever does he have responsibility for the research activity itself, but he is usually included as a part of the director's "team." On the organizational chart he is likely to be found just a little below the director and above most of the scientists. In those organizations publishing reports which include pictures of the key personnel, his picture will usually be included in the report. If the research operation is part of an industrial concern or of a government-bureau operation, the research administrator will usually be included in the top management councils. In contacts with the public, whether they are stockholders, congressional committees, or boards of trustees, the research administrator will usually be included. Yet he is likely to be the only man among high-echelon personnel who is not a scientist and who does not have a Ph.D. As a nonscientist he is regarded by scientists as one of the low men on the totem pole.

Theoretically the research administrator does not make policy nor does he even influence policy. Historically the job arose because the routine and nonscientific aspects of the job of the research director became too burdensome and tedious. In some small research organizations it is still felt that a competent administrative secretary can handle most of these details adequately. Someone must see to it that the scientists get paid, that materials and equipment are ordered and arrive in good condition and within a reasonable time, that technicians and other auxiliary help are recruited as necessary, and so on. But with the growth of the research organization in size and financial status, it has become necessary to employ a full-time administrator. With the employment of a full-time administrator a distinction emerges between the goals of the scientist conducting research and the goals

[4] Although concerned primarily with second- and third-level administrators within a large organization, the evidence from the empirical studies by the Michigan group is extremely suggestive. See especially Howard M. Baumgartel, Leadership Style as a Variable in Research Administration, *Administrative Science Quarterly*, 2 (1957), 344–360; and Donald C. Pelz, Some Social Factors Related to Performance in a Research Organization, *Administrative Science Quarterly*, 1 (1956), 310–325.

of maintaining the organization. Since this is a key distinction in the understanding of research organizations, we turn our attention to this area.

THE GOALS OF THE RESEARCH ORGANIZATION AND THE GOALS OF THE SCIENTIST

The main point at which the goals coincide is in the conduct of research—both the organization and the scientist are agreed on the necessity and desirability of conducting research. To simplify the problem, assume for the moment that this is the sole goal of the scientist. The organization has at least one additional primary goal, namely, the maintenance of the research organization. This is not to say that the research scientist is not concerned with the maintenance of the organization, but only that he is much less concerned than the research director and research administrator. As a goal, the maintenance of the organization may lead to consequences that are in some respects in conflict with the goal of conducting research. For example, one way in which the organization is maintained is through adequate control procedures for receiving and disbursing funds for research. Such controls are considered necessary in order that proper accounting may be made to higher authorities. From the point of view of the scientist this may not always appear as a commendable set of activities or even a very desirable goal, but from the point of view of the director and especially the research administrator this often becomes a primary focus of concern.

The interplay of the values of science and the values of an organization of which science is a major activity has many consequences often unanticipated by either the scientists or the administrators. Thus it is important to the scientist that he be permitted a high degree of freedom in his choice of problem as well as in his decision as to when and how to pursue it. In a sense, therefore, the exact nature of the research problem five years hence is of relatively little importance (and may indeed be unknown) to the individual research scientist. To the director of the research organization and consequently to the administrator, the nature of the research problem five years hence or a year hence is of great importance, especially in terms of the maintenance of the organization. For example, in an industrial research organization it is obvious that the research program must be held within bounds reasonably approximating the profitable interests of the firm. If it is a government research agency, the research program must be held within the bounds set forth in the legislation affecting the agency and its appropriations. So in many research organizations the content of the research becomes of relatively great importance to the top echelons of the organization. This affects the research scientist when decisions have to be made concerning the expansion of some programs at the expense of others, the termination of some programs, and the introduction of completely new programs of research.

In no organization visited has the research administrator himself made such decisions concerning the expansion or termination of a research program. In many, however, the research administrator has influenced such decisions directly or indirectly. He is usually asked for an opinion concerning the availability of space or the possibility of rearranging activities to create more space. Such decisions are ostensibly made on the basis of purely nontechnical considerations, such as the number of square feet of laboratory space available or not being used, and so on. But the administrator usually tries to anticipate the desires of his superior, the scientific director, and when he feels that the scientific director is not enthusiastically in favor of the expansion of a program, for example, he may suggest that there is not really enough room for such an expansion. In some organizations the administrator is deliberately used as a scapegoat for unpopular decisions which the scientific director may have to make.

GOALS AND ROLES

The end product of the research organization is usually an idea or a finding incorporated in a report by the scientists. It may then be developed and end up as a product sold for profit; it may also end up as a published paper or book. Whether or not the research organization is successful or effective is extremely difficult to judge. In any case the research administrator cannot be held directly responsible for the success or effectiveness of the research of the scientists. But the administrator is held responsible for the effectiveness of the operations within the research organization.

If a scientist wants new equipment, if equipment is missing, or if the scientist has exceeded his budget, the administrator must know why. He must have the proper documents to make the organization accountable to the director and to his superiors, whether they are a board of trustees, higher echelons of the company, or perhaps Congress. This gives rise to a number of administrative procedures for obtaining equipment, for keeping inventory of available equipment, for employing new personnel, for traveling to scientific meetings, and so on. As a consequence, practically everything that happens in a research organization is documented and must at some time pass over the desk of the research administrator. Frequently these documents are simply for his information. He cannot evaluate directly the scientific content of a document, but he has to act on it in other ways. Frequently he serves as a source of information, as, for example, when he indicates on a requisition for equipment the fund which is to be charged. Sometimes he must initiate action on his own. He may call to the attention of an investigator the fact that he is temporarily overexpended, that he no longer has any money left in his budget, or that he is not following the proper procedure to obtain equipment. In any case the research administrator becomes an active partner to the research activities of the organization.

The research administrator is frequently the first to admit that he does not have the scientific competence to make many of the decisions that are necessary. But a potential source of conflict within the organization is already apparent, since decisions concerning scientific research are frequently made (in part at least) on the basis of nonscientific criteria. This is at the very heart of the antipathy of the scientist for the administrator and his "red tape."

THE CONFLICT BETWEEN THE ADMINISTRATOR AND THE SCIENTIST

From the point of view of some scientists, the organization would function much more smoothly without a research administrator. But most scientists are more likely to express the opinion that it is the administrator's job to enable the scientist to conduct more research more efficiently. In other words, the best administrator is the one who frees the scientist to do his scientific work and minimizes the routine reports and forms that are admittedly necessary. Most research administrators would be inclined to agree with the statement that their primary task is to free the scientist to do his research. It is only after this general statement that divergences appear. From the preliminary interviews at hand it is possible to describe three types of administrators, with the reservation that these have been somewhat exaggerated to obtain sharper delineations of them.

At the one extreme is the research administrator who feels that freeing the scientist to do research can best be accomplished through rigid adherence to the procedures of the organization. In his view rules, procedures, forms, and other administrative paraphernalia have been developed to assure the greatest efficiency and the greatest control within the limitations of the activities performed. If this is so, it follows that if the scientist would just adhere to the forms and procedures the administrator would have fewer difficulties in trying to iron out problems that have arisen, the organization would run more smoothly, and the scientist would be freer to do his scientific work.

The second type may be found at the other extreme; here the research administrator views his job in somewhat the same way as the scientists do, namely, as a necessary evil. He feels that his job is to save the scientist from as much of the routine forms as possible. He also feels that it is possible, within limits, to circumvent rules and regulations. Just so long as he can construct a reasonable account of what has happened to the funds and the equipment and other such details, he is happy to leave the scientists alone.

Furthermore, he is aware of the fact that the scientist may want to do the same things in different ways at different times for quite legitimate reasons. This of course tends to make his job far more difficult. He not only has more work to do in terms of filling out more of the forms himself, but he also has more adjudicating and more manipulating to do insofar as he has less information for his own reports to the director and other superiors.

The third type of administrator is somewhere in between these two extremes. He tries to introduce as much flexibility as he thinks possible into the administrative procedures, but at the same time he would like to have as much information as possible for his own security. He is constantly caught in the cross fire between the demands of the organization as he sees them and the demands of the scientists as they are transmitted in complaints, bickering, and low morale. In this instance, he is frequently an unhappy pawn in the conflict between the administrative goal of maintaining the organization and the scientific goal of conducting research. He is free neither to change the rules to any considerable extent so as to minimize the scientist's administrative burden, nor to increase the burden very much to make his own job easier. He must wait until enough complaints filter up to the scientific director to cause the latter to ask him why there is so much red tape. After reducing some of the red tape, he may later be asked why there is inadequate information and documentation for reports to the controlling body interested in the nontechnical aspects of operation. Consequently he is a man frequently caught in the middle of the organizational conflict.[5]

Frequently the scientists within an organization tend to view their problems with the administrator in terms of his personality characteristics.[6] Thus the closeness with which an administrator approximates any one of the three types just mentioned is frequently assumed to be a function of different personality types. The rigid authoritarian personality is viewed as inevitably being of the first type, and the nonauthoritarian and flexible personality is viewed as being primarily of the second type. Closer examina-

[5] Terms such as "man in the middle" and "marginal man" have been widely applied to a much more typical industrial role—that of the foreman. See, for example, F. J. Roethlisberger, The Foreman: Master and Victim of Double Talk, Harvard Business Review, 23 (1944–1945), 283–298; and Donald E. Wray, Marginal Men of Industry: The Foremen, American Journal of Sociology, 54 (January, 1949), 298–301. While the analogy between the role of the foreman and that of the research administrator breaks down at many crucial points, the study of such roles with built-in conflicts appears to be a particularly fruitful way in which to approach general problems of organizational structure.

[6] There is frequent and marked reliance, by scientists as well as administrators, on personality as an explanatory variable for a wide variety of problems. Cf., for example, Baumgartel, op. cit., p. 345, for a similar reaction concerning "American administrators."

tion reveals the possibility that, although personality is a factor, for the most part it is the organization and its environment which determine the behavior of the research administrator. Some of these factors may now be discussed briefly.

THE CHARACTERISTICS OF HIGHER AUTHORITY

The specific nature of higher authority will of course vary in industry, government, universities, and private nonprofit institutes of research. It may be Congress ultimately for a government agency, a board of trustees for an institute or a university, or a board of directors for an industry. The greater the number of nonscientists in higher authority, the greater probably will be the demand for controls and information about the nonscientific aspects of the research operation.[7]

If the board of directors or its counterpart does not understand the goals of research scientists, it is likely to demand information on budgets, the disbursement of funds, the purchase of equipment, the number of people working, the square footage allowed to various operations, and so forth. In other words, it will tend to require the kind of information that its members get from the organizations with which they customarily deal. Under such a board the research administrator is likely to be required to collect such information and to be more rigorous in his procedures; consequently, he will have to require the scientists to be more rigorous with respect to such administrative procedures. To this extent the policies and the wishes of higher authority help to define the role of the research administrator.

THE CONTROL AND SOURCES OF FUNDS

If the research organization is dependent on funds from several sources, such as private foundations or government agencies, it is very likely that a number of different accounting and reporting procedures will be required. One government agency may require an annual report, another semiannual reports. Some of these agencies may require financial accounting at stated intervals and others only at the end of the grant period. In any case, to the extent that there are a number of such sources the problem of the research administrator becomes immensely complicated as it is usually his responsibility to help meet these various reporting dates and reporting requirements. In so doing he may institute procedures which the scientist will view as impediments to his research. In fulfilling these requirements, the administrator becomes, in a sense, the agent of these granting agencies.

---

[7] This hypothesis will be explored in a forthcoming paper on the nature of control and authority in research organizations; here its importance can only be noted briefly in relation to one facet of the research administrator's role.

THE SCIENTIFIC DIRECTOR

On the face of it most scientific directors are by definition primarily interested in the scientific research and only secondarily interested in the administrative procedures necessary to sustain it. However, procedures and policies originally designed for one purpose may frequently be made to serve other purposes as well. Thus the necessity for financial accountability and for control of expenditures and other policies affecting the research instituted by the directing body become a major point of control in the hands of the director. The director can use the necessity for such information and such controls as a way of effecting and changing policy. For example, he can stop a project which he feels is not making sufficient progress by informing the project director that it has been impossible to secure additional funds for it. The scientific director can go even one step further; he can get the administrator to do this for him. For example, a scientist reported his director's remarks as follows:

It is not a question of the worthwhileness of this particular project —I, of course, think it's extremely worthwhile—but it's out of my hands. My administrator tells me that the budget is overdrawn and the line item from which this project comes is exhausted. My hands are tied. There's nothing we can do. I'm awfully sorry but you understand it is not my decision.

Another tactic, frequently used by research directors, is to obtain the advice of the administrator concerning the availability of space for a new project suggested by one of the research scientists. Again the decision is not the director's since he can still assure the scientist that he personally favors the project but that the administrator informs him that there is no space available for it.[8] The important point is that the character of a director, his policies, and his goals also serve to influence the nature of the research administrator's job, and what is even more important, the character of the scientific research that is conducted in the organization.

The conflict of roles and goals in the research organization is empha-

[8] Of course, the scientist in question may be aware of the tactics of the director, as is suggested in the remarks just quoted in the text. Whether it serves the director better to have the scientist think that it is the administrator who is blocking his project is a question. Judicious use of this tactic by a director may deflect the potential hostility of the scientist onto the administrator and thus place the director in the position of a man caught in essentially the same organizational vise as the scientist. There is always the danger that the tactic may boomerang if the scientist becomes convinced that the director is not taking responsibility for his own decisions. There is also a potentially serious problem for the scientist in that he may be confused concerning the actual criteria used to reject his idea.

sized further by the divergent perceptions of the individuals involved of the rationale for various administrative procedures. A scientist is usually, albeit reluctantly, willing to accept a certain minimum interference as constituted by these forms if he feels that they are essential for the maintenance of the organization, even though he may not agree with the administrator on the primacy of this goal. If on the other hand the scientist feels that some of the forms are peripheral to this purpose (he usually feels that most forms are peripheral to *his* purposes), then dissatisfaction and ill feeling may result. He is especially irritated if he feels that the forms not only are taking up some of his valuable time and thus keeping him from research, but are actually delaying his research, as for example when he cannot get a piece of equipment because the forms have not been filled out correctly.

Furthermore, scientists' attitudes toward administrative procedures tend to be influenced by perceptions of the administrator's motives. If the scientist feels that the forms or the procedures are simply for the convenience of the administrator and his staff, he attributes them to base motives of the administrator.

Even when all would agree that a certain procedure or form is necessary for the conduct and maintenance of the organization, the administrator may feel that the burden of carrying out the procedure should be shared by those who benefit from it. A research administrator examining a form which requires information that he feels is at the scientist's fingertips and could thus be efficiently filled out by the scientist may, without considering the implications, insist that the scientist fill out the form since in the last analysis this is the most efficient way. The scientist's analysis of the over-all efficiency of the organization does not usually take into account the operations of the administrative functions. Consequently, even though he has the information at his fingertips and even though it may take the administrator somewhat more time to look it up and fill in the form, he may consider this the most efficient way to get more research done.

Such a view on the part of the scientist reinforces the ambiguity of the research administrator's role. To the extent that the scientist can insist that even though it may be more efficient for him to fill out the form the research administrator should do it since the scientist's activity is more important, he reduces the status of the research administrator. On the other hand, to the extent that the research administrator is successful in spreading his own administrative load to the scientists, he asserts the superiority of his own position. It is small wonder then that many organizations are faced with a large number of such minor conflicts of interest.

Having reviewed briefly some of the sources of ambiguity in the role of the research administrator inherent in the conflict of goals in a research organization, we now turn to some of the other problems involved in the role. In particular, we wish to discuss some of the relationships of the research administrator outside as well as inside the research organization.

OTHER ASPECTS OF THE ROLE OF THE RESEARCH ADMINISTRATOR

The ambiguity of the role and the conflict in goals which may exist in the research organization affect still other aspects of the research administrator's role. These assume increasing importance as they, in turn, affect the research operation, the character of the research administrator, and the research organization as a whole.

THE ACCOMPLISHMENT OF THE GOALS OF THE ORGANIZATION

In any report or assessment of the accomplishments of the organization, the research administrator, if mentioned at all (and he usually is mentioned), must list his accomplishments adjacent to the obviously more significant accomplishments of the scientists. At best he can say that his work as administrator helped to advance the research work. He cannot take any credit for the accomplishments of the research workers themselves in any other fashion. The system of assigning priorities and fame in science usually has not included the research administrator. As one research administrator noted ruefully, "About the only satisfactions we do get is when a scientist comes in and thanks us for having made some task easy for him. But these are few and far between—more often he comes in and berates us or complains."

The administrator may have little or no standing in the scientific community, but what is his standing in the administrative community? Again the most he can say is that he "helped," although he was not directly a member of the team that made the achievement. Administrators in other types of organizations might have difficulty understanding the completely auxiliary role that he played. In most other types of organizations the man in the analogous position would have a more direct hand in the accomplishment of the goals of the organization and, consequently, a larger share in the rewards for such accomplishments. Moreover the goals of top administrators in other types of organizations are more likely to be essentially similar to the goals of others in the organization.

POLICIES AND PROCEDURES

The problem of policies and procedures alluded to previously is important here in the context of the comparison which a research administrator might make of his own role with that of chief executives in other types of organizations. In a research organization the lines between the formulation of policy and its execution are considerably sharper. Even in those instances mentioned earlier where the research administrator influences policy, he always does this with the tacit understanding that he is carrying out the research director's desires.[9] At best such policies as the research administrator may formulate are considered necessary evils by the scientists in the organization.

RELATIVE STATUS WITHIN THE ORGANIZATION

As noted previously, the research administrator is usually very near the top of the formal hierarchical structure. His informal status within the organization, however, is often very near the bottom. For one thing, he does not wear a laboratory coat, which is usually a distinct mark of status among the investigators themselves. For another, his salary, while relatively high in most organizations, is likely to be exceeded by that of an increasing number of senior scientists who have few if any administrative duties. In other words, a man who is listed below the research administrator in the formal organizational hierarchy may actually be earning a higher salary than the man listed above him.[10]

Still another aspect of status is intimately related to the possibilities for upward mobility. As has been noted, the research administrator is usually as high as he can go within the research organization itself. With some notable exceptions, the research director is usually a full-fledged scientist. In most cases the research administrator cannot become the research director. He can and occasionally does leave the research operation and go into other areas of the parent organization in order to move into higher echelons. This is true in industry, but in an independent research organization with no other ties, the research administrator is as high as he is ever going to be. Many research administrators have pointed out to me that if they were in an organization not involving scientific research they would have risen to a higher position.[11]

[9] For a discussion of this distinction between the administration and formulation of policy in general, see Herbert A. Simon, "Recent Advances in Organization Theory," in Stephen K. Bailey *et al., Research Frontiers in Politics and Government* (Brookings Lectures, 1955; Washington, D.C., 1955), pp. 23 ff.

[10] This is a growing trend in research organizations, in industry and elsewhere. While contrary to accepted organizational doctrine, the mechanism of a "dual hierarchy" is gaining acceptance as a way of rewarding the scientist without taking him out of research into administration. For a discussion of how one company has worked out this dual hierarchy, see George L. Royer, "Evaluation Programs," offprint of a paper presented at the 34th Annual Meeting of the American Institute of Chemists, Akron, Ohio, May 23, 1957, 12 pp. This mechanism is also discussed in Herbert A. Shepard, Nine Dilemmas in Industrial Research, *Administrative Science Quarterly,* I (1956), esp. pp. 305–306; Francis Bello, Industrial Research: Geniuses Now Welcome, *Fortune,* Jan. 1956, pp. 145 ff.

[11] Despite the many frustrations experienced by the research administrator, our own very limited observations indicate a very low incidence of turnover in the job.

The scientist within such an organization, however, has several avenues for getting to the "top." It is possible for him to become the chief executive, the research director. If he is not inclined in this direction, there are other kinds of "top" positions, which have no relationship to the formal hierarchy. In many research organizations the scientist who has complete freedom in defining his program of research, its size, personnel, and laboratory space, and who commands a salary at or near the highest salary paid by the organization, is frequently considered to be at the "top" by other scientists. Not so with the research administrator, who has only the normal channels for upward mobility, which in his case are closed.

THE TECHNICAL SKILLS OF THE RESEARCH ADMINISTRATOR

While there may be some disagreement as to whether administration is a science or an art and whether there is an adequate body of knowledge for the study of administration, it is agreed that a body of practices and skills which can be transmitted to others has grown up around the administrative role. Some argue that these skills can be as easily applied to one type of organization as to another. Some even argue that skills applicable in any type of organization can be applied to a scientific research organization, but they are in a minority. Many are still inclined to argue that the research organization requires of the administrator a fairly unique set of skills.

Part of the problem lies in the fact that the model for most other types of organizations has been fairly well worked out over the last half-century or so. Whether this organizational model can be improved upon or not is another question, but the fact is that considerable discussion and experimentation have taken place concerning problems such as span of control, levels of organization, communication problems within and among the levels, and formal and informal organization. This is not the case with the research organization, which is still an emerging model. There is considerable disagreement as to whether the model can be simply borrowed from other types of operations and used with minor modifications in the research operation. As one vice-president for research put it: "There are just too many chiefs and too few Indians in a scientific research operation to use the normal organizational models."

One of the other fundamental problems from the point of view of an administrator is that the lines of authority, decision making, and communi-

---

Whether or not these observations are confirmed on a wider scale, more attention should be devoted to some of the positive rewards and satisfactions of the job. While our preliminary data are too scanty on this point, there are some suggestions of counterbalancing satisfactions, especially in the social community, where the research administrator apparently enjoys the reflected glory of being associated with scientists and scientific research.

cation are almost always on two levels, the scientific and the administrative. The division is not always distinct but it is always present, and the ambiguity as well as the necessity for the distinction are ever-present sources of difficulty in a research organization. Given these factors, the question arises: What kinds of skills can the research administrator use in a research organization? Some have argued that he must adapt the usual skills as best he can to a new situation which is not yet well defined while at the same time he perfects new techniques for research administration specifically. In other words, the skills that the research administrator does have may not be viewed as being the best possible skills for an administrator in a research organization; consequently, the research administrator is often stripped of even this aspect of his role and status.

REFERENCE GROUPS OF RESEARCH ADMINISTRATORS AND RESEARCH SCIENTISTS

The structural constraints on the kinds of reference groups possible and considered desirable for research administrators is of considerable interest in the analysis of these roles and of research organization. From what has already been noted, it is to be expected that the reference groups for administrators and scientists would differ both in character and in location. From the evidence at hand this expectation seems to be confirmed. The research administrator is oriented toward management and administration, toward the internal organization, and in general toward groups not concerned with science as such. In contrast, the scientist is not oriented toward any of these groups but toward science, particularly his own area of specialization, and generally to the world of science outside his organization.[12] This contrast in reference groups serves to increase the distance between these two groups and between these two roles.

There are many indications of such differences. For example, research administrators tend to read journals of the American Management Association or other types of executive journals. They tend to belong to associations in the fields of management and administration. Since these are only slightly concerned with research administration, the major focus is on the management of industry or the management of large-scale government operations. Most often it tends to be the former, and thus a concern for efficiency as related to profit is frequently introduced.

---

[12] This distinction has frequently been discussed in terms of Robert K. Merton's "local" and "cosmopolitan" types. See Shepard, Nine Dilemmas in Industrial Research, pp. 298 ff. In the Michigan studies a similar distinction was made between "science orientation" and "institutional orientation." See Pelz, Some Social Factors Related to Performance, pp. 311 ff. Although we can only allude to it briefly here, a forthcoming paper will attempt to build on this distinction through the use of reference group theory and especially through an examination of the implication of differences in orientation of the various participants in a research organization, not just the scientists.

If the research administrator is so fortunate as to live in a large metropolitan area where there are other research organizations, he may have an important informal reference group in research administrators employed by other organizations. A number of these informal groups were encountered in interviews for this study. If, on the other hand, there are few or no other research organizations in his area, then the research administrator tends to interact most frequently with executives in other types of organizations.

The research administrator tends to identify with the organization itself. To the extent that there is any derived benefit and prestige from being associated with scientists and scientific research, the research administrator obtains some measure of it in this fashion. More important, however, is the fact that his job in a sense forces him to put the organization first in his thinking insofar as his major function is to maintain the integrity of the organization.

To the scientist, on the other hand, identification with the organization, if it exists at all, is conditional and can be, and frequently is, cut off at a moment's notice. Should the organization no longer provide him with the opportunity to conduct research freely, he will begin immediately to seek a position elsewhere.[13] His identification is with his field. His reference groups, as noted, tend to a large extent to be outside the organization, and he can maintain his position with these outsiders to the extent that he can conduct research which earns their approbation. Rewards which are solely internal to the organization and which are not recognized outside it tend to have relatively little value to the research scientist. Essentially the opposite is true for the research administrator. Such differing perspectives lead to the cultivation of different reference groups, aggravating some of the initial disruptive and divisive elements in the relationship of the research administrator to the research scientist.

SUMMARY AND CONCLUSIONS

The role of the administrator is far from standardized, as is to be expected from the fact that the research organization itself is far from standardized. This study of some aspects of the role of the research administrator reveals a number of points of strain and potential conflict between the adminis-

---

[13] The scientist is being stereotyped here to some extent in order to emphasize the contrast between the reference groups considered appropriate for him and those considered appropriate for the research administrator. The Michigan studies have shown that scientists may be either "institution" or "science" oriented. Cf. Pelz, *op. cit.* Nevertheless, our data suggest that even where the scientist is oriented to the organization the basis and quality of the orientation differs from that of a research administrator. The fact that scientists, as compared with administrators, perceive many more opportunities to move to other research organizations is only one significant indication of the difference.

trator and scientist. These promise to be important for an understanding of many of the problems encountered in large-scale organizations of research. This analysis is necessarily preliminary because of the relatively small number of organizations studied, and the statements made should be regarded merely as hypotheses worth further study and testing in other research organizations.

The research up to this point reveals the following tentative picture of the role of the research administrator: he is a man in the middle—frequently caught between the conflicting demands of the scientists and those of higher authority within the organization. He is, in significant ways, different from his nearest counterparts in organizations not concerned with research, and he is also unlike the scientists with whom he has to deal in the research organization. His role in the organization is an ambiguous one primarily because the whole problem of organization for research is far from solved. He is frequently viewed as an impediment to the research but a necessity for the organization. He does not usually have the technical skill to make scientific decisions, yet he is usually involved in such decisions. He can never take direct credit for the accomplishments within the organization but must always be ready to receive the complaints of those who feel that he interferes with the accomplishment of these goals. His position in the hierarchy in formal terms is usually high, but in informal terms it is usually low. His status within the organization from the point of view of most of the people with whom he deals is also very low. His job is unrewarding in economic terms as compared with what he could earn in other types of organizations in a similar position, since his salary is held down somewhat by the fact that the scientists themselves have a relatively low salary scale. He can never reach the top of the research organization but must remain an auxiliary near the top. The usual recognition of the necessity of administrative practices is absent among research scientists. The administrator's training and education is usually inferior to that of a large proportion of those below him in the formal hierarchy. His reference groups differ from those of the others in that they tend to be outside of science and outside of research.

In addition to the necessity for much more systematic work on the role of the research administrator, certain other questions must be attacked to aid in the understanding of research organization. Probably the basic question is the type of organization most suitable for the conduct of research. It is by no means widely believed that large-scale organization and research necessarily go together. But where the benefits of large-scale research organization are said to accrue to research as they do to other types of activities, the research administrator plays a key role. Much more needs to be known about the nature of the position as well as the kind of man best suited for this role in a large-scale organizational framework.

Research Administration and the Administrator: U.S.S.R. and United States

NORMAN KAPLAN

In a recent paper I described the newly emerging role of the research administrator in the U.S. and tried to analyze a number of conflicting definitions and problems that stem primarily from the organizational structure in which the role is embedded.[1] During the summer of 1959, an attempt was made to compare these findings on the American research administrator with the situation of the Soviet research administrator. Some preliminary results of this comparative study are reported in this paper.[2]

After a brief description of the study in the U.S.S.R., I will outline a typical large-scale Soviet medical research organization. The administrator is located in this structure and his role is then described and compared with that of his counterpart in American research organizations. Although there are many similarities between these two roles in the two societies, some basic differences emerge, which are of potential significance for both the concrete study of research organization and for organizational theory generally. In a later section of the paper, some of the factors that may account for this basic difference are explored. Finally, some implications of this analysis are discussed.

DESCRIPTION OF THE STUDY

One of the most important objectives of the study in the U.S.S.R. was

Reprinted from the *Administrative Science Quarterly*, June 1961, Vol. VI, No. 1, pp. 51–72, with the permission of the publisher, the Graduate School of Business and Public Administration at Cornell University.

[1] Norman Kaplan, The Role of the Research Administrator, *Administrative Science Quarterly*, 4 (1959), 20–42.

[2] Revision and extension of a paper read at the 127th annual meeting of the American Association for the Advancement of Science, December, 1960. Some of the ideas were initially developed in a lecture on "Comparative Research Organization," delivered at the Fifth Institute on Research and Development Administration, American University, Washington, D.C., April, 1960. This investigation is part of a larger series of studies on the organization of scientific research. Grateful acknowledgment is made for the support of these studies by a Public Health Service research grant (RG 5289), from the National Institutes of Health, Division of Research Grants, U.S. Public Health Service.

229

to obtain data on the organizational structures and practices in research institutes that would permit comparisons with results previously found in the U.S. The study was therefore restricted to research institutes in the medical field, and especially those concentrating on cancer research, so as to examine roughly similar types of organizations engaged in roughly similar activities in both the U.S.S.R. and the U.S.

In all, I interviewed the director or deputy director, as well as a number of department heads and other scientists, in thirteen medical institutes located in Moscow, Leningrad, and elsewhere in the U.S.S.R.[3] Interviews were frequently conducted in a mixture of English, French, and German, as well as Russian. Sometimes we relied on interpreters almost entirely, and in general, either lay or scientific interpreters were almost always available. A qualitative interview guide was used, and on the whole the cooperation in answering questions very specifically was exemplary. Most of the interviews lasted a minimum of two hours, and many were much longer. In a few instances it was possible to conduct several interviews with the same person on successive days.

Most of the organizations visited were under the jurisdiction of the Academy of Medical Sciences, and the majority of these were concerned primarily with cancer research.[4] The smallest institute had over two hundred people while the largest had over a thousand research workers including auxiliary staff. In size, scope, and nature of specific research activities, these institutes were not unlike many to be found in many parts of the U.S.

[3] Most of the Soviet institutes visited were selected prior to my arrival in the U.S.S.R. on the basis of available knowledge here concerning their focus on medical research generally, and on cancer problems in particular. I am particularly grateful for the advice and suggestions offered by the late Dr. C. P. Rhoads, director of the Sloan-Kettering Institute, and Dr. John R. Heller, then director of the National Cancer Institute, and now president of the Memorial Sloan-Kettering Cancer Center. The selection of institutes, as well as initial contact with their directors prior to my arrival in the U.S.S.R., was greatly facilitated by the availability of an excellent document compiled by David P. Gelfand, *A Directory of Medical and Biological Research Institutes of the U.S.S.R.* (U.S. Public Health Service Publication No. 587; Washington, 1958). Finally, Mrs. Galina V. Zarechnak, of the National Library of Medicine, very kindly made available a prepublication draft of her study of the history and organization of the Soviet Academy of Medical Sciences, which provided valuable background information helpful in the selection procedure as well as in the subsequent interviews with Soviet medical scientists.

[4] I am pleased to record my gratitude to the institute directors, vice-directors, and other Soviet scientists who helped me to explore some of these problems of research organization. I am especially grateful to Professor S. A. Sarkisov, a member of the Presidium of the Academy of Medical Sciences, and Professor N. N. Blokhin, the director of the Institute of Experimental Pathology and Therapy of Cancer in Moscow (Dr. Blokhin has since become the President of the Academy of Medical Sciences), for their help in facilitating my visits and interviews, and in general, for enhancing my welcome at the various medical institutes in the U.S.S.R.

STRUCTURE OF A RESEARCH INSTITUTE

As one might expect where most of the institutes studied are under the jurisdiction of a single organization, namely the Academy of Medical Sciences, the basic structure tends to be the same in most of the institutes.[5] Differences were, of course, encountered but these appear to be related primarily to differences in size and especially to differences in emphasis with respect to clinical operations. In this section the basic outline of the structure encountered in most research institutes is described in general terms. No claim is made that this structure is typical of all medical research institutes in the U.S.S.R., let alone all scientific research institutes. My interviews lead me to believe, however, that the deviations and differences which may exist in other research institutes are not basic ones. This will necessarily be an exploratory account, since the primary purpose here is to locate the role of research administration and the administrator.

The director is the chief executive of the research institute and has over-all responsibility for the conduct of the research program and the maintenance of the research institute and its staff. He is appointed by the Presidium of the Academy of Medical Sciences for a three-year term which is renewable indefinitely. Directly below him in the organizational hierarchy is the deputy director or vice-director and typically the title contains the phrase "for research." He assists the director, acts for the institute in his absence, and has primary responsibility for the conduct and co-ordination of the scientific program of the institute. Below the vice-director are the departments into which the institute is divided with the department heads or chiefs reporting directly to the vice-director. The number of departments as well as their composition depends upon the size of the institute and the scope of its program. Below the department heads, one is likely to find a number of laboratories with the laboratory chiefs reporting directly to the department heads.

The basic outline of this type of structure is very familiar and certainly resembles that of most larger medical research institutes in the U.S. and many European countries. Parenthetically, it might be noted that I saw only one organization chart at all the institutes visited, although most of the directors with whom I talked were quite willing to help me draw one up.

Two other elements are always present in the organizational structure

---

[5] For a general, and somewhat critical, review of the history and organization of the Academy of Medical Sciences based primarily on Soviet documentary sources, see: Galina V. Zarechnak, *Academy of Medical Sciences of the U.S.S.R.; History and Organization, 1944–1949* (Public Health Monograph No. 63; Washington, 1960). See especially her charts and descriptions of Soviet research institutes, pp. 12 ff.

and should be described in some detail. The first is the Scientific Council (*Soviet*) which is nominally responsible for the over-all research plan of the institute, evaluating progress of the institute and of individuals, and in general dealing with any organizational or scientific problems that may arise. The director of the institute is the chairman of the Council which is made up of all or most of the department heads. The Party is represented formally on this Council by the secretary of the local Trade Union of Scientific Workers who is normally one of the regular scientists on the staff. Senior scientists who may not be department heads may also be on the Council. In addition, at least two eminent scientists, usually in related fields, but always from other institutes, are also members of this Council. The total number of members varies, of course, according to the size of the institute, and most of the ones about which information is available vary from about twelve to about thirty-five members. The frequency of meetings varies from institute to institute, but in general there are regularly scheduled meetings once or twice a month although they may occur as often as once a week.

The Council appears to combine in a single group the functions normally incorporated in two separate groups in most scientific research institutes in the U.S. One function is that of executive committee for the institute as a whole, which in the U.S. would be composed typically of department heads, the vice-director for research, and the director as chairman, as in the U.S.S.R. The second function is typically carried out by a separate group in many institutes in the U.S. a d is called a scientific council made up of scientists who are not regular members of the organization, but who are invited once or twice a year (or perhaps more frequently) to evaluate the scientific work of the institute. This scientific council in most U.S. institutes has no operating functions. It is difficult to know whether the scientific council in the U.S.S.R. institute would appear above the director's box on an organization chart, or whether it would more appropriately be on the same level as that of the director, with a dotted line denoting a primarily advisory function.

Finally, we turn to the position of the research administrator. Every institute visited has such a person and the title is usually a variant of "vice-director for administration" or simply "director of administration." As in most U.S. organizations, he has primary responsibility for finances, supplies, apparatus, equipment, furniture, repairs, maintenance, and other such service activities. The size of his staff tends to vary with the size of the institute as a whole and in some of the larger institutes the administrator may have a staff of over thirty persons working in a number of separate departments. The administrator's position in the organizational hierarchy is also difficult to locate precisely. He reports to the director of the institute but he has very little if anything to do with any other scientists. Although he reports directly to the chief executive, he is not a part of the executive committee nor is he typically considered a member of the executive hierarchy. Interestingly enough, I did not meet him personally at most of the institutes visited, with one or two exceptions, when the director wanted a precise figure or fact I had asked about and he consulted the administrator. With this background, it is now possible to examine the role of the research administrator in more detail.

ROLE OF THE RESEARCH ADMINISTRATOR

As already noted, the administrator reports directly to the director of the research institute and may have a fairly large staff. Furthermore, he is responsible for more or less the same kinds of activities as is his counterpart in the U.S. Some differences begin to appear as we note that the Soviet administrator is typically trained in what would be the American equivalent of business accounting and business procedures. It is not considered essential, or even desirable (as it is frequently considered here in the U.S.), that he have a scientific background or that he come from the ranks of the scientists. This difference becomes somewhat accentuated when we note his absence in greeting a foreign visitor, where the analogous situation in an American institution would find the administrator one of the more important men present at such a meeting. This is particularly to be expected when that visitor is more interested in problems of organization than in the substantive content of the work of the institute.

It is at first surprising to hear him referred to as the "bookkeeper" and his job described essentially as a bookkeeping one with few if any policy-making responsibilities. This term as used there implies more than simply the keeping of the financial books, referring also to "keeping the books" on maintenance, equipment, and so on. In many respects, we find that he occupies a position sometimes designated in American organizations as that of chief clerk. He has administrative responsibility for the clerks who work under him but has no other decision-making functions.

It is not surprising, therefore, to find that typically he is paid considerably less than most of the research scientists—normally only somewhat above the research technician with no advanced training. While laboratory technicians may earn approximately twelve to fifteen hundred rubles per month and the director of a research institute may have a base salary of at least five to six thousand rubles a month, the chief administrator earns approximately twelve hundred to two thousand rubles per month.[6] The range for

---

[6] These are 1959 rubles. It is difficult to translate these earnings into terms which permit suitable comparisons with the U.S. Furthermore, it is unnecessary to do so for our purposes here since the object is to show that the administrator's salary tends to be much closer to that of technician or beginning scientist, and not, as in the U.S., closer to that of the senior scientists, associate directors, or even department heads.

the administrator indicates primarily the differences in size of organization and length of experience. A researcher starting out with the first advanced degree probably earns about eighteen hundred to two thousand rubles a month. In short, there can be little doubt that the chief administrator, who is referred to as the bookkeeper and whose duties correspond to those of a chief clerk, is in fact paid as one would expect a bookkeeper or chief clerk to be paid compared with the more technically trained research scientists in the research hierarchy.

For the research administrator there is little or no conflict concerning authority and control over science and scientists. These are exercised by the scientists themselves and not by a lay administrator. The Soviet administrator, when compared to his American counterpart, occupies quite a subordinate position in the research organization, despite the fact that the two have essentially the same titles and many of the same functions in a research organization.

The American research administrator is paid a good deal more than most American scientists in the same research organization and frequently is paid nearly as much as many senior scientists. In the organizational hierarchy, he is always at or near the top of the organizational structure. Although his duties may correspond very closely to those described for the Soviet administrator on a formal basis, the American administrator has many decision-making functions, overtly or covertly.[7] Many of these, incidentally, seem to stem from the unwillingness of the research director to make the decisions himself. The American research director often feels that he has little time for purely administrative decisions, and furthermore, the administrator is often thought to be better equipped to make them. In the U.S. it is often considered desirable for an administrator to have a scientific background, and not infrequently chief administrators in research organizations are recruited from the ranks of scientists. The American administrator is definitely a public figure and in fact serves to save the research director's time in public relations. He frequently exercises authority over scientists with regard to the kind of equipment they can get, space allotment, and adherence to budgets, although much of his authority is exercised indirectly, frequently with the budget or some such impersonal instrument as the indirect mechanism employed.[8]

Finally, when the American administrator is not a scientist, it is not very likely that he can move up much higher in the scientific research institute. This is, of course, similar to the Soviet situation. But frequently the American administrator, even without scientific training, who moves

[7] The observations on the role and status of the American research administrator are drawn largely from an earlier paper. Cf. Norman Kaplan, *op. cit.*

[8] Kaplan, *ibid.*, p. 33.

out of the scientific realm whether in the same organization (e.g. an industrial firm or the government) or whether from an organization in one institutional sphere to another, can move up very high in the organizational hierarchy by virtue of his *expertise* as an administrator.

In sum, the American research administrator is better paid, compared with his Soviet counterpart and with scientists in the research organization. He enjoys much higher prestige in America and, of course, he is the source of many more conflicts and problems in a research organization.[9]

This brief description indicates some vital differences in the role of the research administrator in the U.S. and the U.S.S.R. Since we are dealing with essentially similar types of organizational structures and with organizations concerned with roughly similar problems, handled in approximately the same way, and whose over-all size is roughly comparable, we are faced with the question: Why is the role of the Soviet administrator so very different? We are amazed that the Soviet administrator occupies such a subordinate position in the research organization compared with the American administrator. Of course, we could with equal validity ask the question: Why does the American administrator occupy such a superordinate position in the research organization relative to his Soviet counterpart? Asking the question both ways raises interesting subsidiary problems, some of which are considered in the remaining sections of this paper.

POSSIBLE EXPLANATORY FACTORS

As an American commenting on the Soviet scene, it seems to make sense to try to amplify the question in terms of Soviet experiences first. The first obvious question is what happens to all the administrative tasks? Obviously, the American administrator and his staff have much to keep them busy; in fact, they always seem overburdened with a variety of administrative problems. Who takes care of these problems in the Soviet research institute?

This seemingly simple and obvious question turns out, of course, to be fairly complex upon closer examination. For one thing, we must ask whether there is the same "amount" of administrative work and detail in the Soviet and American research institutes. We must also inquire whether the Soviet administrator has approximately the same kinds of duties but simply a lower status, or whether he has lower-status duties and a lower status as a consequence.

[9] *Ibid.;* for other evidence see E. Orowan, Our Universities and Scientific Creativity, *Bulletin of Atomic Scientists,* 15 (1959), 237–238; L. Kowarski, Psychology and Structure of Large Scale Physical Research, *ibid.,* 5 (1949); A. M. Brues, The New Emotionalism in Research, *ibid.,* 11 (1955).

We are almost forced to start with the notion that the Soviet scientists, as compared with their American counterparts, tend to view the content and the boundaries of research administration differently. The Soviet view of the research administrator essentially restricts him to a bookkeeping function and in terms of administrative theory, might be labeled the pure execution of policy.[10] The American view of the chief administrator is often much broader. The hypothetical distinction between the execution of policy and the formulation of policy often does not work out in practice. Furthermore, the American scientist's tendency to delegate any problem that he considers essentially nonscientific results in a concept of the chief administrator's role as essentially residual—it becomes in effect all things and all functions which the director or the other top scientists are unwilling, unable, or reluctant to do themselves. In return for the alleged freedom resulting from a broadly conceived view of administration, the American scientist-director must also give up some of the areas of decision making which at the same time he continues to feel are still his prerogative; hence the almost continual underlying conflict between the administrator and the scientists in many American research organizations.

In the U.S.S.R., and for that matter in most of the rest of Europe, the scientist and the director of scientific research organizations appear to be much less reluctant than their American counterparts to assume administrative duties which have a bearing on the conduct of the research.[11] They

[10] See, for example, the discussion by Herbert Simon, where he questions the distinction (attributed to Frank J. Goodnow) between policy and administrative processes, "Recent Advances in Organization Theory," in *Research Frontiers in Politics and Government,* (Washington, 1955), esp. pp. 24–26. This kind of distinction has been emphasized by many political scientists commenting on the alleged stability and resilience of the civil service apparatus in Great Britain, France, and other nations in the face of marked changes in the political leadership of the state. This thesis is explicitly challenged in a brilliant analysis of the Nazi Germany case by Frederic S. Burin, "Bureaucracy and National Socialism: A Reconsideration of Weberian Theory," in Robert K. Merton *et al.,* eds., *Reader in Bureaucracy* (Glencoe, 1952), pp. 33–47.

To our knowledge, the distinction between the formulation and the (mere) execution of policy has been confined almost exclusively to the political sphere. It has not been studied adequately in other kinds of large nongovernmental organizations. Is there, for example, a "neutral" apparatus in large corporations which remains essentially intact in the face of sharp changes in the leadership and control of the company? Our analysis here points to the possibility that the Soviets effectively avoid the problems which may arise if the distinction is recognized insofar as the scientists keep administrative policy-making functions for themselves rather than delegating these and by downgrading the administrator to the level of a chief clerk.

[11] Published evidence for this statement is admittedly scanty. However, it was strongly supported by my own observations and interview data. In some German laboratories, for example, the Director explicitly provides "on the job training" in administrative duties for his young postdoctoral research assistants. Usually, the young man is given responsibility for "helping" with purchasing activities for a six-month period, and then may be shifted to equipment maintenance for a similar period, and

cheerfully delegate keeping the books and other financial personnel records, and similar bookkeeping-type operations to a chief clerk, who is called a research administrator. But most other so-called nonresearch duties the Soviet scientist, as well as the European scientist generally, seems more willing to do himself. In general, it may be said that scientists at all levels, from the laboratory head to the director, are more willing to involve themselves in the nonclerical aspects of administration—and especially anything which is viewed as connected with the effective conduct of the research itself.

It is not simply as a matter of prestige that the American scientist-director argues in favor of sloughing off administrative duties. Far more important in the eyes of most scientists is the opportunity to concentrate on the conduct of research without being diverted by what seem extraneous organizational and administrative responsibilities. If it is true then, as we have asserted, that the Soviet scientist is far more willing to engage in administrative tasks than his American counterpart, does he in fact spend less time on research, since presumably he has to spend more time on administration?

The answer is paradoxical indeed. Most directors of American research institutes seem to have little, if any, time for their own research. The Soviet director, on the other hand, asserts that he spends most of his day on the conduct of his research and that this is in fact his first duty. When asked for an estimate of how much time a director in the Soviet medical institute had to spend on administrative duties, he typically answered that it was an average of about an hour a day. This increased, of course, at certain times of the year when new budgets had to be in, but generally the time reported spent at the institute not devoted to research was extremely low. We then have the apparent paradox of the Soviet director more willing and more likely to engage in administrative duties than his American counterpart and yet being able to spend considerably more time on his own research than his American counterpart.

Dismissing some of the more tenuous kinds of answers, we can only suggest one rather startling possibility. There is simply less administration. This is exceptional on two counts. We could expect that, given the same type of

---

so on. This is viewed, in part, as a continuation of the traditional apprenticeship pattern to ensure that the young man will have gained the experience necessary to qualify him for a more senior post ultimately. Another consequence, of course, is that the director's own total administrative load is lightened considerably by being shared with subordinates. But, significantly, the director delegates some administrative responsibility to other *scientists*, and not to professional full-time administrators. To some extent, I suspect that this pattern is less a deliberately considered policy and more an extension of the traditional patterns of the small research institutes to the much larger organization which is becoming more prevalent today. The absence of this kind of strong tradition in the U.S. is perhaps partly responsible for the greater reliance on professional administrators here.

activity and the same size in comparable organizations, the administrative duties (not counting the purely routine ones, which are handled by clerks in both situations) would be roughly the same in order to meet the requirements of maintaining the organization. It might even be expected by some that, given comparable organizations, the level of administrative duties in the Soviet organization would be considerably higher because of the nature of Soviet society with its greater emphasis on centralization and its general bureaucratic tendencies.[12] But I must conclude tentatively that there is probably less administrative detail and bureaucratic red tape in the Soviet medical institute.

WHY DOES THIS DIFFERENCE EXIST?

It might be concluded that less administration and red tape would be possible in the U.S.S.R. because of the relative simplicity of the financial support structure. One of the obvious reasons for a complicated and large administrative staff in many U.S. medical institutes is the complexity of the financial structure and the necessity to keep track of the dozens and sometimes hundreds of different grants from different agencies with differing termination dates, differing rules concerning permissible practices, differing

[12] The stereotype of excessive red tape and bureaucracy in the U.S.S.R. is widely supported in the literature and is generally shared by most foreigners visiting the Soviet Union. How much of this stereotype can be attributed to the facts of the case, and how much to preconceived ideas coupled with inadequate comparative analyses is difficult to determine. To our knowledge there have been no studies of bureaucratic tendencies and administrative proliferation in the research institutes of the U.S.S.R. However, medical scientists have commented on the "medical bureaucracy" in the Soviet clinical practices and in the hospitals. Cf. the comments in the U.S. Public Health Service, *The Report of the United States Public Health Mission to the Union of Soviet Socialist Republics* (Public Health Service Publication No. 649; Washington, 1959), especially p. 25.

Much has been written on the bureaucratic facets of Soviet industrial organization, but even here, this notion has been sharply criticized. See, for example, David Granick, *Management of the Industrial Firm in the U.S.S.R.* (New York, 1954), especially the concluding chapter in which Granick makes an explicit attempt to compare the extent of bureaucratization in Soviet and non-Soviet industrial organization. He notes, for example, "It appears an open question whether Soviet industry is not . . . less bureaucratic than are most giant firms in capitalist society" (p. 262). Granick attributes the fact that many Western observers see so much bureaucracy in the U.S.S.R. to their treatment of planned and centralized control over the economy as being synonymous with "bureaucracy." It should also be noted that there has been increasing concern with the growing bureaucratization of private business organizations in the U.S. A study by Seymour Melman of this problem over a fifty-year period in the U.S. cites an increase of 87 per cent among productive workers compared with a 244 per cent in administrative personnel in American manufacturing industries in the period 1900–1940 ("The Rise of Administrative Overhead in the Manufacturing Industries of the United States 1899–1947," *Oxford Economic Papers*, 3, N.S. [Feb. 1951], 62).

requirements for progress reports, renewal procedures, and so on. In the Soviet medical institutes, which are under the jurisdiction of the Academy of Medical Sciences, the budget stems from that single source.

Is it very likely that this difference in the financial support structure accounts for differing administrative loads in similar medical institutes in the two societies? The answer, perhaps strangely, is that this explanation is not very likely because when we examine organizations in the U.S. essentially similar to the Soviet ones with respect to financing, we do not find this to be the case. One of the best examples of such a comparison would be one of the National Institutes of Health, which also has a single source for its budget, namely, the Department of Health, Education, and Welfare and ultimately Congress. Despite this single source, or perhaps because of the characteristic federal accounting and auditing regulations, the reporting procedures and the administrative load generally are probably not very different from that found in most other U.S. medical organizations of similar size and scope. In fact, it may be suspected that the administrative load is at least as heavy, if not heavier, in such an organization.[13] It is probably the case then that the particular kind of financial structure is not of central significance in this context, although as pointed out in the previous paper, it may influence an already existing level of administration.[14]

If it is probably not the relative simplicity of the financial structure, what other possible factors might account for the hypothesized lower level of administrative activity in the Soviet medical research institute? Perhaps the Soviet government is willing to require fewer formal controls which in turn reduces the amount of administrative activity simply because they tend to trust their scientists more than we do. This is an intriguing hypothesis because it is probably true that the average American feels that the Soviet government trusts none of its citizens at all, while the American government,

[13] It must be emphasized that this comparative evaluation is purely impressionistic. It is based largely on available documentary sources and talks with scientists and administrators at the National Institutes of Health. It would certainly be desirable and worth while to check this further in a more precise quantitative fashion.

It should also be emphasized that our impressionistic comparison is between the seven institutes of the National Institutes of Health and their intramural research organization with somewhat similar types of institutes in the U.S.S.R. under the central administration of the Academy of Medical Sciences. This comparison is not intended as a reflection of the effectiveness or policies of the National Institutes of Health administration structure or its administrators. In fact, its administration, as a whole and at the institute level, seems to be highly regarded by the National Institutes of Health as well as by other scientists and research officials who have any familiarity with it. In my own experience, these institutes, when compared with *others of the same size and scope in the United States,* are consistently highly rated in this regard. The comparison with institutes of the Academy of Medical Science, however, highlights the importance of the external environment and the demands stemming from it, which may affect administrative requirements within the organization.

[14] Kaplan, *op. cit.,* p. 32.

industrial firm, or scientific research institute under private auspices would seem more likely to trust their scientists. Unfortunately, it was not possible to obtain any data which would either confirm or deny this hypothesis. If, however, there is less administration in otherwise comparable organizations, then a factor such as this may play an important role.

There is relatively little disagreement that the scientist is accorded considerably more prestige and is relatively better paid and rewarded in the material sense in the U.S.S.R. than he is in the U.S. Conversely, the administrator, at least in the medical research institute, enjoys far less prestige and material reward than the administrator in the U.S. To the extent that the prestige accorded, as well as the material rewards, reflect an evaluation of the relative importance of the activities carried on by scientists and administrators, we have perhaps an additional small bit of evidence in support of the hypothesis that the Soviet scientist is trusted somewhat more.

Another factor of potentially great significance is the nature of higher authority over the organization. The director of the medical institute is responsible to the Academy of Medical Sciences and specifically to the scientists who make up the Presidium of the Academy. He is thus responsible directly to other scientists and not to government administrators or "politicians." His American counterpart is typically responsible to a board composed of laymen who are not often very familiar with the nature of science. Being unfamiliar, they are much more likely to require reports, statistics, and data, which they can understand and which in turn require the services of, and enhance the importance of, the administrator.

Returning to an earlier injunction that the question must necessarily be asked both ways, namely, why does the Soviet institute seem to have "less" administration and why does the American institute have "more" administration, we are led to inquire into some of the consequences of administrative decisions and programs. Administration, in the American sense of the term as defined here, is necessary in order to accomplish a minimum of co-ordination, communication, and control in an organization. But presumably these should be the same in the U.S.S.R. and the U.S. given similarity in organization and its activity. Part of the problem, however, is co-ordination, control, communication for whom and for what purposes? At its simplest, these are necessary for the director; he must be able to exercise control functions and may need help for this. But it becomes more complicated when the director is in turn responsible to other authorities and must provide certain information to them, primarily for purposes of control. As already noted, the complex multiplicity of research budgets in many American institutes may require the exercise of control to meet the differing criteria of a large number of organizations, all of which have provided funds for part of the larger program.

The American research director's having to account for the activities and expenditures of his research organization to a board of trustees or directors—to laymen in general (at least with respect to the intricacies of scientific research)—tends to force the director to provide certain types of nontechnical reports and information. Since these board members may have little technical knowledge of the substance of the research, and since they tend to have a great deal of knowledge concerning the operation of large organizations, both they and the director of organizations responsible to them feel that certain types of reports are most desirable to indicate proper control and reasonable progress although they may have little intrinsic value for the conduct of the research. All of these inevitably increase the administrative load and, in fact, make it very difficult for the director to spend much time on co-ordinating the research itself, let alone doing any of his own.

The additional problem of raising funds, not at all unimportant in most American research institutes, also consumes a good deal of the time and energy of a director and administrators to whom such functions can be, and frequently are, delegated. In the U.S.S.R., on the other hand, whatever the problems concerning the amounts and scope of the financial support, it is a single body of *scientists* to whom the director must go for his financial support for the following year. The men of the Academy of Medical Sciences are presumed to have a fairly intimate knowledge of the scientific character of the work and are less likely to require reports which we might consider normal for boards of trustees here.

Finally, two other far more speculative factors which may affect research administration in the two countries should be mentioned. The first has to do with the contemporary origins of the large-scale research institute in the two societies. In the U.S.S.R., it is apparently the case that the university institute, following the old European tradition, was expanded into a large-scale organization under the Academy. In the process, the high prestige and the relative autonomy of the scientist (with some notable exceptions of political incursions) was maintained. In the U.S., on the other hand, there was little tradition for the relatively autonomous institute, whether attached to the university or not, and the scientist in general enjoyed relatively little prestige or autonomy. By the time research in the U.S. was expanded in the university and outside, and the complexity of the research organization grew with this expansion, the organizational model which many felt worth imitating was the successful big business enterprise. Moreover, the business organization model was borrowed at a time when the organizational specialist—the administrator—was becoming increasingly important.[15]

The other major factor has to do with the diversity of not only our

[15] Some confirmation of the importance of administrative personnel in American industry may be found in Melman, *op. cit.*

financial support structure but also the occupational structure for scientists in the U.S. Titles vary from institution to institution, salary scales vary from one institutional sphere to another (industry versus government etc.), and in general there is diversity with respect to most aspects of the employment, supervision, and evaluation of the scientist. This necessitates the collection of a good deal of information to provide some basis for the evaluation of scientists and institutes.

In the U.S.S.R., on the other hand, there is a single system, with many subdivisions to be sure, defining salary scales in different types of institutes, employment grades related primarily to educational attainment, and other more or less fixed criteria. Thus large areas open to discretion in the U.S. are fixed in the U.S.S.R. and require relatively little administrative action.[16] There are, of course, numerous formal and informal ways of by-passing this otherwise inflexible structure which need not be considered in any detail here. The point to be stressed is that having this centralized and generalized system of promotion policies, grades of employment, salary schedules, etc., may actually reduce the administrative load as well as the amount of discretion that can be exercised in any specific institute. Whether the perceived disadvantages of this centralization outweigh this particular advantage is yet another question.

In closing this section, it must be emphasized again that we are primarily concerned with exploring several significant aspects of the administration of research institutes. Obviously, neither the short period of time spent in the U.S.S.R., nor the preliminary nature of my inquiries permit anything other than a very tentative analysis. It should also be obvious that the various possibilities, theoretical and otherwise, which may account for the apparently sharp differences in the administration of medical research encountered in the U.S.S.R. and in the U.S. have hardly been exhausted. In subsequent studies of this problem, these are among the hypotheses deserving of further exploration. In the final section which follows, I turn to an examination of some of the implications of my observations and the hypotheses just noted.

SUMMARY AND CONCLUSIONS

The observations, that the character of research administration and the role of the research administrator in roughly similar types of medical research organizations in the U.S.S.R. and the U.S. are different, call for an explanation. We want to know why this is so and how these differences operate, as well as how this affects the conduct of medical research.

---

[16] For a comparative study of scientific personnel systems, see: Edward McCrensky, *Scientific Manpower in Europe* (New York, 1958). Chapter vii is particularly relevant inasmuch as it contains a discussion of Soviet practices compared with others.

How this is accomplished is possibly easier to describe, and the main points previously made can be summarized briefly here. The primary difference revolves around the definition of the chief administrator. In the medical research institutes of the U.S.S.R., he is defined primarily as a chief clerk. In the U.S. there is no single clear-cut definition, but in general he tends to be defined as something much more than a chief clerk, varying from general business manager to a general manager of an organization. In the U.S., the chief administrator normally has some decision-making functions while in the U.S.S.R. he appears to have practically none. This difference in definition leads to obvious differences in recruitment patterns as well as in the rewards involved in the job.

For the Russians, there is little or no problem concerning the type of person to be recruited for this job. He does not require any advanced education. He must be a competent keeper of books and records (financial and others), and, to be a chief administrator in a fairly large institute, he must be able to supervise the activities of a number of subordinate clerks. For the American research organization, on the other hand, the character of the desirable recruit for chief administrator tends to vary. Some believe the best sort of person for this position is a man who knows how to run and manage an organization. An underlying assumption is that most large organizations, irrespective of their particular activities, are essentially alike with respect to organizational problems, and consequently the best type of man for this position is a specialist in administration who is, with respect to organizations, a generalist. That is, he can move fairly easily from running a research organization to running a soap factory. Another school of thought, however, believes that there is something fairly unique about the management of a scientific research organization and tends to favor a former scientist or at least a man with scientific background who has administrative experience or at least displays a flair for administration. Involved in such a flair is the ability to deal with people and to talk with scientists, in particular to understand their problems as well as their general antipathy toward large bureaucratic organizations.

Given the Soviet requirements and definition, the man recruited need not be paid a very high salary relative to others in the research organization. He is, in effect, a fairly low-level, white-collar worker among considerably better trained and more advanced personnel in the various scientific fields. In the U.S., on the other hand, the man recruited must be paid a fairly high salary relative to other scientists because he too has advanced training, and what is most important, his market includes other types of large organizations where he commands a high salary.

We should certainly expect that the differences built into these two conceptions of the chief administrator should manifest themselves in other ways in the research organization. As already noted, we can entertain one of the two major possibilities: Either the amount and character of administration (management control, etc.) is roughly equivalent in the Soviet and American medical institute of the same size and character, in which case we should expect that the functions of the administrator in the U.S. setting are carried out by one or more functional substitutes in the organization; or, it is possible that the amount and character of general administration is quantitatively and qualitatively different in the Soviet institutions and hence few, if any, functional substitutes may be necessary. Our tentative analysis appears to favor the latter possibility although some questions and modifications must be considered.

First, it has been suggested that there is in fact "less" administration in the Soviet institutions and that, furthermore, the scientist himself, and in particular, laboratory and department heads as well as the scientific director of the institute, appear to be more willing to carry on some so-called administrative duties, which tend to be shunned by their American counterparts. Most important, these Soviet scientists report that such duties do not infringe on their research time and, in fact, are far more likely to report that they do their research. This suggests the hypothesis that given a reduction of administrative requirements, and an adequate division of labor with respect to the remaining requirements among the scientists, it is possible to have a more effective organization in which the primary goal of the pursuit of scientific research is not diminished significantly.

In fact, it might be argued that the apparent saving of time in delegating many management activities *bearing directly* on research is in the long run a myth. The structure becomes far more cumbersome, cleavages and antipathy may arise between the research people and the administrative people, and the administrator is forced to make decisions in situations where scientific competence and intimate knowledge of the scientific research is necessary. This results in additional mechanisms in the organization to reduce cleavage and to communicate information, which may be far more cumbersome than an ordinary division of labor among the scientists themselves. If the scientist is willing to accept some minimum amount of administrative duty as part of his job, and as part of the price he must pay for the benefits derived from working in a large complex organization, then the net results in terms of what he can accomplish scientifically may be far greater than if he delegates many of these management functions to specialists in management. Such a step would be extremely difficult in many American research organizations because, among other things, it would necessitate the reduction in status, prestige, and monetary rewards of the chief administrator as he is now defined.

It is unfortunately not possible to discuss relative differences in the effectiveness of the conduct of research in the U.S.S.R., and the U.S. medical research institutions.[17] This is so for many obvious reasons, including our lack of adequate measures, but also because of differences in emphases, relative time devoted to the attack on different sorts of problems, and a host of ordinary but complicated problems of assessing the effectiveness of any kind of organization. One point which has some implication for general organizational theory must, however, be stressed. In general, our observation and analysis force us to ask how much administration is necessary in a complex organization. We have tended to assume, perhaps without sufficient evidence, that the level of administrative activity in research organizations (as well as in others) is at, or very near, the minimum necessary for co-ordination, control, and communication considered adequate to maintain the organization. The findings tend to throw some doubt on the validity of this assumption, at least for medical research institutes, and in a very speculative way possibly for most other types of complex organizations as well.

In summary, it seems highly possible that the Russians really do use much less formal administration in scientific organizations than we have thought possible. I have tried to suggest some of the factors that may contribute to this and, in particular, would stress the strategic role of the larger society as well as differences in approach toward large-scale complex orga-

[17] In recent years there have been numerous reports evaluating the "quality" and other characteristics of medical research in the U.S.S.R. by American and other Western medical scientists who have visited the Soviet Union. It would obviously be presumptuous of me, a layman with respect to the medical sciences, to give my own evaluation. However, my impression from reading many of these reports and from talking with some of the medical scientists who have been there, is that Soviet medical research is generally viewed as competent, and in particular subfields, as quite outstanding. The growing program of translation of Soviet medical and scientific journals must also be viewed as evidence of the importance attached to Soviet research.

An extremely useful selected and annotated list of references has been compiled by Elizabeth Koenig of the National Institutes of Health Library: *Medical Research in the U.S.S.R.,* (Public Health Service Publication No. 710; Washington, 1960). Among the most relevant reports in terms of the institutes I visited are the following: J. R. Paul, American Medical Mission to the Soviet Union, *Scientific Monthly,* 85 (1957), 150–156; M. B. Shimkin, "Oncology in the Soviet Union," in *Year Book of Cancer, 1957–58* (Chicago, 1958), pp. 506–510; M. B. Shimkin, and R. E. Shope, Some Observations on Cancer Research in the Soviet Union, *Cancer Research,* 16 (1956), 915–917; J. Turkevich, Soviet Science in the Post-Stalin Era, *Annals American Academy Political Social Sciences,* 303 (1956), 139–151; H. Hamperl, Pathologie in UdSSR (Pathology in the U.S.S.R.), *Deutsche Medizinische Wochenschrift,* 82 (1957), 416–419; C. W. Scull, M. Nance, F. Grant, and G. F. Roll, Some General Observations on Medical and Pharmaceutical Research in the Soviet Union, *Journal American Medical Association,* 167 (1958), 2120–2123; *The Report of the United States Public Health Mission to the Union of Soviet Socialist Republics, Including Impressions of Medicine and Public Health in Several Soviet Republics* (Public Health Service Publication No. 649; Washington, 1959); *U.S. Public Health Service, United States–U.S.S.R. Medical Exchange Missions, 1956; Microbiology and Epidemiology* (Public Health Service Publication No. 536; Public Health Monograph No. 50; Washington, 1957).

nizations. The nature of the financial structure, the kinds of controls exercised by higher authority external to any given organization, as well as the general prestige level of scientists relative to administrators and others seem to affect the situation. It is hoped that additional empirical research can be conducted inside the U.S.S.R., as well as further comparative research in other countries and in other types of organizations in the U.S., to test some of the assumptions and hypotheses suggested here as well as to move closer toward a theory of complex organizations.

Team Work and Individual Work in Research

L. KOWARSKI

STARTING POINTS

Let us begin by asking: 'What is the purpose of scientific research?' Whatever kind of research we consider, its aim always is to acquire new knowledge. But there are different kinds of new knowledge. The aim which first springs to mind is the age-old one of increasing our knowledge of natural phenomena. But there is also another aim, which calls for very much the same sort of effort, that is the aim to achieve something which requires methods or techniques that are still only partly known: for instance to produce a very hard alloy or launch a missile that will go into orbit. Research is also necessary in this case: its object, however, is no longer the knowledge of nature, but what the Americans call 'know-how.' Often, this second kind of research merges into what is called 'applied research.' Often, but not always—for the result sought is sometimes of the kind which will not by itself increase our knowledge of nature, and yet will clear the way towards such knowledge, or else will enhance our prestige. Space research does both. It can hardly be called 'applied research' and yet it aims at achieving a well-defined practical result rather than revealing a new aspect of nature.

The vast expansion of research activities during the last few decades is due mainly to the rapid growth of the second type of research, namely the kind which is more often than not 'applied.' Our knowledge of nature is also growing, but not quite so fast. Intuitively one is ready to grasp the need for putting a whole team to work when a difficult achievement is at stake, whereas it is preferable to be by oneself when it comes to putting a cunning question to nature or reflecting upon its secrets. It is, then, research for a practical purpose which tends to be done by teams, while research of the first type is more for the lone wolf. The present-day evolution, in which the

Reprinted from the *CERN Courier*, May 1962, Vol. II, pp. 4–7, with the permission of the author and the publisher. Talk given in French at the 1962 meeting of the Schweizerische Stiftung für angewandte Psychologie, held in Zurich on 6 March. Dr. L. Kowarski is leader of the Data Handling Division of CERN (European Organization for Nuclear Research) in Geneva. He was Visiting Professor of Nuclear Engineering at Purdue University in 1964–1965.

acquisition of 'know-how' is expanded more quickly than the quest for pure knowledge of nature, can thus be identified to a certain extent with the trend away from individual or solitary research towards research work by teams. This identity is not perfect, for, as we shall see later, even the purest research into the secrets of nature calls for an increasing amount of team work.

It so happens that my own research activities, begun several decades ago when individual work was the rule, are now continuing at a time when team work is the order of the day. I can therefore regard the different stages of my career as illustrating, so to speak, the general trend, and some of what follows reflects my personal experience. Let us consider, then, the state of affairs in physics, and especially nuclear physics, a few years before the last war. We find there such greatly renowned names as Mme Curie and Rutherford, Einstein and Bohr. Apart from a few exceptions, they are all lone workers or else leaders who tower above their colleagues to such an extent that they cannot be regarded as members of a team. As a first exception to this rule, there were even at that time cases where two partners appeared instead of a solitary leader. I mean two partners: there are so few instances when there were more, that they can be almost ignored, whereas duets are fairly frequent, for example in the list of Nobel prize-winners. We find such famous couples as Pierre and Marie Curie, or Frédéric and Irene Joliot; a few pairs of names equally great to the initiated but less well-known to the general public, such as Cockcroft and Walton, or Banting and Best, the discoverers of insulin; or again among more recent Nobel prizemen, the two great Chinese-American theoreticians, Lee and Yang. This two-headed individualism does not yet make a team; it is a relationship in which two personalities add up to a richer whole. This may sometimes lead to true heights, as in the cases I have mentioned, or else follow the well-known pattern of Sherlock Holmes and Dr. Watson.

Alongside these masters, as a rule individual but sometimes twinned, there was a kind of three-tier mediaeval organization made up of the masters themselves and of their journeymen and apprentices. The journeymen, as shown by their name, were birds of passage, already in possession of some status. Younger than the master, they followed his ideas, and the master supervised their work. The apprentices helped the journeymen and the master kept a somewhat condescending eye on them. Many discoveries, especially experimental discoveries, were due to groups made up in this way; there might be three or four essential contributors but the part played by one dominating personality—the master or one of the journeymen who was already taking a lead—could usually be detected. The others were younger and had less experience; they were still learning. In a laboratory of this kind, there were the technical services provided by such people as mechanics and computers with their little old calculating machines, and typists. But a scientist worthy of the name was also expected to know how to use a lathe in the workshop and even a typewriter. The supporting technicians, if any, did not take part in the scientific work itself. It was gradually becoming clear that a discovery, the establishing of a new fact, would henceforth require the work of several people; but this work was still taking place at all these distinct levels: master, journeyman, apprentice, technician. The merger was not complete and team work as such did not yet exist.

THE EVOLUTION TOWARDS TEAM WORK

This state of affairs may not have prevailed in all the sciences, but it did at any rate in those with which I was concerned shortly before the war. Here and there, however, a new style was beginning to appear, where several equals worked together. Why? Because in most of the sciences, and certainly in nuclear science, increasingly powerful tools were being introduced. The assistance of engineers had to be sought for building and operating the big machines. These laboratory machines always had to be adjusted, repaired, etc., as work in a new field always entails straining technology to the limit. Even without the machines, the kind of knowledge required becomes increasingly diversified. A physicist has to work with chemists and mathematicians who are no longer apprentices, nor stooges. The splendid group created by Fermi in Rome included five colleagues of almost his own age. The grouping of these six scientists, although they were completely dominated by the spirit of the leader, could almost be considered as a true team.

In the last few years before the war, particle accelerators made their appearance in nuclear laboratories. Nowadays everyone has heard of cyclotrons; another kind of machine, the linear accelerator, is less widely known. As I have just pointed out, these machines have to operate at the limit of their possibilities; they could not accordingly be put in the hands of routine engineers; the engineers themselves had to have a creative turn of mind. It was already being asked whether an engineer could be the equal of a scientist. Did the two really make a team and work together on an equal footing? Was there sufficient mutual respect to hold the team together and share the fruits of the work? To these questions, which began to arise before the war, no entirely satisfactory answer has yet been found.

It is no use dwelling on the wartime period, because war is abnormally efficient in fostering co-operation and team work, and therefore wartime happenings cannot serve as a guide. During those six years a few projects were extraordinarily successful; they were definitely of the 'know-how' variety but none the less increased our knowledge of nature considerably. Above all, there was the American effort, with many European contributions, which produced the atomic bomb; other efforts of the same kind led to other outstanding results such as, for instance, radar. All this led to a new idea of the kind of co-operation necessary for tackling the great problems of science. From then onwards, as I have already observed, the quest for a given result becomes predominant. In order to achieve this it becomes necessary to harness together the most distinguished and creative specialists in several different sciences: nuclear physics, solid-state physics, electron physics, electrical engineering, mathematics, chemistry, metallurgy, and sometimes biology, when, for instance, the question of radiation protection arises. With so many experts working together, it is difficult to point to a single moving spirit. The leader's role is therefore changing, but there always has to be a leader, as in a symphony orchestra which, if it is a good one, is made up of distinguished instrument-players who are not interchangeable, but there must always be a conductor.

In these new teams, the leader is no longer necessarily the source of all the ideas and inspiration. He should rather have the ability to take a broad view, without entering into too much detail, and display some diplomatic gifts, for care has to be taken of both internal and public relations. Among the members of the team, a specialized idea-monger will sometimes be found, alongside other specialists such as chemists or electrical engineers. Team work is beginning to be the general rule and is developing a style of its own.

NATIONAL AND INTERNATIONAL LABORATORIES

This kind of co-operation flourished mainly in the great national laboratories which sprang up after the war throughout the industrially developed world, in both the East and the West with remarkably little difference. Human nature seems to be the same everywhere, and so are the riddles of nature. The most outstanding of these laboratories were the big atomic centres, like Oak Ridge and Argonne in America, Saclay and Harwell in Europe. Such laboratories are also coming into being in other sciences, such as space research, aeronautics, metallurgy, and electronics. Most of these centres tackle problems of applied science, but some of them are interested in fundamental research. The centres often include several hundred university graduates, scientists or engineers, at different stages of their career which correspond to our classification into masters, journeymen and apprentices. Each of these armies needs a general and several colonels: in each research centre there is a director, who is often a distinguished scientist. Immediately below him there are the heads of divisions or departments, and each department is divided into groups which, even in a very big laboratory, rarely consist of more than, say, four to ten active scientists. These are the groups which correspond most closely to what we might call teams. The group leader, with a higher position in the hierarchy and a higher salary, is not necessarily the most distinguished scientist in the group, but he is the one who co-ordinates and gives a common direction to the work of the group, possibly on account of his diplomatic gifts.

Thus the general idea of a big modern research centre on a national scale gradually begins to take shape. The hierarchy is fairly rigid with its groups, group leaders, division leaders, directors and a great many committees. Scientists complain that they spend an increasing amount of time at committee meetings. However, how can people work together if they do not have an opportunity of exchanging ideas regularly in an organized manner, which means committees? This is an evil one will have to live with. Obviously, all these unpleasant innovations, a hierarchy, committees and the need to fit into a team, go against the grain for scientists of the old individualist school, but the new era is not without its advantages: safe jobs, higher salaries, and no danger of intellectual isolation.

A laboratory following this pattern may also be created on an international scale. CERN is one of the oldest and most successful creations of this kind, but there are others which are still too young for anyone to gauge their chances of success.

Contrary to an opinion that is often expressed—and this is a point I particularly want to emphasize—the problems arising in international laboratories hardly differ at all from the day-to-day problems of national laboratories. As soon as one gets down to group level, viz. the level of a team whose task has been approved, and means supplied, by some outside authority, and whose problems are strictly technical or scientific, it scarcely makes any difference to the team whether it is national or international. The difficulties inherent in international work lie elsewhere: they appear when the organization is being created, when the first financing and the first family trees have to be agreed upon. But once this stage has been passed, the remaining problems are not nearly so serious. Any energetic leader likes to choose his fellow workers and it is generally easier for him to find them in the circles which he knows best. Accordingly, certain cleavages become noticeable: around an Italian master one finds Italian apprentices, or in a technical group under French leadership the second flight may comprise a fairly large proportion of French engineers. All these trends do not represent more than slight fluctuations.

NEW PROBLEMS: PUBLICATIONS

We have thus traced the evolution until its present stage; we started from the image of a solitary scientist, and we arrived at the idea of the team, which seems typical of our times. Let us now consider what concomitant problems have arisen, what would be our reasons to regret the good old days and, failing a return to them, how we can face the snags of the present day.

First of all, let us consider the question of publication. Professional scientific researchers attach much importance to the publication, that is to the appearance in a recognized scientific journal, of an article describing a piece of research and its results, signed by its author or authors. Those not familiar with the course of a research scientist's career cannot understand why this is so important. It is often thought, rather naively, that scientists are vain and like to see their names in print, and that they set so much store by it that they will go to any lengths to achieve it. Once one knows how scientists get their jobs, how they hold them, and how they are paid and promoted, it is easy to understand that having their name on a publication means much more to them than a mere sop to their personal vanity; it is a question of their children's bread and butter. According to the tradition that has ruled science in our world since Galileo's day, the author who signs an original report is taken to be the originator of the ideas expressed. It may then be asked in a team: who originated the new ideas? Where there are only two or three members in the team, it can always be said that all of them did. But nowadays, in the big laboratories, articles signed by ten, twelve, eighteen people are beginning to appear; I have seen one with twenty-nine signatures. Original creators, every one? This is getting hard to believe. Perhaps just some of them were, and the others were technical supporters, servants? Imagine a group of people who have lived together for perhaps weeks on end, day and night (because that's how scientists work when the bug bites them), sometimes in dread of a likely failure or even of accidents. Are we entitled to draw the line: can we say "this man is a creator and the other a stooge"? In actual practice, such distinctions can hardly be made, and that is why it is quite usual nowadays to see twenty names taking up half a page on top of a report which occupies a page and a half, and twenty cards in the library catalogue. The idea of original personal work is headed for the cloud-cuckoo land.

CERN has adopted an ingenious criterion which is probably still suitable for a big laboratory devoted exclusively to fundamental research. Anyone signing a collectively written article should be capable of understanding all the specialized aspects of the work described, to the extent of being capable of taking full responsibility for it. In more strictly technical work, however, specialization may reach a point where this attitude can no longer apply. In the team there may be an engineer, who is the only one to understand how a certain electromagnet works, and a mathematician, who may be the only one capable of following the course of a reasoning involving integral equations. In such cases it is sometimes recommended to split the article up into several separate ones. In practice this sub-division may prove artificial and the separate parts may become meaningless. The various contributions welded together by team work can no longer be easily separated when credit becomes due.

In a few extreme cases a radical solution has been adopted: the work is no longer attributed to such and such an individual but to a whole department or even a whole laboratory. Justice is thus done, but under the present conditions governing scientific careers how are the most deserving to be rewarded?

On the fringe of this yet unsolved problem and under the very impact of team work, two entirely new phenomena may be observed which add a confusing note to the traditional symphony of scientific communications. One of these is the scientific conference. Important results are published to an increasing extent not in journals but by word of mouth at meetings where 200, 300 or 500 colleagues foregather for discussion. This mode of communication is efficient and even pleasant, but it is habit-forming and ends up taking quite a slice out of the addict's working time; the only sure winners in this game are the airlines. Another development is the distribution of what are called 'preprints.' Instead of sending colleagues reprints from a journal in which the article has been printed, copies of the manuscript are multiplied and circulated before the article has appeared in print.

For a while, until the publication in a recognized journal becomes an accomplished fact, the responsibility of the author remains shrouded in a gentle haze; a typescript does not commit so fully as a printed page does. I have known cases where the 'preprint' was circulated before the knotty problem of who was to sign what had been finally solved.

NEW PROBLEMS: THE LEADERS

The spread of team work in research also poses the problem of selecting leaders. In former times this was simple: the leader was the man whose genius was greatest. Nowadays, as I have already said, it is not always the man with the most ideas who becomes leader of a large team. The leader must be able to coordinate, and the financial responsibilities are becoming increasingly heavy. Are those in power always ready to put lots of money in the hands of absent-minded professors?

Finally, leaders are not always chosen; they sometimes choose themselves. In the world of to-day, scientists have prestige and are rather well-paid in senior posts: the profession is beginning to be attractive and this is having an effect on selection, and especially autoselection, in a way that no longer coincides with the interests of pure science as perfectly as it did in the time of the great solitary 'masters.' Increased financial responsibility distorts in another way: caution is beginning to pay and there is a temptation to back only the favourites. For instance, if a daring and even brilliant experiment has been performed somewhere on a certain chemical element, one is tempted not to start another experiment which is just as original but to perform the same experiment on another chemical element. One will thus be sure of obtaining a new result without taking much of a risk. We can therefore see how team work using costly equipment may be led astray by timorous counsel and miss the path leading to unexpected discoveries. Only a few words need be said, in this connexion, on certain temptations which have always threatened the intellectual integrity of research scientists. What is new is that leaders now have much more power, and more power means greater temptations.

Let us also mention, in passing, a more harmless temptation: that of relying on a strong team-spirit built up at the expense of external relations. Individual selfishness, which team work tends to restrict, is then likely to re-erupt, tough and self-righteous, on the higher plane of group relations.

On the other hand, it should also be said that, with the great increase in the number of scientific posts which has occurred in the last 20 years, an ever-growing number of young people have a chance of doing pure scientific work. This has brought about a certain levelling up of temperaments and a certain bureaucratic outlook, especially in the very big establishments. The proportion of individual creative minds goes down, but that of research workers willing to accept the constraints of team work goes up, and it is admittedly easier to do science in this way now than it was 30 years ago, since it suits better the common run of people.

CHANNELS OF INSPIRATION

What can be done to counteract this watering down of creative individualism? There is a remedy which is often suggested in practice: this is a kind of specialization among leading scientists. Certain temperaments are more suited to individual work and others to work in a group. Therefore why should the former not be left to meditate in solitude on profound problems and the others put to directing big teams working on slightly more down-to-earth questions? If this trend becomes established, a new kind of hierarchy is likely to be created; one category, higher and obviously looked upon with greater respect, will be 'real scientists' and, slightly apart, perhaps slightly below, the 'applied scientists,' good for directing teams. The ideal, however, would be to find men inspired with the spirit that fired the best discoveries in the past, and to make sure that this inspiration was accessible to those willing to follow it, to all of the many teams which are needed at present to break new ground. Neither selection, nor walling-off; on the contrary, the channels of inspiration should be kept wide open. To enable a great mind both to create by himself and to inspire others, I feel the only solution is a deliberate partition of his time. The most radical partition is that afforded by the ages of life: it is well-known that the great individual discoverers get fewer new ideas as they grow older. It is relatively rare for really novel ideas to come from a great experimenter after he is 40. The majority of the fundamental theories were put forward before their authors had reached 30. A career can thus be mapped out in which an inspired scientist would spend his youth and make his reputation doing unorganized work; this would apply to the most capable scientists, who once they had advanced in renown and age would become leaders of teams where their subordinates could reap the benefit of their experience, if not of the fullness of their creative gifts.

In certain cases the scientist's time could be divided fifty-fifty: six months' solitary work, then six months as a leader; or two years and two years. It is perhaps such alternating assignment which holds out the greatest hope, but then such a course must be deliberately arranged so that research work in teams can develop without drying up the sources of individual inspiration. In fact, this dilemma threatens the future of science just as it hangs over great restaurants. How to make food available in great amounts and on the spur of the moment, without adopting methods which kill the flavour: the great restaurateurs are already familiar with this problem; organized science is just coming to it.

PART IV

National Science Establishments

The internal organization of a research laboratory, whether in the university, industry, or government—indeed the very distribution of laboratories among these sectors—is closely related to national patterns of organization. Over the years many patterns of support for both individual scientists and the many differently organized laboratories have arisen. Often these have evolved over time in a haphazard and more or less random fashion. These patterns have emerged from responses to specific problems and crises which have arisen and have been recognized in the last fifty or seventy-five years. Only recently have these national patterns of research organization been the object of intense attention and study both by government agencies and by many different investigators interested in problems concerned with societal factors affecting the development of science.

In the first selection included here, A. Hunter Dupree provides us with a much needed historical perspective on the interrelations between science and government in the United States. Dupree sees this as a story of continuing tension, from the beginning of American history, between pluralistic tendencies in government as well as in science and the eternal quest for central organization in both these spheres. There have been times in American history when a single agency has temporarily dominated the government's role in science, but this has always been for a relatively short period of time. Almost all the attempts at a more explicit central scientific organization have been ineffectual and largely "paper" organizations.

By the early twentieth century, there were a number of strong government agencies but all of the coordinating mechanisms were quite weak. At about that same time much of scientific research was rapidly becoming institutionalized in the universities and to some extent in industry, thereby depriving the government of its former virtual monopoly in the conduct of research. The present executive office organization including the President's Scientific Advisory Committee, the Office of Science and Technology, and the Federal Council on Science and Technology could conceivably become the centralized government organization of the future with respect to science. Nevertheless, there remain many strong counterforces toward pluralism both within the government and within science itself. And since these tendencies toward pluralism are likely to remain strong in the foreseeable future, the best solution, according to Dupree, seems to be some sort of balanced harmony.

In a closely related paper, Don K. Price expands on the thesis that science has become a major "establishment" in the American political system. He describes the scientist's emerging role in high administration circles and in the making of policy. Scientists are described as the new "influentials." The extension of the land-grant college system to science in general has led to new relationships between government and private science. We now have administration by contract and not by a giant bureaucracy. It is the rather amiable disorder of the university facility on a national scale. Despite the success of this system there is still the need to strengthen the integrity of the total effort as well as the quality of the Civil Service scientists. But science has (largely inadvertently) played a major role in keeping our political system less bureaucratic and more democratic.

An important and early feature of the development of science in many of the countries of Europe was the scientific academy. In the United States, the establishment of an academy came quite late compared with Europe. In the selection included here, Howard Simons presents a brief history of the development of the National Academy of Sciences on the occasion of its hundredth anniversary. Established by an act of Congress during President Lincoln's term of office, the Academy of Sciences has played a quite varied role in the development of science in this country. To many observers, its importance seems to have been recognized by the government primarily during times of war. Although it has had a varied existence in its first hundred years, the vitality of the Academy has only recently been reaffirmed in the agreement concluded with Congress concerning scientific advice to the members of the Congress.

In the remaining essays of this section, the focus shifts to patterns of national research organizations in countries other than the United States. In the first of these papers, Nicholas DeWitt, a leading American expert on Soviet research organization, discusses the comprehensive reorganization of research which took place in the Soviet Union in 1960. The tremendous expansion of research and development in the U.S.S.R. during the decade of the 1950's led to a re-examination and eventual reorganization at many different levels. According to DeWitt, the major attempt was to achieve a greater degree of coordination especially at the top levels by the national government itself. The Academy of Sciences has been reorganized to achieve more coordination and to concentrate more on the basic sciences. Although the terms of reference often appear to be quite different, the problems discussed in this paper and the solutions which were arrived at in the U.S.S.R. appear to be not too different from those encountered in the United States.

Both the executive and, more recently, the legislative branches of the federal government have concentrated considerable attention on attempts to achieve more effective coordination of the government research effort including the support of research conducted by those outside the government.

The last three selections in this section are illustrative of varying attempts to describe and analyze the critical situation in different parts of Europe leading up to major reorganization efforts at the national level, many of which are still in progress. In the first of these, William Consolazio describes the underdeveloped state of biological research in central and southern Europe. He finds that biologists tend to leave these areas and go to work in other countries because there is a lack of opportunity to grow intellectually and there are very low financial rewards especially for the younger men in science. In Italy, for example, the traditions surrounding the universities do much to impede the progress of science. Consolazio is particularly scathing in his views on the research institutes run by the senior professor. Careers for younger men are almost totally lacking. There are grave difficulties in any attempts to introduce some of the newest scientific specialties because of academic politics. The general need for change is attributed in large measure to the leisurely atmosphere of Italy's ancient universities which, although suited to an upper-class elite system of education and a rich dilettante scientist, seems to be particularly inappropriate to modern science and the professional career-oriented man of today. This paper is of additional interest because of the explicit attempt to compare features of the social structure as well as of the scientific organization within a number of different countries.

Nor are such problems peculiar to the countries of central and southern Europe. In the next selection, Renée Fox reports on certain aspects of her study of medical research in Belgium. The ceremonies in a Belgian Château at which three honorary degrees are awarded to outstanding medical scientists are used by Fox to illustrate the interrelations of the historical, social, and cultural factors affecting clinical medical research in Belgium. The struggle for absolute equality among competing language, status, and research groups as well as others within this tiny country is described in detail. Fox shows how various facets of the Belgian social structure impinge upon the organization and conduct of medical research there.

The juxtaposition of what in some senses is almost a feudalistic social structure with that of a modern scientific effort has grave consequences for the vitality and progress of science. Even before this paper was written, the Belgian government as well as Belgian scientists had already begun intensive efforts to reorganize the national science structure and to modify the effects of the social conditions which were responsible for impeding the progress of the national scientific efforts.

Some of the problems singled out by Dr. Fox are undoubtedly peculiar to the Belgian situation. But the significance of this analysis goes well beyond the particular problems of Belgium. And it should also be emphasized that for the entire period during which there have been many problems in the interrelations of science and society, Belgium has not lacked its Nobel prize winners and other first-rank scientists. But the crucial point that is now becoming increasingly recognized everywhere is that it is not enough to have a handful of truly outstanding scientists who flourish in spite of certain inadequacies in the national science structure and in the interrelations of this structure to the society as a whole.

In a paper closely related to the previous two, Kaplan seeks to identify certain changes which appear to be common to many of the national science establishments in Western Europe. Perhaps the most basic change lies in the rapidly disappearing traditional attitude of laissez-faire toward scientific research in much of Europe. It is curious in some respects that the European governments should have maintained a policy of laissez-faire toward their scientific research efforts. For, unlike the situation in the United States, most European governments had to assume a direct financial responsibility for the support of their universities long before the first halting steps toward indirect and partial subsidization of American private universities were even contemplated. And it was in the universities of Europe that much of the basic research was undertaken, especially after the middle of the nineteenth century. Yet despite this close connection between the central government and the universities, little or no consideration was given to the nature of the total scientific effort being supported by the government.

Since the end of World War II, and even more particularly in the latter part of the 1950's, more and more European governments have begun to re-examine their attitude and policies toward science. More and more of them reached the conclusion that laissez-faire was simply not an adequate policy in the world of today. The paper by Kaplan describes some of the factors responsible for this change. These are traced to the redefined interests of the national governments involved as well as to the changes from within science itself.

There can no longer be much doubt that national governments will play an increasingly more important role in the development of science in the years ahead. As this happens, we can expect many changes in the nature and interrelationships of science and society. The selections included here are concerned, in one way or another, with how we arrived at the present junction. Some of them hint at the possible directions in which we might move in the future. From all of them there is a clear indication of the many gaps in our knowledge which must be filled before a better understanding of the problems involved can be achieved.

Central Scientific Organisation
in the United States Government

A. HUNTER DUPREE

I

Throughout American history the people who have been concerned with the relation of science to the national government have searched for some form of central scientific organisation. This quest has gone on in spite of the fact that the great triumphs of the organisation of science, both within the scientific community and within the government, have tended to come when the guiding theme was not a single central policy of function or concept but rather a scientific speciality or a particular governmental mission. The scientific community is profoundly plural in its structure and the government is equally plural in the agencies it has developed to deal with science. The claims of the centre against the claims of the plurality is one of the fundamental themes of American political experience. However, the forced resolution of the federal balance in favour of union over the sovereignty of the states in the Civil War had the paradoxical effect of merely accentuating the plurality of the scientific establishment instead of providing an effective central scientific organisation. The principle of securing liberty through the rights of concurrent majorities, propounded by John C. Calhoun, the most tragically original political theorist in American history, was vindicated in the scientific establishment even though it irretrievably lost its hold on the government itself.

The strength of the individual entities, which make up the scientific community both within the government and without it, is so overwhelming and the organisations, which have specifically aspired to a central role, have been so feeble that it is tempting to deny the very existence of a central scientific organisation for the United States. Yet the historian cannot accept

Reprinted from *Minerva*, Summer 1963, Vol. I, No. 4, pp. 453–469, with the permission of the author and the publisher. Dr. A. Hunter Dupree is a Professor of History at the University of California at Berkeley and author of *Science in the Federal Government: A History of Policies and Activities to 1940* (Cambridge, Mass.: Belknap Press of Harvard University, 1957). He is currently engaged in studies of the history of science in the United States government, 1940–1960.

a picture of an unqualified pluralism, for he can discern in every generation an attempt both to find a central focus for the total scientific establishment and to counterbalance pluralism with at least some preoccupation with the pattern as a whole. The question whether the focus actually exists is secondary to the fact that pure pluralism has never completely satisfied either the American scientific community or the American government. The units of the plurality—individual agencies within the government, universities, industry, the great foundations—have always dominated, but the quest for a central organisation has gone on.

II

Before tracing this quest through American history, I must pause briefly to justify taking a long historical perspective as the only one which will illuminate a problem which exists in the present and which casts a shadow far into the future. The line which the outbreak of World War II draws across the history of the relation between science and government in the United States does not render irrelevant the older traditions persisting from the American past. The present vast expenditure of money does indeed dwarf past efforts, both relatively and absolutely. A fair judge would also grant that scientific knowledge has accumulated at an accelerated rate. Perhaps even more important, the invisible lists kept by the invisible colleges all over the world have, in recent years, given high place to large numbers of American scientists for the first time in history. Yet, when one examines institutions, both formal and informal, the pace of change is set by forces among which continuity with the pre-1940 past plays an important part. On the government side, the Presidency and the Congress are venerable institutions whose rate of evolution is slow. And in addition to the many layers of scientific institutions which already existed in 1940, the principles that govern the polity of the scientific community are intertwined with the origins of modern science itself, making them among the most venerable of political traditions.

To give just one example of the unexpected relevance of the pre-1940 past to present problems, one can call to mind that the characteristic scientific organisation developed by governments of the Atlantic community in the late eighteenth and early nineteenth century was the surveying and exploring expedition. The rise of the laboratory made this great organisational achievement seem archaic as little as a decade ago. Yet at the Philadelphia meetings of the AAAS[1] in 1962, Dr. Homer Newell, Director of Space Sciences for NASA,[2] discussed at some length the problem of choosing a Darwin to land, *Beagle*-fashion, on the moon from the first lunar excursion module.

---

[1] American Association for the Advancement of Science.
[2] National Aeronautics and Space Administration.

From the struggles of a century and more ago to staff exploring expeditions, to adjust the civil-military relations, and to resolve the conflicting demands of basic scientist and expedition commander, we can gain some insight into problems of scientific organisation for which pallid laboratory dwellers have little background.

To return, then, with some justification for an historical approach, to the problem of central scientific organisation in the United States government, we can distinguish between two broad types of effort to find a unifying focus. For an effort to qualify as a quest for a central scientific organisation as we are using the term, it must comprehend the scientific establishment as a whole, including the government but not being limited to it.[3] The voluntary organisations devoted solely to organising the scientific community itself and keeping its necessary services operating are not within our scope here. The American Association for the Advancement of Science and all of the specialised societies for the individual disciplines, great and small, occasionally play a role in the political community, but observers from the beginning have recognised that they were too far from the government and hence from the sources of political power to take any kind of direct action on those parts of the scientific community which were a part of the government. Hence from the beginning men have dreamed of a central scientific organisation which would give coherence to all of science, both in the government and outside it. They have also, from time to time, adapted agencies which were formally committed to specific missions of limited scope to the more general business of serving as central scientific organisations.

Several basic aspirations account for the perennial revival of the concept of the central scientific organisation. In the first place, some people have always felt the need for arranging the total scientific impact on society into a coherent, if not all-embracing, pattern. Some of those who wish a coherent pattern have believed in the desirability of coherent social goals and have seen the role that science has increasingly played in attaining major purposes in national life. Others have used almost precisely the same arguments for coherence out of a desire to limit the demands that science makes on the community at large. They seek economy in the efficiency of the research effort. In the second place, many have felt the need to coordinate the great variety of scientific activities in the interest of the good administration of government itself. The many layers of scientific institutions within the government raised the problem, which became more pressing as more funds came from taxes, of how to make the government's own response to science one which did not cancel itself out in a welter of com-

---

[3] It should also be understood that "science" is used in a broad sense to encompass applied as well as basic research, and also to include the total range of institutions—including educational institutions—which conduct and promote research.

peting and conflicting organisations. In the third place, nearly all advocates of a central scientific organisation have seen it as adjusting in some way the relations of the government, as the central political authority. with the broader community of science. Even when the government has made an overwhelming contribution to the support of science, the need for the support and approbation of the scientific community as a political community in itself has remained a necessity. Both the centralists and the pluralists have professed to want these things. Disagreement arises because the centralists feel the need for decisive action at the centre to attain their ends, while the pluralists see those same ends accomplished through the vigour of the individual institutions themselves.

Since we have already observed that pluralism has been the major characteristic of the American scientific establishment, we may legitimately expect that the second type of central scientific organisation—that of the predominant agency—has made the more impressive record. And indeed we find that a predominant agency has arisen in every generation since 1830, and each one in turn has seemed invincible during its brief ascendancy Some of the most sentient and energetic institution-builders ever connected with American science have used predominant agencies as their instruments. Not all distinguished scientific groups within the government have achieved the status of a predominant agency. To gain that title an agency must, to further its own mission or in spite of it, have a substantial influence on the scientific community as a whole. It must concern itself with the sectors of science outside the government and its actions must be either large enough or dramatic enough to have a standard-setting effect on other groups.

In theory, the predominant agency is not a central organisation at all but rather the product of a state of mind. Within the scientific community, fields of science vary over time in the ascendancy accorded them by the prevailing opinion within that community. And within the wider lay community certain sciences are held in higher esteem than others and certain problems have a higher appeal or greater shock effect than others. A predominant agency is created by the confluence of these two lines of opinion. It must be able to command on the one hand a series of fruitful research results from the scientists and, at the same time, it must command from the general community the means to accomplish its scientific ends. If the confluence of opinion is strong enough, a predominant agency can convince both of its constituencies—the scientists and the general community represented by such an institution as Congress—that its mission is the most pressing and most attainable one of the age. Out of such a confluence, in a democracy, priority is given to one field of science over another. "Leverage," in the double sense of being able to command support and performance at the same time, is the stuff by which a predominant agency imposes its will on other fields of science and other missions of government.

The first predominant agency was the Coast Survey in the years between 1843 and 1860.[4] The chief of the agency, which was really a temporary organisation stretched out through the years into permanency, was Alexander Dallas Bache. One of the ablest scientific politicians the nation has ever produced, Bache made his agency palatable to Congress, cultivated the research resources in the colleges of the day and maintained civilian control. At the same time, he utilised army and navy officers and gave them advanced training. From the seemingly simple mandate for surveying, he developed basic research programmes in astronomy, terrestrial magnetism, physical standards, oceanography and even biology.

After the Civil War and a period of competition for control of the surveying and exploring function of the government, the Geological Survey emerged as the predominant agency in 1879. Under the leadership of John Wesley Powell, the one-armed veteran of the passage of the Colorado and the peer of Bache as a politician of science, the Geological Survey reigned supreme for the decade of the 1880s. Adept at securing financial support from Congress in a flexible form, Powell's masterpiece was the erection of a truly national scientific organisation from one phrase of an appropriations bill. The Geological Survey had its summer training programme and communications with the scientists in the nascent universities of the day. Its expansion into fields far from its narrow mission showed its scientific reach— even to anthropology and sociology.

The Forest Service of the Progressive Era—the two decades preceding and following the turn of the century—has a less clear claim to scientific distinction than its predecessors, but Gifford Pinchot was the predominant politician of science in the period just after 1900. In the conservation movement, Pinchot and Theodore Roosevelt merged the politics of the scientific community and the politics of the nation briefly into one system. Pinchot broke new ground in the development of the political skills of the scientific administrator. For instance, he was able, for a few years, to gain flexibility for his Service by holding its income from fees for a five-year period, without recourse to Congress. In the national and international conservation movement, he had a communication system which extended far beyond his own bureau. But the price Pinchot had to pay was to become completely a politician of the wider world.

The predominant agency which was already on the rise in Pinchot's time and which continued its reign almost to the Second World War was the Department of Agriculture as a whole. It was built around a system rather than around a single personality. The Department, the land-grant colleges, the state experiment stations, the extension service, formed a com-

[4] An extensive and comprehensive account of the agencies referred to here may be found in Dupree, A. Hunter, *Science in the Federal Government: A History of Policies and Activities to 1940* (Cambridge: Belknap Press of Harvard University Press, 1957).

prehensive research institution of ensured geographical diffusion and great spread of activities. Research and education were institutionally coupled. The whole spectrum from basic research to the application of science by individual farmers on their own farms gave it a comprehensiveness which is still characteristic of scientific work in agriculture and which had no rival in the years 1900–38. The government developed a complete research establishment around the problems of the farmer. Nothing remotely approaching it existed for industry, where research grew up largely in the hands of private corporations. Because the system comprehended whole universities, and because the problems of the farmer extended far beyond his fences, the mission of the Department of Agriculture hardly limited it with respect to scientific discipline. In its heyday, it captured nitrates and meteorology from the military, did most of the chemical research for the whole government, and developed pure food and drug regulation. In the 1920s Herbert Hoover, a much abler politician of science than any single individual in agriculture, tried to put together a rival predominant agency in the Department of Commerce, but his galaxy of bureaux was pale and ephemeral in comparison.

Before going back to trace those explicit central scientific organisations which form another thread through American history, we may pause to make three generalisations about the predominant agencies of the past. In the first place, they were all civilian agencies. The Coast Survey, the Geological Survey and the early Forest Service all fought, sometimes bitterly, to keep military rivals from taking over their missions. And during much of the nineteenth century, the pre-eminence of West Point as an educational institution and extensive experience in scientific exploring and surveying made the military a very possible and even plausible alternative. In the second place, predominance always proved fragile. Bache, Powell and Pinchot lost their touch and usually their position before their sands had completely run out.

To appreciate fully the fundamental reasons for this quick loss of iridescence, one would have to go beneath the politics to the changing pattern of science itself. Perhaps the golden moment when a single mission seems to embody the whole of science is an illusion which cannot be long sustained. In the third place, the loss of predominance has very little to do with the quality of research being done or the justification for the continuation of its programmes. One could almost say that the very success of the predominant agencies freezes their imagination and constricts it in the problems of the period of their greatest success. Certainly the Geological Survey, which gained its hegemony by creatively joining a live and developing science to the expansions of the nation's horizons in the great basin and Colorado plateau, tended to centre on that one region precisely because of its unique capability for dealing with it. The Survey was still there when most people had ceased to get a thrill out of the problems of the trans-Mississippi West, and it was still there when the need for uranium ore brought prospecting on its classic ground back into fashion.

III

In contrast to the predominant agencies, the explicit central scientific organisations seem both more lofty in conception and more ineffectual in practice. They have also been more central when they existed wholly or largely on paper than when, as actual institutions, they entered into the pluralist politics of American science. Thus the national university as envisaged by Thomas Jefferson, Benjamin Rush and Joel Barlow, was both centralised and comprehensive—including many functions now performed not by universities but by research organisations within the government. But by 1830 it was clear that these soaring ideas had come to nothing and from that time onwards Americans were too busy creating a pluralistic scientific establishment, both in the government and in the educational system, to make a national university anything more than a fantasy.

Similarly, during the 10-year debate—1836 to 1846—over the bequest of James Smithson, the need for a national centre for the expedition-oriented science of the day loomed very large. But Joseph Henry as first secretary saw clearly that an endowment of half a million dollars would not get him very far. Besides prudently tailoring his programme to filling gaps with a modest number of research and publication projects, he took money from Congress only very reluctantly, and he gave away projects whenever he could. The weight of Henry's personal influence made the Smithsonian Institution function as a central scientific organisation only during the course of his life. Thereafter, it became, perhaps to the relief of those connected with it, a group of separate bureaux dedicated to special lines of research, often performed with great distinction.

Bache, who had had an important hand in the establishment of the Smithsonian as well as the Coast Survey, came to the conclusion as early as 1851 that none of the institutions of the country were capable of performing the function of a central scientific organisation. An "institution of science, supplementary to existing ones, is much needed in our country, to guide public action in scientific matters." [5] The inclusion of all science and the guidance of public policy are the essence of his call. Historically this statement was an early step on the road to the National Academy of Sciences. But in a broader sense it is the first really clear declaration for what I have called a central scientific organisation. Bache had before him when he asked

[5] Bache, Alexander Dallas, "Address," *Proceedings of the American Association for the Advancement of Science*, VI (1851), p. xlviii.

for such an institution his own predominant agency, the Coast Survey, the five-year-old Smithsonian and the three-year-old American Association for the Advancement of Science. He lived in a world of plural scientific institutions, as we do today.

Although the pluralism of the government's scientific establishment was visible only to a discerning observer in 1851, the pluralism of the political community was one of the great issues of the day. Bache was aware of the strong argument for states' rights which dominated the political scene of his day, and he tried to make a distinction between states' rights in a political sense and the decentralisation of the scientific community. He envisaged a body whose members would belong "to each of our widely scattered states, working at their places of residence, and reporting their results; meeting only at particular times, and for special purposes; engaged in researches self-directed, or desired by the body, called for by Congress or by the Executive, who furnish the means for the inquiries." [6] Thus Bache's central scientific organisation would provide support for research from the central government, an anathema to the states' rights theorists of his day, but he would not centralise the scientific community itself. Indeed, his ideas can be read as a defence of the pluralism of the scientific community. Yet his final emphasis was on the positive role which the scientific community could play in offering advice to the government. Indeed, machinery for scientific advice is always a part of a central scientific organisation. The government "would be saved many times the support of such a council, by the sound advice which it would give in regard to the various projects which are constantly forced upon" the notice of officials, "and in regard to which they are now compelled to decide without the knowledge which alone can ensure a wise conclusion." [7]

Effective steps in the direction of a central scientific organisation have always been closely associated with crises—not the crises of scientific revolutions but the crises of American history. It is the general community and its troubles which make it possible to create central scientific organisations, but equally clearly it is the scientific community which stands ready and impatiently waiting when war or depression provides an opportunity. The leading scientists of the country had been mulling over the project of a national academy throughout the 1850s. One can argue, as I have done in another place with regard to the Morrill Land-Grant Act,[8] that secession rather than war made that legislation possible in the first Congress of the war. The overwhelming republican majority was created by the withdrawal of the delegations from the states which became the Confederacy. The

[6] *Ibid.*, p. 1.
[7] *Ibid.*
[8] Dupree, A. Hunter, "The Morrill Act and Science," lecture delivered 10 April, 1962, at Berkeley, California.

National Academy never performed any study of importance during the war, and indeed three of its founders gave most of the scientific advice which was afforded the military through the device of the Permanent Commission of the Navy. Yet to imagine the Act of 1863 passing at any time except during the war is difficult. By 1867 Joseph Henry saved the Academy from complete extinction by making it less exclusive and turning it almost completely into an honorary society rather than an advisory body.

Between 1884 and 1886 the Congress staged a series of investigations into the government scientific establishment, which afford an insight into the beliefs of the scientists of that day concerning centralism and pluralism. The success of individual agencies, especially the rise of the Geological Survey out of a swarm of competing military and civilian groups, had upset the usual evolution of scientific agencies. Cries of waste and inefficiency had accompanied the increasing support which the government was affording science. A committee of the National Academy suggested a Department of Science to provide "direction and control of all the purely scientific work of the government." [9] Yet it was clear even in 1884 that both the government's scientific establishment and the scientific community with its nascent universities had already grown too complex for an organisational shift to have much effect. Much more important to the actors before the Allison Commission, a joint committee of Congress which conducted the hearings, was the question whether a vigorous predominant agency like the newly arisen Geological Survey was a threat to the freedom of non-government science. Alexander Agassiz, spokesman of private wealth and of private scientific institutions, charged that "the friends of a paternal government would like to see the science of the country centralised, and the work of the bureaux gradually absorbing all the best available men . . . making Washington a great scientific centre." [10] He looked abroad to France, whose scientific institutions seemed highly centralised, and to Germany, which, despite its recent unification, seemed to have gained scientific pre-eminence with a completely plural set of institutions. "It would be a great disaster should Washington ever become the Paris of the United States." [11] Furthermore, Agassiz did not see why "men of science should ask more than other branches of knowledge, literature, fine arts, etc. . . . There is no end to that kind of interesting documents which the heads of bureaux could get printed at Government expense, and which few individuals or societies would print, even had they the means at their command." [12]

John Wesley Powell, the defender before the Allison Commission of his

[9] Joint [Allison] Commission . . . , *Testimony,* March 16, 1886, 49 Cong., 1 Sess., Sen. Misc. Doc. 82 (Ser. 2345), 8*.

[10] Agassiz, Alexander, "The National Government and Science," *Nation,* XLI (1885), p. 526.

[11] *Ibid.*

[12] Allison Commission, *Testimony,* p. 1014.

Geological Survey, replied that Agassiz was trying to make his own privately financed museum "the American centre of scientific research, and the agency which should create, control and diffuse the increasing knowledge of the New World." [13] But in many sciences, especially geology, the support of research by government was a long-established precedent. A "hundred millionaires could not do the work in scientific research now done by the general government." [14] Far from admitting that government science was competing with private science and driving it out, Powell asserted that "all governmental research stimulates, promotes and guides private research." [15] The Allison Commission confirmed the active role of government science enunciated by Powell but turned a deaf ear to the tepid plea for a Department of Science. The immediate future lay with strong agencies rather than with central scientific organisations.

By the early twentieth century two kinds of pluralism had become clearly evident in the American research establishment. On the one hand, the government agencies themselves were very strong and the coordinating mechanisms weak. On the other hand, specialisation of basic research in the universities and of applied research in industry and government had become institutionalised. This change had accompanied the rise of the American university as the home of the scientists who formed the dominant members of the community of science. The shift in prestige in the direction of private research as opposed to government research went so far in this period that one could almost envisage a central scientific organisation outside the government. There was a slight revival of the idea of a national university. And Andrew Carnegie was thinking in these terms when he set up the Carnegie Institution of Washington, which "shall in the broadest and most liberal manner encourage investigation, research and discovery." [16] The Carnegie Institution was destined to make an enviable research record and also to provide a resting place for scientists conveniently close to the centre of government. But its influence was unofficial, and even the generosity of Carnegie was but a small fraction of the contribution to science which the government was already making.

The outbreak of the First World War revived interest in central scientific organisation within the government. Again an external crisis proved necessary. The distinguished astronomer George Ellery Hale had been preaching reform of the National Academy for several years before 1916, but only the conversion of President Wilson to a policy of preparedness made

---

[13] *Ibid.*
[14] *Ibid.* p. 1078.
[15] *Ibid.* p. 1082.
[16] Carnegie Institution of Washington, *Year Book* 1902, (Washington: 1903), p. xiii.

possible the creation of the National Research Council. Hale's ideas, representing a real concern for the problem of central scientific organisation from within the scientific community, are perhaps most fully reflected in the Executive Order of 1918, establishing the National Research Council as a peacetime organisation, but the effectiveness of the organisation in time of war had been much greater than had been that of the National Academy during the Civil War. The post-war NRC had broad terms of reference, which included the injunction "to survey the larger possibilities of science, to formulate comprehensive projects of research, and to develop effective means of utilising the scientific and technical resources of the country for dealing with these projects." [17] It moved away from its direct government connection and set up instead a Division of Government Relations. One representative of each government agency was appointed by the President of the United States, and on paper the new Division appeared destined to provide the bridge between government science and non-government science necessary in any central scientific organisation. However, the Division never performed any important function and soon passed from the scene.

The Great Depression was a sufficiently serious crisis in American history to call forth a special response, again from the scientific community itself. Isaiah Bowman, then head of the National Research Council, was the essential figure in the creation of the Science Advisory Board in 1933. Karl Compton served as its chairman and came to see in its failure lessons which would later serve as a guide in an even greater crisis. When the shadow of World War II fell across the scientific community, its leaders without hesitating looked for a new organisation.

IV

In measuring the strength and nature of the two traditions, it is of course obvious that pluralism has dominated all forms of central organisation. But the scientific community cannot be divided into pluralists and centralists in any simple way. Indeed a recurrent phenomenon is the insight of the leaders of the predominant bureaux that science has problems of its own which transcend what can be done within the confines of their own missions. Bache especially tried to create a central organisation instead of putting this extra and probably impossible burden upon the Coast Survey. Henry Wallace as the titular head of agricultural research did something of the same thing in 1933 when he had a part in calling the Science Advisory Board into existence. Predominant agencies could create the impression that they stood for all of science and set the standards for all of science for a short time, but

[17] National Academy of Sciences, *Annual Report for 1918*, (Washington, 1919), pp. 40–41.

even to contemporaries they did not appear to have the breadth and staying power to handle the central problems imposed upon the scientific community from outside by a crisis which markedly altered the demand for research.

The question may be asked why, in 1939, pluralism still remained strongly entrenched in a country which had moved some distance further toward a national approach to problems in other areas. One obvious answer lies in the pluralism of science itself. Even the central scientific organisations themselves, such as the National Academy of Sciences, tended to become enforcers of pluralism as they drew back from central responsibilities within the government itself. Hence one whole tradition—that of the explicit central scientific organisation—only added to the multiplicity of institutions which made up the scientific community. None could develop the double constituency—the constituencies of the scientific community itself and the larger political community, necessary to make decisions concerning priorities among fields of science and between governmental and non-governmental science.

The other tradition—that of the predominant agency—did indeed provide examples of decisions concerning priorities being made. Yet these periods of command were short in duration and uncertain in authority. They lost their positions as central scientific organisations either when their public constituency changed its demands on science or when the scientific community changed its view of where the most fruitful line of future research lay. The leverage of public support and the opportunity for further research are both necessary for achieving predominance. The feat is so difficult, the timing so hazardous, and the constituencies so far removed from one another that the wonder of the history of science in America is the frequency with which such predominance has been achieved and the talent which has been displayed by a whole succession of leaders. The result of several generations of predominant agencies is, however, again pluralism. Old agencies do not die, and no one with an appreciation of the many paths which science can take, would take the responsibility of wishing them away. It is hard, however, for an agency at the end of its ascendancy to retreat to more limited terms of reference than those it enjoyed during its greatest period. Part of the choler that animated the debate between Powell and Alexander Agassiz stemmed from the latter's desire to shield and protect the Coast Survey.

V

Against this background, a few of the mountain ranges in the confused geography of science and government in the period since 1939 can be dimly discerned. The highest peak of all is the Office of Scientific Research and Development. To a startling extent it took on the characteristics of both a predominant agency and a central scientific organisation at the same time. It had a straight line organisation within the government, culminating in its director, Vannevar Bush. He and his associates had direct access to the President and an accountability to Congress which scarcely affected their major decisions by limitations either of money or timing. They had close liaison with the military, and the ability, in fact seldom used, of going ahead despite the military when they wanted to. They marshalled in the service of the government an array of laboratories undreamed of earlier, by using contractual relationships to secure existing resources in the universities. At the same time they could select the scientific personnel they wanted (and here the "they" was an ever-broadening set of circles, each one known personally to the next above it) and concentrate them as much or as little as the nature of the work and the facilities seemed to dictate. When, as a result of their own ability to make difficult decisions regarding priorities, one part of their operation grew out of balance with the rest and involved them in huge construction and industrial operations, they showed immense administrative ingenuity in assigning the Manhattan Project to the Army Engineers. The device of using Bush and James B. Conant in a double role kept the OSRD and the Manhattan District in step even while they proceeded separately.

The remarkable thing about this performance was the assumption that when the emergency was over the OSRD should go out of business. This was one of the most unusual decisions in all of American political history. Those with experience assert that it would have been impossible to attract and retain sufficiently qualified staff. Yet for any group to possess such power and to display such skill in using it and then to declare as an article of faith that the whole system they had made to work could not possibly continue is by any standard remarkable. There was much realism in the OSRD's position. The leaders recognised the unique forces which gave them the power they had, and they knew that as soon as the threat of Hitler was gone there would be a reckoning not only with the resurgent institutions of the larger society—the Congress and public opinion—but also with the pluralism of the scientific community which would reassert itself. Instead of fighting that pluralism, the leaders of the OSRD thought they could use it to create a set of balancing institutions. Military research, which had been disastrously weak in the 1930s, would have to be strengthened inside the military. Industrial research, then universally considered the strongest sector of science, could take care of itself. Atomic energy would receive special treatment both nationally and internationally. The universities, which had largely shut down both basic research and graduate training for the duration, could clearly not return to the leisurely and penurious pre-war pace, so a National Research Foundation would provide their support. Although this

Foundation would have a broad mandate, with interests in both medicine and military research, the part-time board which would be its executive was a device for guaranteeing pluralism rather than an instrument to make decisions about priorities among the sectors and fields of science. According to these expectations, the OSRD would become superfluous. In this they realistically reflected a state of mind which was widespread just after the end of the Second World War. Pluralism came back to the American scientific community, bringing with it the authority of the success of the only effective central scientific organisation in American history.

These expectations failed to reckon with one important factor. The pluralism which had been expected was put under stress, as always in the past, by an external crisis. The OSRD and those who had looked forward to its abdication did not foresee the Cold War and had no plan for it. Specifically, OSRD made no provision for what it had been itself—a central scientific organisation. While all the generalisations from the long past are still in effect, the new crisis is different in that it is seemingly permanent.

Even without the Cold War, however, the post-war solutions did not go exactly according to the OSRD's scheme. The function of a central scientific organisation was firmly taken over in 1947 by a new agency which was predominant on the day of its birth. The Atomic Energy Commission had the support and the machinery to set standards for American science and to shape the pattern of research in broad terms. Its General Advisory Committee in the late 1940s was a major link between the scientific community and the general policy machinery of the government. It was civilian in form but deeply involved in the production of the warheads which expressed the state of the Cold War.

None of the pale efforts of the late forties and early fifties to create an explicit central scientific organisation went very far. The Interdepartmental Committee on Scientific Research and Development, created in 1947, and the President's Science Advisory Committee in the Office of Defense Mobilisation, child of the Korean War, were useful but obscure in the years before 1957. The National Science Foundation never interpreted its own role as that of a central scientific organisation in the sense used here.

Sputnik is still too close for reliable evaluation in historical perspective. But in its aftermath, as in previous crises, central scientific organisation became a demand imposed on the scientific community from outside itself. And as in earlier crises, the scientific community had solutions to put forward in answer.

By November, 1957, when James R. Killian was appointed a Special Assistant to the President for science, anyone with the long history of central scientific organisation in mind could make certain generalisations and certain predictions.[18] A Department of Science would not work. The National Academy and the National Research Council had no mechanism for the continuous and intense provision of the highly informed advice which was necessary. The National Science Foundation had not yet found its chosen niche of supporting basic research and education in the sciences. The Department of Defense, as had always been true of the military, could not serve as a central scientific organisation for those parts of the scientific community outside itself. The Atomic Energy Commission in the classic manner of predominant agencies, had found that its mission did not envelop the new crisis, which was in delivery systems. A new predominant agency, NASA, was implicit in the situation already. Given the nature of the Cold War and the relation of science to it, the only possible site for a central scientific organisation had become the peak of the government's own organisational pyramid, the Presidency itself.

In November, 1957, it was even possible to see some of the directions in which the organisation within the Presidency would evolve. Statutory authority, a budget, and a position more secure than the White House staff, probably in the Executive Office of the President, would come sooner or later. Some kind of partnership with Congress was necessary. A secure line of communication to the nation's scientists was so obviously needed that it almost immediately engendered the reorganisation of the Science Advisory Committee. A working relationship with the Bureau of the Budget would be the necessary means of influencing the individual courses of the numerous government agencies which in turn affect all the sectors of science. The need for a staff skilled in the analysis of the institutional problems of science also loomed large at the time.

Since November, 1957, the focus of central scientific organisation has lain in the institutional organisation of the Presidency. Yet a choice has never been and is not now between a complete pluralism—a "scientific anarchy" [19]—and a monolithic political control of science by the government. The tripartite structure evolved in the Office of the President has many characteristics of an ideal central scientific organisation. The President's Science Advisory Committee represents the scientific community especially in the universities. The Federal Council of Science and Technology has on it representatives of all the scientific agencies of the government. The Office of Science and Technology provides a staff and head-

[18] What follows draws from my article, "The Real Challenge to Dr. Killian," included in Hearings on S. 3126 and S. 4039, Part 2, Committee on Government Operations, U.S. Senate, 85 Cong., 2 sess. (June 25 and 26, 1958), pp. 304–308.

[19] Jerome Wiesner is quoted as using this term in Marshak, Robert E., "Re-examining the Soviet Scientific Challenge," *Bulletin of the Atomic Scientists,* XIX (April, 1963), 4.

quarters for the Special Assistant to the President for Science, an individual who, by holding multiple positions within the three structures and on the President's staff, is able to coordinate the whole effort.[20]

The post-Sputnik structure of scientific policy has one advantage over all its predecessors which might make it counterbalance the forces of pluralism, including the predominant agencies as they rise and fall. It is close to the President and derives its power from him. It can conceivably reach the President even after the strongest agency has made its plea for priority. Vannevar Bush was able to use his access to President Roosevelt in a manner which gave a single purpose and direction to the many institutions he used. Also he usually confirmed these institutions in their nearly autonomous relations with the government and with one another. Has the post-Sputnik structure under Drs. Killian, Kistiakowsky and Wiesner performed this way?

The greatest danger to the success of the experiment is that it will move too far from the President to draw on the authority of the larger society, which is expressed in the Presidency. Once this happens, one agency or another, with pretensions of predominance, will be able to use the leverage gained from the general community, probably through Congress, to impose priority decisions, despite the organisation which has been constructed around the President. If it ever becomes justifiable to say that the President's Scientific Advisory Committee is doing well at making choices within a field of science, but not so well at making choices between fields, it will be because the presidential structure has lost its momentum as a central scientific organisation and is drifting into the pluralism it was designed to counterbalance.[21]

VI

What instruction may we draw from this historical survey of the interplay of centre and plurality in the history of American scientific organisation? Or, to put it another way, let us suppose that a representative of a developing nation comes to Washington and says: "The research institutions of my country are still in a plastic state. There are few scientists and engineers. We are about where the new United States was in 1789. What is there in the American experience with central scientific organisation from which we can learn?"

[20] See "Reorganization Plan No. 2 of 1962 (Office of Science and Technology—National Science Foundation)" in Hearing before a Subcommittee of the Committee on Government Operations, U.S. House of Representatives, 87 Cong., 2 sess. (April 17, 1962), pp. 2–3.

[21] For a discussion of the process of choice in the President's Science Advisory Committee, see Weinberg, Alvin M., "Criteria for Scientific Choice," *Minerva,* I (Winter, 1963), 3, pp. 159–171.

One simply cannot answer such a question by suggesting that another nation copy the American pattern. The shape of the institutions in the United States is too closely tied to the nation's history and the timing of its development. No one would wish to impose on others the dilemma in which all efforts at central scientific organisation in the United States have found themselves. Still, certain underlying propositions might perhaps hold true in divergent institutional settings.

In the first place, any system of scientific institutions must have in it a large tolerance for pluralism, both of ideas and of their institutional expression. The United States has attained comprehensiveness both with regard to the different fields of science and to the variety of problems to which science is applied by allowing full play of pluralism. The scientific community has a fundamental stake in pluralism and should be expected to encourage it in its relations with the larger community. The scientific community should also give serious thought to the protection of the institutions through which this pluralism is manifested, so that variety and flexibility will be characteristics of the scientific community itself. The nation will be wise which learns from the United States that the scientific future can be prepared for not by prediction but by a healthy pluralism.

In the second place, the nation will also be wise which recognises the need for unity in the midst of plurality. Sooner or later someone must make decisions concerning priorities in science, on behalf of the general community. A central scientific organisation which has an awareness of the social and political impact of science and which can assist the authorities of the larger community in making self-conscious decisions about the society-wide organisation of research is a necessity when science moves into a crucial role in the many various activities of a nation. Democracy is represented in the pluralistic tradition but it is equally present in the responsibility which the scientific community owes to the government as a whole. An adequate provision for central scientific organisation should be an object of intense concern to a developing nation.

Every state must work a balance between the centre and the plurality which is in harmony with its own traditions and its own institutions. Despite the overtones of inadequacy in accomplishment, the American democracy has offered fertile ground for experimentation in the forms of central scientific organisation. From the several attempts made through the last century and a half emerges an ideal of such an institution which is worthy of emulation.

The Scientific Establishment

DON K. PRICE

Now that the federal government is spending more money on research and development than its total budget before Pearl Harbor, American scientists find it hard to figure out their new role in society. They used to assume that democracy would never be a patron of the sciences, and even after the Second World War the Executive had to urge the support of research on a skeptical Congress. But even though the last administration started to cut back on expenditures for science, it ended by quadrupling them. And this was by no means for defense alone; over those eight years the Congress multiplied the budget of the National Institutes of Health more than ninefold, giving them each year more than the President recommended. It is almost enough to make one try to apply to politics the theory of Henry Adams that science, as it becomes more abstract, increases in geometrical progression the power that it produces.[1]

In his farewell message President Eisenhower warned the nation against the danger that "public policy could itself become the captive of a scientific-technological elite." Even though he quickly explained that he was not talking about science in general, but only those parts allied with military and industrial power, this was a shock to the scientists.[2] To one who believes

Reprinted from the *Proceedings of the American Philosophical Society,* June 1962, Vol. CVI, No. 3, pp. 235–245, with the permission of the author and the publisher. Professor Don K. Price is Dean of the Graduate School of Public Administration at Harvard University, and director of its Science and Public Policy Program. His *Government and Science* was a pioneering study of the relations of science and public policy.

[1] Adams predicted that "the future of Thought, and therefore of History, lies in the hands of the physicists . . . ," and went on to speculate that a rapid acceleration of thought in the direction of the abstract sciences might "reduce the forces of the molecule, the atom, and the electron to that costless servitude to which it has reduced the old elements of earth and air, fire and water. . . ." His prediction was uncanny, except for the term "costless." Henry Adams, *The Degradation of the Democratic Dogma* (New York, Capricorn, 1958, first published in 1919), pp. 277, 303.

[2] Quoted in The New York *Times,* January 22, 1961. See also the authorized interpretation of this statement by the President's Special Assistant for Science and Technology, Dr. George B. Kistiakowsky, quoted in "Footnote to History," *Science,* CXXXIII, No. 3450 (February 10, 1961), 355. As Chief of Staff, General Eisenhower had told the Army in 1946: "The future security of the nation demands that all those civilian resources which by conversion or redirection constitute our main support in time of emergency be associated closely with the activities of the Army in time of peace," and advised the Army to contract extensively for scientific and indus-

that science has helped to liberate man from ancient tyrannies—who in short still takes his political faith from Franklin and Jefferson and the Age of the Enlightenment—it is disconcerting to be told that he is a member of a new priesthood allied with military power.

Yet the plain fact is that science has become the major Establishment in the American political system: the only set of institutions for which tax funds are appropriated almost on faith, and under concordats which protect the autonomy, if not the cloistered calm, of the laboratory. The intellectual problems involved in this new status are likely to trouble scientists almost as much as the fears of the apocalyptic uses to which their discoveries may be put by the politicians.

The scientists are not the first, of course, to find it difficult to adjust their political ideals to the new world of technology. For example, the old corporation executive liked the great power technology had given to industry, but wished to limit the role of government on Jeffersonian principles. But the American scientist has a better right to his political nostalgia. For while the Founding Fathers had very little idea that industrial corporations would ever exist, let alone claim freedom of enterprise as a fundamental of the Constitution, some of them had a strong faith that free science would advance the cause of political freedom.

This faith of the Enlightenment tended to persist in the political thinking of American scientists, even in the period between the two World Wars, when it came to seem naïve to their colleagues abroad. Even to this day they have shown singularly little interest in the conservative political theorists who have been telling them that science cannot deal with basic values or solve the major human problems, and the radical theorists who tell them that science can, if it will only join in a political system that will give it real power over society.[3] The conservative theorists have usually supported the conventional views of those in the European parliamentary tradition who believed that major political issues should be dealt with by party leaders and career administrators, with scientists speaking on such matters only when spoken to. And the most important radicals have been the Marxists, who proposed to let science, as they defined it, determine all human values through a disciplined system that would leave no room for the disorder of liberal democracy.

---

trial services. (*Memorandum for . . . General and Special Staff Divisions, etc.,* "Scientific and Technological Resources as Military Assets," April 30, 1946.)

[3] Unamuno, Maritain, and Ortega y Gasset represent the conservative critics of the Enlightenment; J. D. Bernal may be taken as a sample on the socialist side. Judith N. Shklar, whose *After Utopia* (Princeton, N.J., Princeton University Press, 1957) begins with the observation that "nothing is quite so dead today as the spirit of optimism that the very word Enlightenment evokes," goes on to admit that "the less reflective public, certainly until 1914, remained cheerfully indifferent to the intellectual currents of despair. . . . [p. 3]" In this optimistic category, I would include most American scientists, and bring the date up to the present.

If American scientists generally ignored both the conservative and radical critics of the Enlightenment, it was probably, in the main, because they were simply not interested in political theory, or even in politics. But it may have been also because neither theoretical position seemed very relevant to their practical experience. In disregard of the conservative and conventional theory, American scientists have come to have a much more direct role in high administration and in the making of policy than their counterparts in the parliamentary systems of Western Europe. (This is not to say that they had a more satisfactory role in the performance of scientific functions in the government.) And the more influence the scientists acquire, the more they now seem to work toward the dispersal of government organization and the decentralization of decisions, a trend impossible to explain to technocrats or the theorists of Marxism.

If we wish to understand the nature of our present scientific establishment, and its role in the making of public policy, perhaps we should look at the unusual way in which the role of scientists in public affairs has developed in the United States, and what its influence has been on the governmental system. That influence, I think, has been profound, not because of anything the scientists were seeking to do deliberately, at least until quite recently, but because of the special opportunities that were offered them by the nature of American political institutions. From the Jacksonian period, indeed, American scientists rarely had any distinctive opinion about politics or its relation to science; they were most often inclined to combine the anti-political prejudices of the business community with an envy of the social status of the European scientist. But while the American scientist lacked the honorific status of a member of a European Academy, he probably found it easier to play a direct role in government policy-making.

Sir Charles Snow has written with great insight of the Two Cultures, of the persisting failure of the humanists to understand the scientists or the changes they are working in the world, and of the scientists' personal and institutional difficulties in their relationship to government administrators and politicians. He has warned Americans most cogently against the naïve belief that their constitutional system protects them against the dangers that face all countries as the result of the terrible weapons that scientists have put at the disposal of politicians who still think in prescientific terms.[4]

But in the United States we need to understand the idiosyncrasies of our institutions not in order to admire them, but to know how to remedy their shortcomings, which were only a minor nuisance a generation ago, but may be a mortal threat today. Our television experts and editorial writers may be addicted to oratorical overconfidence in our peculiar institutions, but our scientists and intellectuals generally—and government reformers in

[4] See especially C. P. Snow, *Science and Government* (Cambridge, Mass., Harvard University Press, 1961), p. 55.

particular—are rather more addicted to applying constitutional cures that do not fit the disease.

I suspect that Sir Charles has a special degree of popularity in the United States for a reason that he would probably disapprove. We enjoy what he writes not only because we see many important ways that it applies to us, but also because of ways in which it does not. We like it much as we like Anthony Trollope; we like to read about a scholarly world in which the classicists can still snub the scientists and social scientists hardly exist at all, just as we like to read about the squire and the vicar and the butler. And American scientists like to imagine, as they read about the problems that scientists experience when serving under the career administrators of the United Kingdom, that they can blame their own problems on lack of status in the bureaucracy.

Yet a look at the main outlines of the two systems gives a different picture. In Great Britain, in spite of decades of debate about the basis of recruitment of the Administrative Class, it is still dominated by men trained in the classical and historical studies; not one man in twenty among these guardians of public policy has had a scientific or technical education. In spite of recurrent criticism of its role, it still maintains a professional monopoly (though in a studiously amateur and nonscientific way) over the organization of the government departments, and a major share of influence in the formation of national policy. It thus has no great interest in maintaining easy institutional channels by which scientists could move into its membership, or the universities could work closely with it on its major policy problems.[5]

Now that we are both constitutional democracies, it makes much less difference that Great Britain has a king and the United States a president but a great deal of difference how we set up the professional group of men who actually run the government. Our Jacksonian revolution indeed destroyed the hopes of John Quincy Adams for a continuation of the Jeffersonian alliance between science and republicanism. At the same time, by wiping out the beginnings of a career system, it prevented the development of an elite administrative corps and thus cleared the channels of promotion for the scientists who, decades later, were to begin to move up in the civil service. The frontier radicalism of the day distrusted all forms of Establishment; this was the era in which state constitutions forbade ministers to hold public office and prohibited educational qualifications for admission to the

---

[5] Edward McCrensky, *Scientific Manpower in Europe* (New York, Pergamon Press, 1958), pp. 27–29, gives the general picture with respect to salaries and personnel policy. For the classic attitude of the Administrative Class regarding its relation to the scientific civil service, see the testimony of Sir Warren Fisher, Permanent Secretary of the Treasury, before the Royal Commission on the Civil Service, 1929–30, *Minutes of Evidence,* pp. 1276, 1282. For its contemporary attitude, see C. H. Sisson, *The Spirit of British Administration* (London, Faber and Faber, 1959).

bar. But as the business of government got more complicated, the frontier had to admit that certain skills were necessary. Its essentially pragmatic temper insisted, as it became necessary to hire civil servants for merit rather than patronage, that the requirements be defined in terms of the needs of the specific jobs, rather than by general educational status. It was easiest to prove the need for special skills, of course, in technical fields, partly on account of the objective nature of the problem, partly because scientific societies were determined to raise and maintain their professional standards in the civil service as well as in private practice.[6]

As a result, it was in the scientific and professional fields that the career civil service system was first pushed up to the higher ranks. As we developed our top civil service, we made it something quite different from a career Administrative Class; most of its members are not only nonpolitical, but nonadministrative as well, and they are not career officials in the same sense as a U.S. Navy officer or a British Civil Servant.

In recent years, scientists and engineers, while certainly rare among those in high political office, have done reasonably well in the civil service. The positions of administrative continuity and bureaucratic power in Washington are, in the civil service departments, the bureau chiefs. A study in 1958 of the 63 bureau chiefs showed that 9 of them had advanced degrees in the natural sciences, and 17 others had been trained in lesser ways as engineers or technicians. By comparison with these 26 from various branches of technology, there were 9 economists and only 8 lawyers, and 20 from miscellaneous administrative or business careers.[7] Aside from the positions of bureau chief, the top career positions are the so-called "super-grades," which were added above the regular civil service grades to let the government compete for scarce talent.[8] The favorite justification for these positions is the need to employ capable scientists and engineers, notably in the technical branches of the Defense Department and the National Aeronautics

[6] As A. Lawrence Lowell put it: "[T]he great professions, which have secured general recognition in the community, have been strong enough to insist that strictly professional work must not be intrusted to men who have had no professional training or experience." *Public Opinion and Popular Government* (New York, Longmans, 1926), p. 274. Detailed illustrations for specifically scientific fields may be found in the series of "Service Monographs of the United States Government" published by the Institute for Government Research, notably those on the Steamboat Inspection Service, the Office of Experiment Stations, the General Land Office, and the Public Health Service. See also Lewis Mayers, *The Federal Service* (New York, D. Appleton, 1922), p. 21, and Lewis Meriam, *Public Personnel Problems from the Standpoint of the Operating Officers* (Washington, D.C., The Brookings Institution, 1938), p. 317.

[7] Michael E. Smith, "Bureau Chiefs in the Federal Government," in *Public Policy, 1958*, Yearbook of the Graduate School of Public Administration, Harvard University (Cambridge, Mass., Harvard University Press, 1960), p. 62.

[8] U.S. Civil Service Commission, *The Federal Top Salary Network* (Washington, D.C., USGPO, 1960).

and Space Administration. Administrators have ridden along to higher salaries on the political coattails of scientists.

Scientists who become bureau chiefs are, of course, no longer practicing scientists; they are doing work that in the United Kingdom would be done by a member of the Administrative Class educated in history or the classics. But when they are good at their jobs, as some of them are, it is for a reason that would have appealed to Macaulay, who used to argue that he wanted to recruit university graduates in the classics not because they had been studying the classics, but because the classics attracted the best minds, which could adapt themselves to anything.[9] And the American scientist who turns administrator is the equal of his English humanist counterpart in at least one respect: his lack of interest in management as a science, or sometimes at all.

But while the scientists in top civil service posts have not been deeply interested in administration, they have been interested in policy. What chance do they have to make their policy views prevail?

In their influence on policy, as in their advancement in the hierarchy, the scientists in American government had a special opportunity because they did not have to work under a tightly organized governing elite. After the Civil War, there was no strong conservative tradition based on a landed interest and no national party with a coherent ideology to take control.

As a result, policy tended to develop separately in every field. There was no one to tell the scientific experts that they were on tap but not on top; indeed, they were listened to all the more readily because they were usually not thought of as bureaucrats. There was no one from whom Congress wanted advice less than from the regular career service. But each group of scientists had one foot in government, so to speak, and one outside, and the policy views that the insiders developed would come back to the Congress from the National Academy or the scientific societies.[10] In a government of limited constitutional powers, a research program could be

---

[9] Macaulay put it more pointedly in 1833: "If astrology were taught at our universities, the young man who cast nativities best would generally turn out a superior man." Royal Commission on the Civil Service, *Fourth Report*, Cd. 7338, 1914.

[10] "[F]rom the beginning the membership of the Academy included many officers of the Government. . . . On one occasion at least this led to some embarrassment, for the reason that through this double relationship it was thought that the view of subordinate officers might control the action of those higher in authority." Frederick W. True, *A History of the First Half Century of the National Academy of Sciences* (Washington, D.C., USGPO, 1913), p. 202. The same fear, or hope, exists in the present relationship between the Academy and the Federal Council for Science and Technology. F. W. True's history of the Academy, and A. C. True's *History of Agricultural Experimentation and Research in the United States* (Washington, D.C., U.S. Dept. of Agriculture, 1937), Misc. Publ. No. 251, tell a great deal about the role of scientific societies in the development of new federal programs.

justified in a given field when an action program could not. But the research ultimately seemed to lead to action, in spite of the lawyers' scruples and the lack of interest in the party machines. This was only in part because the politicians were persuaded by objective data; it may have been even more because scientists (and in some fields, the economists) were the major organized communities of professional opinion with a continuous interest in specific public programs. This is a summary of the development of many new federal programs: you can trace it in agriculture, in natural resources, in the regulation of business, in labor and welfare, and we now see its beginnings in the support of education.

The most influential pattern was set in agriculture. Washington and Jefferson had been interested in fostering scientific improvements in agriculture, and in federal support of a national university. They were blocked by the lawyers' scruples about states' rights, until the agricultural scientists found a way to get there by a different route—one that evaded constitutional barriers by merging federal and state interests through the device of federal grants to states in either land or money, and by building a program up on scientific and educational bases. The foundation was, of course, the land-grant college; from it grew the experiment station, the extension program, and the whole system of policy which has let the federal government play a more effective role in the agricultural economy than the government of any supposedly socialized state. In all this development, the land-grant colleges and the associations of various kinds of agricultural scientists maintained an important influence on the Department of Agriculture, supplied most of its career personnel, and generally provided the intellectual leadership for national agricultural policy. They thus in effect greatly weakened the old constitutional distinction between state and federal functions, but without subjecting the field of agriculture to the control of a centralized bureaucracy.

The pattern of grants-in-aid, with its new set of administrative relationships, met two cardinal needs: to provide money, as well as national policy direction, from Washington, and to maintain the autonomy of the states. It accordingly became the basis on which new programs were developed—highways, public health, social security, welfare, housing, and others. This was what political scientists came to call the "New Federalism," which has given the scientists and specialists in each field of policy a chance to work out programs without too much constraint by any party doctrine.

An elite administrative corps may look on scientists as properly subordinate, and science as a way of thinking that should deal with the means to support a policy, a tradition, or an ideology, rather than an end in itself. We can understand this relationship in other countries if we recall how until recent years our military services thought that civilian scientists in military laboratories should conduct their research only pursuant to "requirements" defined by military staff work. This notion was exploded as it became apparent that what scientists discovered by unrestricted research might be of greater military importance than the things the military officers thought they wanted—in short, that the means might determine the ends.

This example provides the extreme (and almost the only conspicuous) example in American politics in which scientists have been faced with difficulties in getting a direct political hearing for their policy ideas. The typical editorial writer may still think in terms borrowed from the experience of parliamentary constitutions with tightly knit administrative elites, but all the habits of American public life run on a different pattern.

Its constitutional peculiarities are typified in one trivial incident: in a recent congressional hearing, a friendly Representative addressed the newly appointed political head of the NASA, to his mild embarrassment, as "Doctor." In a legislature that is supposed to distrust eggheads, a Congressman often wants his advice on a specific program undiluted by either party doctrine or the policy views of general administrators; he is so conditioned to go directly to the scientific expert whenever he can that he sometimes treats his witnesses as experts even when they are not. This constitutional model is worth looking at with more critical sympathy. Its essential parts—none of which exists in the classic parliamentary system—are the standing congressional committee that considers policies without being bound by party doctrine; a chief executive who is elected independently of the legislature on a nonideological platform so that he can tolerate loose coordination and experimentation in policy matters; and a civil service which lets scientists move freely up into top administrative positions, and in and out of government, thus maintaining a continuous interchange of men and ideas between the government and universities. This system makes it impossible to maintain an institutional distinction between ends and means, between policy decisions on the one hand, and on the other hand scientific research or administration. Hence it makes party responsibility in the parliamentary sense impossible, and it greatly complicates the task of coordinating either policy or administration.

On the other hand, to deny the distinction between ends and means is a part of the scientific approach: no scientist likes to feel that his basic values and objectives have been set by others so rigidly that he cannot follow where his research leads him. It was, after all, the purpose of the Enlightenment to free both politics and science from the monarchical and ecclesiastical institutions that defined traditional values.[11] It may be even

---

[11] Charles Frankel, *The Case for Modern Man* (Boston, Beacon Press, 1955), p. 58. Ernst Cassirer noted "the almost unlimited power which scientific knowledge gains over all the thought of the Enlightenment. . . . A . . . deeper insight into the spirit of laws, of society, of politics, and even of poetry, seems impossible unless it is pursued in the light of the great model of the natural sciences." *The Philosophy of the Enlightenment* (Boston, Beacon Press, 1955), pp. 45–46.

more necessary to deny the distinction between ends and means, in an institutional sense, in the twentieth century, when it is the requirements of new ideology, rather than old orthodoxy, that threaten freedom. For science itself, by introducing so many complexities into public policy, destroyed the comfortable nineteenth-century notion that public issues could really be determined by the parliamentary competition of two opposing doctrines. At the same time, it made possible, by the development of new techniques of mass communication, the means for producing disciplined support of authoritarian government. If the structure of political institutions does not specifically encourage some social experimentation based on scientific initiative, with some degree of deliberate freedom from the constraints of policy as determined by either partisan theorists or an administrative elite, it will narrow the range of free scientific and political development. Perhaps our eighteenth-century Constitution, with its implied distrust of party discipline, will yet prove to be more adaptable to our scientific era than the classic nineteenth-century parliamentary models of Walter Bagehot or Woodrow Wilson.[12]

At any rate, it is easy to guess why large groups among American scientists—especially in the agricultural sciences—were less pessimistic in the period after the First World War than their European colleagues with respect to the role of science in democratic politics. In two very practical ways their situation was entirely different; in civil service, their advancement was not blocked by a career bureaucracy, and the constitutional system gave them a chance to advocate policies in comparative freedom from administrative or political discipline. It was no wonder that they had not lost faith in the political approach of the Enlightenment, for they had made it work.

Nevertheless, by the time of the Great Depression this naïve faith was least prevalent in the most important universities and the most advanced fields of science. In them, science was supported more by private corporations and foundations than by government, and its leaders in newer fields like nuclear physics and biochemistry had closer intellectual ties with their European counterparts than with the agronomists or engineers of the land-grant colleges. For the loose American constitutional system had worked best in those aspects of public affairs in which the power of government and the power of the great industrial corporations were not in rivalry. The

---

[12] Walter Bagehot, *The English Constitution* (New York, Oxford University Press, 1936; first published in 1867) and Thomas Woodrow Wilson, "Cabinet Government in the United States," *The International Review* (August, 1879; reprinted in 1947 by The Overbrook Press, Stamford). By the turn of the twentieth century, Wilson had apparently changed his mind in view of the new role of the presidency, especially in international affairs: *Congressional Government* (Boston, Houghton Mifflin, Preface to 15th ed., 1900).

scientists in institutions that derived their support from industrial wealth and were interested in problems of the industrial urban economy saw the constitutional model in a different political perspective. Among them, accordingly, were to be found both those conservative scientists who were most distrustful of government, and those radicals who tended to take a Marxist view of the role of science in society.

The Depression had thus made it impossible for the American scientist to avoid the second challenge, explicit in Marxism, with respect to the significance of his role in society: does science as it grows in importance lead us away from constitutional liberalism, and require party dictatorship? In a society of growing complexity, is not an increase in the role of government inevitable, and does not that inevitably lead to a centralization of power that will destroy democratic freedom?

These are still troublesome questions, but they are being discussed on a somewhat higher level of sophistication than three decades ago. The change has come about partly because scientists, under the pressure of the Second World War, worked out a new type of contractual relationship that has brought private scientific institutions into a connection with the federal government as intimate and active as that of any land-grant college. And the extension of this system to industrial corporations may now be bringing about a new relationship between government and business following the quarrels of the Depression era, much as the grant-in-aid system transformed federal-state relations after the Civil War.

Before going into the nature of this new system, let us note two peculiarities of American politics that made it possible. The first was the assumption that it was just as appropriate for the voters and legislators to control the administrative organization and procedures of government as its policies, that is to say, the means as well as the ends. This was a radical departure from British or European assumptions. The political progression from conservatives to liberals to socialists never changed the fundamental European assumption that, while governments might be responsible to legislatures for the substance of their policies, it was better for politics and legislation not to meddle with internal administrative organization or the management of the bureaucracy. The socialist political leaders took the unity of the state and its bureaucracy for granted. If anything, they tended to make it all the more monolithic, and to push to its logical conclusion the tendency of Benthamite liberalism to abolish the privileges of guilds and public corporations. But in the United States the current of radicalism ran in the opposite direction; after the age of Jackson, lobbyists and legislators were likely to concern themselves at least as much with the details of administrative organization as with major policies, generally with the purpose of creating centers of independence within government. This tendency was pushed so far that it destroyed the unity of administration, and had disastrous effects on the competence and the political responsibility of government. But it also made it a mistake to assume—as was often assumed both by those who admired and those who feared socialism—that an extension in the scope of governmental business in the United States would automatically involve a corresponding centralization of power.

The second peculiarity of American politics was the extent to which universities and private foundations had a hand in the initiation of new public policies. Private universities as well as the land-grant colleges were drawn into public service functions, partly because they were, in the absence of a career bureaucracy, the main reservoir of expertise on which politicians could draw for advice, and partly in response to the influence of the philanthropic foundations.

By the 1920s, some of the major foundations had lost interest in the charitable alleviation of social problems, and began to hope that science might solve them. This idea led to a strategy of supporting both scientific research and demonstration projects to test the application of such research, which could then be extended by the greater resources of government. Their aid to scientific education and research is a familiar story, in almost every branch of science. But equally important, they went on to help strengthen the professional organizations of scientists,[13] and to pay for the efforts of governments to improve their organization and administration, and to make use of research and research institutions as they did so. By the time of the Second World War, the leading scientists knew that a grant-making agency like a foundation could initiate nationwide programs by working with independent universities and governmental agencies, as the stories of hookworm control, the foundation of public libraries, and the reform of medical education all suggested. And political leaders were inclined to turn to private funds to help them explore future policy opportunities, or experiment with them, as when President Hoover sought foundation financing for his Committee on Social Trends and for a National Science Fund, and the Public Administration Clearing House provided the initial administrative costs for President Roosevelt's Science Advisory Board.[14]

As scientists learned that the organization of government was something that could be influenced from the outside, and that universities and founda-

---

[13] The National Research Council, created by President Wilson to do in the First World War (in a rudimentary way) what the Office of Scientific Research and Development did in the Second, was supported not by appropriations but by the Rockefeller and Carnegie Foundations. Richard G. Axt, *The Federal Government and Financing Higher Education* (New York, Columbia University Press, 1952), p. 78.

[14] *Report of the Science Advisory Board* (Washington, D.C., USGPO, September 20, 1934), p. 15.

tions could have a substantial influence on public policy, they were in effect freeing themselves from the assumption that government and private institutions were sharply different in nature. They were accordingly ready, at the outset of the Second World War, to work out a thoroughly pragmatic set of arrangements for the conduct of weapons research. The approach that they adopted was simply to enlist institutions rather than individuals in the two great scientific programs of the War: the Office of Scientific Research and Development (OSRD) and the Manhattan Project of the Army Engineers.

To those who expect wartime crises and military authority to produce a centralization of authority, this approach must have been as surprising as if the Army had used the war as an excuse to increase, rather than decrease, its reliance on the state militias. But in the hands of Vannevar Bush, James B. Conant, and Karl T. Compton, the government contract became a new type of federalism. Under the OSRD, the Massachusetts Institute of Technology took on the responsibility for developing radar, and California Institute of Technology rockets, and under the Manhattan District, the University of Chicago set up the first sustained nuclear reaction and the University of California fabricated the first atomic bomb, while DuPont, General Electric, Union Carbide, and other industrial giants built the facilities to produce the fissionable materials.[15]

The postwar sequel is a well known story. Through a continuation of this system of administering research and development programs by grant or contract, the Atomic Energy Commission, which was hailed by the draftsmen of the Atomic Energy Act as a triumph of socialism,[16] supports a program in which some nine-tenths of the employees work for private corporations. The adamant argument of many scientific leaders of the 1930s against federal support of science now seems as ancient and irrelevant as debates over infra- or supra-lapsarianism; no major university today could carry on its research program without federal money. The Massachusetts Institute of Technology, California Institute of Technology, Chicago, and Johns Hopkins, of course, all administer special military or atomic energy programs and consequently draw from three-fifths to five-sixths of their budgets from

[15] See the first volume of the official history of the Atomic Energy Commission by Richard G. Hewlett and Oscar E. Anderson, Jr., *The New World, 1939–1946* (Vol. I. of *A History of the Atomic Energy Commission,* University Park, Pa., Pennsylvania State University Press, 1962).

[16] "The field of atomic energy is made an island of socialism in the midst of a free enterprise economy." James R. Newman and Byron S. Miller, *The Control of Atomic Energy* (New York, McGraw-Hill, 1948), p. 4. Mr. Newman, writing the preface to this book a year after the text was completed, noted that "only one major policy formulation, the decision by the Atomic Energy Commission not to conduct research in its own laboratories, departs sharply from the interpretations of the Act set forth in these pages [p. xi]."

government, while Harvard, Yale, and Princeton now get a larger proportion of their operating revenues from federal funds than do land-grant colleges like Illinois, Kentucky, and Maryland.[17]

In dollar volume, the biggest contracts are between the military services and industrial corporations; while most of this money goes for procurement, much of it goes for research and development, and for the kind of systems analysis and the direction and supervision of subcontractors that in a simpler age would have been done by the technical services of the Army and Navy. And even in the business of procurement, the contractual relation is not the traditional market affair: the contract is not let on competitive bids, the product cannot be specified, the price is not fixed, the government supplies much of the plant and capital, and the government may determine or approve the letting of subcontracts, the salaries of key executives, and a host of other managerial matters. A sizable proportion of the government's (and nation's) business is done this way; any one of six industrial corporations spends more federal tax dollars than any of the four smallest executive departments.[18]

But the significance of this development does not turn on the sheer quantity of money but on the possibilities of institutional development: if a contract can be made with an established academic or industrial corporation, why cannot a new one be set up for the purpose, and if the system will work for scientists and engineers, why not for others? Accordingly we have been seeing not only the splitting off of certain functions that government might have operated directly and their administrative fusion with private institutions, but the creation of entirely new private corporate entities (e.g., the RAND Corporation, the Institute for Defense Analyses, the Aerospace Corporation) for the performance of government business.

As for the kinds of business that can be done under this system, Sir Henry Maine, who believed that progress was measured by the change from status to contract, would be intrigued to note that private corporations have contracts to maintain the Air Force's bombers and its missile ranges, private

[17] See the forthcoming study, to be published by the Carnegie Foundation for the Advancement of Teaching in 1963, on the relationship of American universities to the federal government.

[18] For a general discussion of this problem from the legal point of view, see Arthur S. Miller, "Administration by Contract: A New Concern for the Administrative Lawyer," *New York University Law Review*, XXXVI (1961), 957–90. The economic aspects are discussed in a study by Carl Kaysen, *Improving the Efficiency of Military Research and Development*, to be published by the Committee for Economic Development, and the general problems of weapons development and procurement programs in a study by the Harvard Business School: Merton J. Peck and Frederic M. Scherer, *The Weapons Acquisition Process: An Economic Analysis* (Boston, Harvard University Graduate School of Business Administration, Division of Research, 1962).

institutions make strategic studies for the Joint Chiefs of Staff and foreign policy studies for the Senate Foreign Relations Committee, universities administer technical assistance programs for the State Department all over the world, and telephone and radio companies are about to help the National Aeronautics and Space Administration carry our messages through outer space.

This new system is doubtless breaking down the political opposition to federal programs even more effectively than did the system of grants to the states. State and local governments and private corporations used to join in their jealousy of purely federal activities, any extension of which was considered socialistic. The federal grants to states in the field of agriculture, however, were no longer socialistic in the eyes of the governors and the farm bloc; they were a defense of the American way of life, even though they involved more government controls than some avowedly socialistic states have ever managed. And now that the atomic energy and space and military programs support such a large share of the nation's business, and so much of its enterprise and innovation comes from research and development financed by federal funds, and so much of that innovation and enterprise spills over quite naturally and properly into related commercial fields, it is no wonder that private business corporations are less jealous of government. More accurately, their jealousy no longer takes the form of fighting socialism, but of haggling over the administrative provisions of contracts. A great deal of private enterprise is now secreted in the interstices of government contracts. In short, what the grant-in-aid programs did to the arguments for states' rights, the new contractual systems are doing to those for pure private enterprise.

But the argument for a measure of independence from central authority still remains valid in either case, and so does the need to recognize that the fundamental responsibility of government cannot be delegated. In a proper sense of the term, "sovereignty" is of course not affected by this type of delegation. Policy decisions remain the responsibility of government. But "policy" here means simply those aspects of the business that government authorities consider it important enough to warrant controlling, either because they think them of major importance, or because they realize that voters or Congressmen think so.

This means that they will consider as policy certain aspects of management (for example, fair employment practices or prevailing wage rates). But, as long as they retain ultimate control, they may act on the advice of contractors with respect to the most momentous new issues, or delegate major segments of the business whenever they can specify the purposes to be accomplished: the complex and costly nature of certain types of military studies, and the sophistication of the new techniques of operations research, make the possibility of such delegation very broad indeed. There is nothing in the nature of the contract itself (or the grant, which differs from it only symbolically and in technical detail) to determine whether in this relationship a central bureaucracy will control every detail of the contractor's management, or will leave him free to decide matters in secret that ought to be determined by the President and Congress.

But the general effect of this new system is clear: it has destroyed the notion that the future growth in the functions and expenditures of government, which seems to be made inevitable by the increase in the technological complexity of our civilization, would necessarily take the form of a vast bureaucracy, organized on Max Weber's hierarchical principles, and using the processes of science as Julian Huxley predicted to answer policy questions.[19] To the considerable extent that scientists have shaped this development, its political and administrative patterns have reflected the way scientists actually behaved rather than the way science fiction or Marxist theory would have them behave: they have introduced into the stodgy and responsible channels of bureaucracy the amiable disorder of a university faculty meeting.

Compare, for example, our oldest and least scientific federal agency with a large operational mission with the newest and most scientific—the Post Office with the Air Force or the Space Administration. The Post Office is a relatively self-contained hierarchy. The Air Force develops its policies and runs its program with the advice and cooperation of several dozen of the most influential universities and industrial corporations of the country, whose executives and faculty members consequently have independent bases from which to criticize any policies, strategic plans, or administrative arrangements they dislike—and they can always find a congressional committee to listen to them.

I do not think the role of science in this difference is entirely accidental. This is in part because the pursuit of science itself is a nonhierachical affair; the best scientists either personally prefer, or are taught by their guilds that they should prefer, the university's combination of research, teaching, and irresponsible administration, and to get the best scientists the government took them on their own terms. But more important, I believe, is the long-range and indirect connection: when the revolution of the Enlightenment proposed that the organization and procedures of government as well as its policies should be open to scientific inquiry and independent criticism, they started a process which has had deep effects on the constitutional system. These effects showed first in the relation of scientific administrators to their

---

[19] Julian Huxley, *Man in the Modern World* (New York, New American Library, 1948), pp. 120–21. See also his *Religion Without Revelation* (New York, New American Library, 1957), p. 4.

executive superiors and to congressional committees, and later in the new structure of federalism and in the new contractual relationships between the federal government and private institutions.

As the story of the President's Science Advisory Committee illustrates, to say nothing of the similar advisory groups to the military services and the Atomic Energy Commission, this type of relationship very greatly reduces the possibility that great issues will be decided by closed scientific politics, or that the increase in importance of scientific staff work will reduce the free play of policy debate. For the institutional bases from which advisers operate give them a measure of independence as public critics, and thus provide something of a counterbalance to the centralizing pressures of wars and rumors of war.

American scientists, who have tended to be a little disillusioned about their relationship with politicians ever since the Jacksonian period, are now entitled to look with somewhat greater satisfaction on the domestic Establishment that they have helped set up. For to some small extent science has helped the political system of the United States develop along lines quite different from the classic patterns of either parliamentary government and laissez-faire economics on the one hand, or socialism and one-party rule on the other. Among its essential institutional features are universities that are concerned with applied as well as basic sciences, and continuously exchange personnel with the government at all age levels; a personnel system which puts up no barrier against the administrative promotion of men with scientific training; and grants-in-aid and contracts through which federal agencies may influence or guide the policies, but not direct the detailed management, of certain aspects of local governments, business corporations, and universities. Among these institutions, the connecting links are strongest in scientific and technical fields. And the peculiar looseness of the constitutional system enables the scientists in each field to take the initiative in developing policies—just as their innovations are providing the greatest impetus to industrial enterprise. Most important, science is not restrained in its impact on policy by any rigid distinction between ends and means, imposed by institutionalized systems of traditional ideological values. The key to this is the freedom to influence or determine the organization and procedures of government from the outside, not conceding control over them to professional administrators or party leaders.

But there are some good reasons why scientists should not be too self-satisfied about their new status. A good many of them already think that science has been corrupted by this new system, and the wealth that it has brought.[20] They tend to look back on prewar science as the Re-

[20] Merle A. Tuve, "Basic Research in Private Research Institutes," in Dael Wolfle, ed., *Symposium on Basic Research* (Washington, D.C., AAAS, 1959), p. 178.

formers looked back to the Primitive Church: a period of austere purity, an era in which no vows were needed to guarantee the poverty of the professor, no scientist was seduced by a government contract, and teaching fellows were obedient. One may well be a little skeptical about this point of view, and suspect that poverty probably brought its distractions no less troublesome than those of riches. But even if we discount such dangers so far, the worst may be yet to come. The public and members of Appropriations Committees are being led to think of science in terms of spectacular results like a space satellite or a cancer cure, and the political pressure to pass miracles may lead to some major distortions in our national policy and put some uncomfortable pressures on the independence of scientific institutions. We probably have less reason to fear that major governmental decisions involving science will be secret than they will be popular.

For while our new system of administration by contract temporarily avoids the political problems that come with the growth of bureaucracy, it encounters them again in more subtle and difficult forms. We do well to recognize that a government bureau is tempted to be more concerned with its own status and power than with the purposes of national policy. But if we entrust those purposes to industrialists or even scientists, we do not sterilize that political temptation. We only let it begin to work directly on the industrialists and scientists. If public ownership is no guarantee of unselfishness, neither is private ownership. And it is ironic, in view of the general public image of his political ideas, that it was President Eisenhower who presented most forcefully to the country the danger that, having hired private corporations to further specific public ends, we will see them use the public means for private profit, or even in political efforts to control the policy decisions of the government.

Government policy, like science itself, needs to be conceived and pursued with some regard for its totality as well as its parts. By giving priority to the parts—by turning over the administration of public functions to private institutions—we have strengthened our ability to do a great many separate things, but not our ability to give integrity and discipline and direction to our total effort. Indeed, by relying too much on the contracting method we have probably weakened the quality of the scientists within the civil service, whose help is needed by the executive who seeks to manage our scientific programs as a coherent system.[21]

In the dimensions of its financial support and in the breadth of its influence, science has indeed become a national Establishment. Politicians are more likely to abuse it by calling on it to advance their special causes

[21] Harold Brown, "Research and Engineering in the Defense Laboratories," an address by the Director of Defense Research and Engineering in Washington, D.C., on October 19, 1961.

than they are to ignore it. In this predicament, scientists cannot protect their essential interests in government by setting themselves apart in a separate status or separate department. They used to be content with the control of particular bureaus or programs. Today, in the White House Office or the lobbies of the Capitol, they are obliged by the nature of the system they helped create to play a responsible role in all aspects of national policy, and in the development of a new pattern of relationships between public and private institutions in our society.

The Academicians of Washington

HOWARD SIMONS

Not so very long ago the U.S. Public Health Service, the Federal Reserve and the National Academy of Sciences occupied adjacent buildings along Constitution Avenue, Washington. Sight-seeing guides would identify the three buildings to tourists as "Healthy, Wealthy and Wise."

The Public Health Service has long since moved to larger quarters and its old building now houses the National Science Foundation. But "Wealthy" and "Wise" are still in place, and this year the wise men of Constitution Avenue mark the 100th anniversary of their organisation.

Actually, the Academy came into being on 3 March, 1863 when the Congress enacted and President Lincoln approved the necessary legislation creating a National Academy of Sciences. But, with customary wisdom, the Academy has elected to celebrate its founding this fall—when hotel rooms are more plentiful in Washington and the Academy will not be burdened with elections and the like as happens every spring. The official celebration, therefore, is set for next week (21–24 October) and will feature, among the highlights, an address by President Kennedy.

Architecturally, the long white Academy building defies description, though its architect claimed it was "Alexandrian." In many respects, the Academy itself defies description, though its Congressional mandate is clear enough: to advise the government upon request and to further science. Nonetheless, even the most knowledgeable Washingtonians, such as taxicab drivers, still confuse the governmental National Science Foundation with the non-governmental Academy.

This is not to say that the Academy is not intimately, almost inextricably linked to the federal government. It is. But the Academy still depends upon private capital for a good many of its ventures; describes itself as "a private learned society of elected membership"; and feuds with government when occasion demands.

Historically, credit for the notion that the nation should have an Academy is generally assigned to the Scientific Lazzaroni, a brotherhood of mid-19th century American scientists which included Joseph Henry, Alexander

Reprinted from the *New Scientist,* October 17, 1963, No. 361, pp. 136–139, with the permission of the author and the publisher. Howard Simons is currently the Science Editor of *The Washington Post.*

Dallas Bache, Charles H. Davis, Louis Agassiz and Wolcott Gibbs. As one observer notes, the Scientific Lazzaroni "bore, in effect, the same relationship to the National Academy of Sciences that the 'invisible college' bore to the Royal Society."

There can be little doubt that the scientists' offer to help the federal government, coming as it did midway during the Civil War, in turn helped the Scientific Lazzaroni to realise their goal. The Academy got its charter. Bache became the first president. Six committees were established immediately in response to an equal number of requests for help from the Treasury and Navy departments. It would appear that the Academy was off to a fast start, but this initial flush was illusory. Government requests for assistance dwindled soon thereafter. In 1865, for example, there were none. Even more threatening was the disheartening fact that in January 1867 only seven papers were read before 17 members who appeared for the Academy's annual scientific sessions.

The Academy might have faced the fate of the dodo had it not been for two events: Bache bequeathed the Academy a then sizeable endowment; and the famous Henry became the Academy's second president, determined that it would "not expire in my arms."

Thereupon began a revitalisation process that has not really stopped since. A first and perhaps most significant move on Henry's part was to augment the very limited Academy membership, whose autocratic selection had given the Academy an aristocratic and unhealthy cast.

Over the next several decades, the Academy's role in government affairs took a new tack. Instead of being a technical handmaiden to government agencies, the Academy became a technical adviser without a laboratory. The reason was that government, largely spurred on by the Academy, began to establish its own technical competence. Thus, recommendations by the Academy brought the creation of the Weather Bureau, the Geological Survey and the National Bureau of Standards and, later, influenced the establishment of the Forest Service.

In spite of these impressive achievements, not all the Academicians were pleased with the sum of the Academy's efforts. One man in particular was most unhappy. This was the eminent astronomer and Foreign Secretary of the Academy, George Ellery Hale. On the eve of the Academy's 50th anniversary Hale was of the mind that the Academy was accomplishing only a very small fraction of what it ought to do for science in the United States. Essentially, Hale wanted to transform the Academy from just an honours club into an organisation that could marshal all the nation's scientific and engineering talent to aid governmental and non-governmental projects. The first World War gave Hale and the Academy the chance for this transformation.

In 1916, at Hale's suggestion, the Academy offered its resources to President Wilson. Consequently, one of Hale's dreams was to be realised. This was the establishment of the National Research Council whose purpose was to unite the research capabilities of American industry, universities and government. Then, the nation, the Academy and the Research Council went to War.

The Research Council performed so well during the first World War—overseeing anti-submarine warfare research, raising the production of optical glass and developing the first production of helium from natural gas—that on 11 May, 1918, at Hale's instigation, President Wilson issued an executive order making the Research Council a permanent partner of the Academy.

In the immediate post-war period, again with Hale pulling it forward, the Academy-Research Council took a far more active role in international scientific activities and also established the now familiar National Research Fellowships. There were other pursuits, too. These ranged from the organisation of a Committee for Research in Problems of Sex to a new journal called *Psychosomatic Medicine,* and to a serious attempt to stimulate national interest in oceanographic research.

Soon the post-war period became the pre-war period. And, as they had done twice before, American scientists, acting through the Academy, offered their services to the federal government. Vannevar Bush, like Hale, developed a plan whereby the military services and the Academy could work together. President Roosevelt approved the plan and promulgated the necessary order setting up the National Defence Research Council. In 1941, NDRC became a part of the Office of Scientific Research and Development.

The Academy's role in the second World War extended from helping to inaugurate the Manhattan Project for developing an atomic bomb, to making room in the Academy building for various committees engaged in secret wartime research. Frank B. Jewett was Academy president during these years, and as he put it, the Academy-Research Council "ceased to function as a learned society in the traditional sense. Such scientific sessions as were possible were closed to the public and were confined to the presentation of confidential reports to the members of war research. . . ."

By the war's end, the Academy-Research Council had learned and had demonstrated that in tandem they were an effective mechanism for providing unbiased scientific advice at the highest levels of government.

None the less, the Academy's new post-war period brought new challenges. Not the least of these was the insidiousness of McCarthyism. In one instance, the governing Council of the Academy unanimously condemned an attempt to amend the National Science Foundation bill in such a way that every Foundation scholarship or fellowship awardee would be required to have a loyalty clearance by the Federal Bureau of Investigation. The amendment was eliminated from the bill.

The 1950s also brought new opportunities and a new president, Detlev W. Bronk, who redefined the rather fuzzy relationship between the Academy and the Research Council. In effect, Bronk fused the twin organisations into one in which, as a historian notes, "the Academy, continuing as a learned society, functioned as a board of trustees and the Council as an operating unit of the Academy responsible for the work of its eight divisions." The eight divisions are Behavioral Sciences, Biology and Agriculture, Chemistry and Chemical Technology, Earth Sciences, Engineering and Industrial Research, Mathematics, Medical Sciences and Physical Sciences.

In addition to these divisions, there are a number of independent groups to deal with special areas, such as the Space Science Board, the Committee on the Biological Effects of Atomic Radiation and the Pacific Science Board.

To quote from the most recent history of the Academy-Research Council:

> *The initiative for these activities may arise within the White House, any Department or Office of the executive branch, either House of Congress, the Academy-Research Council itself, the broad scientific and engineering communities, international scientific organisations, or public and private foundations.*
>
> *Their objectives, in the main, fall into five major categories: (1) the advancement of scientific and technological research; (2) advisory services to the Federal Government and other public agencies; (3) the representation of science in the formulation of public policy; (4) the application of science in industrial research, medicine, and agriculture; and (5) the representation of the U.S. scientists and technologists in international organisations and collaborative projects.*

A catalogue of recent and current responsibilities gives a further indication of the nature of the beast. The list would include responsibility for U.S. participation in the International Geophysical Year; extensive studies of the long-term effects of the atomic bombings of Hiroshima and Nagasaki; a national road test to provide data on highway construction; the development of long-range national programmes for oceanography and atmospheric sciences; undersea warfare studies; an evaluation of the scientific and technological future of the Air Force; advice on what can be done to correct protein malnutrition; and the development of a research programme for the National Park Service.

The majority of these activities are done without fanfare. At the same time, most of them are not publicly controversial. Until now, the Academy has tried to avoid controversy by shunning issues of a political nature and staying close to what the 650 Academicians and 3000-odd scientists and engineers serving the Research Council are most competent to judge—science and technology. To be sure, the Academy has handled proverbial "hot potatoes," and has acted the gadfly. The American Miscellaneous Society of the Academy, for example, has been feuding with the National Science Foundation about the management of Project Mohole. The Space Science Board has prodded the National Aeronautics and Space Administration into adopting a sensible space probe sterilisation programme.

But, by and large, as the current president Frederick Seitz said in an interview, up to this time the Academy has been most concerned about whether a given project called to its attention "is technically good or not."

Today, a subtle change is taking place. And the reason is not hard to discern. Hitherto the Academy has responded to national crises. Presently, there is a crisis of a different kind confronting the Academy and it is a crisis for American science.

For the first time since the second World War the scope and direction of the national science effort are being seriously challenged by the Congress. At the same time, it is being made clear to scientists that the executive is about to turn down the spigot on its largesse to scientists.

Congress is concerned that the rate of government research spending is increasing too rapidly and that it, the Congress, lacks the wherewithal either to understand or to effectively control the government's $15 billion research effort. So, the Congress has decided to investigate the how and the why of this research and one expects that, until the congressmen are satisfied that all is reasonably well, American science will have a bad time of it.

That the storm is near was indicated last week when the House Committee on Appropriations roughly halved the budget request of the National Science Foundation; forbade the Foundation to start any new programmes; and told it not to transfer its funds to support research by another government agency.

The fact that the Administration plans to tighten up on science spending was the theme of a recent and little publicised address by William D. Carey, the Budget Bureau's science accountant. Carey said, in effect, that the 16th and 17th billion dollars are going to be harder to come by than was the first billion for American science.

"I would further hazard the view," Carey said, "that this tightening of the federal purse strings will cause some convulsions in the scientific community. When dollars for big science become scarcer, the science community can be expected to break ranks and form clusters of opinion and dissent to a greater extent than is the case today."

What has this two-pronged attack on science have to do with the Academy? It is becoming clear to observers that the Academy may be the logical choice to provide the Congress with the kind of advice the Congress thinks it lacks but that the Executive has enjoyed for two decades. Indications are that the Congress is moving in this direction.

Moreover, the Administration, which already makes considerable use of the Academy—appointees to high science positions are usually drawn from a list made up by the Academy—may turn to the Academy to arbitrate among the "clusters" vying for finite federal funds.

In addition to responding to these needs, the Academy appears destined for a totally new role as it turns the corner on a new century. It arises from the decision taken more than two years ago to put the Academy into the business of taking stands on a number of public issues affecting national policies, especially those issues with substantial scientific and technological aspects. And the means by which the Academy has chosen to pioneer this route is the establishment of a Committee on Science and Public Policy. Its chairman is George B. Kistiakowsky, Harvard chemist and former science adviser to President Eisenhower. Its membership is comprised of 14 others, one from each of the Academy-Research Council's disciplinary sections.

COSPUP, as it is called, was responsible for the highly praised commentary on "The Growth of World Population." More recently, the committee has begun a survey of facilities for astronomy in the U.S., and an analysis of the federal government's grants programme. It also is conducting a study on the uses of computers and plans studies of the plant sciences, general physics and chemistry. The aim is to take a broad looksee and prepare a "white paper" on its findings. There is every reason to anticipate that COSPUP will, when occasion demands, tackle challenges more akin to the sociology of science, than to science *per se*.

Internationally, too, the Academy-Research Council is stirring grandly. In July of this year the office of the Foreign Secretary, who is now Harrison Brown, was reconstituted. In the short period since that time, the Academy, at the request of the Agency for International Development, has organised a Latin American Science Board to advise the U.S. Coordinator for the Alliance for Progress; established an African Advisory Committee; and set up a programme to distribute science and technology reference books in less developed nations.

"In almost every country," Seitz said, "the national academy or research council is becoming involved in the national planning of domestic science. Our intent is to invite representatives of these academies and research councils to a major conference here to discuss patterns of action on a domestic scale."

How successful will the Academy be as it takes on these additional challenges? The odds are that it will be very successful. After all, the Academy is not only the most august body of American scientists, but the most influential, as well. Seitz and Kistiakowsky, for example, are members of the President's Science Advisory Committee. Conversely, Jerome B. Wiesner, the President's Science Adviser, is a member of the Academy. And former Academy president Bronk is still the head of the National Science Board which governs the National Science Foundation.

Moreover, the Academy is still regarded as the most impartial judge of differing scientific and technological views in the country. Evidence of this can be seen in the fact that a maritime union and a shippers association had no qualms about letting the Academy evaluate mechanisms for speeding up ship loading at a West Coast port.

Of course, the Academy-Research Council will still do "a hundred things you could not think of," such as choosing paints for ships. But it is safe to assume that wherever there are new science areas to explore, including urban renewal, the Academy will explore them.

If the centennial year is a critical time for American science, it is also an opportune time for the Academy.

Reorganization of Science and Research in the U.S.S.R.

NICHOLAS DeWITT

On 12 April 1961, while the world was caught up in the excitement of the Soviet cosmonaut, *Pravda* published a major decree of the Central Committee of the Communist Party of the Soviet Union and the Council of Ministers of the U.S.S.R., entitled "Concerning Measures To Improve the Coordination of Research and Development Work in the Country and the Activities of the Academy of Sciences of the USSR." This official decree, first disclosed at a meeting of the Academy of Sciences on 10 April, resolved, finally, the protracted institutional debate which had raged since the mid-1950's concerning the management of the Soviet Union's burgeoning research and development effort, a debate overshadowed by Soviet technological spectaculars.

Some observers have looked upon the Soviet scientific organization as a carefully charted administrative pyramid with a well-developed decision-making mechanism. In some strategic areas of research, the Soviet principle of centralized decision-making has indeed been often and easily translated into the mobilization of human and material resources for the attainment of given objectives. Without separating civilian or military, political or scientific, objectives, once a decision was reached, the planning mechanism set in motion the priorities to allocate the human and physical resources from different institutions and from diverse jurisdictions and localities. This was not true, however, of all areas of Soviet research and development. The current decree of the Soviet government and Communist Party forcefully pointed up the problem: "The presence at the Academy of Sciences of the USSR of a large number of specialized research institutions diverts its attention from the long-run basic problems of science, splinters its work force and material resources on many technical problems of a departmental nature, which can be handled successfully in specialized research and development institutes. These shortcomings in the work of the Academy and in other research and development organizations are largely a result of the absence in

Reprinted from *Science*, June 23, 1961, Vol. CXXXIII, pp. 1981–1991, in its entirety (with the exception of the descriptions of the then current Soviet leaders in the top echelons of the various committees on Research and Development) with the permission of the author and the publisher. Professor Nicholas DeWitt is Director of the Non-Western Studies Project in the School of Education of Indiana University. He has published widely on various aspects of Soviet education and science.

the country of a single governmental unit which could coordinate research on a national scale. The absence of such a unit in many cases has led to unjustifiable duplications in research and the irrational use of scientific personnel and material resources" (1).

While this problem has existed in the past, it is the recent expansion of the Soviet research establishment which has brought it most clearly to the fore.

GROWTH OF THE SOVIET RESEARCH ESTABLISHMENT

Table 1 provides data (2) on professional higher-education graduates and on research and academic personnel engaged in the Soviet economy in

TABLE 1. TOTAL EMPLOYMENT OF PROFESSIONAL GRADUATES AND RESEARCH PERSONNEL IN SOVIET RESEARCH ESTABLISHMENTS, IN JANUARY OF THE YEAR INDICATED (FIGURES IN PARENTHESES, INDEX)

Item	Number employed (in thousands)		
	1941	1956	1961
Workers and salaried employees in the national economy (total)	31,500.0 (100)	47,900.0 (155)	62,000.0 (197)
Workers and salaried employees in research and development and science service (total)	361.0 (100)	992.0 (275)	1,732.0 (480)
Workers and salaried employees in research and development only	267.0 (100)	585.0 (220)	1,220.0 (457)
Graduates of professional institutions of higher education employed in the national economy	908.0 (100)	2,340.0 (258)	3,570.0 (394)
Graduates of professional higher-education institutions employed in research and development establishments	91.0 (100)	240.0 (256)	449.0*(494)
Research and academic personnel (total)	98.3 (100)	223.9 (227)	354.2 (361)
Research and academic personnel employed in research and development establishments only	26.4 (100)	96.5 (365)	200.1 (760)
Research institutes			
Total number	1,821	2,797	3,548*
Number of main research institutes	786	1,210	1,608*

* Data as of January 1960.

TABLE 2. SOVIET RESEARCH AND ACADEMIC PERSONNEL, BY FIELD, JANUARY 1960

Field	Number	Percent
Physical sciences		
Engineering	106,960	34.5
Physics-mathematics	24,831	8.0
Chemistry	22,724	7.3
Geology-mineralogy	8,990	2.9
Subtotal	163,505	52.7
Biological sciences		
Biology	13,611	4.4
Agriculture and veterinary science	20,210	6.5
Medicine and pharmaceutical science	31,004	10.0
Subtotal	64,825	20.9
Arts, education, humanities, social sciences		
Philology	19,489	6.3
History and philosophy	17,490	5.6
Pedagogy	13,099	4.2
Economics and planning	12,227	3.9
Art and art history (fine arts, painting, sculpture; music; theater, cinema, and related fields)	4,805	1.6
Architecture	1,339	0.4
Geography	3,890	1.3
Jurisprudence	2,112	0.7
Subtotal	74,451	24.0
Other (unspecified)		
Subtotal	7,241	2.4
Total	310,022	100.0

general, and in the research establishment proper. During the last two decades, while the total nonagricultural employment of workers and salaried employees about doubled in the U.S.S.R., the over-all number of professionals and of research and academic personnel increased about four times. If we consider employment in the Soviet research establishment only, however, the number of professional graduates of institutions of higher education and of researchers increased at rates substantially higher—five and eight times, respectively.

What is particularly important, however, is that the most rapid growth of the Soviet research establishment has taken place in the last 5 years. Between 1956 and 1961 the total employment, the number of professional graduates, and the number of research and academic personnel engaged in Soviet research establishments has about doubled. This enormous quantitative expansion of the Soviet research establishment has constituted the moving force behind the recent institutional reorganization.

SOVIET RESEARCH EFFORT BY FIELD

In the last two decades the dominant emphasis of Soviet research activity has been in the area of the natural sciences. This is shown by the data in Table 2, which indicate that in January 1960 an overwhelming 73 percent of all Soviet research and academic personnel were concentrated in the physical and biological sciences. Within these areas, engineering fields alone accounted for over one-third of all research and academic personnel.

Furthermore, the expansion of the Soviet research establishment in the late 1950's was again most rapid in the fields of physical sciences and engineering, as revealed by a comparison of the numerical growth of research and academic personnel by field between 1956 and 1960 (Table 3).

The current trends in training professionals (two-thirds of all graduates of institutions of higher education are in engineering and scientific fields) and research personnel (about three-quarters of them in the natural sciences) indicate that the emphasis in physical sciences and engineering will undoubtedly continue in the 1960's. This quantitative expansion, though achieved at the expense of the humanities and social sciences, has not lowered the quality of scientific or engineering education, which has improved steadily over the years.

The Soviet research establishment today employs a total of 995,000 workers and salaried employees; among them 449,000 are professional graduates, and of these, 188,000 are research personnel. Well over half of the researchers work in the physical sciences or engineering. They are employed in a maze of institutions united under different lines of subordination.

TABLE 3. Research and Academic Personnel in the U.S.S.R., by Field,
1956 and 1960

Field	Jan. 1956		Jan. 1960		Index of growth
	Number (thousands)	%	Number (thousands)	%	
Physical sciences and engineering	103.3	46.0	163.5	52.7	159
Biological sciences, medicine, agriculture	51.5	23.0	64.8	20.9	121
Arts, humanities, social sciences	62.6	27.9	74.4	24.0	119
Other	6.5	2.9	7.2	2.4	110
Total	223.9	100.0	310.0	100.0	138

HISTORICAL ROOTS

The Soviet scientific research and development effort is presently an extremely complex and highly organized area of human activity, where external institutional machinery determines to a large degree the vitality of scientific progress. In the last few decades in the Soviet Union, as well as in the rest of the world, the role of the individual scientist as a vehicle of theoretical discovery has remained strong, and in many fields Soviet theoretical and basic research has displayed excellence precisely because the scientist was left to his own devices. In other fields of research, however, individual endeavors gave way to a mass experimentation approach with two notable characteristics: on the one hand, a continuing process of differentiation of fields and ever-increasing specialization within each field, and, on the other, the emergence of the "problem approach," the interpenetration of distinct fields of science in the study of various natural phenomena and the resulting establishment of interdisciplinary fields. It is the latter which requires increasing attention to basic and theoretical research.

Ever since the golden age of Russian theoretical science, in the second half of the 19th century, there has been an institutional separation of scientific functions. Russian universities and institutes of higher education concerned themselves with professional education primarily and, to some degree, with broad theoretical research. In addition, however, there was a separate network of scientific research establishments which dealt with experimental research, applied sciences, and highly specialized theoretical investigations. In the latter category there were two types of institutions: (i) the Academy of Sciences, dating back to 1724, under whose auspices a number of specialized institutes were set up, and (ii) a number of independent research institutes, which began to emerge at the turn of the century, serving the applied technological demands of various industries or the research needs of specific fields in medicine, agriculture, and so on. The Soviet regime inherited this institutional setup, in which the bonds between universities and research institutes were loosened long before the Communist Revolution.

Until 1929 all Soviet research and development organizations (except those concerned with military areas) were directly subordinate to the Supreme Council of the National Economy, the highest governmental body in charge of industry, agriculture, and other production activities. It coordinated all research activity. In 1929, Pandora's box was opened, however, when individual research and development institutes were placed under separate departmental auspices in order to intensify their work on practical applications and to identify them more closely with service to individual sectors of industry. In the 1930's the Supreme Council of the National Economy itself was broken up into a variety of administrative departments, called "commissariats" (renamed "ministries" in 1945), each of which took charge of a given sector of industry. Under their auspices, specialized, functional research and development institutes were established and expanded in number and size.

The Academy of Sciences of the U.S.S.R., since 1933 subordinate to the Council of People's Commissars (later Ministers), was under increased pressure to engage in applied research. In response to this pressure it set up many specialized engineering and technological institutes. In 1935, in order to handle these applied-research tasks, a new Division of Engineering Sciences was added to the Academy's other two divisions—those of natural sciences and mathematics and of the humanities. The Academy was again reorganized in 1938, when the number of its divisions reached eight; and in order to broaden the regional base in scientific research, it was empowered to supervise the regional academies of science set up in the various Soviet republics first as branch offices, then as divisions, and, ultimately, as quasi-independent union-republic academies of science.

It should be noted parenthetically that the Russian word *nauka,* though translated as "science," has the broader connotation of the German *Wissenschaft* and is not limited to the natural sciences; rather, it embraces all fields of human knowledge, and accordingly the Soviet academies of science and various departmental research institutes concern themselves not only with basic and applied natural sciences but with the whole spectrum of knowledge—the humanities, fine arts, and social and political disciplines.

But whatever the agglomeration of the fields of knowledge included in the term *nauka,* there are essentially three distinct pyramids in the Soviet research establishment. As of January 1960, these were as follows.

1. Institutions of higher education—universities and institutes (766 institutions in all), employing 138,000 research and academic personnel, of whom about one-third were actively engaged in research. Their research was coordinated by the Scientific-Engineering Council, established in 1956, within the Ministry of Higher and Secondary Specialized Education.

2. The Academy of Sciences of the U.S.S.R. and the 13 union-republic academies of science (603 institutions), employing 39,317 research workers (*3*). Their research was directed by the Presidium of the Academy of Sciences of the U.S.S.R., which had a special Council for the Coordination of Research Work of the union-republic academies of science.

3. Departmental (ministerial) research and development establishments (1005 institutions), employing 125,413 researchers (of whom 18,830, in 494 research institutes, were under the jurisdiction of 13 functional, specialized academies). No central body for coordinating the research activities of these establishments existed until recently, and "institutional research" mush-

TABLE 4. Soviet Academies of Sciences, Research Institutes and Research Personnel, January 1960

	Year founded	Academicians: full and corresponding members (No.)	Research institutes (No.)	Research personnel (No.)
Academy of Sciences of the U.S.S.R.	1725	503	238	23,150
Republic academies*				
Ukrainian S.S.R.	1919	208	60	3,274
Belorussian S.S.R.	1928	76	30	1,250
Uzbek S.S.R.	1943	60	30	1,838
Kazakh S.S.R.	1945	76	37	1,500
Georgian S.S.R.	1941	70	44	2,084
Azerbaidzhan S.S.R.	1945	39	24	1,612
Lithuanian S.S.R.	1941	35	15	499
Latvian S.S.R.	1946	37	20	819
Kirgiz S.S.R.	1954	26	12	544
Tadzhik S.S.R.	1951	29	27	709
Armenian S.S.R.	1943	59	28	1,074
Turkmen S.S.R.	1951	37	21	466
Estonian S.S.R.	1946	32	17	498
Subtotal, republic academies		784	365	16,167
Academy of Construction and Architecture of the U.S.S.R.	1956	196	33	2,642
Academy of Construction and Architecture of the Ukrainian S.S.R.	1956	31	26	1,628
Academy of Arts of the U.S.S.R.	1947	109	4	92
Academy of Medical Sciences of the U.S.S.R.	1944	216	32	2,678
Academy of Pedagogical Sciences of the R.S.F.S.R.	1944	92	13	577
Academy of Communal Services of the R.S.F.S.R.	1931		4	359
Subtotal, functional academies		644	112	7,976
All-Union Academy of Agricultural Sciences	1929	142	165	4,758
Academies of Agricultural Sciences of				
Ukrainian S.S.R.	1957	45	76	1,744
Belorussian S.S.R.	1957	28	23	833
Uzbek S.S.R.	1957	15	41	1,222
Kazakh S.S.R.	1957	20	51	1,142
Georgian S.S.R.	1957	21	11	564
Azerbaidzhan S.S.R.	1958	6	15	591
Subtotal, agricultural academies		277	382	10,854
Grand total		2,208	1,097	58,147

* The Moldav branch of the Academy of Science of the U.S.S.R., which had eight institutes and 272 researchers in 1960, is scheduled to begin functioning as a republic academy of sciences in 1962.

roomed along functional lines, research institutes being formed by the appropriate commissariat or ministry as the need arose—whether for steam turbines, coal mining, school construction, or space research.

The growth of the Soviet research establishment in the last three decades, and particularly since the mid-1950's, was most intensive in pyramids 2 and 3. Table 4 provides data, as of January 1960, on the number of institutions and of research personnel in the Academy of Sciences of the U.S.S.R. and its regional units (the 13 union-republic academies of science) and in the 13 functional academies. The remaining research personnel (106,653 in 509 research institutes) were employed in departmental research and development institutes under a variety of auspices—of state committees, ministries, and other administrative bodies.

EARLY STEPS IN REORGANIZATION

The debate concerning the Soviet science and research setup originated in July 1955. In February 1956, at the 20th Communist Party Congress, Khrushchev declared: "The separation of research activity of the Academy of Sciences, departmental research institutes and higher educational establishments can no longer be tolerated. This separation and lack of coordination prevent the concentration of research activity on the solution of major scientific and engineering problems, lead to duplication of effort and waste of resources, and retard the introduction of research and engineering achievements into production" (*4*).

Although similar thoughts had occasionally been expressed by other Soviet leaders, the demand to streamline the organization of Soviet research and development had never before been presented so forcefully. In 1956 and 1957 a veritable flood of proposals by prominent scientists appeared in the Soviet press, all aimed at streamlining the research organization along the lines of consolidating the fragmented, specialized units and breaking up departmental boundaries.

Meanwhile, beginning in May 1957, the management of Soviet industry was also reorganized, and as a result, a number of departmental research institutes, originally under the auspices of central ministries in charge of particular branches of the Soviet economy, were transferred to regional economic councils or to the newly formed state committees. Among these, the most important was the State Planning Committee, the *Gosplan,* and to it was delegated supervision of the major industrial research and development institutes. By 1958, 323 industrial research institutes, employing 19,000 re-

---

Figure 1. Organizational structure of Soviet agencies concerned with research and development.

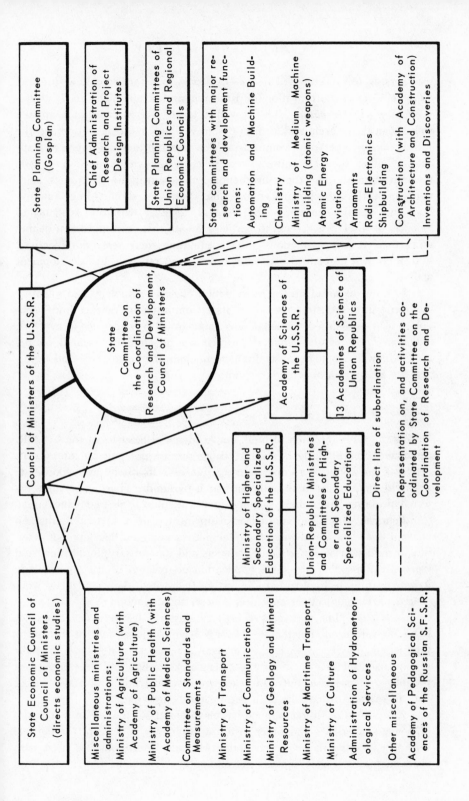

searchers, were subordinated to the *Gosplan*, which formed a new directorate, the Chief Administration of Research and Project Design Institutes (*Glavnüproekt Gosplana*). This new directorate was to coordinate applied technological research and project-design activity in areas not under the jurisdiction of other state committees. The research and development institutes of other state committees were to carry on both applied and basic research in areas under their jurisdiction,—that is, in radio electronics, aviation engineering, armaments engineering, chemistry, shipbuilding, automation, and machine building. The *Gosplan*, together with the Academy of Sciences of the U.S.S.R., was to participate with these committees in delineating their research functions and coordinating their research objectives. Still, there was no central body to coordinate *all* research and development activity.

In order to speed up the introduction of new technology and scientific discoveries into industry, a separate State Committee on Science and Technology was established (called *Gostekhnika* in 1955, and since May 1957, *Nauchno-Tekhnicheskii Komitet*), which was to conduct research on the uses of new technology, disseminate technological information, and supervise the adaptation of foreign technology.

ACADEMY OF SCIENCES IN A SQUEEZE

During this reorganization turmoil, the Academy of Sciences of the U.S.S.R. came under particularly heavy fire, being pressed not only to intensify its activities on applications for industry but also to direct and coordinate research applications in the other research pyramids. There were three external pressures upon the Academy: political, industrial, and educational.

Political. The Communist leadership insisted upon certain results: an efficient and economical way of conducting research and development activities, a reduction of departmental barriers and unnecessary duplication, and especially a speeding up of the application of research results (particularly in engineering technology) to industry. It wanted the Academy's work geared to these objectives and made "closer to production."

Industrial. The managers of Soviet industry, who were sometimes not eager or were even reluctant to use new technology for fear of disrupting production activity, wanted the Academy's researchers not only to make general scientific investigations and to engage in design and development of products and processes but also to engage in model production and testing and, thereafter, to participate in getting the "bugs" out.

Educational. Although much has been said about the research activities of Soviet universities and other institutes of higher education, for the last three decades the main preoccupation of these institutions has been with academic tasks largely separated from applied research. Universities had indeed carried out some highly theoretical work, but they had only limited access to experimental research facilities. Their applied (contractual) research for industry was small in terms of funds and facilities, though academic personnel frequently participated in the research effort through multiple-job holdings in facilities outside higher education. The educational reforms introduced in 1958 demanded the expansion of research work in higher educational institutions proper, and universities and institutes turned their attention toward the possibility of merging with or absorbing some of the separate research institutes. In order to strengthen instruction in practical applications and to increase research activity, demands were made that a number of the research institutes of the academies should be transferred to higher education auspices.

These three external pressures, however, were counteracted by one fundamental internal force. The scientists engaged in fundamental and theoretical research and the leaders in numerous research institutions of the Academy not concerned directly with applications desired greater emphasis on basic research. They urged the separation of activities and the setting up of new research institutes, not along specialized functional lines but as research task forces or problem areas with an interdisciplinary orientation. In effect, the working theoretical scientists and the leaders of the Academy wanted to rid it of activities which were not genuinely scientific. Largely in compliance with this view and, indeed, in full recognition of the problem, A. N. Nesmeianov, then Academy president, suggested in 1958 that Soviet science "can no longer rely upon foreign basic science . . . what we need now first of all is to develop the fundamental sciences. . . . We need to take decisive measures for the speediest and most widespread development of basic science" (5). He then proposed a sharp reorganization of scientific inquiry, with the Academy dealing only in basic research; applied research in technical and engineering fields was to be carried on by industrial institutes. The radical nature of Nesmeianov's proposals—that is, the separation of basic and applied research activities—was a blow at a cardinal assumption of Soviet dogma, that the "unity of theory and practice" is fundamental to dialectical materialism and that the separation of applied and theoretical objectives in research is inadmissible.

In the summer of 1959 Khrushchev recognized that a "difficult situation exists in some institutions of the Academy" (6) and suggested that some technical institutes be removed from its jurisdiction since the work of the Academy had become too big and complex for it to continue to have so many technological research functions. The Academy was to continue with experimental research in biology, geology, and some other areas of the natural sciences, but not in such areas of technology as mining, coal, metallurgy, transportation, and other kinds of industrial research.

In keeping with Khrushchev's proposals, Academician N. N. Semenov suggested that the technical sciences division of the Academy be abolished altogether and that its other divisions be consolidated into three major groups: experimental, geological, and social sciences (7). Research in engineering and the humanities should be carried on elsewhere. Such an arrangement would break down the narrow disciplinary lines of former Academy divisions and institutes. In the newly organized institutes, the departmental assignment of specialized fields to separate research institutes would thus be abolished. In the ensuing debate Semenov's proposals were supported by many leading scientists but were opposed by the applied-technology hierarchy within the Academy's Engineering Sciences Division, who wanted the Academy to retain tasks in applied technology so as to have a link with industry and production. Despite the opposition, Semenov continued to contend that the "responsibility to the state for developing science should rest with the Academy, and for its technical application with the appropriate research institutes elsewhere" (8). The same note was struck again in 1960 by other theoretical scientists, and Nesmeianov declared anew his belief that the Academy should engage primarily in basic research (9).

The new governmental decree resolves the issue in part at least. It declares: "Institutes of applied specialized profiles, upon the recommendation of the Academy's Presidium, will be transferred to other state committees, ministries and departments" (10). If all the Academy's institutes with a technological profile were thus affected, it would mean the transfer of up to 50 research institutes with an estimated 8000 researchers. Furthermore, the regional branch offices of the Academy of Sciences of the U.S.S.R. will be transferred to the jurisdiction of the Council of Ministers of the Russian S.F.S.R. and will be operated by regional economic councils.

In fact, such a decision has already been adopted at the plenary session of the Presidium of the Academy of Sciences of the U.S.S.R., held on 10 April (11). Accordingly, exclusive of the Academy's affiliates (branch offices) (12), the transfers have so far affected about 30 research institutes, employing between 2000 and 3000 researchers. Affected were not only the industrial research institutes of the Academy's Engineering Sciences Division (13) but also institutes under other divisions of the Academy (14), the latter also engaged primarily in applied technical research. Despite these proposed cuts, the Academy will still remain the U.S.S.R.'s largest research unit.

The decree stipulated further that "the work of the Academy should be focused primarily on the most important long-run problems of science undergoing rapid development." These functions are precisely the ones which the Academy leadership has been asking for. The Academy will continue to (i) exercise scientific and methodological leadership and conduct research in the area of the natural sciences (physics, mathematics, biology, and sciences of the "universe and earth"—that is, geology, oceanography, astronomy, and so on) ; (ii) aid the academies of science of the union republics in their research; (iii) coordinate the activities of all the Academy's institutions; (iv) maintain scientific ties with foreign countries; and (v) engage in the training of research personnel.

The Academy's role in regard to the first of these functions was clarified further to include the coordination of work in those areas conducted not only at the Academy but by other institutes as well, especially by institutes of higher education (*15*). Although the decree does not make it clear, according to Topchiev, the Academy's role in maintaining scientific ties with foreign countries (function iv) will be to coordinate scientific exchanges with foreign countries, and particularly to expand its activities in the exchange and dissemination of scientific information.

REPLACEMENT OF ACADEMY PRESIDENT

Closely associated with the reorganization moves was the sudden replacement of the Academy's president, A. N. Nesmeianov, by academician Mstislav Vsevolodovich Keldysh, who was elected to that post at an extraordinary general meeting of the Academy on 19 May 1961 (*16*).

The official version of the meeting was that former president Nesmeianov had petitioned to be relieved of his duties because of the "expiration" of his second 5-year term. Technically, however, his term would not expire until October 1961, for he had been elected by the general assembly of the Academy on 13 October 1956. Furthermore, the extraordinary plenary session of the Academy was called together on 19 May by its presidium (governing board) to "ratify" the resignation of Nesmeianov, which had already been "accepted," and to elect a new president, whose candidacy was already endorsed by the Academy's presidium, the "Communist Party group" of the Academy, and by the Academy's eight divisions. Each of these moves indicates clearly that Keldysh, the new president, was co-opted prior to the formal election.

The new president, professor and doctor of mathematical sciences, had a meteoric rise in the largely conservative body of the Academy. Elected as a corresponding member in 1943, he became a full member in 1946 (the span between the two ranks is usually at least 10 years). In 1953 he was elected a member of the Academy's ruling body, the Presidium, and became its vice president in February 1960. He did not at any time belong to the internal managerial hierarchy of the Academy; all of his research work in mathematics, aerodynamics, and aircraft and rocket technology was done outside the Academy's research institutes. He thus belonged to that group of academicians (about half of the total of 161 full and 369 corresponding members) who are in the Academy of Sciences of the U.S.S.R. as honorific members and top-level research coordinators rather than staff scientists in one of its many research institutions. Keldysh has strong ties with the new head of the Committee on Coordination, having worked in research organizations headed by Khrunichev. In addition, he has a long-standing working relationship with other members of the new committee active in the Soviet military research and development effort.

Keldysh's appointment to the presidency was undoubtedly influenced by the fact that in addition to his scientific competence he has had wide organizational experience with the large-scale research and development effort outside the Academy. It is this research-management experience which is needed in the institutional reorganization and streamlining of the Academy's research functions that are presently under way.

FUNCTIONS OF THE NEW COMMITTEE

The State Committee on the Coordination of Research and Development will supervise the work of research and development establishments in fulfilling the most important scientific research and engineering objectives in accordance with the directives of the party and the government. It will coordinate work of the Academy of Sciences of the U.S.S.R., of the academies of science of the union republics, and of ministries and departments in fulfilling the most important research objectives of an interdepartmental or interdisciplinary nature, and it will guide the direction of research and development work up to the point of its adaptation in the national economy.

On the recommendation of the Council of Ministers of the U.S.S.R., the councils of ministers of the union republics, and ministries and departments, the State Committee on the Coordination of Research and Development, together with the State Economic Council (17) and the State Planning Committee, will develop plans for research and development work in the country at large and for the introduction of scientific and engineering accomplishments in production. The task of the new committee will be to propose these plans for approval to the Council of Ministers of the U.S.S.R.

The Committee on the Coordination of Research and Development will have the following specific areas of responsibility.

1. National control over the fulfillment, by all ministries, departments, and organizations, of the most important research objectives, and supervision, on an operational basis, of the introduction of scientific and engineering accomplishments into production.

2. Preparation of proposals for research and development work of greatest national significance, and concern with problems posed by new discoveries and inventions.

3. Preparation of proposals concerning the supplying of research and development organizations with special equipment, installations, and instruments.

4. Study and evaluation of scientific and engineering accomplishments (both domestic and foreign) with a view toward their possible introduction into the national economy.

5. Coordination of all interdepartmental activities of ministries, departments, and research and development organizations in the area of science and technology.

6. Preparation of annual and long-run plans for financing material-technical supply of research and development work, including plans for capital investment for the development of science.

7. Certification of major research and development institutes; such institutes may be opened only with the committee's consent. Particular attention of the committee will be devoted to designating "major" institutes (*golovnyi instituty*) which are interdisciplinary or "problem" research centers. They have been set up under different departmental auspices in recent years, and it is anticipated that a number of additional such centers will be established in the near future.

The former State Committee on Science and Technology has been absorbed by the new State Committee on Coordination. The All-Union Institute of Scientific and Technical Information, which was originally subordinate to this State Committee (though operated jointly with the Academy of Sciences of the U.S.S.R.), has now been transferred to the new State Committee on Coordination. As in the past, the Institute of Scientific and Technical Information will be the central translating, abstracting, and disseminating organ for domestic and foreign scientific information.

Except for this scientific information institute, the new State Committee on the Coordination of Research and Development will not operate any research institutes directly; rather, its function will be to guide research activities of an interdisciplinary nature, or of great importance, in research units under the jurisdiction of other state committees or departments. However, as in the past, specialized research and development work not of national significance and not of an interdepartmental or interdisciplinary nature will be coordinated by ministries, departments, and regional economic councils.

COMPOSITION OF COMMITTEE ON COORDINATION

The new decree, which establishes for the first time in Soviet history a central coordinating agency (see Fig. 1) for research and development for the country at large, is to be headed (see pages 1986 and 1987, original article) by a Deputy Chairman of the Council of Ministers (Rudnev, replacing Khrunichev who died on 2 June).

It is to be composed of the President of the Academy of Sciences of the U.S.S.R. (Keldysh); the Minister of Higher and Secondary Specialized Education (Eliutin); the Chairman of the State Committee on Automation and Machine Building (Kostousov); the Chairman of the State Committee on Chemistry (Fedorov); the Chairman of the Committee on Inventions and Discoveries (Garmashev); one of the deputy chairmen of the State Economic Council; and one of the deputy chairmen of the State Planning Committee.

There will also be "other members" of the Committee on the Coordination of Research and Development from other state committees dealing with research and development work (page 1989, original). They were not identified by position in the official decree, but definitely the heads of other governmental departments dealing with research and development will be represented. These are chairmen of the following agencies: state committees on aviation engineering (Dement'ev), armaments engineering (Smirnov), radioelectronics (Kalmykov), electronics (Shokin), shipbuilding(Butoma), and atomic energy (Emel'ianov) and the Minister of Medium Machine Building (atomic, and other, weapon development and production) (Slavskii).

The State Committee on the Coordination of Research and Development will form a permanent scientific council, consisting of leading specialists and scientists of the country, with advisory functions, and when the occasion arises, will call for special boards to study specific problems. Particular significance should be assigned to this latter function. Soviet sources indicate that "although about 80 permanent scientific councils are in existence today . . . about one-half of these are inactive" (15). The new State Committee on Coordination will thus streamline and activate the work of scientific councils in diverse areas of research, whose activities will now be coordinated by a permanent scientific council (18). Through these measures, it is hoped, the "leadership role of scientists now working within the Academy of Sciences of the U.S.S.R. will intensify in the work of the nation's research organization" (19).

The new measures to coordinate research and development are obviously designed to give even more emphasis to the physical sciences and engineering and to complex interdisciplinary problems. The important consideration is that the new chairman of the State Committee on Coordination, Khrunichev, is a person with a strong military research and development background. This is also true of the new president of the Academy, who has not only general background in military research and development but also specific experience in rocket and space technology. In addition, most of the heads of the state committees with research and development functions have similar backgrounds. All are former engineers active in defense fields, now turned industrial managers and political leaders. Upon examining their background, it is hard to resist the view that their past interests have profound implications for the future of Soviet efforts in applied research—that these efforts will be technological in nature, with strong military overtones.

Whatever the outcome may be, however, the intended result of the establishment of the State Committee on Coordination will be the synchronization of the Soviet research and development effort in the distinct institutional pyramids—academies, institutions of higher education, and departmental research institutes. What is even more significant, perhaps, is that responsibility for decisions on scientific research and development has now been lodged at the pinnacle of the Soviet power hierarchy; for the first time in Soviet history the Deputy to the Prime Minister (that is, Khrushchev himself) has been charged with the supervision of these tasks.

In regard to other areas of research, it appears that the earlier setup will continue, as follows.

1. Research on economics will be coordinated by the State Economic Research Council of the Council of Ministers, which was set up in 1959, with the chief role assigned to the economic research outlets of the *Gosplan* and with ever-increasing use of mathematical methods of centralized planning and production programming.

2. As in the past, the Academy of Medical Sciences will supervise and conduct medical research, largely sponsored by the Ministry of Public Health.

3. The Ministry of Agriculture, with its All-Union Academy of Agricultural Sciences and five other regional agricultural academies set up since 1957, will coordinate agricultural research and manage experimental agricultural stations. In the areas of medicine and biology, the Academy of Sciences of the U.S.S.R. will not be involved, save for basic research in biology.

4. The State Committee on Construction, with its own Academy of Architecture and Construction (organized in 1956), will coordinate construction and architectural research.

5. Political studies (especially "philosophy") will be guided largely by the Academy of Social Sciences of the Central Committee of the Communist Party.

6. In the field of education, the Academy of Pedagogical Sciences of the Russian S.F.S.R. remains the national clearinghouse and conducts major research.

The new centralization of the decision-making mechanism in Soviet research and development will no doubt be manifested in the near future.

Freed from burdensome technological tasks, the Academy of Sciences will be able to concentrate more effort on basic research. Many of its institutes are expected to be reorganized. The Soviet authorities hope that the new measures will (i) improve the system of both long-run and current planning of research and the coordination of research and development activity; (ii) further strengthen theoretical research on the most important scientific problems (within the Academy); (iii) allow for closer ties between departmental research institutes and industry; and (iv) allow more rapid introduction of research-and-development results into production technology and the economy.

The separation of functions must be clearly recognized. On the operational level the Academy will delegate some of its former functions in applied industrial research to other agencies, and within the Academy, institutes will be reorganized in such a way as to cope with complex interdisciplinary and basic research problems, including a very likely increase in the Academy's role in space exploration. On the consulting and decision-making level the prestige and resources of the Academy will, as in the past, be utilized, though now there will be an intermediate link—the Committee on Coordination—which will in turn exert pressure upon the Academy.

Perhaps these measures are a recognition of a turning point in Soviet technological development: the point of diminishing returns from adaptation of Western technology has been reached, and new and vigorous domestic technological development becomes a necessity. The Soviet political leadership appears to be convinced that the invigoration of technological research activities can be more profitably achieved by separating functions, and by freeing the Academy of Sciences of the U.S.S.R. to concentrate its attention on basic research and the long-run problems of science. Reorganization of the Soviet research setup could provide an effective mechanism for channeling scientific manpower and material resources into strategic areas of the physical sciences and engineering toward the achievement of the most ambitious long-run goal of Soviet power—world leadership in science and technology.

Note added in proof. Right after this article had gone to press, Mr. Khrunichev died of a heart attack on 2 June. His successor, Konstantine N. Rudnev, was named on 10 June.

REFERENCES AND NOTES

1. *Pravda* (12 Apr. 1961).
2. Some of the statistical information in this article is taken from N. DeWitt, *Education and Professional Employment in the U.S.S.R.* (National Science Foundation, Washington, D.C., in press).

3. A 14th union-republic academy of sciences is scheduled to begin functioning in the Moldavian S.S.R. in 1962; it is presently a branch of the Academy of Sciences of the U.S.S.R.
4. *Pravda* (14 Feb. 1956).
5. *Uchitel'skaia gazeta* (20 May 1958).
6. *Pravda* (2 July 1959).
7. *Izvestiia* (9 Aug. 1959). Semenov was a Nobel prize winner in chemistry.
8. *Ibid.* (16 Dec. 1959).
9. *Pravda* (31 Dec. 1960).
10. *Ibid.* (12 Apr. 1961).
11. This information was given me by A. V. Topchiev, vice-president of the Academy of Sciences of the U.S.S.R., in Washington, D.C., on 26 and 27 April. Dr. Topchiev attended the plenary session just before his trip to the United States. He indicated that no public announcement of this decision has been made as yet, since the Presidium is still considering the possibility of additional transfers of research institutes.
12. There are seven branches: Bashkir, Dagestan, Karelian, Kazan', Kola, Komi, and Ural. An eighth branch—Moldav—is currently being reorganized into a union-republic academy. The seven branches are being transferred to the jurisdiction of the Council of Ministers of the Russian S.F.S.R.
13. Dr. Topchiev gave as examples the Institutes of Complex Transportation Problems, Metallurgy, and Hydraulic Engineering and Water Economy. In addition, the Institute of Mining will be transferred from the Academy [*Vestnik Akad. Nauk.* 31, No. 4, 3 (1961)].
14. Dr. Topchiev gave the following as examples: in the Geography-Geology Division, Institutes of Geological Prospecting and of Coal Geology; in the Chemical Division, Institutes of Silicate Chemistry and of Forestry and Wood Chemistry; in the Biological Division, the Institute of Soil Sciences.
15. *Ekonomicheskaia gazeta* (20 Apr. 1961).
16. *Pravda* (20 May 1961); *Ekonomicheskaia gazeta* (20 May 1961).
17. Some of the Academy's institutes which deal with long-range planning, such as the Institute of Complex Transportation Problems, have been transferred to the operating auspices of the State Economic Council.
18. This was especially emphasized by Dr. Topchiev.
19. *Pravda* (21 Apr. 1961).

Dilemma of Academic Biology in Europe

WILLIAM V. CONSOLAZIO

The observations reported in this article are the result of approximately a year's stay in Europe, recently made possible by the National Science Foundation in its newly inaugurated advanced study program set up for the purpose of augmenting the skills and understanding of its career scientific staff.

The deeper I probed into this survey of the organization and the needs of European academic biology, the more I became convinced that whatever I reported would be a first approximation to a most complex and singularly important subject. In spite of extensive effort, the time I spent abroad proved much too short for the needs of the task. Several specialized biologists could have been profitably occupied at this chore, each spending as much time in each of the countries I visited as I did on my entire trip.

I would like to begin by defining a few terms. Although I have used the term *science* throughout this article, I refer specifically to the biological sciences in the broadest sense. I have written about European science. Actually, I refer to science in Europe west of the Iron Curtain. I visited all but two countries in Western Europe. I include Israel, not only because I visited there but also because, intellectually, Israel is part of the West.

I visited as many centers of research as time and my professional interests permitted; however, I visited people rather than institutions. Before I left the United States I prepared an itinerary based on the recommendations of many American experimental biologists who know Europe and whom I hold in great respect.

It is a truism that science is international; it knows no national boundaries. It is also axiomatic that whether or not there is science in a country, or whether there is a good or a bad science, depends on the number, quality, and training of the nation's scientists, the availability of research funds, the extent of the nation's educational facilities, and the state of its research equipment and laboratories. But more than this, the nature of a nation's science depends on the intellectual and scientific traditions and attitudes of that country—I would say on the intellectual and scientific receptivity of a

Reprinted from *Science,* June 16, 1961, Vol. CXXXIII, pp. 1892–1896, with permission of the author and the publisher. William V. Consolazio is currently with the Office of Program Development and Analysis in the National Science Foundation.

nation. One thing is clear: no nation has a monopoly on intelligence and on scientific potential. Bright young men and women are just as common in the more unfortunate and poverty-stricken countries as they are in the wealthier and intellectually more highly developed nations. The only difference between the haves and the have-nots with respect to scientific potential lies in the fact that in the more fortunate countries young people are better trained and utilized, and that the potential is thus more fully exploited. Despite our self-castigation, we in the United States don't waste nearly as many young people as are wasted in Central and Southern Europe.

It is well known that, of the countries I visited, science is most highly developed in the British Isles, in Israel, and in Sweden. There are pockets of scientific activity of very high quality in most of the other countries of Western Europe, but on the whole one can say that as one proceeds south, both the quality and the quantity of scientific activity decline. But let me add quickly that the best southern European scientists are as good as the best Swedish and British; they are fewer, and they work under considerably more stressful and less rewarding conditions. Southern European scientists are considerably more isolated; they have heavier teaching loads; their facilities are more primitive; their pay scales are very low; and the student body is unselected and is rarely trained to follow a career in science.

The most productive European scientists I met all had a common training. In general, they had all been trained in the same scientific centers, both in Europe and in the United States. All came from a common mold and had become siblings through education. It also is a fact that all productive scientists in Europe read and speak English, most of them fluently. English and American journals and monographs predominate in their libraries—an indication of the dependence of European science on English and U.S. publications and of the universality of English in the scientific world.

Of great interest in this connection is the significant number of productive European scientists who have at some time in their careers received support from the Rockefeller Foundation, either in the form of a fellowship or indirectly through grant funds. This record of the Rockefeller Foundation is one of which Americans should be exceedingly proud. It also demonstrates the value of the grant-in-aid system of supporting science. Rockefeller Foundation funds have always been in very short supply. They have always been employed as catalysts, and the high points of European science attest to the past effectiveness of this system.

World Wars I and II played a significant role in the decline of science in Central and Southern Europe. The disruptive effects of the two wars, of course compounded by Fascism and Nazism, drove some of the best experimental biologists out of Germany and Italy. A few of these experimental biologists went to the British Isles and Scandinavia; the majority came to the United States. Europe still has to recover from this catastrophe. But it seems to me that Europe has lost its dominance in science for reasons other than the wars. Independent developments in the new world; nationalistic, linguistic, and cultural barriers; and economics—all have taken their toll. It is to some of these issues that I address myself.

WHY BIOLOGISTS LEAVE EUROPE

Scientifically, Europe is being outstripped at a relatively fast rate by the United States. Although Great Britain, Sweden, and Israel are increasing their research activities, by comparison with the increase in the United States, the increment is small. This results in the emigration of far too many able young people from Europe to the United States. Very few Americans seek permanent scientific employment in foreign countries, with the exception of those who seek it in Israel, so that the movement of scientists is practically all in the direction of the New World and, primarily, of the United States. Emigration begins when young people seek further training abroad. Exposure to the great scientific centers of the United States and a taste of our high standard of living exert an irresistible pull on them. By contrast, a return home often means a lack of opportunity to grow intellectually and difficulty in supporting oneself and one's family. It is logical, then, for these young people to seek permanent residence in the United States.

Europe has neither enough trained people nor the facilities to exploit the many scientific breakthroughs that still occur there. This discouraging state of affairs is very frustrating to an individual who makes a fundamental discovery and then has to stand by and watch it being exploited in a prosperous country like the United States. Those who have had this experience once or twice soon break out and leave.

With respect to the criticism leveled at the New World for proselytizing these young people, my answer is that society is the beneficiary when there are nations that, from whatever motivation, give assistance to deserving young people.

However, we in the United States should make every effort to encourage the young people who come here for training to return home when they have completed their training. I believe we should do it by persuasion and by helping to modify conditions at home and not by legislation. Nevertheless, it is good for Europe to find the United States competing for its young people. This competition forces political and educational authorities to focus attention on the problem of emigration. When attention is drawn to the problem, reforms are inevitable. We ourselves can help these returning young people by giving them financial aid until they become established in their home environment. It does no good to train them in the techniques of modern experimental biology and then banish them to a desert to count sand particles.

The late Enzo Boeri, who had to live with the problem, described it more dramatically than I can. "History teaches us that when freedom of thinking, speaking, and writing was acquired, a second step appeared necessary: freedom from want. What is the use of my freedom of thinking, speaking, and writing—claimed the poor—if I starve? What is the use of my freedom of thinking, speaking, and writing if I am a teacher of experimental science and I have no money to plan and make experiments? We must extend the old concept of academic freedom and take it also to mean freedom to act, freedom to perform one's academic function without being compelled by poverty to inactivity"(1).

Unfortunately, any system of foreign aid that absolves the home country from financial responsibility for establishing its young people encourages further irresponsibility. It may well be that foreign aid should be tied to a matching-fund system irrespective of whether the aid or the matching-fund comes from private or public sources.

SCIENCE IN ISRAEL

The size, population, and economic status of a nation bear little relationship to the quality of that nation's science. In my opinion science in Israel—a relatively new state not much bigger than New Jersey, with a population of some 2 million and with phenomenal social and economic problems still to be solved—is of higher quality and better developed than that in any country in Western Europe, with the possible exception of Great Britain and Sweden. The Israelis have harnessed their energies collectively to raise the intellectual standards of their country. Their political and scientific leaders are responsive and responsible. This is a country where intellectual ability is held in very high regard, and where the people are willing to impose on themselves a tax structure which is practically confiscatory to raise the standards of living, higher education, and science. These people make the most of every foreign opportunity available to them. They spare no effort or expense to send their best young people abroad for training, and then they make it advantageous for them to return. As I said earlier, Israel is the only country that has been able to attract U.S. scientists as permanent residents. Part of this, of course, is due to the fact that some American Jews have identified themselves with Zionism, but a good deal is also due to good working conditions in Israel. Scientific tradition in Israel is but one generation old. But Israel has imported and adopted the best of the Western scientific tradition—scientific honesty, respect for merit, self-criticism, and rewards based on competence.

TRADITIONS AND NATIONALISM

Italy and Southern Europe, on the other hand, where the scientific tradition is old, have retained many of the symbols but few of the ideals of science. I am convinced that the "institute"—the administrative unit for academic science and education—is partly responsible. It is headed by a director who is also, except in rare instances, the only full professor. An institute may contain any number of staff members, varying from one or two (usually the rule) to numbers that approach those of our more highly developed university departments, but staff members are usually junior and subservient. The few able and productive directors make a substantial effort to develop an attractive environment for a creative staff, but attractive environments are the exception rather than the rule. The director of an institute holds power of livelihood and promotion over his assistant. As someone put it, the institute directorship, at least in Southern Europe, constitutes the last stronghold of feudalism. The director is a potent force because in Europe the university is usually a federation of colleges or institutes, or both. He holds membership in the academic senate, which is in most cases the administrative and executive arm of the university. Rectors and deans are rarely selected for executive ability; positions are usually honorary—a relic of the pomp and pageantry of the past. It is this academic senate that stands in the way of many of the reforms that are so badly needed in the European university.

Junior faculty members seeking permanent university appointments tend to cultivate the good will of the institute director and of members of the academic senate rather than to concentrate on scholarly accomplishments. It is the tragedy of many European universities that their young people must cater to the powers that be if they are to receive rewards. In a system where youth is subordinate to age and the elder scholar happens to be a brilliant individual, the young man may suffer but society and science nevertheless gain. If, on the other hand, the same youth is exploited by mediocrity, everyone loses. Unfortunately, in any society mediocrity is more apt to be prevalent than genius.

In many of the old and great medical schools of Europe there are still no institutes or departments of biochemistry and microbiology. Every European university has an institute of zoology and one of botany, but none of biology. Under the present system, if one wanted to introduce genetics, embryology, microbiology, or biochemistry into a university curriculum, it would be necessary either to create new "chairs" (new institutes) or to see to it that an individual who received his earlier training in an older discipline seeks further training in the newer one. Institute directors will be likely to resist appointing, for example, a biochemist or microbiologist to an existing "chair," such as human physiology or comparative anatomy, unless the candidate began his career as a human physiologist or an anatomist. Efforts to introduce the newer disciplines through this system have not been very successful.

Even more resistance greets proposals to create new institutes. Creation of new institutes would encroach upon the prerogatives of existing institutes and directors and threaten the present power structure. The professor's salary still depends to a large degree on the number of students registered in his course. In many European medical schools the funds resulting from clinical analyses (blood and urine analyses) revert to an older department within the medical school. It would be natural for the professor of an older department to resist the creation of new institutes with which such funds might have to be shared. There is also severe competition in the graduate faculty for the few graduate students. No one wishes to diminish the number of students in his own course by sharing them with a new colleague.

Does the size of a nation bear any relationship to the breadth and depth of its science? The fact that a nation is small does affect the type and the variety of its science, the example of Israel notwithstanding. It is economically impossible for a small nation to support research of the breadth and depth of that going on in the United States today. One finds very highly advanced physical and chemical biology in Sweden, for example, but one doesn't find the same depth in the other branches of biology. One finds some of the world's best intermediary metabolism and protein chemistry in Great Britain, but not an equally potent genetics. It is economics, to a large extent, that stands in the way of developing breadth. But economics is by no means the only or even the primary factor. Nationalism and the limitations imposed by the manpower pool play an even more significant role. The manpower limitation, however, could be overcome were it not for nationalistic barriers. The European environment is not conducive to the importation of scholars from foreign countries. In the United States, academic and scientific personnel at least cross state boundaries. Such exchange, of course, is the source of our national strength economically and of our scientific strength, too. But in Europe scientists do not often settle in countries other than their own. The many national and intellectual barriers get higher and more difficult to surmount, with the result that European science becomes more isolated and provincial.

European universities are old. Some go back to the 10th and 11th centuries. They began as institutions for the training of the clergy and were used later for training in professions associated with the humanities—law, linguistics, literature, and so on. It seemed to me that too many European universities are much as they were when they were established; they have changed very little. They are still dominated by classicists. Descriptive biologists still speak for biology, and they cling to what they have. Just as long as these groups are dominant, they are a power to be reckoned with. Classicists and descriptive biologists tend to delay modernization of the university to accommodate modern science and seem fixed in their belief that one professor suffices for a department. In many respects the professors in old-line disciplines fulfill their responsibility to the university by their teaching. They need nothing for their research but their collections, the library, paper, and pencils. Consequently they seem to have little appreciation of the nature and needs of modern experimental science. Modern laboratories and the establishment of a departmental structure are matters foreign to their understanding.

The academic atmosphere in Europe is somewhat more relaxed than its counterpart in the United States. In spite of this, in the past Europe has produced much of the great science of the world. There is no paradox here —all agree that great thoughts are nourished in a leisurely atmosphere. The combination in the past of a relaxed atmosphere at the summit and an ever-replenished pool of youth dedicated to furthering the aspirations of the leader proved most profitable. Unfortunately for this system, young people the world over are in rebellion against exploitation and especially against traditional ways that perpetuate the status quo. But although there is a stirring and an unhappiness, little change will occur till the youth are encouraged to develop independently, till those who have emigrated are encouraged to return home, and till scientists and teachers are encouraged to cross national and disciplinary barriers.

For comparison, one can point to the fact that no small part of Israel's scientific success can be traced to its spirit of internationalism. Its scientists and its science are truly international. Our strength here in America stems from a highly competitive system and from the same international outlook. As long as universities in the United States continue the practice of competing vigorously with each other and with international universities for the best minds, just so long will our science remain strong.

ECONOMICS OF ACADEMIC BIOLOGY

The creative life of the university in Europe is still best suited to the upper-upper classes, those of noble birth and wealth. Not too long ago those seeking careers in the university were expected to be individuals of private means. The university was not an employer of educators and scientists, as it has come to be in the United States. Many universities still fail to realize that teaching and research are professions associated with a livelihood. Consequently, academicians without private means of support must look to extracurricular sources for their living, for the university is often incapable of meeting its financial obligations to its employees. There is no longer a place for the dilettante in science; science has become much too complicated, too expensive and competitive, and government, the major source of support of European universities, has not yet assumed its full responsibility.

In 1953 Italy spent $23 million on its universities and high schools (*1*). This amount was to meet the educational needs of a population of approximately 40 million people. These figures include all expenditures—for buildings, salaries, libraries, research, and so on. If I can trust my memory, figures for the United States for higher education alone and for the comparable period were of the order of $3.5 billion. The U.S. expenditure was for a population approximately 4 times the population of Italy but, as I said, for higher education only. What can one do but keep salaries low if the funds available for education are so pitifully small? And how can we expect more than one professor per institute? Under these circumstances, the talented youth without hope of tenure or the security of a sponsor would be foolish to elect academic science as a career, for he could never give his full energy to research and teaching. To expect to do so would be unrealistic.

Except in rare instances, all support for higher education in Europe comes from taxes. Consequently, salaries are generally standard and comparable throughout universities and throughout the civil service structure. Therefore, there is little incentive to move from university to university and from civil service to university, and vice versa. There is still too little competition from industry, since there is little intellectual and social reward associated with an industrial career. The academician is held in great respect in Europe, but prestige in itself is insufficient to make the academic career attractive. I do not want to create the impression that salary is the only motivating factor in a scientist's life, but where the standard of living is low, money takes on great importance. Under low-income conditions creative people who are wholly dependent on salary will and do seek other professions or leave for greener pastures.

A NEED FOR CHANGE

Governments in Europe, it seems to me, have leaned over backward in their effort not to interfere and have deferred too much to university committees, sometimes piling one committee on top of another and thus further weakening university administration. The academic world in Europe in thus without "executive" officers who could become responsible for modernizing and upgrading the university.

I am convinced that the individualistic, "efficiently" administered

American university, both public and private, with all its disadvantages, is to be preferred above any of the types of institutions of higher learning I have seen in Europe. If nothing else, American universities at least offer variety and competition.

Ways must be found to upgrade science and the teaching of science in Europe. Modification of the existing university structure offers hope. But this avenue of approach from within is slow and painful. The most logical and most effective device lies in the development of international institutes of science and technology. Those Europeans who think about such problems strongly advocate such a development. Institutes of this kind are the Technion in Haifa and the Institute of Science and Technology at Imperial College, London. A study group of the North Atlantic Treaty Organization has recently advocated similar developments (2). In contrast to the over-all institute, covering science and technology, establishment of specialized institutes has been suggested, such as institutes of cell biology. The advantages and disadvantages of these approaches have been discussed by many, and I do not consider them here. Suffice it to say, I feel quite strongly that international institutes, to serve as model systems, offer the only real hope of change, and that the more specialized institutes hold the greater promise.

These model institutes should be under international management and, preferably, funded from private sources. At the beginning they ought to be staffed by nonnationals. Only an international institution can be free from local economic pressures and from efforts of competing institutions to attract teachers and scientists of high caliber. Foreign professional staff is as essential as foreign management if tradition and local political considerations are not to have the upper hand. At present, local customs are steeped in the past, pay scales are too low to make academic science an attractive area of employment, and local talent tends to be too provincial. In my judgment only the establishment of an international institute can shake European scientific education to its roots, and only an international institute can show Europe the modern way.

One frequently hears it stated that the way to uplift European biology is to put more money into the system. Heaven forbid! It does no good to develop programs of general support to science in "depressed areas," including some areas of Europe, without first introducing and fixing within the populace those scientific ideals that reward honesty in science, that recognize the value of self-evaluation and self-criticism, and that place scientific accomplishment above all other gains. These ideals are the core of the successful scientific environment. Scientifically "depressed areas" need assistance of a bread-and-butter nature. They don't need caviar. They need teachers, textbooks, journals, audio-visual aids, and the like. They need scientific instruction and examples of the "scientific method" at the most primary level. Giving research funds of a general support nature to existing institutions would only continue the present intellectual stagnation and perhaps even deepen it.

International institutes of cell biology can bring some of the ideals of science to these "depressed areas" and can serve as models, setting standards of research and education now lacking in all but a few nations of Europe. Through them young people would be exposed to the highest ideals of science, trained in the most recent techniques, and thus enabled to take over the training of subsequent generations. To my way of thinking, one model institute strategically placed would be of far greater value than all the foreign grant-in-aid, training, and fellowship assistance now made available to each of the countries I visited.

U.S. AID FOR RESEARCH AND TRAINING

Of the many problems facing European science, a few can be solved with money. The amount isn't very large by U.S. standards, even though it is far too large to be attainable from present European sources. It is not our responsibility to underwrite European academic science, but it certainly is in our national interest to render some financial aid. We need a strong European science not only because Europe still is a producer of many original ideas but because we need competition to keep our own science healthy and dynamic. We also need training centers for seasoning our young people —training centers, different from our own, where, for example, the mind gets greater play than the machine. The Europeans have had to make do. Lack of funds to some extent has been a blessing in disguise—it has forced Europe to stress conceptualization rather than experimentation.

The kind of aid European science needs from us is of two types—support for its best young people and support for a few of its more creative scientists. Some of this we are already giving. Support for the young people should be in the form of postdoctoral fellowships for training in the United States and of support for a few years of subsequent research to help establish them at home. A fellowship program without some support at home is of little value. The Rockefeller Foundation was very successful with this type of program a generation ago, and it should not be too difficult for us to emulate its success. The other type of program can be in the nature of grants to help the more creative people establish and maintain training programs. There are very few postdoctoral students in Europe—first, because few training centers exist, but even more because there are few sources of funds to support these young people during an additional few years of training.

Of course we can make available textbooks, journals, audio-visual aids, and other teaching essentials. These items are desperately needed, but federal and private U.S. overseas agencies exist that can handle these needs. We can, however, make available our surplus, unused scientific equipment and periodicals now gathering dust and deteriorating in a large number of laboratory storerooms throughout the nation. A small investment to recondition and redistribute this equipment will gain us many friends and at the same time help familiarize many young people with laboratory techniques with which they are now unfamiliar. A simple expansion of existing book exchanges can accomplish the rest. Europeans are too desperately in need of scientific equipment and periodicals of any kind to let pride stand in the way of acceptance.

Whatever financial support is made available to Europe from U.S. sources should be direct—from the primary agency to the scientist. It should come from many of the same agencies, both private and public, that are now functioning in the United States, and certainly not from any specially created agency of the federal government. For whatever reason, we now tolerate a multiplicity of agencies for the support of science in the United States; that same reasoning obtains for Europe. But I repeat—aid should come directly and not through any middle-man international organization.

EUROPE CAN HELP ITSELF

Europe can begin to help itself too, for the manpower it is wasting constitutes a valuable and irreplaceable natural resource. European economic recovery has been dramatic. European citizens of wealth, industrial corporations, and governments have a responsibility to finance the education of their youth and the research of their scholars. Public organizations do now exist, but they are much too inadequately financed and managed for the task at hand. Tax incentives will, to some degree, further the development and growth of philanthropic organizations. It will take Europe a long time, even with the best of intentions, to approach anything like the present American response to the needs of its science.

Before I close I should like to leave one more thought. Anyone who has traveled about Europe or in other parts of the world in the last few years is aware that the world is in a deep ferment, politically, socially, and economically. Fundamentally, as in all such awakenings, it is the young people who are stirring. They are aware of the strangle hold of tradition and the dead hand of the past, and they are losing patience with delays and, yes, even obstruction. We, one of the youngest nations of the world, one born of rebellion, the most powerful economically and intellectually, can easily afford to share a bit of our good fortune and wealth with them. Any assistance we can give them will eventually be of benefit to us as well as to them. Such aid may spell the difference between survival of life on this planet as we now know it or total destruction. Will it be possible for responsible people and nations to move before the help provided is, once again, too little and too late?

REFERENCES

1. E. Boeri, *Bulletin of the Committee on Science and Freedom* 11, 34 (1958).
2. "Increasing the Effectiveness of Western Science" (Foundation Universitaire, Brussels, 1960).

Medical Scientists in a Château

RENEE C. FOX

On Sunday afternoon, 15 November 1959, a medical scientific colloquium was held in the château at Laeken, which belongs to the royal family of Belgium. This was a meeting officially devoted to accomplishments and problems in the field of cardiac surgery. The conference was held in honor of three foreign medical scientists, A. G. Brom of Leyden University, André Cournand of Columbia, and Robert Gross of Harvard, who, through their trail-blazing experimental work, have made outstanding contributions to this field. The three men had traveled to Belgium in order to personally receive the "doctor *honoris causa*" degree that each was to be awarded in the course of the following week. Along with King Baudoin of Belgium, who was honored with the same diploma, Cournand subsequently received his honorary degree from the Free University of Brussels on the same day that Gross and Brom were awarded their degrees by the Catholic University of Louvain.

According to accounts in Belgian newspapers, among the persons invited to the medical scientific gathering in the royal château were the following: numerous members of the royal family (King Baudoin, ex-King Leopold, Princess Lilliane, Prince Alexandre, Prince Albert, Princess Paolo) ; the ambassadors of France and the United States; various ministers, present and past, of Cultural Affairs, Public Instruction, Social Security, Public Health, and so on; the rectors and deans of each of the four major Belgian universities (Ghent and Liége, as well as Brussels and Louvain) ; professors of the medical faculties of each of the universities, and numerous other professors; medical specialists from various university-connected centers; certain young Belgian physicians who were members of cardiac teams; mature physicians in private practice, specializing in cardiology; Belgian physicians who had received some training in the United States; the director and various members of the Princess Lilliane Cardiology Foundation; representatives of the Belgian Academy of Medicine and the Royal Flemish Academy of Medicine; the president of the Fund of Medical Scientific Research; the president of the Red Cross; a commissioner from EURATOM; Belgian

Reprinted from *Science,* May 11, 1962, Vol. CXXXVI, pp. 476–483, with the permission of the author and the publisher. Professor Renée Fox is in the Department of Sociology at Barnard College, Columbia University. She has published widely in the field of medical sociology and the social aspects of medical research.

patients with heart maladies who had undergone cardiac surgery outside of Belgium, chiefly in the United States (there were approximately 40 of these); Belgian patients who had undergone cardiac surgery in Belgium (there were 400 such individuals at this time—how many of these came to the colloquium was not specified in the newspapers); some candidates for cardiac surgery; and the families of all these patients.

Before the colloquium, a tea was served in the Palm Rotunda of the château. In the midst of the reception a sudden failure in electricity extinguished all the lights of the château. Members of the palace staff had to be summoned to bring candles, and for a while the reception proceeded in the at once eerie and romantic "ambiance" of candlelight.

After the tea (electricity restored), a speech was delivered in French by a professor of medicine of the University of Brussels, who was also Belgium's delegate to the International Council of Cardiology. Another professor then gave a complementary speech in Flemish. Prince Alexandre, the son of ex-King Leopold and Princess Lilliane, who had himself undergone cardiac surgery as a patient of Gross, was the next to speak. He delivered an address, thanking modern medical science and the physicians and surgeons who are its agents for what it had done to help patients like himself. The speech was delivered first in Flemish, then in French.

Following this, the colloquium proper took place in the small and elegant theatre of the château, in the presence of the royal family and their invited guests and of many of the assembled medical personages. The guests of the royal family included certain members of the nobility and a number of prominent businessmen, several of whom were believed to be important Free Masons. A professor of medicine from each of the four Belgian universities and several foreign physicians participated in the discussion. This was on a rather elementary scientific level, out of consideration for the persons in the audience who were not medically or surgically trained.

After the colloquium there was a cold supper, to which all who had been present at the meeting in the afternoon seem to have been invited, with the exception of the patients and their families. In addition, the five bishops of the Belgian Catholic Church, some more members of the nobility (counts, countesses, barons, baronesses), and various members of Parliament were cited in the newspapers as having attended the supper.

A SYMBOLIC GATHERING

Nothing could more dramatically suggest some of the ways in which various social, cultural, and historical factors affect clinical medical research (1) and research careers in Belgium than this medical colloquium that took place in a château. This is not to imply that Belgian medical congresses are usually held in such a setting, or that medical scientific work necessarily proceeds under the direct surveillance of the royal family. [In fact, in certain specific ways the "story of cardiac surgery" in Belgium is atypical, involving as it does the personal medical history of Prince Alexandre and the consequent interest of his immediate family in medical and surgical developments that bear upon his congenital heart condition (2).] However, in several respects this medical gathering in a château may be said to be a symbolic expression of the complex social structure and cultural tradition within which a good deal of medical research in Belgium functions, and of the rather special psychological atmosphere that consequently surrounds it (3).

To begin with, the extraordinarily long and sociologically encompassing list of guests present at this colloquium is representative of virtually every social institution, organization, and group that affects medical research and researchers in Belgium. The diversity and importance of extramedical influences on research and research careers is suggested by the presence at the colloquium of political and religious personages, nobles, financiers, and patients and their families, in addition to the expected array of physicians. The fact that such a range of persons was invited; that two different Belgian universities had chosen to award honorary degrees at the same time to medical scientists of French, Dutch, and American origin; that each address given by a professor from one of the four Belgian universities was paralleled by an address given by a comparable professor from at least one of the other three; that Prince Alexandre's speech was delivered in both Flemish and French—all these are outward manifestations of the continuous vying for absolute equality that characterizes the many competitive groups involved in Belgian medical research, and of the exponentially complicated attempts that are made to try to meet their rival demands.

In a more abstract and general sense, this medical colloquium held in the royal château may be viewed as symbolic of social conditions under which medical research proceeds in Belgium. Metaphorically speaking, Belgian medical scientists can be said to operate continuously in a "château." The word is used here in much the same way that it was used by Raoul Kourilsky (professor of clinical medicine at the University of Paris)—to symbolize those still-unchanged aspects of traditional social structure which tend to curtail medical scientific creativity and productivity and the possibilities for careers in medical research: "The great sacrifice has been research," Kourilsky said (4). "We have conserved the old 'chateau' and its arrangements that belong to another age. . . . We have watched from afar the triumphant ascent of biology. . . ."

Here Kourilsky was referring to the predicament of medical research in present-day France, rather than to the situation in Belgium. His comments suggest, however, that it is not only in Belgium that certain aspects of the traditional social structure within which medical research is carried out are unsuited to the fullest development, exchange, and application of medical scientific talent, facilities, and knowledge. Throughout a significant part of Europe, with the notable exception of England and the Scandinavian countries, a good deal of medical research is still housed, sociologically as well as architecturally, "in ancient buildings, remnants of a glorious past" (5).

Finally, this particular medical colloquium held in a royal château symbolizes to some extent the psychological milieu within which many Belgian medical researchers feel they are forced to operate by the intricate, time-entrenched *système* of which they are a part—a highly elaborate, ceremonial, delay-ridden, often paralyzing, enigmatic kind of atmosphere.

The purpose of this article is to describe and analyze the social structure within which clinical medical research is carried out in Belgium, and to suggest some of the problems that this structure creates for Belgian medical science and scientists. Although, in concrete detail, some of the phenomena discussed may be peculiar to Belgium, I hope that perhaps there is also a more general level on which the descriptive analysis that follows is relevant to problems of medical research in other European settings as well.

SOME GENERAL CHARACTERISTICS OF BELGIAN SOCIETY

The tiny, densely populated country of Belgium, smaller in area than the state of New Jersey, is a very complex, diverse little society—in the words of one Belgian physician, a "veritable social mosaic." With every few miles one travels in Belgium one finds marked differences in landscape, architecture, language, tradition, and orientation. For, within the 11,779 square miles that comprise Belgium, its more than 9 million inhabitants distribute themselves in countless ways between two cultures, French and Flemish; two languages (each with numerous dialects) ; two sharply contrasting philosophical-religious attitudes toward life (traditional Catholicism and anticlerical Masonic "Free Thought") ; and four political parties (Social Christian, Liberal, Socialist, and Communist). They are distributed, too, among the nine provinces and the 2633 communes (6) that make up the highly autonomous local governments of the constitutional monarchy; within an elaborate hierarchy of social classes that include peasants, factory and mine workers, white-collar workers, industrial and commercial bourgeois, professionals, members of the clergy, and members of the nobility; and among more than 15,000 social organizations—societies, clubs, associations, academies—formed around special interests (which, to take an extreme case, can become so special as to give rise to an "Association of Hammer-Handle Makers of Lower Ixeles") (7).

Belgium has been described as "surely one of the most particularistic societies in the world." (8). The reference is not only to the great diversity of social and cultural groupings that exist in Belgium but also to the emotionally charged, central role that ethnic, linguistic, philosophical, religious, political, community, class, and special-interest differences play in every aspect of Belgian life. At one and the same time there is a tendency for individuals to deeply identify themselves with what they consider to be "their" groups and a tendency to regard the groups to which they do not belong with apprehension, suspicion, animosity, and competitiveness. As John L. Brown (former American cultural attaché to Belgium) has remarked, given the "rivalries and resentments that smoulder under the surface" of Belgian life, "it is sometimes hard to understand how the country holds together and functions at all" (7). These particularistic groups keep a close jealous watch over each other, devoting at least as much energy to trying to prevent opposing groups from outdistancing them as to advancing their own interests through efforts devoted to self-improvement and achievement. A very literal "it-must-be-identical-and-not-simply-equivalent" conception of equality is imposed by one group upon the other. This gives rise to a number of phenomena highly characteristic of Belgian society.

One of the consequences of these rival demands for exact equality in the distribution of material resources, status, and authority is the development of numerous social organizations that replicate each other in all respects except that of the particularistic group from which each draws its membership. Thus, for example, in Belgium there is both a Royal Belgian Academy of Science, Letters and Fine Arts and a Royal Flemish Academy of Science, Letters and Fine Arts; a Royal Belgian Automobile Club and a Royal Flemish Automobile Club; Boy Scout and Girl Scout organizations and a Catholic Scouts organization.

Still other consequences are suggested by the following ironic, but nonetheless telling, description (9) of the inner political life of Belgium (the phenomena depicted characterize more than just political groups): "Once in power the [political] parties are equally consecrated to impotence. The necessity to act splinters all their divisions: in the face of this kind of peril, without fail, they put off until tomorrow what they could not settle today. Thus, nothing ever comes to pass in Belgium. . . ."

What is implied here is that the continual vying for equality between groups often leads to a kind of impasse between them. Opposing groups are deliberatively so evenly balanced and so unyielding in their relations with one another that it frequently becomes impossible to initiate any particular course of action. To do so would be construed as honoring and favoring one group's opinion more than another's. Furthermore, under the circumstances, when a particular group is faced with the challenge of trying to make and implement a decision, it often begins to split internally into smaller and smaller particularistic groupings. This, then, makes it unlikely that the original group will be able to maintain enough inner unity to take any kind of definitive and effective stand on behalf of what presumably were the shared interests around which it was organized in the first place. The internal factions that emerge also tend to engage in the same kind of divisive struggle for exact equality. Not infrequently, what results from this is an amoeba-like fission process, through which still other evenly balanced formal organizations, offices, and so on are created; this, in turn, produces another impasse of even greater social complexity.

The King and the Parliament, of course, through the symbolic and operational executive and legislative powers invested in them by the constitutional monarchy, represent and provide a certain overarching national coherence, direction, and unity. The Council of Ministers (presided over by the Prime Minister), formally appointed by the King according to which parties predominate in Parliament, has the most effective voice in introducing and administering legislation. Each minister has a permanent official (the secretary-general) at the head of his staff and, in addition, appoints his own bureau of advisers, who retire with him. But here again the characteristic particularism of Belgian society and the continuing pressures to achieve and maintain a literal kind of equality between all vying groups manifest themselves, creating impasses and the proliferation and still further decentralization of ministries, ministers, and ministerial advisers. Thus, in the 20th century most Belgian ministries have been formed by coalition, since the electoral system has rarely returned a party with a working parliamentary majority. And new kinds of ministries and ministerial posts have again and again been created in the face of impasse, conflict, and crisis; they have simply been added on to those already existing (10).

It is partly because of the proliferation of officials, agencies, and so on, as well as because of the particularistic rivalry among them, that the formal processes by which decisions are made and actions are taken in many areas of Belgian life are typically slow-moving, often delay-ridden, and sometimes indefinitely blocked. This leads, in turn, to still another characteristic Belgian phenomenon—a widespread tendency to try to find ways around the cumbersome formal structure (*"petits chemins"*), chiefly through the use of personal, often covert, influence, in order to get things more efficiently, speedily, and assuredly done.

Intricately connected with this "mosaic" of particularistic groups that make up Belgian society, and sharing many of its characteristics, is the complex of social organizations, within which most of the clinical medical research in Belgium takes place.

SOCIAL STRUCTURE OF CLINICAL
MEDICAL RESEARCH IN BELGIUM

Most clinical medical research in Belgium is carried out in a department, hospital, or institute affiliated with one of the four major universities (*11*). Each of these universities represents a different combination of some of the social and cultural distinctions that dominate so many sectors of Belgian life. To be more explicit: Brussels is a Free Thought (largely anticlerical, Free Mason), non-state university. Originally, all its classes were taught in French, but since World War II, various parts of the university have doubled their faculties, adding professors who give in Flemish the same courses that are given in French. Ghent is a state university, officially neither Catholic nor Free Thought, but with a great many practicing Catholics in the student body and on the faculty. Since the early 1930's all classes have been taught in Flemish. Liège is a state university, neither Catholic nor Free Thought, but with the greater number of its students and faculty nonpracticing Catholics or non-Catholics. All classes at Liège are taught in French. Louvain is a Catholic, non-state university with a double, completely replicated faculty and student body, the one section of the university being Flemish, the other French.

Because each of the universities represents a particular constellation of some of the social and cultural differentials that truncate Belgian life, each tends to seal itself off from the others. As some Belgians put it, the universities are "veritable cloisters," with a very limited interchange of ideas and information and an even more restricted exchange of personnel. The faculty of each of the universities is drawn almost exclusively from its alumni.

The creation of a new, fifth university, in Antwerp, is presently being considered. This would be a non-state, Free Thought, Flemish-speaking university, differing from the Flemish section of the University of Brussels in that it would be located on what is considered part of the mother soil of Flanders. Given the mounting fervor of Walloon as well as Flemish nationalism during the past few years, it is predicted by many that not only will a "Flemish" university be built in Antwerp but that its Walloon equivalent will immediately be founded either in Mons or in Charleroi. This anticipated sixth university would be non-state, Free Thought, French-speaking, and located on the soil of Wallonie.

The structure of the staffs of the university departments, hospitals, and institutes where medical research is carried out is, in the words of a young research physician, "like a building in which the ground and top floors have been constructed, but in which they haven't gotten around yet to putting in the floors in between." Research units are typically headed by one full professor, with all of the authority and responsibility of a "*patron*." Generally, the other members of the research staff are junior to him and greatly subordinate in status. A few such junior research workers may have university positions—for example, that of *chargé de cours* or *assistant*—but usually these are not positions with tenure. The greater number of researchers hold no formal university appointment. Rather, their positions (often title-less) exist only by virtue of the fact that the *patron* has been able to raise a sufficient sum of money temporarily to pay them a salary and support their research. Usually there is no formal assurance of funds for continuing their research from one year to the next. It is only in the course of the past year that a law has been passed (*12*) officially creating two kinds of tenure positions in the structure of Belgian universities, in addition to that of full professor. These new positions are those of *chargé de cours associé* and *professeur associé*. In effect, they represent some of the "floors in between" the ground floor and the top floor which hitherto have been completely missing in the formal status system of Belgian university faculties (*13*).

An integral relationship between medical research and research careers in Belgian universities and the national government is already suggested by the fact that legislation was required to create these positions. The determining influence of the government in the progress of Belgian medical research stems primarily from its important role as financier. To begin with, chiefly through the Ministry of Public Instruction, the government has the major responsibility for the support of the two state universities, Ghent and Liège, and the subsidies it has given to the "free" universities of Brussels and Louvain in the past few years have been almost as great. Above and beyond this, it is not an exaggeration to say that practically all the government ministries have some control over medical research in Belgium, through their authority to pass judgment on requests relevant to research that are submitted to them (for personnel, equipment, buildings, and so on), and, of course, ultimately through their willingness or refusal to grant the funds to meet these requests. Some of the ministries which affect medical research in Belgium are the ministries of public health and family, public works, finance, economic affairs, cultural affairs, interior, national defense, and agriculture. Perhaps more striking than the mere number of governmental bodies involved in the control and support of medical research is the fact that no one ministry or council of ministers is responsible for the overall coordination of the many agencies involved and for the development of medical scientific research as a whole. The closest approximation to such a committee is the Conseil National de la Politique Scientifique, created only 2 years ago, by a legislative act. This National Council of Scientific Policy is made up of 28 regular members drawn primarily from the four universities and from various sectors of the worlds of industry and finance. The council also has two consultant members: the secretary-generals of the ministries of public instruction and of economic affairs. The council has no executive power. Its function is purely an advisory one—that of helping to integrate and advance scientific research in Belgium through formal and informal interchange with the ministers who make up the Ministerial Committee and the Interministerial Commission of Scientific Policy, created under the legislative act that created the council. It is as yet too early to predict whether this strictly advisory council will carry enough moral weight and will remain sufficiently free of political pressures and particularistic loyalties to fulfill its hoped-for goals.

It is not only the national government that affects the execution and development of clinical medical research in Belgium. The governments of local communes in the cities of Brussels, Ghent, Liège, and Louvain also have a considerable influence. This is because, in each of these four cities in which a university is located, at least one major hospital, used by the Faculty of Medicine to carry out research (as well as to teach and to help care for patients), is owned, partly financed, and administered by the local Commission de l'Assistance Publique. The commissions of public assistance in Ghent and Liège, cities which have state universities, are required by law to put their hospitals at the disposition of the faculties of medicine of those universities; the commissions of public assistance of Brussels and Louvain, although not legally obligated, have voluntarily done the same. The commissions of public assistance, which exist in every commune of Belgium, date from the era of the French Revolution. They were originally charged with two missions: to prevent poverty and to organize hospital services. Their primary obligation was to give free care to the indigent sick of their communes in the civil hospitals that they had created, but from the very beginning they also cared for patients from the local community who were capable of paying (*14*). Direction of the hospitals of the commissions of public assistance rests in the hands of a special commission, made up of five to 12 members according to the size and population of the commune. These members of the commission, elected by the communal council, hold office for 6 years and may have their terms renewed. Any resident of the local community who is a Belgian citizen, is 25 years of age or older, and has never committed a serious legal offense is eligible to be nominated for this office. Nothing else is required. The commissions of public assistance function under the "protectorship" of the government of the commune, the government of the province in which the commune is located, and the national government. They must obtain formal authorization for many of their decisions and actions from each of these governing bodies.

In addition to the various local and national governmental agencies, a number of *oeuvres nationales* (against cancer, poliomyelitis, tuberculosis, and so on) and foundations of a private or semiprivate nature (the National Fund of Scientific Research, the National Fund of Medical Scientific Research, the University Foundation, the Francqui Foundation, the Queen Elisabeth Medical Foundation, the Inter-University Institute for Nuclear Sciences, and so on) are involved in the conduct and support of Belgian medical research.

Perhaps the most important of these agencies is the Fonds National de la Recherche Scientifique (FNRS), or National Fund of Scientific Research, founded in 1928 in response to a speech made by King Albert in which he declared that a "state of crisis [existed] in the scientific institutions and laboratories of Belgium" and that something must be done to "arouse, encourage and sustain" scientists and their work. A large-scale public drive for funds resulted from this speech, and within a relatively short time enough money was raised (chiefly from banks, industry, commerce, and contributions by private individuals) to launch the FNRS. Such a drive was unprecedented in Belgium, and nothing comparable has occurred since.

The 30-member board of directors of the FNRS is composed of nine representatives of the institutions of higher education and research of Belgium (the rector of each of the four universities and the rectors of five other institutions) ; the permanent secretaries of the four major academies of Belgium (the Royal Academy of Sciences, Letters and Fine Arts; the Royal Academy of Medicine; the Royal Flemish Academy of Sciences, Letters and Fine Arts; and the Royal Flemish Academy of Medicine) ; 14 members nominated by the University Foundation (eight professors, evenly distributed between the four universities; one of Belgium's most important businessmen, who is president of the FNRS board of directors; the director general of the Ministry of Public Instruction, and four other persons) ; the secretary-general, of the FNRS; and finally, its director and first vice president.

Decisions about the granting of funds to the various research groups who apply to the FNRS for subsidies are made by its 25 scientific commissions. Each of these commissions, organized around a different subgroup of sciences, is comprised of four professors (one from each of the four universities) and a president (20 of the presidents are university professors—five from each university—and the other five are professors at several nonuniversity institutions of higher education). All told, then, 125 different professors are members of the scientific commissions of the FNRS—virtually every university professor of science in Belgium. Since, as we have already seen, most research in Belgium is carried out in the universities in a group headed by a full professor, most of the research projects reviewed by the commissions of the FNRS are being conducted under the aegis of one or another of the commission members.

Although originally the major part of the funds distributed by the

FNRS came from private sources, the organization now receives more than two-thirds of its annual income from grants made to it by the state (chiefly via the Ministry of Public Instruction). In addition, during the past few years (by virtue, first, of custom and now of royal decree), the FNRS has become the direct recipient of funds allocated by the national government to some of the other foundations. The FNRS passes these funds on, in turn, to the designated foundations. For example, the FNRS receives the subsidy granted to the National Foundation of Medical Scientific Research by the Ministry of Public Health. It then turns this money over to the president of that foundation (who is also secretary-general of the Ministry of Public Health).

The FNRS, the National Fund of Medical Scientific Research, the University Foundation, the Francqui Foundation, and the Inter-University Institute of Nuclear Sciences (as well as several other foundations with somewhat different functions) are all housed in the same building, the Club of the University Foundation, 11, rue d'Egmont, Brussels. The director and first vice president of the FNRS has his office there. He is the effective director, first vice president, and cashier of *all* the foundations at 11, rue d'Egmont and is on the boards of directors of a number of other foundations. The secretary-general of the FNRS also has his office in this building. He is secretary of each of the 25 scientific commissions of the FNRS and of every one of the rue d'Egmont foundations. A close examination of the membership of the board of directors of each of these legally independent foundations reveals a considerable amount of further overlapping.

These are the outlines of the formal structure of medical research in Belgium—the empirically built, time-encrusted "château," with all its separate-but-identical "rooms" and its maze of winding, interconnecting "corridors," within which Belgian medical science and scientists function. It is a paradoxical structure characterized in some respects by extreme decentralization; in others, by what appears to be an extraordinary concentration of authority and power in the hands of a few agencies and persons. And this dualism is being perpetuated by recent, slowly implemented efforts to modify the existing structure.

SOME PROBLEMATIC CONSEQUENCES

What are some of the observable consequences of the structure of clinical medical research in Belgium—with its particularism, its pluralism, its centralization and decentralization—for the advancement of medical investigation and for the careers of researchers?

Although in the various institutes and departments of the four universities there are well-trained medical investigators of ability carrying out competent research, often this work is being done under adverse social and psychological conditions, or in spite of them.

The salaries of men engaged in research are generally so low that they cannot support themselves, much less their families, unless they supplement their incomes by doing some work in addition to research. (Typically, most medical researchers who are physicians see a number of private patients.) Everywhere researchers lack the funds, equipment, and personnel that would help them carry out their work. At the same time, one finds very expensive equipment duplicated in the four universities, rather than some sort of cooperative arrangement worked out between departments, institutes, and universities for the joint use of such equipment. (At last count there were 16 artificial heart machines, four artificial kidney machines, four betatrons and four cobalt bombs in Belgium—a country, it must be remembered, smaller than the state of New Jersey.)

Most of the hospitals of Belgium were built in a much earlier historical era—several of them even date back to the Middle Ages—and thus are not appropriate for medical research (or, for that matter, ideal for modern medical care). New hospitals, institutes, and laboratory buildings are obviously urgently needed, yet one university hospital which was started 25 years ago is still not completed and has only several departments functioning within it; another university hospital stood completely ready but unaccountably closed and unused for almost 2 years, until its doors were virtually forced open in the spring of 1961 by a threatened strike of medical students and "assistants"; and a crated betatron delivered more than a year ago can still be seen in the corridor of a third university-affiliated hospital building, which is too old and fragile to withstand the operation of such a powerful machine.

In the various university settings one finds medical researchers with only the most provisional of positions, and in private practice, any number of physicians who were forced to give up the idea of a research and teaching career because of the lack of reasonably well insured positions. At the same time, in departments of several medical schools there are professorial chairs, long vacant, for which occupants have still not been definitely chosen. Furthermore, especially in certain university milieus, such particularistic considerations as the political, ethnic, linguistic, philosophical, religious, class, and family affiliations of candidates play as important a role as their scientific competence in determining whether or not they will be named to an available university position. Indeed, this state of affairs is quasi-institutionalized in that each university represents a distinct political, ethnic, linguistic, and religious-philosophical cluster and that almost all faculty appointees are chosen from among the graduates of the university in question.

Despite the good relations that exist in a number of settings between professors of medicine who head a research unit and the younger medical investigators who work under their jurisdiction, a great gap in attitudes as well as in status often characterizes the outlook and interchanges of these two groups. Young research physicians speak of their "*patrons*" and professors of their "*jeunes*" with a degree of incomprehension that suggests a far greater lack of certain kinds of communication than generally would characterize, for example, the relations between an American professor of medicine who heads a research group and individuals of junior status who work under his supervision.

The professors of medicine who are the chiefs of research units—the *patrons*—spend a good deal of their potentially creative time and energy simply in coping with the burdensome administrative responsibilities that running a department or an institute entails, given the complicated network of university, governmental, and private agencies of which it is necessarily a part in Belgium. Above all, these professors are engaged in what they refer to as the "*chasse aux subsides*" (the "hunt for subsidies"). This "hunt" involves them in a complicated, time-consuming, never-ending process of writing eloquent, inquiring, imploring, demanding, grateful letters; of making formal and informal visits to strategic officials; and of sitting on numerous commissions. For, in the words of a recent report by the Conseil National de la Politique Scientifique, since "the universities insure their Faculties of Medicine with [funds] that one would hesitate to call a 'decent standard for research,'" money must be sought largely outside the universities. The funds for any particular department or institute must be procured from a great many different agencies; it is altogether unlikely that large enough grants could be obtained from only one or from several extrauniversity sources. This is because, as we have already seen, a great deal of the money given for medical research in Belgium, even when it comes from funds and foundations, is supplied by the national government. In particularistic Belgium these agencies are under political pressure to try to allocate their resources equally between the different university groups that apply for aid. Since the research-designated funds of any ministry, foundation, or fund must be evenly distributed among a large number of the hundreds of medical research groups that exist in Belgium, the absolute amount that any one group receives will be very small. And so, the professors who are chiefs of research units must apply to many different agencies in order to amass enough funds for salaries and needed equipment. Grants are usually given only on an annual basis; this makes it necessary to repeat the "hunt" for subsidies each year. In view of the limited money available for research from universities and formal extrauniversity agencies, the typical professor who heads a research unit must also spend a great deal of time skillfully cultivating and elaborately tending personal social relationships with individuals who, if astutely handled, may be willing to donate substantial private sums of money for research.

Whatever the specific nature of the problems of medical research and researchers in the various university milieus of Belgium—problems of procuring funds and equipment; of modifying, building, and opening hospitals; of utilizing facilities; of creating and establishing research positions and appointing competent, committed investigators to fill them—there is usually a long delay in trying to deal with them, and sometimes utter paralysis. It is these delays and impasses above all that erode the morale of junior and senior researchers alike—that encourage them as one research physician put it, "to seek [their] own ways, . . . licit if possible, illicit if not, . . . independent and outside of the system" to speed matters on in what might otherwise be hopelessly deadlocked or infinitely delayed situations. It is only by circumventing the formal structure and engaging, if need be, in "*sous la table*" tactics that, to quote another researcher, you can "work your way out . . . put your situation on more firm grounds . . . insure your happy survival . . . and hope for the development and expansion of the research group with which you work. . . ."

Perhaps more striking than any of these concrete problems faced by Belgian medical researchers is what might be termed the psychological atmosphere or climate in which they work. In discussing their problems with us, many researchers talked of the "absurd," "ridiculous," "arbitrary," "irrational," "undecipherable," and ultimately "absolute" ways in which, it seems to them, things come to pass or are blocked in the milieus in which they work. They frequently expressed apprehension and frustration over the "capricious, all-or-nothing, arbitrary game" of which they feel themselves a part, and which gives them the sense (as one Flemish researcher put it) that they are "tussling with phantom windmills." Even researchers relatively satisfied with their professional situations voiced a considerable amount of disquietude over the reasons for their "exceptional good luck" in having a fairly well insured position, an adequate salary, needed equipment, and a *patron* who understands, supports, and facilitates their research (*15*).

The seemingly absurd, enigmatic, arbitrary qualities of the milieus in which these medical investigators conduct their work are partly a consequence of some of the characteristics of the social structure of medical research in Belgium already discussed. To begin with (as a group of young research physicians put it, in a document of grievances they drafted) in a Belgian research institute or department "one finds one's self confronted with such a maze of entwined organizations that it is remarkably difficult to know who determines policy. . . ." Formal authority to make and implement decisions is divided between so many different groups that it is especially hard for younger medical researchers to identify all the agencies and officials involved, and to trace out the long sequence of steps by which decisions are supposed to be made. For, unlike their *patrons*, these young investigators have not been directly involved with these agencies and officials year after year in the "hunt for subsidies."

The lack of interchange of information, ideas, and opinions between departments, institutes, and universities and, in general, between persons who belong to different particularistic groups and live in different local communities also contributes to the sense of mystery about "who determines policy" and "who really has the power of decision" that is expressed by many researchers. For this insulation of one group from another means that one cannot easily develop a view of the forces larger and more general than those originating and immediately perceivable in a given research institute or department which might be affecting its progress (*16*).

The fact that so many of the decisions that affect medical researchers and the institutes and departments in which they work are made in ways that circumvent the complex, delay-ridden means that are formally prescribed also accounts for what many researchers find incomprehensible, unpredictable, and arbitrary in their professional situations. For such informal, ex officio negotiations are less "visible," less subject to control by surveillance, and more likely to be influenced by particularistic factors (as opposed to medical scientific considerations) than negotiations conducted in the formally designated ways.

Finally, many of the feelings of apprehension and indignation expressed by researchers about the apparently inscrutable or capricious forces that affect their professional activities and destinies seem to focus around certain persons in strategic positions, who, it is assumed, determine, often covertly and prejudicially, what does and does not happen in the various worlds of Belgian medical research. Sometimes these "*messieurs les responsables*" are cited by position and name; sometimes they are referred to half jokingly, half fearfully as "*Esprits Directeurs*" or "*éminences grises*." As we have seen, there is some realistic basis for attributing a great deal of authority and power to certain individuals who simultaneously hold many different offices in various of the organizations which are part of the intricate social structure of medical research in Belgium. However, the extraordinary amount of power and the nature of the power ascribed to such persons by medical researchers who discuss them; the vague and sinister allusions to still other influential, and invisible, "*messieurs*"; the remarkable lack of agreement even within a particular department or institute as to who these persons with "special powers of decision" actually are—all point to their somewhat legendary character. In part, what Belgian medical researchers seem to be doing is projecting some of their uncertainty, bewilderment, frustration, and anxiety about the social structure of which they are a part and the problems to which it subjects them onto these presumably all-powerful "*messieurs les responsables*" (*17*).

REFERENCES AND NOTES

1. I use the term *clinical medical research* in a relatively loose, descriptive sense to refer to medical research which has some ostensible, intended relationship to an understanding of the etiology, diagnosis, treatment, or prognosis of disease, or of the maintenance of health, in human beings. In the particular case of Belgium, almost all such research is conducted under the aegis of the medical school faculty of a university, most frequently by investigators who are graduate physicians.

2. A potential new link between medicine in Belgium and the royal family was forged in the fall of 1961 when Prince Alexandre enrolled as a first-year student in the Faculty of Medicine at the University of Louvain.

3. The medical colloquium seemed symbolic not only to me but also to a number of physicians with whom I had occasion to discuss it in each of the four Belgian universities. Several of the physicians with whom I talked had been present at the colloquium; others had merely read accounts of it in the newspapers or had spoken with colleagues who had been invited to attend.

4. R. Kourilsky, "Leçon inaugurale" [reprint from "L'Expansion scientifique française" (1958), pp. 27–28].

5. D. M. Gates, *Science* 128, 227 (1958).

6. Of these communes, 1733 have a population of less than 2000 inhabitants. The smallest Belgian commune, Zoutenaaie, has 25 citizens, who belong to five families. It has been necessary for Zoutenaaie to "borrow" two inhabitants from a neighboring commune to sit on its council, since there is a law forbidding two members of the same family to be members of the council at the same time. Symbolic of the proud, traditional insistence on local autonomy in Belgium are, on the one hand, the red, yellow, and black national flag, which represents the heraldic *émaux* (enameled colors) of the provinces of Brabant, Flanders, and Hainaut in the Middle Ages, and, on the other hand, the fact that the official title of the King is the "King of the Belgians" rather than the "King of Belgium."

7. J. L. Brown, in *Discovering Belgium* (Lumière, Brussels, 1960), preface.

8. The adjective *particularistic* (or *particularist*) was frequently and spontaneously used by many of the Belgian physicians with whom I talked. Interestingly enough, they used the term in almost the same way that it is used by Talcott Parsons, the well-known American sociologist, though few of these physicians have had work in formal sociology, and none of them has any knowledge of Parsons' writings.

9. R. Micha and A. de Waelhens, *Les Temps Moderne* 4, 432 (1949).

10. This was illustrated in recent Belgian history (September 1960), when, as a result of the Belgian public's reaction to the uprisings in the Belgian Congo, Gaston Eyskens, the (Social-Christian) Prime Minister, was obliged to reorganize his cabinet. The new cabinet with which Eyskens emerged on 3 September typified some of the processes I have been describing. The preceding government had consisted of 20 ministers, of whom 13 were members of the Social-Christian Party and seven belonged to the Liberal Party. The new cabinet was made up of 24 ministers, 15 of them Social-Christians, nine of them

Liberals. Thus, two ministers from each of these political parties were added to the original number. Furthermore, four new ministerial posts were created—so-called Under-Secretaries of State; two of these posts were filled by Social-Christians and two by Liberals. Commenting on this reconstitution of the cabinet, the French newspaper *Le Monde* expressed the opinion (4–5 Sept. 1960) that there was essentially nothing "new" about it, and that "the Prime Minister will more than ever be paralyzed." The nation-wide, violence-accompanied strikes which occurred in Belgium little more than 3 months later dramatically bore out this prediction. For now a "whole nation" seemed to be "revolting against itself" as, for 27 days, "nearly everything that keeps a modern nation going—trains, busses, trams, gas and light works, garbage and mail deliveries, schools, shops, ports, steel mills, coal mines, even football teams—stopped still" [C. Sterling, *The Reporter* (16 Feb. 1961)]. The origins of these strikes, of course, were very complex. But from one point of view they may be regarded as extreme outward manifestations of some of the contending, recalcitrant forces that continually threaten the progress of Belgian society.

11. It is informally estimated that there are at least 1200 separate university research institutes in Belgium. This number includes institutes in fields other than medicine, of course. Nevertheless, it suggests the wide dispersion and the duplication of research facilities and efforts characteristic of this tiny country, in which cooperation and collaboration between different groups is so difficult to effect in any domain.

12. This law came into being on 14 December 1960, when it was signed by the King, the Minister of Public Education, and the Minister of Justice.

13. Thus far, the creation of these posts has had only a token effect in increasing the number of stable, prestigious, adequately remunerated positions in Belgian society from which one can do research. For only 30 such positions have been created in each of the four universities, and these 30 must be distributed between all the departments of the university. What is more, the problem of where the funds for financing these positions will come from has not been fully resolved.

14. In 1958 a new law was passed, giving these hospitals two additional formal obligations: those of caring for patients with prepaid health insurance and of caring for all emergency cases which occur within the confines of the commune in question.

15. These descriptions of what many Belgian researchers find absurd, inscrutable, and arbitrary about the atmosphere in which they work forcibly reminds one of the novels of Franz Kafka—especially *The Castle* and *The Trial*. In this connection it is interesting to consider that Kafka, a Czech, was also a citizen of a small country of Continental Europe. Perhaps that accounts in part for the striking pertinence of his writings to Belgium.

16. As a sociologist from a foreign society I was accorded a privilege that no Belgian enjoys: I was permitted to move freely from one university to another and between departments and institutes within each university. As a result, I was able to directly observe and discuss many things about which Belgians themselves can only conjecture. Most striking of all was the opportunity I had to see that, irrespective of the particular university settings in which medical research groups were located, they were all faced with many of the same problems. That this is only guessed, not really known, by Belgian researchers is suggested by the fact that many of them asked me whether, without being

indiscreet, I could tell them if I had observed difficulties similar to their own in other groups that I had visited.

17. The materials on which this article is based were gathered during the summers of 1959, 1960, and 1961. The research was made possible by special grants from Columbia University's Council for Research in the Social Sciences and from the Belgian-American Education Foundation, and by a fellowship from the Guggenheim Foundation. I wish to thank Dr. Norman Kaplan for the opportunity of reading a first draft of a chapter he has written on "The organization of research in Belgium" and Dr. Francis X. Sutton and Carol A. Feist for critical readings of the manuscript of this article.

The Western European Scientific Establishment in Transition

NORMAN KAPLAN

Europe is on the verge of abandoning its laissez-faire attitudes and organization with respect to scientific research. The last five years or so have seen changes made or contemplated in the national organization of science which are clearly revolutionary in character. The hotly debated question of the 1930's—whether science *should* be planned—has been turned into the question of how it *can* be planned. Perhaps even more significant is the explicit linking of the scientific research effort to a nation's political, social and economic goals and policies. The revolution in thinking about these problems is already well advanced; the revolution in the actual organization of the research effort is still in its infancy. This paper examines the background or antecedents of these changes in an effort to account for what is presently happening and to anticipate the probable directions of future change.[1]

The term "European scientific establishment"[2] is used to denote the general organization of the national scientific research effort of most of the countries of Western Europe.[3] The establishment includes the individual laboratories, institutes and other research organizations actually engaged in the conduct of research in any of the natural, physical or social sciences. It also includes the various scientific bodies such as academies and scientific associations concerned with the promotion and dissemination of science. All of these constitute the organizational component of what is here called the internal system of science.

Those agencies and organizations concerned with the support or promotion of scientific research—financially and in other ways—are labeled the "external" system of science. This would include government ministries, public and private foundations, the educational system insofar as it is an agency of recruitment and training for science, and any other organizations whose activities impinge on science or scientific research.

Reprinted from *The American Behavioral Scientist*, December 1962, pp. 17–21, with permission of the publisher.

THE BREAKDOWN OF THE LAISSEZ-FAIRE ESTABLISHMENT

The dominant research organizational pattern in most of Europe for over a century has been the university as the center of scientific activity. Here, in a vast multitude of relatively small research institutes, dominated by *the* professor, much of a nation's scientific effort was carried out. The over-all emphasis tended to be on basic research,[4] but this was not dictated by any central body, whether of scientists or non-scientists. Choices of scientific work were largely an individual matter and were neither coordinated at the level of the university nor at the national level. The system was largely self-starting, self-maintaining and self-regulating—to a degree unparalleled in almost any other institution in society.

While developing what might be characterized as a real laissez-faire system, the scientists always welcomed "bounties" from the government in order to enable them to carry on their scientific pursuits. But this financial support from the government typically involved no advance commitment to any specific area or project. The money provided was to be used at the discretion of the scientist in any research direction he wished to follow. Far from interfering with the autonomy of science, these government bounties enabled the autonomy of science to grow and flourish by providing scientists with the means to pursue their work. The importance of research as an integral function of the university was thus recognized and upheld earlier and in a much stronger fashion in Europe than in the U.S.A. Under this system, it is generally agreed that science flourished in much of Western Europe and the newer, less developed nations of that era (the U.S.A. among them) went to Europe to observe and emulate this model scientific establishment.

It is important to note that this model worked with varying degrees of success for varying periods of time in the different nations of Europe. The specific social and cultural features of the different nations affected the vigor and growth of this scientific establishment in different ways.[5] Among these features were relatively small-scale universities, educating a small, socially elite group with high prestige for the professor but limited opportunities to achieve a professorship. It was not until quite recently that it became apparent to so many that the once proud scientific edifice of Western Europe was in the process of crumbling. In the discussion which follows, some of the more significant aspects of this crumbling process are examined, as seen from within and from without the system of science.

PRESSURES FOR CHANGE FROM THE EXTERNAL SYSTEM OF SCIENCE, ESPECIALLY THE GOVERNMENT

In almost every nation of Europe two related events growing out of the Second World War, and a third growing out of the Cold War, served to bring science to the attention of the highest government officials and to bring scientists in closer contact with them. The one was the development of atomic energy, and the other two focused attention on the role of science in the development of military technology. These problems emphasized to almost all governments the importance of scientific research on a grand scale, and the importance of having competent scientific advice. It emphasized, perhaps more clearly than ever before, the importance of "keeping up" scientifically. This was, of course, considerably reinforced by the general Soviet challenge prior to 1957 and even more so after Sputnik. While the ravages of the Second World War could be blamed for a slowdown in the rate of scientific advancement in many of the nations of Western Europe, it was also apparent, at least in some cases, that this alone was insufficient to account for the state of the scientific establishment. In particular, attention was focused on at least three problems: (1) the development, or the lack of development, of the newer areas of science; (2) the relative underdevelopment of the applied sciences in most of the European nations; (3) the general problem of allocation of scientific and other resources, especially with respect to the development of atomic energy, space research, and other such large, complex and costly scientific undertakings.

The rate of economic recovery and subsequent economic growth in most of the nations of Western Europe has been amazing. In the early years, much was accomplished simply through the rebuilding of old productive capacity and the building of new. But it soon became apparent, at least to some of the national leaders, that this rate of continued growth was not likely without a substantial increase in the resources devoted to applied research. And where specific national governments remained unaware of this, international bodies, particularly the old Organization for European Economic Cooperation (OEEC), [now the Organization for Economic Cooperation and Development (OECD)], and its off-shoot the European Productivity Administration (EPA), did much to stimulate an interest among all the Western European nations in building an adequate industrial research establishment.[6]

Finally, the active role of the national governments in planning and stimulating their economic recovery and subsequent growth served to bring the importance of science and technology to the highest levels of government in yet another way and from another direction. While the central government[7] played a significant role in research, it exercised almost no control, or to put it more mildly, influence, over the way in which the funds were used. Whatever the problems of exercising such influence from the point of view of scientists, it became apparent to some within the government that this would be extremely difficult because of the dispersal of research funds among a variety of ministerial budgets.

Another factor was the increasing recognition by heads of state of their own need "to know" something about scientific developments both within their own countries and in other countries as well. A larger and larger proportion of political, social and economic decisions now seemed to involve at least some question of science and scientific research. This was not a very difficult problem in most of the nations of Western Europe because of the size of the country, since frequently much of this was done on a highly informal basis among government officials and scientists who already knew each other. But the need for some kind of formal mechanism to keep the prime minister posted on the latest scientific developments, and to enable him to have the necessary information to make decisions relating to or impinging upon scientific developments, soon became apparent.

Finally, we come to the nebulous factor of national prestige. On the one hand it became clear (and in most cases was quite clear for a long time previously), that scientific achievements contributed materially to the domestic and international images of a nation's prestige. It also became apparent that this image of scientific achievement and scientific greatness had persisted in some countries long after it was justified. But perhaps even more important, in an era of disintegrating empires and the emergence of giant world powers on either side of Western Europe, it is not quite so surprising that many of these nations should have sought alternative means to continue the traditions and images of their former "greatness."

To a large extent, all of the factors just discussed provided fairly explicit recognition of the relationship between a variety of political goals and decisions and the health of the scientific establishment.[8] Perhaps any one of them might have proved sufficient to cause a reexamination of that scientific structure. The fact that they occurred more or less simultaneously and reinforced each other to a considerable extent, undoubtedly contributed to the strength of the move to reexamine and overhaul the research structure. But it must be recognized that there were a host of other factors which also played a significant though not as visibly recognizable role in the same direction. In particular we might mention the importance of changes in the stratification system, leading to a more mobile system which opened up for the first time opportunities for many of the sons of the middle classes, and to some extent even of the lower classes, for a higher education and for careers in science. This, plus the changing conceptions of the functions of the educational system,[9] contributed in some measure to the increasing numbers of students entering the educational system at all levels. Changes in occupational recruitment patterns reflecting the increasing desirability of certain of the newer occupations, and the decline of the more traditional occupations of previous eras, also contributed to the changes about to be discussed.

PRESSURES FOR CHANGE FROM THE INTERNAL SYSTEM OF SCIENCE

One of the most striking changes in the conduct of scientific research since World War II has been the enormously increased cost involved. Much of the new equipment could no longer be made adequately in the local laboratory workshop, but had to be imported from abroad and was enormously expensive. The lack of the latest equipment plus the poor condition of the basic laboratory facilities dating back long before the war, combined to emphasize the problem of facilities to most scientists all over Europe.

It was clear to practically all the scientists concerned, that the normal budgetary allowance for research was hopelessly inadequate at present. And even if new facilities were not required and it was not necessary to buy new equipment, the regular budgetary allowance would hardly have been enough to keep the laboratory going because of inflation and rising costs generally. Of course the government was approached through its many ministries to increase the support of science and scientific research. But since most governments' total allocations for research were so pitifully small, it was not infrequently the case that scientists competed with each other in quite bitter ways for these very scarce resources. It was not strange to hear that Professor "A" had requested a certain expensive piece of equipment purely for international showmanship, or that Professor "B" had outfitted a complete laboratory with the latest equipment from the U.S.A. and did not have a single person who knew how to use it.[10]

One of the other more serious problems apparent to most was that of the recruitment and retention of new scientists. While an earlier trend to train young men abroad was further accentuated in these postwar years, especially with respect to training in the U.S.A., one of the major changes was that these young men did not always go back home.[11] The most facile explanation was that salaries were so inordinately high in the U.S.A. compared with their own countries'. But it soon became apparent that this was only part of the story. Many of these young men who did not go back home felt that there were insufficient opportunities both for their career and for their research in their own countries. While it is very difficult to obtain accurate data on the extent of this exodus, it is clear that many scientists as well as others in a number of the European nations were very much concerned with this problem.

For at the same time that they were losing some of their very best men to the United States or the United Kingdom, the problem of training new recruits in science, particularly in the newer fields, was becoming more and more acute in much of Europe. The acute shortages of people in certain areas was further highlighted by the absence of these areas in the regular university departmental structure.[12] So that even if a man went abroad to get training in one of the newer specialties, when he returned it was often very difficult to find a specific position for him within the university structure.

All of this called attention to something which had been apparent to many for a long time: namely, that the rigidity of the university departmental and research institute structure was not always very favorable toward the development of scientific research. Others have put it more bluntly and said that it was definitely impeding the continued growth and development of science.[13] This was especially apparent in those cases where the senior professor was himself either not very active in research or not very "modern" in his approach to the research problems within his area.

Still another problem which began to plague many university departments was the ever-increasing student load. This increase in the number of students meant still less time for research and involved more and more of the younger men in assisting in teaching duties rather than in research programs *per se*.

It seems quite reasonable to assume that these problems within the internal system of science might have been sufficient by themselves to cause some major changes in the overall organization of scientific research. But the fact that they were coupled in time with the equally serious concerns of the national government, reinforced the existing tendencies to change. In the next section we examine some of the changes which were instituted, as well as the way in which governments and scientists went about introducing such changes.

THE TRANSITION TO A "PLANNED" SCIENTIFIC RESEARCH ESTABLISHMENT

As a result of the problems discussed in the previous section, almost all the European nations have begun to consider, and in some cases have taken action, leading to changes in the national organization of science. While there has been considerable variation among the nations with respect to the specific steps contemplated or taken, there has been remarkable unanimity on at least the following important items:

—It has been the government, and not the scientist, which has initiated formal action.

—The basic ingredients of the change in policy toward science are essentially the same.

—Scientists have been actively involved in helping the government to define the "means" to achieve pre-determined objectives.

—There has been at least implicit, if not explicit, recognition of the distinction between the internal and external systems of science, inasmuch as almost all the changes already made, or in the offing for the immediate future, deal exclusively with the external system. No country has exhibited undue haste in "tampering" with the internal system.

THE GOVERNMENT AS THE INITIATOR OF FORMAL CHANGE

While many, if not most, of Europe's leading scientists were well aware of the growing inadequacies of their scientific research establishment, it was the government and not the scientists who were the formal initiators of change. Scientists were by no means inactive in obtaining, and in sometimes speeding up, government action, but they were often actively encouraged by government officials. Moreover, no official scientific organization seems to have been active.[14] On the other hand, there are numerous well-known instances of individual scientists having played a very crucial role (often in a highly informal "behind the scenes" fashion) in hastening action of the government.

The actions taken by the government and the new policies formulated most often involved the active participation and cooperation of the scientists. But it was the government which formed these new agencies and staffed them with scientists which it chose—even though in most cases it was with the advice of other scientists involved on this highly informal level. The main point is that the scientists did not seem to possess any mechanism or agency within the internal system of science for dealing with recognized inadequacies and instituting new changes in the structure of science. And it should be added, since European research was so deeply imbedded in the university system, that there seemed to be few if any "self-correcting" mechanisms within the university either.[15]

THE OBJECTIVES OF AN EMERGING NATIONAL SCIENCE POLICY

The main objective of the newly emerging science policy is to provide for more adequate support of the national scientific research effort. Almost all the Western European Governments have now recognized this as a clear and major responsibility.[16] But in a basic break with past traditions, science is to be supported and promoted in conjunction with the nation's basic political, economic and social goals and objectives. With the advice and help of the scientists themselves, the governments propose to establish agencies to promulgate and carry out plans and policies designed to fulfill these objectives. Various mechanisms are being devised or are under consideration to enable the governments to make a more rational determination of the resources to be allocated to science, to establish priorities among competing scientific projects, and to formulate long-range plans for the development of science in terms of other national objectives.[17]

Typically, these objectives were not announced explicitly but rather have emerged from the various actions taken to correct the deficiencies in the scientific establishment discussed above. In the case of France, for example, they emerge from a series of decrees issued in late 1958 establishing a new Interministerial Committee of Scientific Research under the Prime Minister, the appointment of a Délégué Général à la Recherche Scientifique et Technique, a scientific advisory committee of twelve scientists, and a series of other such actions designed to reorganize the entire governmental structure impinging on the nation's scientific effort.[18] In the other countries, these objectives emerged from similarly established research councils, scientific advisory groups, and new agencies within the governmental structure itself.

These objectives clearly signal the end of an era of relative autonomy within the house of science. Given the tremendous importance and emphasis scientists have attributed to the autonomy of science, it is somewhat surprising to find few, if any, voices of protest. Without a much more thorough study it is not possible to do more than speculate about the factors involved in the scientists' apparent acceptance of the new objectives announced by the various European governments with respect to science. It may be that many of the scientists involved were not particularly concerned with, or aware of, the manifold consequences of this change in policy. It may well be that the scientists were concerned primarily with the immediate, short-run period. For in the short run, the effect of these changes will undoubtedly be to increase substantially the financial support for scientific research. Moreover, everyone involved seems to be proceeding quite gingerly with respect to altering any of the major features of the internal system of science. The major emphasis to date has been on alterations in the external system directly impinging upon the internal one.

SOME TENTATIVE STEPS TOWARD CHANGING THE
ORGANIZATION FOR THE SUPPORT OF SCIENCE

Although there have been considerable variations within the different countries with respect to the exact organizational revisions or new units created, there is still sufficient similarity in the underlying patterns to warrant a general description. At least three distinct phases are involved: (1) the reorganization of the government agencies, or the creation of a new unit within the top echelons of the government, whose main function is to carry out the major objectives of this changed policy towards scientific research; (2) the creation within the government of an organization or a body of scientists whose main function is to provide continuing advice for the government and to assist in formulating plans and policies for the development of science as a continuing operation (this agency may or may not be organizationally incorporated within the first one); (3) the revisions, if any, in the organizations actually conducting research—especially the research institutes and the university generally. Considerable progress has been made in most Western European nations with respect to the first two items, but almost all of them have postponed any direct action with respect to the last.

The first problem is a familiar enough one in most governments, and there is considerable experience in planning and carrying out such internal reorganizations. The main problems appear to be straightforward enough: (1) Far too many ministries had some interest in scientific research and provided some support for it, but no one ministry had overall responsibility.[19] Scientific research was therefore usually neglected as it was not a top-priority item for any one of the ministries. And even where it was not wholly neglected, there was relatively little coordination of the total effort. (2) It was apparent that some agency had to be created whose main job it would be to coordinate the various government research programs and to provide central information to enable those in charge of planning to make realistic decisions. (3) The importance of science in the modern world can be seen from the fact that the agency created in most of the countries was placed on a par with the other more traditional ministries.

Interestingly enough, in no case was a traditional ministry of science created. Even in the United Kingdom, which came close to doing so, a Minister for Science was appointed, but a Ministry of Science was not created. This apparently was due to the expressed fears of scientists in all countries about the disadvantages of yet another large-scale government bureaucracy hamstringing the progress of science. Instead, relatively small agencies were created which usually had fairly direct access to the prime minister and were in turn very accessible to at least some segments of the scientific community. Whether a new research council was created (as in Belgium), or a separate agency such as France's Délégation Générale à la Recherche Scientifique et Technique, or a Ministry of Coordination (as in Greece), the primary objective was to place the organization of the government's efforts in some kind of rational order. It was an attempt to clean up all the bits and pieces that had developed over the years in response to numerous specific crises and events. The government wished to provide a more effective means whereby it could take strong action, collect information as necessary, formulate new plans with respect to its scientific and other goals.

The need to revitalize the internal system of science was equally obvious to most of those involved. However, almost nothing specific to achieve these ends has been tried in any of the Western European nations. The major exception to this statement is the attempt to raise the general level of support for science everywhere. Most of the governments are increasing substantially the general level of resources available to all universities, including raising salaries and the provision of new facilities. Through this as well as their own reorganization, they seem to be hoping that some of this "new look" will trickle down and somehow change the picture within the universities and the research institutes themselves.

It should also be added that at least in some of these countries, a limited attempt to introduce immediately provision for selective support of new research has been introduced. In most cases where this is being tried, it is some variation of the device of the project grant long familiar in the U.S.A. Both the government officials and the scientists involved seem agreed on the necessity to move cautiously in trying to effect changes within the university system.[20] And in most cases, because of the smallness of the country, the relatively small number of scientists and universities involved, and the limited facilities generally, there seems to be little alternative than to try to work through the universities.[21]

Thus, it is still too early to be able to say with any assurance exactly what changes will take place within the universities. It seems likely that the old style, small-scale university research institute dominated by *the* professor is likely to disappear. But this is likely to happen as much because of the changing nature of research requiring large-scale facilities and teamwork, as it is because of the social and economic changes in Europe. The universities in Europe face difficult years, not only because of the problems of research and the so-called feudal research institutes which they have spawned, but because of the tremendous increase in the number of students which is likely to occur in the next few decades.

CONCLUSIONS

We are witnessing the emergence of new patterns of cooperation between scientists and government officials in the revision and creation of a new national research establishment. The basic problem to which these men are addressing themselves remains one about which we know relatively little: namely, what kind of society, and what kinds of specific organizational forms are most appropriate to the effective and optimum development of science. This is a question to which social scientists should be addressing their attention. But it is difficult to find many with such concerns either in Europe or the U.S.A. In their absence, and in the absence of any tested knowledge, the government officials as well as the scientists are proceeding according to their best guesses, common sense, and their most prominent prejudices.

REFERENCES AND NOTES

This is part of a larger study of the organization of scientific research supported, in part, by grants (RG 5289 and currently RG 9225) from the National Institutes of Health, Division of General Medical Sciences, U.S. Public Health Service.

[1] This report is based largely on personal observations and interviews with scientists and government officials in Europe during two recent field trips in 1959 and 1962.

A more detailed description and analysis of these problems will appear in a forthcoming monograph: "European Scientific Research Organization: A Comparative Analysis."

[2] This term was suggested by a recent article by Don K. Price: "The Scientific Establishment," *Proceedings of the American Philosophical Society,* Vol. 106, No. 3, June 1962, pp. 235–245. In this paper he traces the developments leading to "the plain fact that science has become the major Establishment in the American political system . . ." (p. 235). The interested reader will find many points—both similar and diverging—in Dean Price's analysis of major American trends compared with my analysis of European trends in this paper.

[3] Almost all the major countries of Western Europe, with the exception of Spain and Portugal, were visited at least once. In focusing on the European scientific establishment we must necessarily blur or omit entirely many significant differences in patterns and processes among the various European nations. While the ensuing description and analysis does not apply precisely to any one particular country, it does provide a model which permits us to detect variations and deviations for subsequent analysis.

At least two other recent reports on this subject have used the same approach in treating European science organizations as a whole, and thus increase our confidence in the assumption of underlying patterns common to most of Europe. Cf. Alexander King, "Towards a National Science Policy," *Impact of Science on Society* Vol. XII, No. 3 (1962) pp. 157–175, and *Increasing the Effectiveness of Western Science* (Fondation Universitaire, Brussels, 1960) 19 pp.

[4] Cf. David M. Gates, "Basic Research in Europe," *Science,* Vol. 128, No. 3318, Aug. 1, 1958, pp. 227–235.

[5] Cf. Joseph Ben-David, "Scientific Productivity and Academic Organization in Nineteenth Century Medicine," *American Sociological Review,* Vol. 25, No. 6, Dec. 1960, pp. 828–843; and, Joseph Ben-David and Awraham Zloczower, "Universities and Academic Systems in Modern Societies," *European Journal of Sociology* Vol. III #1 1962, pp. 45–84.

[6] See especially: Organization for European Economic Co-operation, *The Organization of Applied Research in Europe, the United States, and Canada.* Paris, OEEC, 1954, 3 vols. A. King, *op. cit.,* and *Increasing the Effectiveness of Western Science, op. cit.*

[7] The major exceptions: West Germany and Switzerland where the Länder and Cantons, respectively, play an important role in such support, although this is becoming more of a technicality in West Germany in recent years.

[8] See, for example, A. King, *op. cit.,* who notes: "It is obvious therefore that, irrespective of the economic structure, political ideology or state of development, governments now have a major stake in scientific activity, maintaining their own laboratories, recruiting their own research staffs and, above all, accepting responsibility for future developments—these being assumed inevitably as a consequence of the gradual recognition of the role of science in economic growth, security, social development, foreign policy and general national well-being . . ." pp. 164–5, and the statement in the report *Increasing the Effectiveness of Western Science, op. cit.,* if the West's lead in science is to be main-

tained, " . . . closer liaison between governments and science will be required" (p. 7).

[9] Cf. A. H. Halsey, "The Changing Function of Universities," pp. 456–465, Chapter 32 in A. H. Halsey, F. Floud and C. A. Anderson (eds.) *Education, Economy, and Society* (New York, Free Press, 1961).

[10] For some other examples and manifestations, see Renée C. Fox, "Medical Scientists in a Château," *Science,* Vol. 136, No. 3515 (May 11, 1962) pp. 476–483.

[11] For a recent discussion of this problem by a nuclear physicist cum sociologist of science, see: Stevan Dedijer, "Why Did Daedalus Leave?" *Science,* Vol. 133, No. 3470 (June 30, 1961) pp. 2047–2052. Also: William V. Consolazio, "Dilemma of Academic Biology in Europe," *Science,* Vol. 133, No. 3468, June 16, 1961, pp. 1892–1896.

[12] See esp. Ben-David and Zloczower, *op. cit.*

[13] See Consolazio, *op. cit.,* who makes reference to the institute directorship as the last stronghold of feudalism (p. 1894). Also, the statement in *Increasing the Effectiveness of Western Science, op. cit.* "Scientific Education is hampered in many Western Countries by the archaic administrative structure of the universities. Science departments are handicapped because they must conform to conditions which were designed to meet the very different needs of teaching the humanities." (p. 9.)

[14] An important exception: The Royal Society has continued to play a significant formal role in advising the British Government on scientific matters. But even in the U.K., a separate Advisory Council on Scientific Policy was set up shortly after World War II.

[15] In my forthcoming book on European scientific organization, a number of such patterns are described. Of particular interest is yet another manifestation of the "two step flow of influence pattern" and the tremendous significance of internationally recognized scientists in influencing the adoption of new policies and procedures within specific countries.

[16] See esp. the following: Ben-David and Zloczower, *op. cit.,* A. H. Halsey "British Universities" pp. 85–101; Raymond Aron, "Quelques problèmes des universités françaises," pp. 102–122, *European Journal of Sociology,* Vol. III #1, 1962. Also: Dietrich Goldschmidt, "Teachers in Institutions of Higher Learning in Germany," pp. 577–588 in A. H. Halsey, *et al. op. cit.,* and Lucien Massart, "The Belgian Universities: A Note on Their Problems and Prospects," *Science and Freedom,* No. 19, June 1961, pp. 21–25.

[17] Cf. A. King, *op. cit.*

[18] Cf. "La France Devant les Problèmes de la Science": Dévelopements récents de l'Organisation de la Recherche en France (1958–1960), 30 Novembre 1960, No. 2.721, La Documentation Française.

[19] Strictly speaking this is not correct since the European equivalent to the U.S. Bureau of the Budget (usually the Finance Ministry in Europe) has, in effect, assumed overall responsibility for the nation's total research expenditures. But this was usually in the role of "guardians of the purse strings" rather than as a coordinating science ministry.

[20] See, for example, Lucien Massart, "The Belgian Universities," *op. cit.* This statement is especially significant in view of Professor Massart's position as Chairman of the Belgian National Advisory Council for Scientific Policy, established September 16, 1959.

[21] On the differences in attitudes and approach to the integrated and planned

utilization of the universities as research producers in Europe and the U.S.A., see: Don K. Price, *op. cit.,* and N. Kaplan, "Research Overhead and the Universities," *Science,* Vol. 132, No. 3424, August 12, 1960, pp. 400–404.

PART V

Science and Policy

In the 1930's, a great debate raged among scientists, especially in Great Britain, on the question of whether or not science could be, or should be, planned. Those who argued against planning said, in effect, that science *could not* be planned because the results of science were essentially unpredictable. They also argued that it *should not* be planned because to do so would seriously restrict and impair the fundamental freedom of scientists and would result in their stagnation. Those who argued in favor of planning did so primarily in terms of a desire to harness the benefits of science for the social good. In the 1960's, both the character and the focus of this debate has changed considerably.

In the 1960's, hardly anyone argues that science cannot be planned at least within a restricted notion of planning. Admittedly, the results of research are not always predictable in advance and thus it would be impossible to lay down a precise course to be followed in any particular branch of science. It is possible, however, to lay out certain guidelines for future development. This might involve the expansion of certain fields and the contraction of others, either because of important new developments within the field and the expectations based on these developments or because of the social (or political or economic, etc.) importance of a particular line of research. For example, it might be agreed by both scientists and laymen within a society that it would be desirable and important to find solutions for the cancer problem. As a result, the decision might be made to encourage an all-out effort in the cancer battle by creating new research institutes devoted to this subject, by making large sums of money available for research in this area, and by other means. At the same time, a decision might be made in one country that the fight against cancer is so important that it would be carried out at the expense of alternative research possibilities either in the field of health or in completely different fields. In another country, the decision might be made that while cancer is very important, it cannot be investigated at the expense of certain other equally important areas. Such choices have always been made, sometimes consciously, but most often on a covert basis. Sometimes the main criterion has been emotional

365

appeals or political influence. Those who would argue in favor of the planning of science argue for more conscious choices based on more explicit criteria.

Most national governments and many scientists now appear to be convinced that science can be and *must be* planned. Differences of opinion still persist with respect to exactly what should be planned, in how much detail, how this should be done, and by whom. The papers included in this section are addressed to various aspects of these questions.

Near the end of 1963, the Organization for Economic Cooperation and Development convened a meeting of science ministers and others concerned with questions of national science policy. This received only a few inches of space, at most, in the newspapers, but it is quite likely that historians of the future may accord it considerably more importance. This was probably the first meeting of its kind and it is most certainly not the last. The very fact that there were science ministers (or ministers for science) in existence was in itself a development no more than five years old at most. To serve as a basis for discussion at this meeting, a document was prepared by the advisory group on science and its secretariat which laid out the problem areas. Several sections of this document are presented here.

In the first part the problem and its boundaries are defined. The main emphasis is on the fact that the development of priorities and policies with respect to science is inescapable in the world of today. This is so because of the scope and significance of science generally, but even more important, because of the opportunities to harness science to the needs of economic development. Since economic development and growth are a primary concern of the OECD, it was only natural that the relationship with science should be stressed. The support of scientific research, and the support of education generally as a necessary foundation for science, is viewed as an investment in economic growth for the more industrially advanced countries as well as for the developing countries.

Science and policy are viewed in terms of two conceptually distinct components. The one is concerned with policies *for* science. Here are included considerations for establishing priorities and for allocating resources of all kinds among competing scientific programs and objectives. The second component concerns the implications of science (potential and actual) for policy making in all other spheres of national life. These include economic, political, social, military, and other areas. In the world of today science has implications, sometimes very direct and immediate ones, for all these other areas, and the connection between it and them must become far better understood. This report presents a strong case for the explicit recognition of the connections between science and almost all other national activities. Perhaps when this does actually happen in the not too distant future, it will become possible to begin to study the problems involved more deeply and more seriously than we have in the past.

As the OECD report makes clear, it is important to distinguish the problems of policies for science from those dealing with the implications of science for other policies. As we shall see in a number of the other selections included in this chapter, there is an increasing awareness of the necessity to make explicit choices in allocating scarce resources among competing scientific proposals. On what basis can such choices be made? It must be emphasized again that we are not now concerned with the individual scientist frequently facing a choice of whether to devote the next year or the next five years to project A or project B. We are concerned with choices which must be made by government agencies and others supporting scientific research which involve the selection of alternatives, the establishment of priorities, and the encouragement of field A more or less at the expense of field B. Even when decisions can be made to support research in both fields, a further decision must be made whether to allocate, say, 60 per cent or 10 per cent to one or the other.

In the next selection, Alvin Weinberg discusses some of the criteria involved in making such scientific choices. He distinguishes internal criteria which involve questions of whether the field is ready for exploitation and whether the scientists in it are competent enough to warrant a certain level of support. If we could stop right here we would have a decision based on technical considerations. However, in the normal course of events we can expect to find many scientific areas with equally valid technical claims while at the same time the resources available for the support of research are necessarily limited. This means that choices have to be made among competing fields which are technically equivalent. Consequently, certain external criteria must be introduced. According to Weinberg these revolve around technological, scientific, and social merit. Weinberg then discusses how these external criteria might be applied in concrete situations by examining five different fields of scientific endeavor. It is of considerable interest that Weinberg, applying his own criteria, finds that the present level of financial support for his own field (nuclear physics) may in fact be too high vis-à-vis the competing alternatives. Whether or not we accept Weinberg's analysis and his criteria, it is certainly clear that such questions will have to be asked much more frequently in the foreseeable future. Dr. Weinberg has provided us with a provocative beginning.

While the OECD document presents the general outline of science policy problems, the next selection deals with some problems specific to a particular country at a particular time. In these excerpts from a statement made by Paul Gross, when he was President of the American Association for the Advancement of Science, before a congressional committee, he views the total research and development picture in four separate parts: (1) The largest fraction (approximately 90 per cent) of the national research and development budget is devoted to applied research where the objectives are reasonably clear and the results reasonably predictable. Even here, however, it is often found that there are serious gaps in basic knowledge, and the solution in the past has too often been an attempt to remedy this on a "cut and try" basis. (2) Basic research remains the most essential and at the same time the most difficult to explain to Congress as well as to the public at large. (3) Advanced scientific education claims the next fraction. (4) Primary and secondary science education complete the picture. Gross insists that each of these must be viewed separately in trying to assess government policies toward science. In doing so it would be possible for Congress and the President to maintain their responsibility for the total budget amount as well as its division into these four categories. Responsibility could also be maintained for subdividing the first area involving development to meet specific defense and other national objectives. On the other hand, scientists themselves together with the basic research granting agencies might best decide how to subdivide the money available for basic research.

The support of research in the universities is beset by many problems often involving contradictory objectives. An example may be found in the recurring clamor for a more equitable geographical distribution of funds rather than the present concentration in the so-called high-quality universities. However, long-range planning and the recognition of two quite different and specific objectives are necessary. One of these involves the support of research strictly on the basis of quality which would probably continue the present pattern of concentration in the few first-rate universities. The second objective however is to build up quality on a geographically distributed basis, and one possible solution is to allot a greater fraction of research funds for institutional grants to the so-called weaker universities. The Gross statement is a good summary of some of the issues, problems, and solutions considered by scientists in the emerging problems of government-science relationships.

In the 1950's the federal government expenditures in support of research and development expanded at an unprecedented rate. In the early 1960's, a reaction had begun to set in, and observers both from the government and from science began to question the assumption that research and development could or would continue to expand at the same rate in the future. In the next selection, William D. Carey of the Bureau of the Budget presents the case for a "slowed down" expansion of science in the years ahead.

The Bureau of the Budget is the chief executive branch "watchdog" agency overseeing the separate executive department and agency budgets of the federal government. Although it was never intended as a formal planning agency, the Bureau of the Budget acts in such a capacity by default whenever decisions are made on the budgetary requests of the many different federal agencies.

Carey expects a very slow expansion in the expenditures for science over the next few years which will then level off. Science must now justify itself and its costs in fair competition with other social priorities and preferences. There is too much danger, in his view, of the "pork barrel" mentality developing in science. Scientists can no longer expect to get as much money as they want.

If the Carey statement becomes official policy, and the expectation is that it will, then the implications for science are quite clear. In the first place, hard choices will have to be made among competing scientific claimants for the scarce dollar. Purely technical and scientific criteria will undoubtedly play a considerable role in making such choices. But other kinds of criteria, involving social, political, and other considerations, will undoubtedly become more important. In the second place, as Carey clearly points out, the total outlay for science will be determined by the grand total available for all governmental activities. Science will have to compete with other activities, and here the role of technical and scientific criteria may be a very minor one indeed. The choices in this case would be primarily political—involving judgments about whether the government should spend more money for missiles or hospitals or roads or research or hundreds of other such choices. This is precisely the point at which the informed layman, whether he be private citizen or a member of Congress or member of the executive agencies, is vital if science is to be adequately supported.

As the need for new kinds of choices and decisions has become apparent, the roads to Washington have become more familiar than ever to many scientists. Scientists have been called upon increasingly by the federal government to act as advisers on a variety of questions ranging from purely scientific choices among competing research proposals to scientific advice which is heavily tinged with political considerations and implications. In the selection included here, Meg Greenfield, an outstanding political journalist, reports on the advisory setup in Washington and, in the process, raises some basic questions about the role of science and scientists in a democratic society.

Greenfield finds an invisible elite of perhaps two hundred scientists who must fill many more than the two hundred separate advisory jobs. The organization of the major science advisory groups is described. In discussing the nature of science advising, Greenfield points out the difficulties of distinguishing between purely scientific and political questions, especially in relation to such questions as the nuclear test ban, disarmament, etc. Some of the difficulties which scientists experience in distinguishing between their private and public areas of responsibility are discussed. This is the system which grew like Topsy, and why it works as well as it does is something that is still not entirely clear to most observers.

So much for discussions about the machinery of science policy making and about policy in general. In the next several selections, we turn to one important substantive question involved in the formulation of science policy in any country. The concern of these selections, however, is with the specific situation in the United States, and the substantive question concerns the role of the universities in the nation's scientific effort. A substantial foundation for considering the role of the universities as one of the most significant elements in a national scientific effort has already been covered, especially in the first and second chapters of this volume. The importance of basic research, of training new scientists, and of fostering scientific development generally places a university in a particularly crucial position.

One of the first, and most significant, of the "official" studies of the role of the universities in the national science effort was that of the President's Science Advisory Committee, which was first issued in 1960. It is a pioneering attempt to identify the ways in which the universities and the federal government are linked to each other in promoting scientific progress.

The importance of this problem is documented further by the fact that several years after the appearance of the PSAC report, the National Academy of Sciences undertook a kind of follow-up study. As Frederick Seitz, the president, notes in the preface: "The present report, which is addressed to a very basic issue involving the relationship between science and our society, was undertaken by the National Academy of Sciences on the request of its membership at an annual meeting of the Academy in April of 1963. There was an overwhelming opinion among the members, not only that the issue is an exceedingly urgent one to study, but also that the Academy's committee on science and public policy was a most appropriate body to explore the views of the scientific community and to formulate responsible conclusions." Due to limitations of space, only the prefatory remarks and conclusions are reproduced here. For those interested and concerned with the problems raised, the entire report is earnestly recommended.

But even the conclusions alone provide us with very instructive clues about the actions and reactions which followed the earlier PSAC report as well as some of the newer issues which had come to the fore. Among the latter, we might mention a growing clamor within Congress for "tighter" fiscal supervision of research grants. The conclusions of this National Academy report reaffirm and remind the scientific "community" of the necessity for fiscal responsibility while providing for the maximum possible scientific freedom.

There can be little doubt that the implementation of the National

Academy and the PSAC reports on the universities' role in the nation's science effort will tend to improve the present situation *within the present context*. For the fact is that both of these reports accept the project grant system as the basic mechanism linking the federal government's effort to support science to the scientific community in the universities who are actually conducting the research. This is not to deny that other forms of support are also suggested. But the grant system was a somewhat accidental adaptation to specific circumstances; in the view of many observers a very brilliant adaptation indeed. Whether it is, and will be, the best mechanism in view of the changing conditions remains an open question. It is a question which should become the focus of systematic research efforts by many different kinds of specialists in addition to the subject of studies by committees composed primarily of natural and physical scientists and interested particularly in immediate action and application.

One research study, which was at the same time concerned with practical recommendations, was actually undertaken by Harold Orlans of the Brookings Institution in Washington. The main focus of this study was on the impact of federal research support programs on higher education in this country. Much of the support for basic research in the universities has tended to be concentrated in a relatively small number of the so-called top universities of the country. From a purely technical point of view, this concentration of support was not only inevitable but desirable. In this view, support should be extended on the basis of capacity and quality, and the best men do tend to be concentrated in the best universities. (It is an interesting sidelight that this fairly obvious concentration of high-quality talent in a small number of high-quality universities is only recently becoming a subject of concern.) On the other hand, there are some observers who are somewhat worried about this concentration of support in a small number of universities and would like to see federal support distributed in other ways. In the selection included here, Orlans presents a somewhat modified and summarized version of his main findings and conclusions of this larger study.

In Orlans' view the concentration of federal funds in a few major universities has done most damage to the liberal arts colleges and the state universities. Undergraduate teaching and the humanities have been devalued. The increasing volume of funds to this small number of institutions has not resulted in an increased return for each dollar invested but rather in a dilution in the quality of research which, although still competent, is quite often mediocre. Orlans advocates that research funds should not be used as hidden subsidies and stresses the need for the development of more open policies of support of higher education. Funds should be directed toward the teaching and small colleges, toward the humanities and social sciences.

While this is by no means a balanced account, nor is Orlans' analysis the only acceptable one, the issues he raises and the questions he discusses are vital to an understanding of these problems.

The selections which have been included in this section have been chosen for their contribution to a broader and more comprehensive perspective on problems in science policy. Several general comments and observations might be offered at this point. The first is that only one of the selections included here stems from a research study strictly speaking. All the others represent individual or group efforts to define the relevant problems, to record observations and experiences, and to recommend solutions to pressing practical problems. Even the single research study is probably best classified as applied rather than basic research.

We are faced with dilemmas within dilemmas. The problems of science and its organization and support are pressing and immediate. Solutions are needed today to the crises as they occur. There is no time for research. Besides, some may well ask whether we are prepared to undertake any meaningful research in this area. Who would undertake such research? Do we have enough of a foundation and sufficiently well-trained experts prepared to launch such research undertakings?

The answer must be based on a large measure of faith. Certainly there are not a large number of well-trained experts who can hardly wait to embark upon research on science policy. And certainly there is much that we do not know about this area. And certainly we have perfected neither the conceptual nor the methodological tools to undertake such studies. Nevertheless, it is precisely because all this is true that it is all the more important to encourage the development of concepts and methods and of people who will use them. And despite all the immediate pressures, the urgent necessity for long-range basic research programs must be recognized.

Science and the Policies of Government

ORGANIZATION FOR ECONOMIC COOPERATION AND DEVELOPMENT

THE PROBLEM

THE NEW DIMENSIONS OF SCIENCE AND TECHNOLOGY[1]

The great recent growth and impact of science and technology are common knowledge. They involve more people and bigger budgets than ever before. They have generated increasing specialisation within and at the borders of traditional scientific disciplines. They are today engaged in by industries, governments, and independent institutions, as well as by universities. They

---

Only Chapters 2, 3, and 4, pp. 14–32 in *Science and the Policies of Government* by the Advisory Group on Science Policy, September 1963, Paris, are reprinted here with the permission of OECD. The report, from which the section reprinted here was taken, was prepared by the Ad Hoc Advisory Group on Science Policy appointed by Thorkil Kristensen, Secretary-General of the Organization for Economic Cooperation and Development. The members and staff of this group are listed at the end of this excerpt. This report served as a background document for a Ministerial Meeting on Science called by OECD in Paris in October, 1963. Needless to say, this report does not necessarily reflect the official views of the Organization or of its Member Governments.

[1] DEFINITIONS: The intimate interrelation of science, technology, and education often requires that the respective terms be mentioned together. The following text nevertheless often employs the word "science" generally, to connote all three activities. The context should make clear when the word is so used, and when it serves the narrower purpose of designating scientific research alone, as distinct from technology or education.

The distinction between what have traditionally been called "basic" and "applied" research is daily growing more blurred and confusing. This text will therefore generally embrace them both in the single word "research," except when there is a specific purpose to be served by stressing the difference. The phrase "technological development" or simply "development" is used in its normal connotation of activities designed to embody scientific knowledge in new machines, devices, products, and processes for useful purposes.

The phrase "science policy" is used no more frequently than necessary because of the ambiguity of its meaning explained on Page 376 below. When used, it is, where possible, with the narrow connotation of a policy specifically for the advancement of science. The more descriptive and univocal phrase "science and policy" is often used to connote the broader interaction of scientific progress and national and international policies generally.

have led to strengthened science and engineering curriculums and to changes in the content, pattern, and conduct of education in general. They have created new kinds of tools for management, and they have spawned new kinds of institutions and agencies in an increasing mixing-up of the public and private sectors of nations. In association with sound policies, they can contribute essentially and increasingly to national safety, physical health, adequate nutrition, economic growth, improved living standards, and more leisure for the populations of the world.

THE PUBLIC STAKE IN SCIENCE

The state and progress of science and technology have thus become matters of immediate concern not only to scientists, but also to peoples generally and to national governments in particular. Except for its implications for human welfare and therefore also for policy, few but professional scientists would care how fast or whether science advanced, or in what directions. But since the strength, progress, and prestige of countries are today measured in part by their achievements in science and technology, scientific excellence is more and more becoming an important national goal. National resources are therefore increasingly devoted to research and development.

But resources, however plentiful, are always inadequate to all the demands placed upon them. Choices must therefore be made between the claims of science and other national objectives, and priorities must be established among the multiplying and competing opportunities that modern science offers. The choices must moreover be made in the light of long-term national goals and expectations, since the research supported today may take a decade or more to flower into a useful technology. It is clear, of course, that these choices will often have to be made in situations of great uncertainty, but that is an inescapable characteristic of all policy decisions, and must be an element in the form they take.

The scientist, therefore, has not only his age-old responsibility to guide his work according to its promise and his lights, but also the opportunity to co-operate with the educator, the economist, and the political leader in deciding how science as a social asset can be furthered, and how a nation and the human community can best benefit from its fruits. Science, in a word, has become a public concern.

SCIENCE AND ECONOMIC GROWTH

The most striking recent example of the impact of science on the policies of nations has been in the field of military technology, especially among the major powers. The needs of military research and development have provided at once the impetus and funds necessary to the rapid growth of science and technology during and since World War II. Many new possibilities for scientific investigation and engineering achievement have been opened up as a result which promise continuing contributions not only to national defence, but also to many other socially beneficial activities as well. Nations are therefore seeking ways to support the advancement of science, and to make decisions about general directions in which inquiry and technological development might most usefully move.

A growing opportunity for science and technology lies in the field of economic development. Economic theory to date has tended to concentrate on explaining relatively short-term fluctuations in employment, incomes, and prices, and to see the problem of economic growth as restricted to increases in national income. The relevant parameters have been capital accumulation and labour productivity. Science and technology have always, of course, influenced economic growth, but this influence has generally been assumed rather than accounted for explicitly by traditional theory.

An increasing number of economists are nowadays taking a new look at the relationship of science and economic growth. In seeking the factors that make an economy grow in the longer term, they are giving more direct attention to research, invention, and development as governing the extent to which investment in capital equipment can result in increased productivity. Economic growth, in other words, is seen as the result, not only of capital investment in machines and labour, but also of national resources devoted to research and development, since these lead to improvements in the quality of capital and labour. Investment in science, on this view, is investment in growth.

Analogously, investment in education is investment in growth. Just as the productivity of capital equipment is seen to depend on technological innovation, so can the efficiency of labour be seen to depend on the education made available to a population. The traditional incentives to labour efficiency are the material rewards of work. But the kind and degree of efficiency that these rewards produce depend on the general education and particular skills of the labour force. Both science and education, therefore, can be seen as basic factors in the process of economic growth.

THE BREADTH OF ECONOMIC OBJECTIVES

Economic analysis that approaches problems of growth from this fundamental and long-term point of view takes on a breadth of character not alien to the classical concept of political economy. Economic growth is now more than synonymous with increases in national income. It is seen as a part of general social development. Traditional economic procedures—i.e., establishment of criteria and priorities, calculations of costs and benefits, selection of courses of action in the light of expected consequences—apply, on this wider view, not only to economic, but to sociological and political choices as well.

It is in the wide sense, too, that the concept of development is most usefully understood when applied to the needs of the world's newly advancing countries. Those countries require not only industrialisation and improvement of agricultural methods, but also concurrent development of general education, technical training, modern cultural attitudes, new social-psychological patterns, some research activity of their own, and sophisticated political leadership. No effective policy for the economic development of such countries can ignore these essential elements of the problem. Science, technology, and education can to some degree contribute to all these aspects of development, in advanced countries as well as in the less advanced. A broad view of economic objectives can therefore provide a fruitful context for formulating comprehensive national and international policies designed to derive maximum benefits from the resources devoted to science.

SCIENCE POLICY

The term "science policy" is ambiguous. It too often connotes only a policy limited to the needs of science *per se,* and excludes the effects of science and technology on the full spectrum of national policies in such disparate fields as agriculture and industry, defence, education, and domestic and foreign political affairs. Maximum exploitation of scientific opportunities requires programmes that combine concern for the growth of science itself and provision for the rapid, deliberate application of its fruits to human welfare. That is the substance of science policy in the full sense, as denoting consideration of the interactions of science with policy in all fields.

In this sense, a nation's science policy is the same kind of thing as its economic policy, or its foreign policy. The idea of an explicit national science policy is new—as those of an economic or foreign policy are not—because science has only recently taken on major public dimensions. But the idea is no more alien than that of any other policy. To say that a government needs an articulated science policy is simply to note that there has devolved upon that government a major and continuing responsibility to make choices about issues that involve science. Nor is science policy an abstract concept. It names the complex of individual ideas, organisational biases, institutional attitudes, operational realities, temporary working arrangements, and necessary compromises out of which emerge national decisions about where and how fast science will go, and about the national goals to which it should contribute. The existence of a national science policy implies no abridgment of the scientist's autonomy in the conduct of research. As the sequel will be devoted to showing, it simply means that scientists must now get together with public representatives to decide how this major new resource can best be used for the common weal.

POLICY FOR SCIENCE

POLICY PLANNING AND SCIENTIFIC FREEDOM

A nation needs a comprehensive and consistent policy for the support and advancement of science, because there are more opportunities to advance science and technology than there are resources available to exploit them all. Government authorities who are subjected to continuing requests for support from industry, universities, scientific institutions, individual scientists, graduate students, and international scientific organisations, as well as from consumers of science within various departments and agencies of government itself, need guidance on how to allocate their funds and their trained manpower. The purpose of a national policy for science is to provide such guidance.

There is no necessary conflict between the need for policy and the intellectual autonomy of the scientist, especially so long as research ideas are more numerous than the possibilities of implementing them, and so long as the scientists themselves, through their advice to policy-makers, can discourage unwarranted compromises with scientific worth. Many scientists nevertheless realise that the complex organisations and diverse skills required by modern scientific work imply some modification of traditional views of academic freedom. Not every investigator can now expect a distinguished solo career untrammeled by institutional considerations. Many need to work as members of teams on projects whose magnitude exceeds the capabilities of single workers. Today's senior scientist, therefore, must often possess also the skills of the administrator, to maintain a research atmosphere conducive to discovery and to allocate his manpower and financial resources according to the promise of each inquiry. This task cannot be shunned, and is analogous to the professional's traditional responsibility to teach.

THE WORK OF POLICY

The principal purpose of this chapter is to identify the large number and great variety of factors that must enter within the purview of a national policy for science.

Making a nation's science policy is a matter of projecting future research and technological needs, as well as requirements for trained manpower, of assessing the adequacy and over-all balance of the country's civil and defence research effort, of programming or co-ordinating diverse government-supported science programmes, of keeping generally informed about research and development activity in the private sector and within other nations, of identifying relatively neglected areas requiring additional attention, and of evaluating accomplishment in the light of objectives sought and resources expended.

Science policy is moreover but an aspect of over-all national policy, and cannot be formulated in isolation. Plans to satisfy manpower needs, for example, cannot be made except in relation to educational policies and technological objectives. Government investment in research must be decided upon in the light of the over-all national budget and of the extent and kind of research being conducted in the private sector, and must take account of the relative economic advantages of alternative technological opportunities. Development decisions must be made in the context of such expected social consequences as temporary unemployment, labour mobility, and new needs for job retraining. This complexity imposes upon a nation a formidable yet essential policy task.

SOME DETAILED CONSIDERATIONS

The detailed considerations are legion. Balanced scientific growth requires support of fields temporarily neglected because of unclear practical utility or because they happen to be out of scientific fashion. Resources must be properly distributed between basic and applied research to encourage exploitation of knowledge without at the same time drying up its fundamental sources. The social sciences and humanities cannot be allowed to wither in the face of urgent needs to support the natural sciences.

Further, the question of patents and licenses must be examined to assess a nation's relative standing as a knowledge-generating or a knowledge-exploiting power. Security considerations should not exclude judging the military research and development budget in the context of total national expenditures on science, nor deprive civilian scientific programmes of the applicable fruits of military research.

MANPOWER PROBLEMS

Another category of policy issues arises in connection with manpower training and encouragement of fruitful scientific careers. The objectives of a nation's science programmes require concern with patterns of scientific education. New disciplines may require curriculum changes. Special needs foreseen may call for altering educational and career incentives to avoid future manpower shortages in one or another specialty.

Mobility of scientific and technical personnel—both among nations and within most—becomes an important issue for policy as a result of changing technological needs, and with recognition of the values of inter-disciplinary co-operation and of combinations of experience in different fields. This in turn imposes a need to equalise in so far as possible the opportunities and rewards of scientific careers in government, industry, and universities, partly to remove disincentives to excellence, and partly to minimise the costs of mid-career changes in employment.

It is naturally in the manpower context that the intimate relation of science and education emerges most clearly, since trained personnel is at once necessary to scientific advance and a resource contributing to over-all national growth, both economically and in virtually every other respect. It is at this point, therefore, as will be further suggested in the next chapter, that a serious question arises about the degree to which a country's science policy and educational policy need to be integrated, or at least made consistent with each other.

INSTITUTIONAL AND MANAGEMENT QUESTIONS

There are in addition a host of problems relating to science organisation and management that fall within the purview of policy. There is often a need to encourage increased industrial expenditures on research by means of tax or other incentives, and to incorporate this effort in the over-all fabric of the nation's research. The research contract as a new form of government-industry scientific co-operation needs study and refinement. Mechanisms may be necessary to bring new knowledge to experimental demonstration pending industrial interest in commercial exploitation.

New phenomena of modern science, such as extremely costly experimental equipment and the frequent needs for interdisciplinary research teams, require policy attention to the size of research establishments, to the need for co-operative regional facilities for university research, and to the value of industrial research associations. The high costs of modern engineering development, finally, require vigilant concern for the efficiency with which resources are expended. This raises problems of the sequence and nature of technical decisions in the course of a programme, and imposes the need to test research ideas so that the risks inherent in scientific uncertainties can be anticipated and minimised.

SCIENTIFIC COMMUNICATION

Particularly important is the subject of scientific communication. This encompasses problems of documentation, which are generally known and receiving considerable attention, as well as how other means of communication among scientists—correspondence, personal visits, formal conferences —can insure adequate exchange of information without excessive compromise of research time and other resources.

To the extent that policy must see to the effective transfer of scientific knowledge into useful technology, there arises a problem of adequate communication between the scientist and the user of his product. Government departments or industrial concerns often impose requirements on their research scientists and engineers based entirely on operational or economic needs in ignorance of scientific feasibility. The scientists may thus be faced with the need to make some compromise in the stated requirements, but may find themselves inadequately instructed in the user's problems to make intelligent choices from among alternative technical possibilities arising in the course of research. This failure of communication can lead to performance inefficiencies, high costs, and intolerable delays. A major contribution of policy consideration of this question would be to devise some mechanism, institution, or service designed to give scientists and consumers of their products a necessary insight into each other's problems.

In general, scientific communication has to date been interpreted as no more than a matter of making scientific information *available*. Yet there is a long step between this and genuine communication. Communication requires also a process of selection by the user of information, as well as translation of his needs into terms with which the scientist and engineer can come to grips. A genuine solution of the growing communication problem calls for research into the possibility of combining these processes of selection and translation with effective dissemination, probably by means of some man-machine system that can deal at once with the qualitative and the quantitative factors involved.

R & D STATISTICS

Informed policy decisions on such questions as those listed in the preceding ten paragraphs must be based on accurate information about the extent and forms of investment in research, technological development, and scientific education. There must be data available on numbers of persons engaged in the various activities, on research and education budgets, and on expenditures for technological development. Data must be broken down into appropriate categories, and should preferably be comparable from nation to nation. Such statistics are inadequate in many countries and virtually non-existent in some, partly because there are few bodies specifically charged with collecting and analysing them, and partly because considerations of privilege make them difficult to acquire, particularly from industry and the military. Provision for compilation of such data is an indispensable prerequisite to formulating an effective national policy for science.

BASIC RESEARCH AND THE UNIVERSITIES

There is always the danger that exclusive policy attention to urgent near-term problems will result in failure to maintain adequate financial and institutional support of basic research activity, particularly since practical utility and policy relevance are more remote here than in any other part of scientific endeavour. No failure could be better calculated to bring all scientific advance to a stop within a very few years. Pending development of satisfactory means of measuring the return on investment in basic research, it should be a fundamental tenet of every nation's policy for science to devote a generous proportion of its total scientific resources to the support of a balanced, continuing, healthy basic research effort. No precise percentage figure can be applicable in all cases, so that it becomes a primary concern of policy thinking to arrive at the appropriate sum for each nation. Errors in this calculation should be allowed only on the generous side.

The increased volume and enhanced practical utility of research can also threaten the traditional role of the university as the sanctuary of basic research. Some research scientists are overburdened by administrative and contract-monitoring responsibilities. Others find too heavy a teaching burden an obstacle to creative research. Large and expensive research equipment requiring elaborate engineering maintenance can induce imbalances in departmental strengths, hiring procedures, and pay scales. Yet the university remains the proper home of basic science because of its free environment, the stimulus of young minds, and the seminal influence of interdisciplinary contact. A principal objective of national science policy must be to insure that university administrations, budgets, laboratories, and standards of excellence are maintained at the highest levels possible.

IMPLICATIONS OF SCIENCE FOR POLICY

THE NEED FOR UNDERSTANDING

The preceding . . . is essentially a catalogue of considerations that must enter into any comprehensive national policy for science. This one discusses some of the respects in which the formulation of national policies in other fields must take account of the achievements and expectations of science and technology.

That science has essential implications for national policy generally is widely recognised. Systematic knowledge of the specific nature of these implications from case to case is little advanced, however, except in the military field in some countries where research organisations or institutes of experts have been established to study and consider questions of the relation of technology and defence policy. In other fields, the scientific component often enters policy-making only in intuitive ways, by rule-of-thumb, or on the basis of personal advice from technical experts.

There is a great need for studies of the several fields and ways in which science and policy interact, and there is a need above all for a continuing and intimate working relationship between officials responsible for science policy and other policy makers. Only thus will governments be able to take

maximum advantage of the opportunities offered by scientific advance, and
to insure against policies that may be inadequate to a world that technology
changes from day to day.

ECONOMIC POLICY

An important proportion of economic growth is attributable to the
effects of technological change, and hence to inventive activity as the carrier
of change. There is, further, a good deal of evidence to show that inventive
activity in the twentieth century is far greater in industries based on modern
physics, chemistry, and biology than in those deriving from crafts and simple
mechanical engineering. The clear conclusion is that a large measure of economic growth in advanced countries is the result of new knowledge produced by scientific research, and of the material capital that embodies it.

It follows that long-term economic planning in an industrialised or
industrialising country or region cannot be carried out without taking
account of advances in science and technology. It must provide for allocation of resources to encourage the growth of science and technology, consider science-induced changes in industrial structures, and plan for a continuing search of basic science for innovation.

Economic policies can be effectively adapted to advances of science
only if means can be devised to arrive at reliable evaluations of the economic return from investment in research and development. This is currently a crucial problem facing economists, with criteria now employed
being largely empirical and qualitative. Any serious effort at economic
planning in modern technological societies must strive to improve these tools
of measurement.

Measurement of the economic return from basic research, however, is,
as noted on Page 380 above, hazardous and very difficult. It is for this
reason, as well as for the added cultural value of fundamental scientific
endeavour, that investment in basic research should not be planned according to the usual economic criteria, but should, in some appropriate percentage of total investment, be axiomatic in any plan.

SOCIAL POLICIES

Science and technology also affect directly policies concerned with the
social environment. Urban problems are largely created by the increasingly
technological character of civilisation, and are in turn likely to be amelio-
rated only by still further improvements in engineering systems for construction, transportation, communication, and sanitation. Situations of temporary
or regional unemployment may often be dealt with by replacing traditional
manufacturing institutions and methods with newer, science-based industries.

The over-all health and sophistication of a population, as well as productive use of its leisure, depend in large part on progress in medical research and on refinement of technical media for widespread distribution of news, literature, and art.

MILITARY POLICY

Military policy is dependent on science in virtually all its aspects, as might be inferred from the continually increasing proportions of military budgets devoted to research and development, at least among the major powers. Strategies, tactics, logistics, the organisation, size, and composition of forces, as well as structures of defensive alliances depend directly on the new products of weapon technology, and today's soldier must often add a technical education and some degree of scientific imagination to the traditional tools of his profession.

FOREIGN POLICY

The influence of science on foreign policy is deeper and more pervasive than normally appreciated. Some of the connections are well known. National prestige is in many cases sensitive to achievements in science and technology. Exchanges of scientific information and personnel, international scientific exhibitions and fairs, specific agreements for scientific and cultural co-operation, and scientific expertise in diplomatic missions all can serve as means of friendly communication among nations. Scientific considerations enter specifically and directly into such problems as

1. co-ordination of a nation's participation in, and allocation of fiscal and trained manpower resources to, international scientific programmes,
2. negotiation of treaties having a significant technical content, and
3. establishment of regulatory agreements governing international technological systems in communications, transportation, and defence.

Beyond that, however, there are important technical aspects to the very substance of foreign policy making. Economic strength itself is a principal instrument of national policy, and is crucially dependent on technological progress. The direct influence of science on military power takes the form in international affairs of the over-all defence strategy and degree of manœuvre possible to a nation. Technical considerations are central not only in international negotiation of such questions as arms limitation or disarmament, but in the very way in which a country formulates its policies regarding them. A nation is unlikely nowadays to maintain a successful posture in international affairs unless its diplomats, scientists, and soldiers are in continuous and effective communication with each other.

AID POLICY

It is generally accepted that the problems of development facing the world's newly advancing countries are potentially very sensitive to solution with the help of science and technology. These countries need to build themselves up as nations, to induce very rapid economic growth, to restructure their economies to the demands of industrialisation, and to create institutions to meet the requirements of international communication and commerce. The scientific resources and capabilities that could respond most directly to such needs, however, are either unavailable or insufficiently available in the developing countries themselves. The advanced countries in turn, which enjoy most of the world's scientific resources, naturally apply their science to their own needs, which are of a quite different nature. They are not strongly motivated to seek scientific solutions to the problems peculiar to other countries.

The long-range solution is to help the new countries to develop adequate scientific resources and capabilities of their own, which could then respond directly to the challenges and pressures that they face. The problem of the advanced countries in the interim, however, is to insure that their scientific efforts on behalf of the new nations are given a sufficiently high priority in their own over-all scientific programmes. Policy planning for aid must include consideration of what proportion of total resources devoted to the new nations can usefully take the form of scientific activities designed specifically to meet their needs. Present aid programmes in science, technology, and scientific education should be re-evaluated, and modified as necessary, in that light.

EDUCATION AND MANPOWER POLICIES

The influence of science on the general spectrum of government policies is perhaps most intimate in the case of education, as already suggested. Since expenditures on both education and research represent long-term investment in economic growth, there is at least this point of view from which integrated science and education policies would seem to be called for. In most countries, government responsibility for activities in research and education is scattered among a number of ministries, agencies, or boards charged with various kinds of education, with health, industry, agriculture, defence, and so forth. At a minimum, there is an evident need for some sort of co-ordination of these various activities at some point in government structure, although how this is done must necessarily depend largely on the particular institutions and conditions of individual countries. In any case, most governments need top-level advice on such matters from experts in education and science. Whether there are arguments other than from the point of view of economic growth for a more extensive integration of policies in the particular case of science and education requires considerable detailed study of a sort not attempted in this report. Further, still other points of view may suggest that similar integration would be desirable beween science policy and government policies in addition to those for education.

Specific points at which science touches educational policy include the effect on curriculums of rapidly accumulating new subject matter, the requirement to develop the new kinds of specialists demanded by large-scale and complex modern technologies, and the need to continue education of the adult population throughout life if it is to remain sophisticated and politically responsible. Allied problems of manpower policy include the responsibility to anticipate future needs for trained manpower, and to provide mid-career retraining for a highly mobile labour force and for professional scientists and engineers who are increasingly finding that specialties in which they were initially trained are shorter-lived than they.

It should be clear in the context of the questions discussed in this report that one of the most important problems of educational policy in the immediate future will be to train scientists who are also knowledgeable about the essential and varied policy implications of their work, and above all to develop an essentially new breed of public servant who is sufficiently trained in the methods and ways of science to be equal to the increasing number and importance of policy decisions having a high technical content.

TRANSFER AND FEEDBACK

The problems connected with identifying in detail the implications of science for the various facets of a nation's policy, and with taking advantage in policy formulation of opportunities inherent in science and technology, are part of the enterprise of transferring knowledge to use. Such transfer has by and large in the past been accidental and haphazard. The fruits of science are now so abundant, and human problems so staggering and complex, that nations and the world can no longer afford the luxury of being casual about knowledge. That is why problems of the interaction of science and policy are demanding and should be receiving increasing attention on both a national and an international scale. Only consistent and deliberate attention to them can result in effective policies for exploiting knowledge for human welfare.

The scientific enterprise itself can only benefit from enhancement of the enterprise of transfer. Really new ideas have always been scarce, and have depended in the earlier days of science only on the intuitions of great men. That source remains indispensable, but can now be supplemented by the added stimulus that comes from putting knowledge to work. This is the phenomenon of feedback. Wrestling with problems of formulating policies in disparate fields that take maximum advantage of scientific opportunities can in turn suggest still newer opportunities, as yet beyond the ken of science, in the form of further ideas for basic inquiry, more effective methods and institutions for research and development, and widened educational horizons.

* * *

The Secretary General's Ad Hoc Advisory Group on Science Policy

Professor Dr. Karl Herz (Germany).[2]
Sir Willis Jackson (United Kingdom).
Mr. Robert Major (Norway).
Professor Lucien Massart (Belgium).
Mr. Pierre Piganiol (France), Chairman.
Professor Norman F. Ramsey (United States).
Mr. Erik Ib Schmidt (Denmark).
Professor Theodore William Schultz (United States).
Dr. Edgar W. R. Steacie (Canada).[3]

* * *

Professor Pierre Auger (France), Consultant.
Mr. Henning Friis (Denmark), ex officio.[4]
Dr. J. G. Malloch (Canada), Observer.[5]
Professor C. L. Wilson (United States), ex officio.[6]

* * *

Alexander King, O.E.C.D. Director for Scientific Affairs.
Emmanuel G. Mesthene, Rapporteur Général.
Jürgen Schmandt, Secretary.

[2] Professor Herz was unfortunately unable to participate in the Group's deliberations.
[3] Deceased August, 1962.
[4] Chairman, O.E.C.D. Committee for Scientific and Technical Personnel.
[5] Former Chairman, O.E.C.D. Committee for Scientific Research.
[6] Chairman, O.E.C.D. Committee for Scientific Research.

Criteria for Scientific Choice

ALVIN M. WEINBERG

I

As science grows, its demands on our society's resources grow. It seems inevitable that science's demands will eventually be limited by what society can allocate to it. We shall then have to make choices. These choices are of two kinds. We shall have to choose among different, often incommensurable, fields of science—between, for example, high-energy physics and oceanography or between molecular biology and science of metals. We shall also have to choose among the different institutions that receive support for science from the government—among universities, governmental laboratories and industry. The first choice I call scientific choice; the second, institutional choice. My purpose is to suggest criteria for making scientific choices—to formulate a scale of values which might help establish priorities among scientific fields whose only common characteristic is that they all derive support from the government.

Choices of this sort are made at every level both in science and in government. The individual scientist must decide what science to do, and what not to do: the totality of such judgments makes up his scientific taste. The research director must choose which projects to push, which to kill. The government administrator must decide not only which efforts to support; he must also decide whether to do a piece of work in a university, a national laboratory, or an industrial laboratory. The sum of such separate decisions determines our policy as a whole. I shall be concerned mainly with the broadest scientific choices: how should government decide between very large fields of science, particularly between different branches of basic science? The equally important question of how government should allocate its support for basic research among industry, governmental laboratories, and universities will not be discussed here.

II

Most of us like to be loved; we hate to make choices, since a real choice alienates the party that loses. If one is rich—more accurately, if one is growing richer—choices can be avoided. Every administrator knows that his

387

job is obviously unpleasant only when his budget has been cut. Thus the urgency for making scientific or institutional choices has in the main been ignored both in the United States and elsewhere because the science budget has been expanding so rapidly: the United States government spent $1,600,000,000 on research and development in 1950, $9,000,000,000 in 1960, $14,000,000,000 (including space) in 1962.

Though almost all agree that choices will eventually have to be made, some well-informed observers insist that the time for making the choices is far in the future. Their arguments against making explicit choices have several main threads. Perhaps most central is the argument that since we do not make explicit choices about anything else, there is no reason why we should make them in science. Since we do not explicitly choose between support for farm prices and support for schools, or between highways and foreign aid, why should we single out science as the guinea pig for trying to make choices? The total public activity of our society has always resulted from countervailing pressures, exerted by various groups representing professional specialties, or local interests, or concern for the public interest. The combination that emerges as our Federal budget is not arrived at by the systematic application of a set of criteria: even the highest level of authority, in the United States, the President, who must weigh conflicting interests in the scale of the public interest, is limited in the degree to which he can impose an overall judgment by the sheer size of the budget if by nothing else. But because we have always arrived at an allocation by the free play of countervailing pressures this does not mean that such free interplay is the best or the only way to make choices. In any case, even if our choices remain largely implicit rather than explicit, they will be more reasonable if persons at every level, representing every pressure group, try to understand the larger issues and try to mitigate sectional self-interest with concern for broader issues. The idea of conflicting and biased claims being adjudicated at one fell swoop by an all-knowing supreme tribunal is a myth. It is much better that the choices be decentralised and that they reflect the concern for the larger interest. For this reason alone philosophic debate on the problems of scientific choice should lead to a more rational allocation of our resources.

A second thread in the argument of those who refuse to face the problem of scientific choice is that we waste so much on trivialities—on smoking, on advertising, on gambling—that it is silly to worry about expenditures of the same scale on what is obviously a more useful social objective—the increase of scientific knowledge. A variant of this argument is that with so much unused steel capacity or so many unemployed, we cannot rightly argue that we cannot afford a big cyclotron or a large manned-space venture.

Against these arguments we would present the following considerations on behalf of a rational scientific policy. At any given instant, only a certain fraction of our society's resources goes to science. To insist or imply that the *summum bonum* of our society is the pursuit of science and that therefore all other activities of the society are secondary to science—that unused capacity in the steel mills should go to 'Big Science' rather than a large-scale housing programme—is a view that might appeal strongly to the scientific community. It is hardly likely to appeal so strongly to the much larger part of society that elects the members of the legislature, and to whom, in all probability, good houses are more important than good science. Thus as a practical matter we cannot really evade the problem of scientific choice. If those actively engaged in science do not make choices, they will be made anyhow by the Congressional Appropriations Committees and by the Bureau of the Budget, or corresponding bodies in other governments. Moreover, and perhaps more immediately, even if we are not limited by money, we shall be limited by the availability of truly competent men. There is already evidence that our ratio of money to men in science is too high, and that in some parts of science we have gone further more quickly than the number of really competent men can justify.

III

Our scientific and governmental communities have evolved institutional and other devices for coping with broad issues of scientific choice. The most important institutional device in the United States is the President's Science Advisory Committee, with its panels and its staff in the Office of Science and Technology. This body and its panels help the Bureau of the Budget to decide what is to be supported and what is not to be supported. The panel system, however, suffers from a serious weakness. Panels usually consist of specialised experts who inevitably share the same enthusiasms and passions. To the expert in oceanography or in high energy physics, nothing seems quite as important as oceanography or high energy physics. The panel, when recommending a programme in a field in which all its members are interested, invariably argues for better treatment of the field—more money, more people, more training. The panel system is weak insofar as judge, jury, plaintiff and defendant are usually one and the same.

The panel is able to judge how competently a proposed piece of research is likely to be carried out: its members are all experts and are likely to know who are the good research workers in the field. But just because the panel is composed of experts, who hold parochial viewpoints, the panel is much less able to place the proposal in a broader perspective and to say whether the research proposal is of much interest to the rest of science. We can answer the question 'how' within a given frame of reference; it is impossible to answer 'why' within the same frame of reference. It would therefore seem that the panel system could be improved if representatives, not only of the field being judged but also representatives of neighbouring fields, sat on every panel judging the merits of a research proposal. A panel judging high energy physics should have some people from low energy physics; a panel judging low energy physics should have some people from nuclear energy; a panel judging nuclear energy should have some people from conventional energy; and so on. I should think that advice from panels so constituted would be tempered by concern for larger issues; in particular, the support of a proposed research project would be viewed from the larger perspective of the relevance of that research to the rest of science.

In addition to panels or the bodies like the President's Science Advisory Committee as organisational instruments for making choices, the scientific community has evolved an empirical method for establishing scientific priorities, that is, for deciding what is important in science and what is not important. This is the scientific literature. The process of self-criticism, which is integral to the literature of science, is one of the most characteristic features of science. Nonsense is weeded out and held up to ridicule in the literature, whereas what is worthwhile receives much sympathetic attention. This process of self-criticism embodied in the literature, though implicit, is nonetheless real and highly significant. The existence of a healthy, viable scientific literature in itself helps assure society that the science it supports is valid and deserving of support. This is a most important, though little recognised, social function of the scientific literature.

As an arbiter of scientific taste and validity, scientific literature is beset with two difficulties. First, because of the information explosion, the literature is not read nearly as carefully as it used to be. Nonsense is not so generally recognised as such, and the standards of self-criticism, which are so necessary if the scientific literature is to serve as the arbiter of scientific taste, are inevitably looser than they once were.

Second, the scientific literature in a given field tends to form a closed universe; workers in a field, when they criticise each other, tend to adopt the same unstated assumptions. A referee of a scientific paper asks whether the paper conforms to the rules of the scientific community to which both referee and author belong, not whether the rules themselves are valid. So to speak, the editors and authors of a journal in a narrowly specialised field are all tainted with the same poison. As Einstein said, 'Eigener Dreck stinkt nicht.' [1]

Can a true art of scientific criticism be developed, *i.e.*, can one properly criticise a field of science beyond the kind of criticism that is inherent in the literature of the field? Mortimer Taube in *Computers and Common*

---

[1] As quoted by Dyson, Freeman J., in a review of Sweber, S. S., *Mesons and Fields*, in *Physics Today*, IX (May, 1956), pp. 32–34.

Sense[2] insists that such scientific criticism is a useful undertaking, and that, by viewing a field from a somewhat detached point of view, it is possible to criticise a field meaningfully, even to the point of calling the whole activity fraudulent, as he does in the case of non-numerical uses of computers. I happen to believe that Taube does not make a convincing case in respect to certain non-numerical uses of computers, such as language translation. Yet I have sympathy for Dr. Taube's aims—that, with science taking so much of the public's money, we must countenance, even encourage, discussion of the relative validity and worthwhileness of the science which society supports.

IV

I believe that criteria for scientific choice can be identified. In fact, several such criteria already exist; the main task is to make them more explicit. The criteria can be divided into two kinds: internal criteria and external criteria. Internal criteria are generated within the scientific field itself and answer the question: How well is the science done? External criteria are generated outside the scientific field and answer the question: Why pursue this particular science? Though both are important, I think the external criteria are the more important.

Two internal criteria can be easily identified: (1) Is the field ready for exploitation? (2) Are the scientists in the field really competent? Both these questions are answerable only by experts who know the field in question intimately, and who know the people personally. These criteria are therefore the ones most often applied when a panel decides on a research grant: in fact, the primary question in deciding whether to provide governmental support for a scientist is usually: How good is he?

I believe, however, that it is not tenable to base our judgments entirely on internal criteria. As I have said, we scientists like to believe that the pursuit of science as such is society's highest good, but this view cannot be taken for granted. For example, we now suffer a serious shortage of medical practitioners, probably to some extent because many bright young men who would formerly have gone into medical practice now go into biological research; government support is generally available for post-graduate study leading to the Ph.D. but not for study leading to the medical degree. It is by no means self-evident that society gains from more biological research and less medical practice. Society does not *a priori* owe the scientist, even the good scientist, support any more than it owes the artist or the writer or the musician support. Science must seek its support from society on grounds

---

[2] (New York: Columbia University Press, 1961).

other than that the science is carried out competently and that it is ready for exploitation; scientists cannot expect society to support science because scientists find it an enchanting diversion. Thus, in seeking justification for the support of science, we are led inevitably to consider external criteria for the validity of science—criteria external to science, or to a given field of science.

V

Three external criteria can be recognised: technological merit, scientific merit and social merit. The first is fairly obvious: once we have decided, one way or another, that a certain technological end is worthwhile, we must support the scientific research necessary to achieve that end. Thus, if we have set out to learn how to make breeder reactors, we must first measure painstakingly the neutron yields of the fissile isotopes as a function of energy of the bombarding neutron. As in all such questions of choice, it is not always so easy to decide the technological relevance of a piece of basic research. The technological usefulness of the laser came after, not before, the principle of optical amplification was discovered. But it is my belief that such technological bolts from the scientific blue are the exception, not the rule. Most programmatic basic research can be related fairly directly to a technological end at least crudely if not in detail. The broader question as to whether the technological aim itself is worthwhile must be answered again partly from within technology through answering such questions as: Is the technology ripe for exploitation? Are the people any good? Partly from outside technology by answering the question: Are the social goals attained, if the technology succeeds, themselves worthwhile? Many times these questions are difficult to answer, and sometimes they are answered incorrectly: for example, the United States launched an effort to control thermonuclear energy in 1952 on a rather large scale because it was thought at the time that controlled fusion was much closer at hand than it turned out to be. Nevertheless, despite the fact that we make mistakes, technological aims are customarily scrutinised much more closely than are scientific aims; at least we have more practice discussing technological merit than we do scientific merit.

VI

The criteria of scientific merit and social merit are much more difficult: scientific merit because we have given little thought to defining scientific merit in the broadest sense, social merit because it is difficult to define the values of our society. As I have already suggested, the answer to the question: Does this broad field of research have scientific merit? cannot be answered within the field. The idea that the scientific merit of a field can be judged better from the vantage point of the scientific fields in which it is embedded than from the point of view of the field itself is implicit in the following quotation from the late John von Neumann: 'As a mathematical discipline travels far from its empirical source, or still more, if it is a second and third generation only indirectly inspired by ideas coming from reality, it is beset with very grave dangers. It becomes more and more pure aestheticising, more and more purely *l'art pour l'art*. This need not be bad if the field is surrounded by correlated subjects which still have closer empirical connections or if the discipline is under the influence of men with an exceptionally well-developed taste. But there is a grave danger that the subject will develop along the line of least resistance, that the stream, so far from its source, will separate into a multitude of insignificant branches, and that the discipline will become a disorganised mass of details and complexities. In other words, at a great distance from its empirical source, or after much "abstract" inbreeding, a mathematical subject is in danger of degeneration. At the inception the style is usually classical; when it shows signs of becoming baroque, then the danger signal is up.' [3]

I believe there are any number of examples to show that von Neumann's observation about mathematics can be extended to the empirical sciences. *Empirical* basic sciences which move too far from the neighbouring sciences in which they are embedded tend to become 'baroque.' Relevance to neighbouring fields of science is, therefore, a valid measure of the scientific merit of a field of basic science. In so far as our aim is to increase our grasp and understanding of the universe, we must recognise that some areas of basic science do more to round out the whole picture than do others. A field in which lack of knowledge is a bottleneck to the understanding of other fields deserves more support than a field which is isolated from other fields. This is only another way of saying that, ideally, science is a unified structure and that scientists, in adding to the structure, ought always to strengthen its unity. Thus, the original motivation for much of high-energy physics is to be sought in its elucidation of low-energy physics, or the strongest and most exciting motivation for measuring the neutron capture cross sections of the elements lies in the elucidation of the cosmic origin of the elements. Moreover, the discoveries which are acknowledged to be the most important scientifically, have the quality of bearing strongly on the scientific disciplines around them. For example, the discovery of X-rays was important partly because it extended the electromagnetic spectrum but, much more, because it enabled us to see so much that we had been unable to see. The word

[3] Heywood, R. B. (ed.), *The Works of the Mind* (University of Chicago Press, 1947), p. 196.

'fundamental' in basic science, which is often used as a synonym for 'important,' can be partly paraphrased into 'relevance to neighbouring areas of science.' I would therefore sharpen the criterion of scientific merit by proposing that, other things being equal, *that field has the most scientific merit which contributes most heavily to and illuminates most brightly its neighbouring scientific disciplines.* This is the justification for my previous suggestion about making it socially acceptable for people in *related* fields to offer opinions on the scientific merit of work in a given field. In a sense, what I am trying to do is to extend to basic research a practice that is customary in applied science: a project director trying to get a reactor built on time is expected to judge the usefulness of component development and fundamental research which bears on his problems. He is not always right; but his opinions are usually useful both to the researcher and to the management disbursing the money.

VII

I turn now to the most controversial criterion of all—social merit or relevance to human welfare and the values of man. Two difficulties face us when we try to clarify the criterion of social merit: first, who is to define the values of man, or even the values of our own society; and second, just as we shall have difficulty deciding whether a proposed research helps other branches of science or technology, so we will have even greater trouble deciding whether a given scientific or technical enterprise indeed furthers our pursuit of social values, even when those values have been identified. With some values we have little trouble: adequate defence, or more food, or less sickness, for example, are rather uncontroversial. Moreover, since such values themselves are relatively easy to describe, we can often guess whether a scientific activity is likely to be relevant, if not actually helpful, in achieving the goal. On the other hand, some social values are much harder to define: perhaps the most difficult is national prestige. How do we measure national prestige? What is meant when we say that a man on the moon enhances our national prestige? Does it enhance our prestige more than, say, discovering a polio vaccine or winning more Nobel Prizes than any other country? Whether or not a given achievement confers prestige probably depends as much on the publicity that accompanies the achievement as it does on its intrinsic value.

Among the most attractive social values that science can help to achieve is international understanding and cooperation. It is a commonplace that the standards and loyalties of science are trans-national. A new element has recently been injected by the advent of scientific research of such costliness that now it is prudent as well as efficient to participate in some form of international cooperation. The very big accelerators are so expensive that international laboratories such as CERN at Geneva are set up to enable several countries to share costs that are too heavy for them to bear separately. Even if we were not committed to improving international relations we would be impelled to cooperate merely to save money.

Bigness is an advantage rather than a disadvantage if science is to be used as an instrument of international cooperation: a $500,000,000 cooperative scientific venture—such as the proposed 1,000 Bev intercontinental accelerator—is likely to have more impact than a $500,000 Van de Graaff machine. The most expensive of all scientific or quasi-scientific enterprises —the exploration of space—is, from this viewpoint, the best-suited instrument for international cooperation. The exchange between President Kennedy and Chairman Khrushchev concerning possible increased cooperation in space exploration seems to have been well received and, one hopes, will bear ultimate fruit.

VIII

Having set forth these criteria and recognising that judgments are fraught with difficulty, I propose to assess five different scientific and technical fields, in the light of these. The five fields I choose are molecular biology, high-energy physics, nuclear energy, manned-space exploration, and the behavioural sciences. Two of these fields, molecular biology and high-energy physics, are, by any definition, basic sciences; nuclear energy is applied science, the behavioural sciences are a mixture of both applied and basic science. Manned exploration of space, though it requires the tools of science and is regarded in the popular mind as being part of science, has not yet been proved to be more than quasi-scientific, at best. The fields which I choose are incommensurable: how can one measure the merit of behavioural sciences and nuclear energy on the same scale of values? Yet the choices between scientific fields will eventually have to be made whether we like it or not. Criteria for scientific choice will be most useful only if they *can* be applied to seemingly incommensurable situations. The validity of my proposed criteria depends on how well they can serve in comparing fields that are hard to compare.

Of the scientific fields now receiving public support, perhaps the most successful is molecular biology. Hardly a month goes by without a stunning success in molecular biology being reported in the *Proceedings of the National Academy of Sciences*. The most recent has been the cracking by Nierenberg and Ochoa of the code according to which triples of bases determine specific amino acids in the living proteins. Here is a field which rates the highest grades as to its ripeness for exploitation and competence of its workers. It is profoundly important for large stretches of other biological sciences—genetics, cytology, microbiology—and, therefore, according to my criterion, must be graded A+ for its scientific merit. It also must be given a very high grade in social merit, and probably in technological (that is, medical) merit—more than, say, taxonomy or topology. Molecular biology is the most fundamental of all the biological sciences. With understanding of the manner of transmission of genetic information ought to come the insights necessary for the solution of such problems as cancer, birth defects, and viral diseases. Altogether, molecular biology ought, in my opinion, to receive as much public support as can possibly be pumped into it; since money is not limiting its growth, many more post-graduate students and research fellows in molecular biology ought to be subsidised so that the attack on this frontier can be expanded as rapidly as possible.

The second field is high-energy physics. This field of endeavour originally sought as its major task to understand the nuclear force. In this it has been only modestly successful; instead, it has opened an undreamed-of subnuclear world of strange particles and hyperons, a world in which mirror images are often reversed. The field has no end of interesting things to do, it knows how to do them, and its people are the best. Yet I would be bold enough to argue that, at least by the criteria which I have set forth— relevance to the sciences in which it is embedded, relevance to human affairs, and relevance to technology—high-energy physics rates poorly. The nuclear forces are not being worked on very directly—the world of subnuclear particles seems to be remote from the rest of the physical sciences. Aside from the brilliant resolution of the τ-particle paradox, which led to the overthrow of the conservation of parity, and the studies of mesic atoms (the latter of which is not done at *ultra*-high energy), I know of few discoveries in ultra-high-energy physics which bear strongly on the rest of science. (This view would have to be altered if machines such as the Argonne Zero Gradient Synchrotron were exploited as very strong, pulsed sources of neutrons for study of neutron cross sections.) As for its bearing on human welfare and on technology, I believe it is essentially nil. These two low grades would not bother me if high-energy physics were cheap. But it is terribly expensive— not so much in money as in highly qualified people, especially those brilliant talents who could contribute so ably to other fields which contribute much more to the rest of science and to humanity than does high-energy physics. On the other hand, if high-energy physics could be made a vehicle for international cooperation—if the much-discussed intercontinental 1,000 Bev accelerator could indeed be built as a joint enterprise between East and West —the expense of high-energy physics would become a virtue, and the enterprise would receive a higher grade in social merit than I would now be willing to assign to it.

Third is nuclear energy. This being largely an applied effort, it is very relevant to human welfare. We now realise that in the residual uranium and thorium of the earth's crust, mankind has an unlimited store of energy—enough to last for millions of years; and that with an effort of only one-tenth of our manned-space effort we could, within ten or fifteen years, develop the reactors which would tap this resource. Only rarely do we see ways of *permanently* satisfying one of man's major needs—in this case energy. In high-conversion ratio nuclear reactors we have such means, and we are close to their achievement. Moreover, we begin to see ways of applying very large reactors of this type to realise another great end, the economic desalination of the ocean. Thus, the time is very ripe for exploitation. Nuclear energy rates so highly in the categories of technical and social merit and timeliness that I believe it deserves strong support, even if it gets very low marks in the other two categories—its personnel and its relationship to the rest of science. Suffice it to say that in my opinion the scientific workers in the field of nuclear energy are good and that nuclear energy in its basic aspects has vast ramifications in other scientific fields.

Next on the list are the behavioural sciences—psychology, sociology, anthropology, economics. The workers are of high quality; the sciences are significantly related to each other, they are deeply germane to every aspect of human existence. In these respects the sciences deserve strong public support. On the other hand, it is not clear to me that the behavioural scientists, on the whole, see clearly how to attack the important problems of their sciences. Fortunately, the total sum involved in behavioural science research is now relatively tiny—as it well must be when what are lacking are deeply fruitful, and generally accepted, points of departure.

Finally, I come to manned-space exploration. The personnel in the programme are competent and dedicated. With respect to ripeness for exploitation, the situation seems to me somewhat unclear. Our 'hardware' is in good shape, and we can expect it to get better—bigger and more reliable boosters, better communication systems, etc. What is not clear is the human being's tolerance of the space environment. I do not believe that either the hazards of radiation or of weightlessness are sufficiently explored yet positively to guarantee success in our future manned-space ventures.

The main objection to spending so much manpower, not to say money, on manned-space exploration is its remoteness from human affairs, not to say the rest of science. In this respect space (the exploration of very large distances) and high-energy physics (the exploration of very small distances) are similar, though high-energy physics has the advantage of greater scientific validity. There are some who argue that the great adventure of man into space is not to be judged as science, but rather as a quasi-scientific enterprise, justified on the same grounds as those on which we justify other non-scientific national efforts. The weakness of this argument is that space requires many, many scientists and engineers, and these are badly needed for such matters as clarifying our civilian defence posture or, for that matter, working out the technical details of arms control and foreign aid. If space is ruled to be non-scientific, then it must be balanced against other non-scientific expenditures like highways, schools or civil defence. If we do space-research because of prestige, then we should ask whether we get more prestige from a man on the moon than from successful control of the water-logging problem in Pakistan's Indus Valley Basin. If we do space-research because of its military implications, we ought to say so—and perhaps the military justification, at least for developing big boosters, is plausible, as the Soviet experience with rockets makes clear.

IX

The main weight of my argument is that the most valid criteria for assessing scientific fields come from without rather than from within the scientific discipline that is being rated. This does not mean that only those scientific fields deserve priority that have high technical merit or high social merit. Scientific merit is as important as the other two criteria, but, as I have argued, scientific merit must be judged from the vantage point of the scientific fields in which each field is embedded rather than from that of the field itself. If we support science in order to maximise our knowledge of the world around us, then we must give the highest priority to those scientific endeavours that have the most bearing on the rest of science.

The rather extreme view which I have taken presents difficulties in practice. The main trouble is that the bearing that one science has on another science so often is not appreciated until long after the original discoveries have been made. Who was wise enough, at the time Purcell and Bloch first discovered nuclear magnetic resonance, to guess that the method would become an important analytical tool in biochemistry? Or how could one have guessed that Hahn and Strassmann's radiochemical studies would have led to nuclear energy? And indeed, my colleagues in high-energy physics predict that what we learn about the world of strange particles will in an as yet undiscernible way teach us much about the rest of physics, not merely much about strange particles. They beg only for time to prove their point.

To this argument I say first that choices are always hard. It would be far simpler if the problem of scientific choice could be ignored, and possibly in some future millennium it can be. But there is also a more constructive response. The necessity for scientific choice arises in 'Big Science,' not in 'Little Science.' Just as our society supports artists and musicians on a small scale, so I have no objection to—in fact, I strongly favour—our society supporting science that rates zero on all the external criteria, provided it rates well on the internal criteria (ripeness and competence) and provided it is carried on on a relatively small scale. It is only when science really does make serious demands on the resources of our society—when it becomes 'Big Science'—that the question of choice really arises.

At the present time, with our society faced with so much unfinished and very pressing business, science can hardly be considered its major business. For scientists as a class to imply that science can, at this stage in human development, be made the main business of humanity is irresponsible—and, from the scientist's point of view, highly dangerous. It is quite conceivable that our society will tire of devoting so much of its wealth to science, especially if the implied promises held out when big projects are launched do not materialise in anything very useful. I shudder to think what would happen to science in general if our manned-space venture turned out to be a major failure, if it turned out, for example, that man could not withstand the re-entry deceleration forces after a long sojourn in space. It is as much out of a prudent concern for their own survival, as for any loftier motive, that scientists must acquire the habit of scrutinising what they do from a broader point of view than has been their custom. To do less could cause a popular reaction which would greatly damage mankind's most remarkable intellectual attainment—Modern Science—and the scientists who created it and must carry it forward.

R & D, and the Relations of Science and Government

PAUL M. GROSS

. . . I should like to try to get behind the specifics of particular fields of research and particular aspects of their administrative management to consider some of the basic, persistent problems of government-science relationships. Because these problems are fundamental and persistent, they deserve the thoughtful consideration of the Subcommittee, of the Congress, and of the scientific community.

I start with the premise that the present character and size of federal research and development expenditures owe their initiation in large measure to ideas and concepts originating in the scientific community. The basic research supported by the National Institutes of Health, the National Science Foundation, and other agencies is almost wholly determined by the scientists themselves, who decide what seems worth working on. The applied research and developmental programs of the Department of Defense, the Atomic Energy Commission, NASA, NIH, and other agencies have become possible as a result of work which, in the main, was initiated by scientists. As some of that work developed, it became clear that it could and should be exploited to serve military, industrial, health, and prestige goals of the nation.

In appropriating funds for research and development, the Congress has certain objectives in mind, as have the executive agencies in submitting their R&D budgets. In submitting proposals for work that is to be funded from these appropriations, scientists and engineers on the staffs of university, industrial, and other research laboratories also have certain objectives in mind. In the long run and in general, there is agreement between the objectives of the government and those of the scientists and engineers, but the match is not always a perfect one, and the amount of agreement may be greater in the long run than in the short run, and greater for some kinds of research activities than for others.

Reprinted from *Science*, November 8, 1963, Vol. CXLII, pp. 645–650. The first part of this article, pp. 645–648, is reprinted here with some minor omissions, with permission of the author and the publisher. Dr. Paul M. Gross is a Professor of Chemistry at Duke University in Durham, North Carolina. He was the retiring President of the American Association for the Advancement of Science at the time this statement was prepared.

Both scientists and government officials understand, however, that there is a strong interdependence between the government, which depends upon industrial and educational research laboratories to conduct research, and those laboratories, which depend upon the government for a large fraction of the necessary financial support. Because of this interdependence, there is need for mutual understanding, and sometimes for compromise and adjustment. There is also need for the kind of analysis of basic problems that this Subcommittee is undertaking.

A FOUR-PART SUBJECT

Some of the problems could be clarified if we think of the whole subject as having four main parts:

1. *Applied research.* I place this first because much the largest fraction of the total R&D budget is spent for the development, the testing, and the associated applied research involved in perfecting or bringing into use new equipment, new methods, and new products. A great deal of money is required to develop—for example—a new weapon system, but the objective can be foreseen with reasonable clarity, and it is thus reasonably easy to make some of the necessary decisions. Nevertheless, it is rare that such a system can be perfected without our first finding gaps in our fundamental scientific knowledge. Thus we do not go very far in a broad consideration of applied research before we find ourselves thinking about the second of the four main parts of our subject, namely, basic research.

As an example of how our applied-research objectives press upon our achievements in basic research, let me consider in general terms the development of a weapon system. It began to appear feasible to develop an effective anti-missile when three essential components became available: radar adequate to track a missile, very fast computers that could quickly plot the required interception course for an anti-missile, and a small nuclear war head. These were the principal necessary components, but as work on an anti-missile progressed, it soon became apparent that they were not sufficient and that without substantial additions to basic knowledge the work could not be successfully completed.

In my experience, the same kind of situation arises frequently in industry: a new development is delayed by the necessity for further research. Industry frequently solves such problems by a cut-and-try process involving the use of a large number of scientists. With a more adequate store of basic knowledge available, the objective could frequently be attained more quickly and with a more economical and efficient use of scientific manpower.

2. *Basic research.* In the abstract, people would agree that the purpose

of supporting basic research is to strengthen the nation's scientific competence, to gain a better understanding of the processes of nature and to acquire new knowledge, some of which will prove to be of practical usefulness. But it is in basic research that the scientist finds it most difficult to explain to Congress, to the general public, and sometimes even to scientists in disciplines other than his own, just what he is doing and why he thinks it worth while. It is also usually basic research that is involved when journalists and others poke fun at whole research enterprises by selecting from a list of studies a title which they do not understand and which may appear trivial or even ludicrous out of the context of technical language of the particular field concerned.

3. *Advanced scientific education.* At the advanced level, science education is closely allied to research, for it consists largely of a kind of research apprenticeship and is supported primarily by graduate fellowships and by research assistantships.

4. *Science education at the primary and secondary levels.* At these levels, and even to a substantial degree at the collegiate level, science education is of course much less intimately connected with research. Its improvement consequently poses somewhat different problems from those of graduate and professional training, and the appropriate methods of support also differ. A major reason for differentiating between research training at the advanced level and science education at earlier levels is the fact that the problems of segregation, of religious versus secular control, and of the fear of federal government control, which cannot be avoided at the levels of general education, are comparatively irrelevant in considering support for research and research training at the advanced level.

Some of the executive agencies—the National Institutes of Health, the National Science Foundation, the National Aeronautics and Space Administration are examples—are involved in more than one—even in all—of these four kinds of activities. Because of the way in which responsibilities are assigned to committees of the Congress, several of the committees have responsibility for all or several of them. I would not suggest that the four be separated by agencies—with some agencies responsible, for example, only for applied research and development and forbidden to interest themselves in basic research or science education—nor is it realistic to suggest that congressional committees have their responsibilities similarly differentiated. I would suggest, however, that in the formation of policies, and at some stages in the consideration of appropriations, we can think more clearly about government-science relations if we think separately about each of these four categories. If we do that, we will have clearer opportunities for reaching decisions concerning both policy and operational management.

ALLOTMENT OF FUNDS

Let me suggest several advantages of such a separation. First, we could establish more firmly our policies concerning support for fundamental research. In the current budget of approximately $15 billion for research and development. 10 percent or less is devoted to basic research. A wealth of experience tells us that when money gets tight, it is this category that is most likely to suffer. If we differentiated more clearly between basic research, on the one hand, and applied research, development, and testing, on the other, it would, I think, be easier to agree upon the appropriate level of support that the nation can afford. We are now spending a billion and a half dollars or less a year on basic research. I would contend that the nation is getting its money's worth for this amount, for this is the money that we spend to renew and extend our fundamental stock of scientific knowledge.

The issue is not whether x dollars is too little or too much for science, but whether the nation's investment in research is producing results that are desirable for the American people. With our investment in basic research we have built a reputation as a great scientific leader among nations—witness the number of Nobel Prizes that have been awarded to Americans. We have made the United States the mecca for scientists throughout the world. We have learned much about the nature and history of the universe and of our planet, about the mechanisms of cellular growth and reproduction. And basic research has been leading with increasing rapidity to applied research that has been of widespread benefit to the American people. A few examples may be quickly cited.

1. Great advances in the health of the American people have coincided with the expansion of federal investment in medical research and public health measures.
2. The nation's military might is a direct outgrowth of the scientific community's responsiveness to the needs of national security.
3. Civil aviation's high degree of safety stems from research that is fundamental to traffic control and navigation devices.
4. The productivity of the nation's farms is directly related to seed and fertilizer developments that originated in the laboratory.

Finally, let me cite a single concrete example as evidence of the value of basic research. This is in part from fundamental research in radiation biology, a field with which I have some acquaintance because of my association with the Oak Ridge Institute of Nuclear Studies.

First let me give the title of an early paper published in the *Journal of Economic Entomology* in 1951. This was "Experiments with screw-worm flies sterilized by x-rays." If one did not live in Florida or Texas and knew nothing about screw-worm flies, this might at first glance indeed seem a subject of doubtful merit on which to spend federal research funds; it is easy to imagine what a journalistic wit might make of it. A little inquiry, however, would reveal the following facts:

1. Fatal wounds in cattle in Florida and Texas caused by maggots from eggs of the screw-worm fly led to losses estimated by cattlemen to aggregate at least $100 million a year.
2. Basic research on the ecology of this insect, its flight, mating, feeding, and other habits has led to a method for eliminating its occurrence, at least in Florida.
3. Stated simply, the method consists of breeding large numbers of the fly and sterilizing them. After wholesale release, the sterilized males mate with naturally occurring females, but only sterile eggs result.
4. After systematic application of this quite new and novel technique of insect control in Florida for about two years, the insect was practically eradicated and its serious menace to the Florida livestock eliminated.
5. From my general knowledge of research costs, I would estimate that the cost for the basic research involved did not exceed $1 million in all. The annual savings to the livestock industry of Florida alone would pay many times over not only for this but for much other basic research.

One of the advantages of treating separately the costs of basic research and the much greater costs of development is that it becomes easier to see what we are paying for. For $1.5 billion a year we get our whole basic research program, including many examples such as the one I have cited on the mating habits of the screw-worm fly. The more frequently cited figure of $15 billion a year includes the developmental costs of military, atomic energy, space, and other large programs. Scientists, the executive agencies, and Congress can defend a billion and a half dollars a year for basic research, and can point to such examples as one kind of justification. It is not so easy to justify such work or the level of expenditure if the budget is thought of as $15 billion a year, a budget that includes a great deal of work that the country has decided is necessary but that does not belong in the basic research category.

The second advantage of a clearer separation of basic research from applied research, development, and testing would be in the clarification of our worries about duplication. Congress has very rightly been worried about the duplication of effort in the R&D sphere. Scientists equally correctly deny that there is any intentional duplication in basic research. Congress wishes to save money, and can very properly raise questions about duplication of developmental efforts in the programs of agencies that have overlapping responsibilities. But duplication of effort in basic research is a quite different matter. The scientist's own motivation, his concern for his reputation among fellow scientists, and the elaborate procedures that prevail for exchanging information about the research being undertaken in different laboratories constitute much better guarantees against unnecessary duplication than could be provided by any set of governmental regulations or congressional hearings.

Third, questions of overhead, of the kinds of reporting required, of the relative merits of grants versus contracts, and other problems of management would, I believe, be easier to agree upon if we took them up separately for basic research and for applied research and development than they have been when these have all been lumped togther into an undifferentiated category.

Fourth, the government supports science education in a variety of ways in order to have a continuing supply of people qualified in pure science and its applied fields, but there is a considerable amount of confusion in the process. For example, much of the money that is allotted for research purposes is, in fact, used for the advanced training of graduate students. I said earlier that education at this level consists largely of a research apprenticeship. A great number of the grants for basic research and many of those for applied research that are carried out in university laboratories include funds for graduate assistants. The money is usefully spent, and the training received by graduate students contributes to our future supply of scientists and engineers. But some of the issues are clouded, because money that appears in the budget for one purpose is expended for a related but nevertheless different purpose.

There are, as I have said, some major differences between the proper methods of support for science education at the graduate level and for science education for younger students. The budgets upon which Congress has to act include funds for both these levels. But at no point in their consideration is there a clean separation between the two, and consequently there is never an opportunity for a clear decision as to how much money can appropriately go to each and the differences in arrangements that will most effectively foster each set of objectives.

DIVISION OF RESPONSIBILITY

Fifth, a clearer separation of the four main categories would make it easier to define the kinds of responsibility that can most appropriately be carried out by Congress, by the executive agencies, and by the scientists who are ultimately responsible for the research and educational activities that are being supported. The lines are not completely sharp, but I would suggest that Congress and the Office of the President have primary responsibility for deciding what the total budget shall be and how it should be divided among these four broad areas. Within the area of development, testing, and associated applied research, Congress and the Office of the President also have primary responsibility for subdividing funds, for here are involved specific goals—for defense, for public health, for our activities in space, for industry, agriculture, and for national prestige. On the other hand, the cognizant agencies, such as the National Science Foundation or the National Institutes of Health, and their grantees have a better basis for deciding how money for basic research should be spent and how money for the advanced and graduate education of prospective scientists should be spent. Confusion, mistrust, and a considerable amount of wasted effort result when either group tries to make decisions that might better be made by the other. In his testimony a few days ago, Dr. Wiesner spoke of the great speed with which a new finding in science may alter a variety of research activities. When this happens, a great deal of time can be wasted by going through a lot of bureaucratic red tape in order to secure permission to alter the direction of a study or to obtain a piece of equipment the need for which was not foreseen when the proposal was originally submitted. Congress and the Office of the President have great and overriding responsibilities for the health of the nation's research and development effort. They need not and should not dilute that responsibility by attempting to exercise a kind of control in one area that is only appropriate in some other area, or by attempting to make detailed research decisions which they are not truly qualified to make. Who is responsible for what would be easier to decide if we were thinking separately about the four parts of the total R&D effort rather than trying to establish rules and procedures for R&D as a whole.

To summarize: It seems to me altogether desirable that the Subcommittee study seriously and thoroughly the general question of the relationships between government and science, and I believe that you can do so most constructively if the four categories that I have discussed are taken up one at a time.

GEOGRAPHIC DISTRIBUTION OF RESEARCH FUNDS

The second general problem that I would like to discuss is closely related to the first. The problem is that of the geographic distribution of federal research funds.

The facts are perfectly clear and are a matter of record for each agency. A few states get a great deal more money than do all the rest. In general, the states that get the most money for research are such populous states as California, Massachusetts, and New York, but even on a per-capita basis the disparities among the states are tremendous. Whether the distribution is what it ought to be has been and no doubt will continue to be subject to a good deal of argument. A considerable part of the argument has been confused and confusing because we have been trying to use the same money for objectives that in the short run are mutually contradictory. In the abstract, most people would, I believe, agree that it is desirable that research be done on a variety of problems and that the research be of as high quality as we can procure. In the abstract, I believe also, most people would agree that it would be desirable to have a larger number of research and educational institutions of high quality than we now have, and that such institutions should be located in various parts of the country instead of being concentrated in a few.

In practice, there has been conflict between these two objectives. The need for defense, the fear of possible attack, the desire to ameliorate or eradicate crippling and disabling diseases, and the desire to achieve other national goals as rapidly as possible have all argued in the direction of placing research grants and contracts with those institutions that are best qualified to conduct the desired research. There are not many such institutions. Consequently, there has been a pile-up of federal research funds in a relatively small number of universities. In order to fulfill their obligations, these universities have recruited competent scientists from other universities and colleges, and so there has been further concentration of research talent in the best institutions. From time to time, this system has been criticized and the claim advanced that research funds should be more broadly allocated among the 50 states. The concentrated distribution has often seemed necessary in the past. The urgency of attaining some of the goals we have had in mind would have made anything like an equal distribution among the states a serious mistake.

But this situation has posed a dilemma for Congress, one that was illustrated—to take a single example—by the hearings of a subcommittee of the Committee on Appropriations of the House of Representatives earlier this year. In the review of the 1964 budget of the National Science Foundation, officers of the National Science Foundation were criticized several times for what members of the subcommittee considered undue concentration of NSF funds in a few states. The same hearings, however, resulted in striking out of the NSF budget the funds that had been requested for developmental grants that would have enabled NSF to assist a number of universities to attain greater research competence, and thus on merit to secure a larger proportion of funds handled through the regular grant procedures of the National Science Foundation and other agencies.

We cannot let down our guard, but I suggest that we have reached a stage where we can do some longer-range planning, and that it would now be appropriate to allot funds specifically to each of the two purposes. That is, some funds should be allotted for research support, with selection of recipients to be made strictly on grounds of quality, as has been the policy of the agencies in the past; and some funds should be allotted specifically for the purpose of building up a broader base of high-quality institutions scattered throughout the land.

Here, clearly, is a matter of high policy for the Congress and the President's Office. The change of policy would recognize that there is now an overemphasis on research at the expense of teaching and an overemphasis on short-term research goals at the expense of a broadened research competence.

When the establishment of the National Science Foundation was first being debated in Congress, consideration was given to the possibility of allotting some portion of its funds—perhaps 25 percent—among the several states on a formula basis and of allotting the rest strictly on the basis of merit. This proposal was killed, partly because the pork-barrel label got attached to it, but the objective is still desirable. I propose, therefore, that the government's total objective in supporting science would be better served if immediate research competence were not the only criterion for the distribution of funds and if some grants for research and for the improvement of science education were to be made either on a formula basis or by selection of especially promising institutions, with the intent to develop first-class institutions in parts of the country in which they do not now exist.

To the extent that federal funds can be used to accomplish this purpose, it will be necessary to use a larger fraction of that money than we have been using in past years in the form of institutional grants rather than individual project grants, and it will be necessary frankly to recognize the desirability of placing a larger amount of the total budget into universities that have the potential of reaching top rank but that have not yet done so.

All in all, I would list as one of the most fundamental problems in government-science relations the need to arrive at a better adjustment between the immediate, short-term research goals and the long-term goal of attaining for the nation a broadened educational and research competence.

Research Development and the Federal Budget

WILLIAM D. CAREY

I take for my opening text the observation of Malcolm Muggeridge that human beings suffer more as a result of being unduly serious than of being unduly flippant; their worst blunders arise out of their solemnity, not out of their mirth.

The relationship of government to science in the postwar years is a case in point. Without very much visible deliberation, but with much solemnity, we have in little more than a decade elevated science to a role of extraordinary influence in national policy; and now that it is there, we are not very certain what to do with it. We have evolved a variety of rationalizations for what we have done and for what we doubtless will continue to do: science for national security, science for a better life, science for a growing economy, and science as a cultural end in itself. What we have done less well is to employ research support as an effective agent in upgrading higher education not just for a few leading institutions but at its broad base, provide safeguards against expediency in influencing career and vocational commitments, and establish a truly competitive market place within which science and technology must justify itself and its costs in fair competition with other social priorities and preferences.

We have gone through a whole generation of science administrators and political executives who developed ulcers in bringing science and technology to its present dimensions. Now we are inducing ulcers in another generation of scientists, administrators, economists, and politicians who are trying to solve the problems left by their predecessors. Is big science and technology for space and defense in fact bleeding the private economy of the incentive and capability for innovation and creativity? Where is the high-grade intellectual manpower coming from to make good the commitments we are so freely entering into for the next decade? How are we to make certain that rising expenditures for research and development are not lost

This paper was delivered at the 17th National Conference on the Administration of Research, Estes Park, Colorado, on September 11, 1963, and it is reprinted here with the permission of the author. William D. Carey is Executive Assistant Director of the Bureau of the Budget. He has published several other papers on the role of the Executive Branch of the federal government on supporting science. In 1964, he was a recipient of the Rockefeller Public Service Award.

by dwindling productivity and quality in research? Can some way be found to ensure an adequate spinoff from space and defense research for the benefit of civilian technology? Have we approached the time for a healthy shaking-down of our Federal science and technology for purposes of taking stock and consolidating our efforts where the priorities lie?

In short, reaction is at last setting in. It is apparent in the scientific community, perhaps because of fears lest major programs and enormous hardware costs will push less exotic science to one side. It is apparent also in the Executive Branch of the federal government, where the budgetary pinch is becoming acute. And it is perhaps most spectacularly apparent in the Congress, where a mounting wail of frustration and uneasiness is being reflected in a rash of proposals to bring science and technology to heel, possibly reflecting a thought uttered by the quotable Mr. Justice Holmes, who said "We need education in the obvious more than investigation of the obscure."

The point I want to make is that government's part in the research and development business has now reached the point where it commands attention because of its sheer size and propensity for growth. From here on, we will have to be more choosy in what we do, and better prepared to supply answers to questions about marginal costs and benefits. The budget this year for research and development is a husky $15 billion. Its growth potential dwarfs anything else in the budget. Someone has figured out that the doubling time for R & D as a fraction of national income is only seven years, and that if this continued for 30 years research and development would rise to one-half of the national income. Dr. James Killian estimates that on the basis of present trends, total national expenditures for research and development could exceed $40 billion by 1970, with the Federal Government tagged for most of it.

In my judgment, without for a moment discounting the talent of the R & D community for finding new and expensive frontiers, these trends are not realistic. In absolute terms, I expect the level of Federal support for R & D to rise, but at a diminishing rate which could produce a leveling-off of the budget for science and technology over the next few years. Nevertheless, even a moderate upward trend is not to be taken for granted. Funds for R & D have come so easily during the past decade that in some quarters of the scientific community we find a state of mind that assumes that the miracle of the loaves and the fishes will go on indefinitely, and that the mere assertion of a valid scientific need will suffice to turn on the financial gusher once more. I should like to make it plain that the justification for the sixteenth and seventeenth billion will have to be very different from the justification which sufficed for the first billion. We have arrived at the point in the government's budget where the trends of the past are meaningless. A budget which quadrupled in the forties and doubled again in the fifties is extremely unlikely to behave in that style in the sixties, even for science and technology. And so that next billion dollars will come under both executive and legislative scrutiny of a kind previously unknown. And the scientific community will have to take a major responsibility for being sure that government chooses to put its dollars behind the best of many choices.

I would further hazard the view that this tightening of the federal pursestrings will cause some convulsions in the scientific community. When dollars for Big Science become scarcer, the science community can be expected to break ranks and form clusters of opinion and dissent to a greater extent than is the case to date. If a massive program for high-energy nuclear physics costing six to eight billion dollars, or a development program for a supersonic commercial air transport costing even one billion dollars, has the effect of heralding the displacement of other urgent claims for Federal support, we can expect the fur to fly and the issues to be illuminated with far more pungency than we have seen thus far. And this is precisely as it ought to be. This is the competitive market place at last.

To be sure, with this comes a new hazard, and one which is already visible. This is the danger of injecting the technique of the "pork barrel" into the area of science and technology. While I run some risk of excommunication for even bringing the matter up, it is a risk someone needs to take. We are talking about large sums of money, highly attractive physical plant, research tools to tantalize any self-respecting scientist with a forgivable eye on a Nobel Prize. We are speaking of national prestige science and technology which can be vital to the intellectual standing of a university or a group of universities. Where the tools are located, where the facilities are built, how funds are disbursed to equalize research opportunity among the various sections of the country—all these are very real issues in the era of Big Science. Scientists and educators with all this at stake are already learning how to bring pressure on their political representatives on their behalf, first for the approval of the programs and then for the location of facilities and the disbursing of operating funds. As new thresholds of research and experimentation materialize requiring highly sophisticated hardware, this phenomenon will become a force to be reckoned with. If I may say so, we can expect to face this not only in the area of applied science and technology, but even within that cloistered and rarefied world concerned with basic research. But if I am right about all this, and I think I am, one result will be to make science somewhat less luminous and other-worldly than it has been to date, and add a slight tinge of green to its halo.

As a more or less living example of the type of people who work on the federal budget, I should like to venture some general observations about that operation in so far as it touches science and technology.

To begin with, the budgetary process is the closest thing we have in government to a systematic effort at resource planning. Imperfect as it is, we would probably have to invent it if it did not already exist. What it provides is a round-the-year examination and re-examination of needs and resources in a changing society, in a setting of economic purposefulness and a Presidential program of political action. It is a process which stresses challenge and the evaluation of responses to that challenge. It reaches for rational criteria against which to sift competing claims and demands, and it aims toward a workable synthesis of goals within a financial and economic plan. In our framework of government, the budget process is the President's chief tool for facing up to the issue of what must be done now and what must wait. Underlying the exercise of this process there must, of course, be some basic strategy, and this will vary with Presidents and their public philosophies. One President may view the budget as a built-in Maginot Line against further extension of the arc of public action and intervention, while another will recognize it as an opportunity to advance our society purposefully in many fields of action important to both internal and external progress.

The Bureau of the Budget has never agreed with suggestions that it should establish within its structure a Division of Science, staffed with qualified scientists and engineers, to review R & D proposals. We prefer to do our work by using a broad approach which examines program issues in the field of science and technology from the standpoints of public policy, soundness of justification, the availability of money and manpower, and the balance of financial effort as among alternative program commitments. To be sure, our analysis frequently requires inputs of sophisticated professional judgment as to technical feasibility, state of the art, and possible alternatives to a proposed line of development, as for example in the moon program or in the missile field. In recent years, however, we have been able to obtain this kind of judgment through the Office of Science and Technology and the President's Science Advisory Committee. We have also arranged each year to undertake an overview of selected fields of science with the objective of relating levels of effort and support in particularly vital areas of science and technology to our general budgetary planning. This year, for example, we selected the areas of atmospheric science, oceanography, water research, high-energy nuclear physics, basic science, and science information for special review, and we conducted this exercise jointly with the office of the President's Science Advisor. I might say that the budget review process is not slanted toward exposing the weaknesses and follies of science proposals, although at times it has that result. But the process we employ is also calculated to bring out situations where we feel that there are distortions and imbalances in the government's support of science and technology and education, and in such instances we look for corrective solutions even though this might actually run the totals up.

I would like to be able to assure this select company that the budget process employs an ideal combination of criteria which guarantees a fully rational exercise in decision-making where we are dealing with science and technology. The truth is that we have a long way to travel before achieving that Utopia. There are still too many variables, too many unknowns, to leave us comfortable. We have no way to measure satisfactorily the potential yield to civilian technology from military and space R & D. We lack dependable data to judge whether we are approaching—or have already reached— the point where government-supported science and technology is displacing or impeding private investment in the R & D which feeds economic growth and creates the new products and markets needed for an economy on the path to full employment. Our crystal ball is still very foggy in forecasting what all this scientific and technical exuberance may mean in accelerating automation with all its implications on the mix of skills and utilization of our basic labor force. After twelve years of the National Science Foundation, we are as far away as ever from any clue as to how much basic research should be supported, year in and year out, as a national purpose, and we continue in that area to depend too much on the oversimplified formula of budgeting for some rough percentage of the worthwhile acceptable research proposals that are expected to roll in. We have found no absolute answers to the dilemma of priorities when we are faced with a well-reasoned but vastly expensive long-range program in high-energy nuclear physics and simultaneously programs for major outlays for oceanography, supersonic aircraft development, and the moon program; how does one assign relative values to the spectrum of opportunities to advance knowledge? James Reston of the *New York Times* has seen fit to draw attention to the dilemma of priorities in a piece entitled "Kennedy and the Scientists: the Quiet War." It is not a war at all, but an abundance of opportunities which government itself has invited and which only government can seize for the benefit of its people. The problem is that government today cannot take the easy way of recognizing them all and endowing science and technology with an unlimited drawing account. As I said earlier, the sixteenth and seventeenth billion are harder to come by than the first. Our problem is an embarrassment of intellectual riches which is not matched by the affluence to employ them fully. While Mr. Reston is entitled to his doubts about the adequacy of the government's method for reaching sound choices, it is my view that the difficulty here is not one of inventing more super-authorities but rather one of organizing "research about research," of developing more adequate insights into cost-benefit relationships, of illuminating our value analysis so that we can with greater confidence strike a balance between being "first" in high-energy accelerators and being first in education and in decent living and job opportunity. I do not think that government alone can reach these answers, but perhaps government can—and indeed I believe it must—be as proportionately lavish in stimulating this kind of intellectual inquiry as it has been in endowing science and technology.

Perhaps, after all, Mr. Justice Holmes had the right perspective. He observed, half a century ago:

> *If I am right, it will be a slow business for our people to reach rational views, assuming that we are allowed to work peaceably to that end. But as I grow older I grow calm. If I feel what are perhaps an old man's apprehensions, that competition from new races will cut deeper than working men's disputes and will test whether we can hang together and fight; if I feel that we are running through the world's resources at a pace that we cannot keep, I do not lose my hopes. I do not pin my dreams for the future to my country or even to my race. I think it probable that civilization somehow will last as long as I care to look ahead— perhaps with smaller numbers, but perhaps also bred to greatness and splendor by science. I think it not improbable that man, like the grub that prepares a chamber for the winged thing it never has seen but is to be—that man may have cosmic destinies that he does not understand. And so beyond the vision of battling races and an impoverished earth, I catch a dreaming glimpse of peace.*

Science Goes to Washington

MEG GREENFIELD

In the beginning, a current saying in Washington goes, were the lawyers; next came the economists; and then came the businessmen. Now it is the scientists' turn. This new breed, or more precisely, these new hybrids, who began their more or less reluctant ascent to power during the Second World War, are now so thoroughly enmeshed and infiltrated into every level of government that no one seems capable of stating with any precision just what their function is.

The role of the scientist-in-government as it has evolved in Washington in the past twenty years has been interpreted so loosely, by both the scientists and the administrations that have dealt with them, that each has inflicted punishment on the other, and neither, so far, seems to show any genuine understanding of the duties or requirements of the other. Invariably, science in Washington is science under pressure; it is science having to react to something, science having to hurry along, science having to worry about what the Russians might do, what the Congress may say, what Bertrand Russell is likely to think of next. The government in turn has yet to get accustomed to this strange community whose members are given in the best academic tradition to squabbling, back-scratching, and casting doubt on one another's competence—a community that cannot help being politically minded and yet cannot possibly resolve its dissensions according to majority principle.

It is a measure of the difficulty that nobody has—or could—come up with a readily comprehensible table of organization to explain the labyrinth of agencies, foundations, consultantships, academies, and committees that has grown up in Washington in recent years. A simpler guide might begin with the new Office of Science and Technology, created a year ago. The OST, which is directed by Jerome B. Wiesner, is part of the Executive Office and is accountable to Congress. It is charged, formally, with evaluating the programs of other agencies, and with helping to formulate national science policy.

Reprinted from *The Reporter*, September 26, 1963, Vol. XXIX, No. 5, pp. 20–26. Copyright 1963 by The Reporter Magazine Company. Reprinted with the permission of the author and the publisher. Meg Greenfield is Washington Correspondent for *The Reporter*.

Next, there would be the Federal Council for Science and Technology, a subcabinet group of which Wiesner is the chairman. The Federal Council is composed of a ranking member of each of eight government agencies along with a few official observers, and its purpose is to co-ordinate government programs in science. The task is a formidable one, since even such agencies of government as the Small Business Administration engage in some sort of scientific activity, while the giants such as the National Aeronautics and Space Administration (NASA), the Atomic Energy Commission, and the Department of Defense maintain their own laboratories, award their own contracts, and employ their own private armies of consultants. But the Federal Council's aims are modest. According to one staff aide, it is presently working against the day when ships from two of the twenty government agencies presumed to be involved in oceanography collide and sink while trying to take the same soundings.

In yet another of his capacities, that as Special Assistant to the President for Science and Technology, Wiesner and his staff of thirty-five function as personal advisers to the President. Here they work with the President's Science Advisory Committee (P-SAC), eighteen distinguished and more or less nongovernment scientists and engineers who meet monthly under their chairman, who, again, is Wiesner. P-SAC members are organized into standing committees and *ad hoc* panels, and for assistance they draw on a pool of around two hundred part-time panelists and consultants whose identity is kept secret. (Reportedly, about half the mystery guests come from private industry, and of these the largest single group is said to be from Bell Telephone Laboratories.) P-SAC may also receive what are known as "inputs" from committees of the National Science Foundation, which is concerned with the development of science and science education. Finally, the Foundation, P-SAC, the Federal Council, the individual agencies, and Wiesner in any of his multitudinous roles may request advice from the National Academy of Sciences, a quasi-official agency that has close ties to the Federal government.

One consequence of this chaotic institutional structure is that no one can be sure exactly what a government scientist is or, more to the point, when he is acting as one. It is not unusual to find a scientist like biologist H. Bentley Glass serving simultaneously as an adviser to the AEC on the effects of atomic radiation, as one of the independent experts selected by the National Academy to pronounce upon the same subject, and as a participant in such private groups as the Congress of Scientists on Survival and the Pugwash conferences, which on occasion deplore what the AEC is doing. One effect of the now-they-have-it-now-they-don't relationship many scientists enjoy with government has been to make remarkably vague the degree of their officialness at any given moment in terms of both their rights and their responsibilities.

THE STATUS OF SCIENCE

When is a government scientist speaking for government, and when is he speaking as a private citizen? Government has provided few guide lines, and those adopted by the scientists themselves have been, by and large, unsatisfactory. Last summer, for example, UCLA physicist Joseph Kaplan, who serves as an adviser to both the White House and the Air Force, was asked by a television interviewer for his opinion of the high-altitude nuclear test that had recently been conducted over Johnston Island. He emphatically regretted that the United States had been first to violate "an international agreement" to submit any such potentially harmful experiments in space to international scientific judgment. Yet questioning disclosed that the United States government was not a party to the agreement at all. The "agreement" had been subscribed to by official delegates of the semi-official National Academy at a conference of the International Council of Scientific Unions (ICSU), an organization that is remotely connected with the U.N.

When the scientists are unable to distinguish between their private and their public areas of responsibility, it frequently is government that ends up being embarrassed. Regularly, for example, members of P-SAC go off to the Pugwash conferences. There on occasion they have agreed to disarmament schemes less stringent than those they presumably support as members of government. In explanation of this practice, it has been said that they are acting in their capacity as private citizens, and no doubt they are. The problem has been the Russians' persistent refusal to take the disclaimer seriously, partly because the concept of "private capacity" is unfamiliar to them and partly because it is logical to expect that the views of the President's advisers—public or private—may ultimately carry some weight and even prevail. The effect has sometimes been confusion over U.S. policy, a fact that has begun to trouble even some former enthusiasts of Pugwash. "I think," I was told by one, a P-SAC member presently trying to devise a new format for the conferences, "that Khrushchev may have been misled by some things that were said in private on Berlin in 1961." Not long ago, in fact, Khrushchev, in a correspondence with President Kennedy, alluded to the views of U.S. scientists at Pugwash to bolster his own position on the monitoring of a test ban. In reply, the President was obliged to point out that the scientists "were speaking as individuals."

Painful as such effects of the scientists' irregular status may be, there is little that is likely to be done about it. For most attempts to bring scientists further within the framework of ordinary governmental procedures are suspected as attempts to compromise them; and many scientists who have no trouble understanding, say, the need to "muzzle" the military on subjects that may affect the conduct of foreign affairs consider a call for restraint on the part of government scientists an attack upon their intellectual freedom.

This confusion, institutionally blessed, that characterizes their relationship to government in general, leaving them never quite free but never quite responsible either, also characterizes their manner of functioning within it.

"Who is providing the facts ... ?" Representative Melvin Price (D., Illinois) demanded a while back. "By what authority do they act? ... Are they qualified?" It was the familiar cry of a congressman who has learned that government scientists have lately put the kibosh on one of his favorite projects—the nuclear-powered aircraft in this instance—and who also knows that his questions will not be answered. For the system and its mode of operation are such that even well outside areas of security classification it is rarely possible to determine who has acted, for what reason, or even in what capacity.

What with everyone participating *ex officio* in everyone else's business and regularly exchanging an embarrassment of inputs, the point has finally been reached where it is no longer clear at a given meeting who is advising and who is consenting and, in either case, on behalf of whom. Thus physicist James A. Van Allen complained last winter that he had been "intimidated" by members of a P-SAC committee before which he twice appeared, only to learn that he had never appeared before a P-SAC committee. It turned out to have been an interagency group convened by Wiesner in P-SAC headquarters under the auspices of the OST. There were P-SAC members present in some capacity and outside consultants too, but they were agency advisers on this occasion. For having failed to grasp this distinction, Van Allen was later charged by one of Wiesner's aides with a lack of "sophistication." In other words, what began as a laudable exercise in co-ordination has ended by almost completely dissolving lines of responsibility in government science, a process that has been hastened by the informal out-of-channels way in which the Kennedy administration likes to operate. In contrast with the two Special Presidential Assistants who preceded him, for example, the somewhat stately James R. Killian, Jr., and the respected scholar George B. Kistiakowsky, Wiesner is widely and admiringly held to be "an operator" in Washington.

Whether or not, as it is claimed, Wiesner accomplishes more this way, there has been a further loss of visibility in an already dim area of activity, and government scientists themselves have begun to complain. What once might have been public reports, according to some consultants who prepare them, are nowadays treated as documents for Wiesner's own guidance, and panel findings that seem to be going the wrong way are apt to meet untimely and mysterious ends more often than was thought practical in the past. The secrecy of preparations for the Johnston Island shot, for instance, bothered many scientists more than the test itself. Joseph Kaplan, who thought the test a "very good experiment," claims to have written Wiesner some "rather frank and strong letters" on the subject. "You were quoted . . . ," Kaplan's TV interviewer said apropos of his displeasure, "that the only way to get any information on what we're doing in the scientific space experiments was to sit around the Cosmos Club in Washington. Is that an accurate quote?" "No," said Kaplan, "that's simply one of the better ways. . . ."

For each of the factors that tend to put the scientists beyond accountability and their work beyond review—the maze at the working level, the fuzziness of authority at the middle and the top, and the unorthodoxy of present operations—good reasons and even necessity can sometimes be adduced. But taken together with the part-time nature of many scientists' employment, they have undeniably encouraged on more than one occasion a quick, casual, and even sloppy approach to problems, one that the scientists themselves would be the last to tolerate in their own laboratories. And, as is often the case, an inadequate system has begun to become a justification for its own inadequacies. For even though the government scientists' footlooseness and relative obscurity tend to promote careless work and to make its discovery by others difficult, the possibility of such work occurring has been offered by Wiesner and others as a reason for making their activities even more obscure. The point, as it is often argued in Washington, is that government simply could not get scientists to come down to perfunctory, accident-prone, potentially embarrassing work if even so much as their identity were revealed.

Partly on the basis of such unreassuring logic, a kind of secrecy has been maintained about government scientists that is practiced elsewhere in Washington only on behalf of intelligence agents. Not only are the names of some two hundred P-SAC consultants kept secret, but so are those of other paid scientific advisers to government. Spokesmen for both the Air Force and the Arms Control and Disarmament Agency recently refused to divulge the identity of certain of their scientific advisers on the grounds that to do so would (1) expose them to "pressure," (2) ensure that they would receive unwanted mail, and (3) put them under public scrutiny, which was exactly where they did not want to be.

Why shouldn't government scientists be under public scrutiny? The prevalent view seems to be that since science is more or less objective truth, scientists themselves are all but interchangeable, and their individual identity need not be a matter of concern. It is a view that, oddly enough, the public and the press seem to share. "A noted biologist," the New York *Post* declared not long ago, had made a certain comment about radioactive fallout. The *Post* quoted his comment and proceeded to base a passionate editorial upon it, never bothering to reveal which noted biologist he was, one presumably being as good as the next. The government scientists' exemption from public responsibility, in other words their relative freewheeling and remoteness, are more than side effects of the curious ways in which most of them have been organized into government; it is thought that they should be thus exempt, freewheeling, and remote.

Not long ago, a press officer of the Arms Control Agency informed me that the identity of ten scientists working full-time as civil servants *within* the agency could not be disclosed to the press. He reluctantly produced their names only when he had come to understand the difference between managing the news and managing civil-service regulations. "We claim Executive privilege," he said quite seriously at one point. And at another: "What good would it possibly do you? Why do you want to know who they are?"

THE INFLUENTIALS

Well, who are they? Who are the government scientists? One answer, of course, is practically everyone who has an advanced degree in science or engineering. For taking account of government contracts with universities, industry, and nonprofit organizations, it is estimated that between sixty per cent and seventy per cent of the nation's scientists and engineers are directly or indirectly employed by Washington. According to the Science Foundation, scientists and engineers account for 128,000 of the government's white-collar workers, or about eight per cent of the total. But in discussing those of their number whom they consider "politically relevant," scientists do not speak in thousands but in hundreds. One study, after investigating the subject, posited an "elite" of nine hundred and an "active elite" of 392. Killian reportedly has arrived at two hundred as the number of government scientists who are "consistently influential."

Because of the mystery in which they move and the frustration of those who have tried to find the locus of scientific decisions in Washington, the "active elite" has become subject to vague and contradictory accusations. Characteristically, suspicion on the Right and despair on the Left have produced two abiding myths about where the weight lies in government science and who the Influentials actually are. They are, to hear it told on Capitol Hill, the "fuzzy-wuzzies," by which is meant, roughly, the do-good, left-wing, academic basic-research set. "Like Rabi," they say to cover the other few hundred; ". . . like Bethe." At least, however, proponents of the fuzzy-wuzzy theory can produce a name or two upon request. The same cannot be said for the other side, the believers in the omnipotence of someone called the Military Scientist, a heartless, scheming, and above all irresponsible fellow who would just as soon blow up the Taj Mahal as look at it.

Neither of these devil theories makes much sense. For while it is true that military experiments often develop from recommendations made by the working scientists in the labs of the AEC and the armed services, higher approval has often come from none other than the so-called fuzzy-wuzzies. This was true, for example, of the two experiments most loudly denounced as Pentagon plots in recent years—the Johnston Island test and Project West Ford, a communications experiment that involved creating an orbital belt of copper needles around the earth.

Actually, the academic-military distinction is a false one, and not only because "fuzzy-wuzzies" may claim credit for having invented much of the infernal modern machinery of war. Most of the "active elite" could qualify either as military scientists *or* as fuzzy-wuzzies, whichever they themselves found less disturbing in terms of their personal politics. For the main thing to understand about the "active elite" is what makes it so active in the first place: there are many more influential jobs, it would seem, than there are influential scientists to fill them. Indeed, one reason all the institution-building and committee-creating of the past few years has brought relatively little order to science advising is that the new positions have gone, by and large, to the same old frantic, multi-hatted, overworked, exclusive crew. There exists at the top in government science not an academic-military split but what political scientists have politely described as a "self-selecting group" that "intercommunicates," and what congressmen rather more bluntly have called a game of musical chairs. In part it exists by default, and in part it exists by design. "Only those who circulate . . . in the right circles," as an editorial in *Science* magazine puts it, "who have the right connections, are likely to be called on to give advice . . ." Not long ago a prominent government consultant with whom I was discussing the controversy about the effect of the Johnston Island test on the Van Allen Belt thought it relevant to point out that Van Allen was "just a little man from Iowa." The question I should have asked, he said, "was whether we would hire him at MIT."

The "right connections," by all accounts, were made during and shortly after the war. Those most multifariously involved in government science are likely to be wartime veterans (or students of the veterans) of one of two institutions: Los Alamos or the MIT Radiation Laboratory (Rad Lab), which was run by Lee DuBridge during the war. After the war there was further commingling on military projects and science advisory committees. According to one scrupulous historian of these matters, some time around 1954 the "core group of the Rad Lab and the old Los Alamos people seemed to merge." Los Alamos as an institution has declined since then. California, on the other hand, has gained ground. And people have moved from place to place. At the present time, government science advising might best be described as a sort of Harvard-MIT-Bell Telephone-Caltech situation, with lines out to a few Eastern universities and to Palo Alto, Berkeley, and the RAND Corporation.

While the number of posts held simultaneously or in succession is one index of a government's scientist's influence, it doesn't tell the whole story. Being appointed is one thing; being listened to is another. Friendship, skill, chance, willingness to work, and a little bit of auld lang syne have combined in various ways to make some of the elite more elite than others. Certain members of P-SAC are called on for advice more often than is P-SAC itself— Edward Purcell, Wolfgang Panofsky, Jerrold Zacharias, George B. Kistia-kowsky, Harvey Brooks, who is Dean of Engineering and Applied Physics at Harvard, and Paul Doty, a Harvard chemist who is a close friend of the President's special assistant, McGeorge Bundy, and who has taken an active interest in disarmament and the test ban. Also, government has its favored businessmen-scientists, such as James Fisk, president of Bell Telephone Laboratories, and Emmanuel Piore, who is vice-president for research and engineering at IBM. Similarly, the advice of certain lab directors in the field often carries more weight in Washington than that of their nominal superiors. One of these is Norris Bradbury, director of Los Alamos. Another is John S. Foster, Jr., who is director of the Lawrence Radiation Laboratory in California and who, along with Richard and Albert Latter of the RAND Corporation, John Wheeler of Princeton, and a few others, represents what has come to be thought of as the scientific shadow cabinet or loyal opposition on questions having to do with nuclear armament and disarmament.

From the days of the Manhattan District Project there has existed within the community of government science a political split over the proper use and control of atomic weapons, a split that was exacerbated by the Oppenheimer hearings and subsequent controversies over fallout and the technology of a test ban. For several years after the war, power shifted from side to side as scientists of opposing views swept in and out of control. The hegemony of the General Advisory Committee of the AEC (I. I. Rabi, Du-Bridge, Fisk, et al.) ended with the Oppenheimer hearings and was followed by a period of hegemony on the part of the Teller group. The ascent of Sputnik in 1957, and a new interest in a test ban on the part of the Eisenhower administration, combined to bring on Period 3. Killian became Eisenhower's Special Assistant for Science and Technology and P-SAC, formerly part of the Office of Defense Mobilization, was elevated to the White House. Its members included Fisk, Kistiakowsky, Rabi, Wiesner, and Zacharias, and for about two years they were again at the undisputed center of scientific power in Washington. The creation of other agencies and advisory groups in government—largely at their own recommendation—has dissipated P-SAC's power since then and given the loyal opposition at least a chance to speak if not always to be heard.

If most of those in the new positions have been around before, one reason may be lethargy and indifference on the part of the out-group scientists as well as finickiness and snobbery on the inside. "You sit on the sidelines and complain," Wiesner chided a convention of scientists in Washington recently. But, he added, it was "surprising" how many scientists when approached by the government made it plain that they only were willing "to come down and help out occasionally." Indeed, the chairmanship of the National Science Foundation went begging for nine months until Atomic Energy Commissioner Leland Haworth, still a member of the "in-group," finally took it this spring. And it took Wiesner more than a year after OST had been established by law to oversee all scientific operations in government to acquire the deputy director provided for in the act. Some people said he couldn't find one, others that he wouldn't; writ large, the argument was whether the dearth of government scientists was due to the fact that no one has been knocking at the door or to the fact that no one has been answering. But whatever has caused the scarcity, it still exists.

What has happened since Sputnik rattled the china in 1957 has been an elevation of scientists, who were for the most part already there, to posts of new responsibility with access to the top. P-SAC moved up to the White House; scientists were taken on by the departments for the first time at the secretariat level; advisory groups were established to communicate directly with Congress and with agency heads; a scientist, Glenn T. Seaborg, became chairman of the AEC. The movement has been upward, and the harassed few now constitute a new class in Washington. They are scientific upper-middlemen—translators, reviewers, communicators, monitors of what goes on below in the labs and agencies, as well as participants in what goes on above, namely policymaking.

THE NATURE OF SCIENCE ADVISING

In a series of Godkin Lectures delivered at Harvard a few years ago, C. P. Snow related a story of conflict between two British science advisers during the war, laying stress on the intractable mysteries of scientific knowledge and its inaccessibility to those in government who had to base decisions upon it. Though Snow's lectures were widely challenged, this chilling and romantic version of science advising dies hard. For the least argument, accident, or admission of uncertainty related to science these days continues to bring on that now familiar host of editorial warnings about how the nation and its leaders must learn science while there's time, or it's curtains for the democratic process. Are the warnings justified? Is radiophysics, like democracy, really everybody's job?

According to those who give and receive advice in Washington, the answer is "No." Wiesner, speaking of the President, and Harold Brown, Director of Defense Research and Engineering, speaking of Secretary McNamara, both concede that there have been times when they had trouble communicating information because of its technical complexity. But such trouble is said to be rare and relatively easy to overcome. "If you can't put it into English," as Jerrold Zacharias has summed up the prevailing view, "it means you don't understand it yourself." Far more troublesome to those who receive advice from Washington's new class of scientific watchdogs, consultants, and policymakers has been the seemingly simple matter of figuring out what is a scientific question in the first place, and what is a scientific answer.

No one was in a mood to make such discriminations in the period immediately following Sputnik I. "They gave us a flabbergasting array of responsibilities," Killian has recalled of those days in 1957 and 1958 when a kind of desperate blur characterized official thinking about the scientists' newly announced purpose of bringing their wisdom to bear on such policy matters as military security and the space race. They were looked upon by the White House and by many in Congress as saviors and miracle workers who could solve, rather than merely assist in, the problems of defense.

The problem of determining what exactly is a scientific question was nowhere so acute and is nowhere better illustrated than in the general field of disarmament and the test ban, largely because science slips so easily and imperceptibly into non-science at almost every point on both issues. Last spring, for example, the following statement was made before the Joint Committee on Atomic Energy by Air Force seismologist Carl F. Romney: "Based on all the information now available, we can conclude that it is feasible to design a detection system, based entirely outside the Soviet Union, which is capable of detecting explosions of about 1 kiloton in granite, 2–6 kilotons in tuff, and 10–20 kilotons in alluvium." As a statement of fact, it was agreed to by government scientists. Yet the old quarrel over our detection capabilities immediately broke out anew among them. Why? They were arguing about many things—whether the Soviet Union would go to the expense of developing weapons below that threshold of detection, whether such weapons would be worth not only the cost to them but the opprobrium of getting caught—whether, in fact, such weapons would have any decisive military value at all. In other words, they were arguing about Soviet intentions and Soviet strategy, not about science. Failing to appreciate the distinction, many people continue to invoke the scientist of their choice in support of their own test-ban and disarmament positions in the happy belief that they are citing unchallengeable scientific authority.

The associative process whereby a physicist's special knowledge of nuclear weapons is transformed into an equally special knowledge of all the political, military, and diplomatic problems in which they figure has got the government into trouble often enough now to be fairly widely recognized for what it is—though not by everybody. In one case, when I asked a member of P-SAC not long ago if he could describe the extent to which government scientists found themselves marshaling facts in support of decisions already taken, he replied with great feeling, though a little off the point, "Never! Because we have always told them what's coming. *They* ask *us*."

His subsequent account of the astuteness and foresight scientists have displayed as instructed military thinkers has been challenged lately by a number of non-scientists in and around government. Albert Wohlstetter, formerly of RAND, in a recent speech presented an imposing collection of mistaken predictions and judgments made by such scientists as Bethe, Teller, and Rabi on such subjects as air defense, civil defense, Soviet behavior, and military strategy in general since the onset of the cold war. "I believe neither Dr. Teller nor Dr. Bethe has done . . . systematic analysis of the military worth of these weapons they talk about," he said. "Both are experts on the technology of bomb design. But that is quite another matter."

CONGRESS EYES THE "EXPERTS"

Predictably, the newly gained insights into what is and what is not a scientific issue in government have suggested to some that time is ripe for that classical counter-revolution against the government scientist—back to the bevatron and speak only when spoken to. Something of the sort, for instance, was in the mind of Congressman Craig Hosmer (R., California) last March when he demanded that a statement made before the Joint Committee on Atomic Energy by scientist Jack Ruina be stricken from the record since, even though Ruina had identified the statement as an opinion, it dealt with aspects of a test ban that were outside his special competence as an electrical engineer. "This witness is stating an opinion in an area in which he is not an expert," as Congressman Hosmer summed up the New Thinking, "and therefore it clutters the record." Ruina, who was then Director of the Defense Department's Advanced Research Projects Agency, has probably been one of Washington's most careful and sensitive scientists where infringements of this kind are concerned. At the level of government where he operated, it would be highly impractical to try to keep science advisers in bottles. The genuinely scientific part of most issues in government is so thoroughly entwined with and dependent upon other considerations that it is at best an imperfect, partial science. Thus, Wiesner, at the time of the United States' resumption of atmospheric nuclear testing in 1962, was not called upon to deal absolutely with the question of how much radioactive fission release would be permissible or safe. Rather, he is said to have mediated a behind-the-scenes dispute on the matter between the Public Health Service on the one hand and the AEC and Defense on the other, balancing potential risks to health against potential risks to military security in the light of what the Russians were thought to have achieved in their tests.

The word "potential" was the key on both sides of the radiation dispute, since the ultimate effects of radioactive fallout were—and are—if anything more a subject of conjecture among scientists than the achievements of the Soviet test series. But the sacred distinctions that scientists normally make between scientific fact and scientific theory, or that which is known because it has been proved and that which is still a matter of speculation, have all but gone by the boards in government.

Even making allowance for the fact that government scientists are often pushed into making such premature judgments, however, too often they seem to volunteer them as well. Accordingly, some people have begun to speak wistfully of the need for some sort of self-enforced fair labeling practice among scientists, one that would require them to indicate (as Ruina, in fact, did) when they are departing scientific fact for scientific speculation and when they are departing science altogether. Take the affair of the "black boxes"—the unmanned detection stations that were set forth last winter as a means of policing a test-ban treaty. The scientists had said they were "safe," as people liked to point out. But what exactly had they meant by "safe"? "There never was much enthusiasm around here for the black-box concept," an Arms Control Agency scientist explained to me. "But after the Russians made it plain that they wouldn't take internationally manned stations, we began to find the idea more attractive. Black boxes aren't very reliable when you compare them with manned stations. But they are reliable when you compare them with nothing." So much for the policy judgment and the meaning of "safe." What precisely had the scientists meant by "black box"? There was and still is no such thing—except in theory. Understandably, this bit of news came as something of a shock to legislators who were pondering its place in our then current test-ban proposal last March. Was the black box real or was it "imaginary," as Senator John Pastore (D., Rhode Island) finally put the question to J. H. Hamilton, who is responsible for the project. "I think this system is essentially within the state of the art," Hamilton replied. ". . . I would say to assemble these components, to test, and be reasonably sure of yourself, we are talking about eighteen months."

Such canny questioning of scientists is a relatively new development on Capitol Hill, and its meaning has not been lost on the administration. The plummy days of the hushed hearing room and the reverential "Well, now, Doctor . . ." are becoming a thing of the past. And for once, the narrowing squint of Congress has been turned on the scientists' science rather than on their political upbringing. Consequently, not only have the President and his advisers themselves learned that the phrase "The scientists say . . ." may carry any number of meanings and degrees of authority; they have also learned that simply to quote them will no longer do to persuade Congress of the wisdom of a particular decision. For the Congress has learned that a scientist's own emotions and his personal politics may well affect the advice he gives.

The repugnance with which most people respond to the idea that a scientist may even have such things as emotions and politics, let alone that either might influence his work, is a tribute to the durability of some rather odd beliefs about both science and politics, and about any encounter that takes place between them. Science is the man in the white coat, the thinking goes, and politics is the man with the stale cigar, from which it follows that a politically motivated scientist must be a venal one, a passer along of equations that don't prove out. The truth is considerably less dramatic. P-SAC, for example, has a reputation for scientific rashness where the test ban is concerned and for scientific skepticism about proposed military weapons systems. Among Defense Department scientists, quite naturally, it has been the other way round. "It's hard to separate emotion from hard facts," an Arms Control Agency scientist explained. "We can get agreement on the facts, but not on what we could do on the basis of them. We can't get agreement on the scientific promise, on where it will lead."

He was talking about the test ban, and his first point was illustrated— and continues to be—in the scientists' quarrel over the meaning of the element of uncertainty in test detection. To those scientists, such as Teller, who oppose the ban, the uncertainty meant danger: we could not be sure of detecting Russian evasions. To those who favored the ban it meant increased safety: the Russians could not be sure of evading detection and therefore would be less apt to cheat.

The test ban serves equally to illustrate the way in which the scientists' political inclinations have affected their intuition and inventiveness—their actual scientific creativity. In Washington the process is known as "finding ways that things won't work." Both Teller and Bethe have proved masters of the art. Teller, as Wohlstetter has pointed out, has been particularly adept at imagining weapons that the United States could not develop under the terms of a test-ban treaty. Bethe, on the other hand, has generally responded to such imaginings with imaginings of his own—"enemy counter-measures which would reduce their military worth to zero." The scientists' advice has not only been affected by their political preference. Their curious status between and betwixt government and private roles has left room for any number of interests to inspire their advice in both areas. As presiders over the national science purse, are the scientists speaking in the interest of science or in the interest of government or in the interest of their institutions? Is their policy advice, on the other hand, offered in furtherance of national objectives or agency objectives—or their own objectives based on their political thinking? It has begun to become apparent that wherever they have favored the more private aim over the more public one, they have not only limited their usefulness to government—except as checks and balances to each other—but undermined their own influence as well. The extent of the confusion that exists on the subject became apparent at a meeting of the Federation of American Scientists not long ago when Wiesner was asked rather imperiously from the floor how he could justify the way in which government annually disposed of its $12-billion budget for science when there were so many neglected projects more worthy of support. The funds, Wiesner pointed out, were not being spent *for* science but *on* it. They were being spent *for* government, he said.

SHOOTING THE MOON

Despite its many achievements, the present balancing act has proved inadequate for the chores the scientists in government set for themselves. It has not been possible to make even a start on the establishment of scientific priorities and long-range plans for science. Agency monitoring proceeds on a helter-skelter basis. And chaos and frenzy are at least as common to the process of advising as order. "Valuable as such [*ad hoc*] advice is," as Kistiakowsky has summed up the problem, "it does not fill today's requirements for a continuing and intimate involvement in the policymaking process of competent people who understand science and its significance to policy . . ." Indeed, six years after the ascent of Sputnik, what might be called the state of space in Washington is a fairly good index of what the scientists have and have not been able to achieve—and why.

"The scientists cringe when you call it science," a NASA administrator recently told me on the subject of Project Apollo, the moon-flight program. He added that of course it wasn't supposed to be "science"; science was only one part of the program. In return, many scientists have pointed out that while science is a relatively small part of the program, the program will still have an enormous impact, by reason of money spent and manpower committed, on the future of science itself.

But to some extent the fault was their own. The point has been made that the initial response of the newly elevated P-SAC and of other leaders of the scientific community in 1957 to the post-Sputnik space emergency was almost entirely geared to the interests of science—from the original proposal for a research-oriented space agency to the casual dismissal of both the military and diplomatic ramifications of a space program. "There is plenty to do without trying to nail the American flag on the whole solar system by next week," Lee DuBridge put it at the time. By speaking mainly for science conceived as basic research, P-SAC saw its power over the program diminish and with it the chance to influence the program's impact on science.

The moon program was worked out over a hectic weekend in May of 1961 at the Pentagon following Alan Shepard's successful suborbital flight. It was a political response to the Gagarin venture and to the Cuban disaster, among other things. Reportedly, Secretary McNamara, James Webb of NASA, and a few others met round the clock starting Friday evening and worked out the crash program that was presented to the President for a decision the following Monday. "We had been told," as one of the participants puts it, "not to fool around." What was Wiesner's role? "Jerry was associated with the decision. He was called in. He was there. He wanted everything to be done right by the administration. And he had his constituency of scientists he was worried about too. As I remember, he was torn."

In Washington these days, the definition of a truly hip science adviser is one who knows that the moon money could be better spent on other scientific projects and who also knows that Congress won't appropriate it for any of them. The kind of passive in-betweenness this suggests is more or less the state of science advising now. "The scientists think you are a tool of the administration," Wiesner told me in summing up the predicament not long ago, "and the administration thinks you are a tool of the scientists."

Federal Support of Basic Research in Institutions of Higher Learning

NATIONAL ACADEMY OF SCIENCES

PREFACE

This report had its origin in a resolution, passed by the American Society of Biological Chemists in April 1963, urgently requesting the National Academy of Sciences "to enunciate the principles and philosophy which could serve as a basic policy in the future conduct and administration of federal programs in support of fundamental research." The resolution described the situation that impelled the request in the following terms:

> "The condition of mutual dependence between the federal government and institutions of higher learning and research is one of the most profound and significant developments of our time. It is abundantly clear that the fate of this nation is now inextricably interwoven with the vigor and vitality of these institutions. In turn, the fate of these institutions is dependent upon the wisdom and enlightenment with which federal funds are made available in support of their activities. It is imperative, therefore, that the conditions governing this mutual interdependence be subject to continuing appraisal and that the policy underlying administration of federal programs in support of research assures that this relationship will continue to be mutually beneficial."

Several other scientific societies passed similar resolutions calling for consideration by the National Academy of Sciences of federal support of basic research in institutions of higher learning.

The Academy voted at its annual meeting of 1963 to undertake an appraisal of the subject as defined in the resolution. In June, the Council of the Academy asked the Academy's Committee on Science and Public

Written by the Committee on Science and Public Policy, Washington, D.C., March 1964, and reprinted with permission of the Chairman of the Committee on Science and Public Policy, the President, and Publications Editor of the National Academy of Sciences. Only the preface and the conclusions are reprinted here. The members of the Committee on Science and Public Policy of the National Academy of Sciences are listed at the conclusion of this excerpt from their report.

Policy to prepare a report. Almost the entire membership of the Committee has participated actively in its preparation. Moreover, in response to announcements in several scientific periodicals and to personal letters soliciting the views of the membership of the National Academy of Sciences, many comments and constructive suggestions were submitted to the Committee. It is against the background of the thoughtful expression of many individual investigators, therefore, that the Committee has prepared this report, taking account of a broad spectrum of opinion among scientists. The Committee accepts full and sole responsibility, however, for its conclusions.

The resolution that called for this report was prompted by an increasing concern, both in the Congress and in the scientific community, about the principles that guide the federal government's system of science support in the universities. The sheer size of the government's financial stake in research and development might alone have triggered this stock-taking. The figure of $14.9 billion, so often heard, is not fiscal year 1964 government investment in *basic* research, but rather in its *total* research and development effort, encompassing many military and space development programs. Nevertheless, a figure of nearly $1.5 billion (this year) for basic research in the United States, of which almost half goes to institutions of higher learning, is sufficient cause for thought and discussion.

More immediately, reports of the Intergovernmental Relations Subcommittee of the House Committee on Government Operations, dealing with grant policy and administrative practices of the National Institutes of Health, have marked the beginning of a period in which government agencies have been revising their policies. Much of the discussion within the scientific community has been closely focused on administrative changes of direct consequence to the individual investigator. Even the original resolution of the American Society of Biological Chemists, however, envisaged not a narrow examination of specific issues but a study covering the general policies of all the government agencies supporting basic research in the universities. The action of the National Academy of Sciences confirmed this concern with principles rather than specific cases. The swift-moving events of the last half of 1963—the period of the deliberations relating to this report—have amply justified the wisdom of emphasizing the fundamental relationships of the government and institutions of higher learning, rather than specific incidents.

Three main elements have entered into the Committee's consideration —the federal government, the institutions of higher learning, and the community of professional scientists in these institutions, most of whom are also members of teaching faculties. These are the same three elements dealt with in the statement of the President's Science Advisory Committee entitled, *Scientific Progress, the Universities, and the Federal Government,* issued in November 1960. That report set forth a rationale for federal support of basic research in institutions of higher learning and reasons why the support of basic research and the support of graduate education must be merged. The present report is a sequel, in that it accepts the major assertions of the report of the President's Committee and moves on to consider how the donors and recipients of government support should manage their inter-relationship.

One principle dominates all others in the present report: The government and the universities must work within two noble traditions character-istic of all free societies—the political freedom of a democratic people and the freedom of scientific inquiry. The scientific community, the Congress, and the Executive have long since agreed both that a strong and free devel-opment of science is a national necessity and that accountability for the use of government funds is a fundamental part of the exchange by which a people in a democracy entrusts power to its leaders, who are in fact and theory public servants. Can freedom of scientific inquiry and accountability be reconciled? We believe that they can be and must be. We ask in this report: What are the policies by which accountable support can effectively advance scientific inquiry in the common interest? How can inaccurate con-ceptions of both *the necessary freedom for scientific research* and *the ac-countability of funds* be prevented from stifling the fruits of research—a potent resource of our society not only for today but for the future?

Many important matters cannot receive full consideration here. Devel-opment and applied research claim and will continue to claim a large share of money and talent in both government and industry. In many instances, the scientific community has found the surroundings it needs for outstanding work within the walls of both governmental and industrial laboratories as well as in the universities. Moreover, the universities have essential purposes that transcend basic research, graduate education, and science itself. Never-theless, we shall give but little attention to these considerations, and will limit our report for the most part to consideration of federal support of basic research in institutions of higher learning. It is at this point, where the universities, the government, and the scientific community come to-gether, that the issue of reconciling scientific freedom with fiscal responsi-bility appears most clearly and is in greatest need of wise formulation of policy and mutually satisfactory means of implementation.

*   *   *

CONCLUSIONS

The commitment of large public funds for the support of basic research in universities has led not only to spectacular growth of the scope of scientific effort but also to advances in quality: American science has reached a position of world leadership. We attribute this in no small measure to enlightened policies of several federal agencies committed to furtherance of basic research; specifically to the current emphasis on support by research project grants and by fixed-price research contracts (not too unlike grants), coupled with an extensive use of advisory scientific bodies, such as panels or study sections, to select scientifically meritorious projects for support. We believe that research project grants and contracts should remain the backbone of federal policy in support of basic research in science in universities. The emphasis on large programmatic ventures and laboratories which has been manifest in recent times must not lead to a loss of emphasis on individual scientists: the individual investigator has been and will remain the source of strength in American science.

CONCERNING FEDERAL AGENCIES

1. The criterion of selection for grant or contract support of basic research has been primarily the scientific quality of the work proposed. The selection of projects on this basis has come about in various ways, but particularly as a result of the judgment of scientists well versed in the areas concerned. We believe this merit judgment should be retained as a prime basis for federal support. The methods of obtaining this merit judgment at present vary; the following measures will strengthen and bring greater effectiveness to the judging process.

a. Federal agencies not presently using study sections or advisory panels for the merit rating of research proposals would improve the quality of their research programs by the adoption of these or similar devices.

b. Membership in the panels and sections should be on a relatively short-term rotating basis, and wide circles (in terms of scientific disciplines, geography, and function) of the scientific community should be tapped for this service. This is necessary because conscientious service on such panels is very costly in time to consulting scientific personnel. Moreover, we are convinced that infusion of new blood into the sections and panels is conducive to the maintenance of high scientific standards and helps to induce the selection of the most original and promising research proposals.

c. When panel, section, or consultant activity has resulted in ordering of proposals by scientific merit, the order suggested should be seriously considered by the federal agency staffs and modified only in special circumstances which are explained to the panel or section members.

d. Panels and sections should not be involved in detailed evaluation of proposed budgets, although panel judgments on the general reasonableness of proposed budgets should be seriously considered by agency staffs. Detailed budget considerations should be the responsibility of agency staffs alone.

However, panel or section judgments as to the proper duration of grants or contracts should be given considerable weight by the agency staffs. While panels and sections must supply the primary judgments regarding scientific merit, questions of administrative responsibility and agency policy must be dealt with by full-time staff members, and the agency itself must assume responsibility for the final decisions with regard to awards of grants and contracts. For this reason, we strongly endorse the efforts of the government to improve the quality of the career service, by providing compensation at levels comparable with private salaries, and by encouraging staff members to continue their scientific and professional advancement.

e. Consultation with scientific referees by mail is less satisfactory than the panel-section procedures. Where this procedure is used, however, it is essential to keep the referees informed as to the effect of their advice in each case. Failure to do so is bound to lead to less responsible attitudes among referees and in the end to purely administrative choices of projects. We do not believe that personnel whose main functions are administrative can for long retain keen judgment as to what is most promising in science. We believe, therefore, that purely administrative mechanisms for selection of worthy research proposals would lead to inferior programs and thus to a waste of public funds.

2. The advantages of grants generally outweigh those of fixed-price contracts for basic research. However, research contracts have been developed into legal instruments that place few restrictions on the principal investigator beyond those imposed by grant arrangements under present regulations. Unfortunately, there is a current trend toward introducing into grant and contract negotiations and regulations administrative restrictions that are inimical to effective basic research. We believe that this trend should be reversed, with the universities taking increasing responsibility for proper administration of grants and contracts.

3. We recognize and endorse the fundamental legal principle that public funds may be spent by contractors and grantees only for stated purposes, and thus that diversion of funds to other purposes cannot be tolerated. We welcome in principle the issuance of guidelines concerning the expenditure of grant and contract funds. But we discern a recent trend toward unnecessary restriction of scientific freedom and increases in the bookkeeping chores of scientists in both grants and contracts; we believe that this trend will result in lower returns on the investment of public funds in science.

4. The project proposal by an applicant states the purpose of the requested grant. The implications of this are not always understood by applicants. We believe that many difficulties could be avoided if the federal agencies, in their printed instructions for the preparation of research proposals, explained clearly the relation between the contents of a proposal and

the purpose of the grant. Scientists should bear in mind in making application for grants that the preambles of their proposals define the purposes for which granted public funds may be spent. We believe that a project proposal should include:

a. Broad objectives of the proposed research in terms of areas of scientific knowledge to be advanced.

b. Specific early research objectives stated as illustrative of the broader aims.

c. Scientific tactics (experimental methods) to be employed. We also hold that the grant or contract instrument should explicitly recognize the broad objectives (a) as its legal purpose. Only a deviation from the broad objectives of a project proposal, thus stated, should be considered as constituting a change in the purpose of the grant, thus calling for special approval from the federal agency.

5. Current regulations concerning the expenditure of grant moneys restrict the transfer of funds from one budgetary item to another. We believe that these regulations are quite proper insofar as they deal with the compensation of senior personnel, with travel (especially travel abroad), and with improvements in the facilities of the grantee institution. On the other hand, we believe that the principal investigator should be given maximum latitude in spending other grant moneys for the stated purpose of the grant as he sees fit. Ordinarily, so much time passes between the preparation of a proposal and the expenditure of grant funds that preferred tactics change, new equipment becomes available, and so forth. We believe that the principal investigator should be free to shift funds between budget items of equipment and expendable supplies, and that a provision that the principal investigator explain the reasons for substantial shifts, in his application for renewal or continuation of the grant, would provide an adequate safeguard against misuse of grant funds. At the very least we urge that the present limit (usually $500) on purchase of initially unspecified equipment be increased in some proportion to the total value of the grant. Thus principal investigators will be spared a great deal of wasteful paper work to obtain, necessarily, either perfunctory approvals or arbitrary refusals from remote agency staffs.

6. The accounting for part-time service of principal investigators and other academic personnel in projects supported by research grants or contracts, whether or not such service is paid for with grant funds, must be realistically related to the input of professional effort on the project. We believe that accounting for research effort in terms of time input, i.e., in terms of days or hours, is unrealistic and can lead to fiscal policies that fail to make allowances for the nature of scientific research. We recommend that accounting for effort of professional personnel on a grant or contract be

expressed in terms of some fraction of the total effort applied by the individual to his university duties.

The full fiscal year of a grant, or the full academic year, is recommended as the minimum period of time for which accounting of service should be made by a university. However, the time periods in which individual scientists have no university duties, such as summer vacations, may be accounted for separately.

7. We are not competent to enter into a detailed discussion of the problem of appropriate overhead costs. We believe, however, that inadequate provision for such costs is harmful to the universities as communities of scholars dedicated to the balanced education of American youth. We urge that overhead payments be provided for, on grants as well as on contracts, based on application of essentially the same formula in both instruments.

8. While we strongly endorse the project grant/contract system of research support, we believe that three auxiliary types of support are also necessary for the healthy growth of American science.

a. The first of these are institutional or general research grants related to existing totals of project grants, now being made on too modest a scale by the National Institutes of Health and the National Science Foundation. These should be strengthened and broadened in purpose to overcome serious imbalances created in the universities by the growth of existing project research support and to meet the need for initial support of new projects.

b. The second type is necessary to meet the problem of junior faculty members who have difficulties obtaining support for independent research. We believe that a system of *small research grants*—on a modest scale—should be introduced. These would be awarded to junior scientists for individual research on the basis of a very general outline of their research interests, supported by letters of endorsement from senior scientists personally acquainted with the work of applicants. Aside from an agreed sum as reimbursement to the grantee institution for work of the applicant, the budget should provide only for supplies and smaller items of equipment, but should not be broken down into component parts. The grantee investigator should, within the purpose of the grant, be allowed to pursue such researches as appear most fruitful to him in the broad area defined in the application. Some truly original ideas and discoveries have come from young scientists, and we cannot afford to tie them down to narrowly defined research objectives.

c. The nation faces the problem, in addition to that of rapidly growing population, of an even faster-growing need for highly educated personnel. This, we believe, makes the efforts to increase the number of strong educational institutions a matter of first importance. Therefore, we urge a third type of auxiliary support: a distinct and selective program of research grants to be made available to some weaker institutions on the basis of demonstrated will to utilize new funds to raise the level of research and graduate education. The number of strong institutions must grow. We recognize that the framing of criteria by which such grants can be awarded is not an easy task, and invite careful study of the problem by a competent task force.

9. We subscribe to the conviction, expressed in the President's Science Advisory Committee 1960 report, *Scientific Progress, the Universities, and the Federal Government,* that research and the graduate education of young scientists are intimately related. Considerable progress has been made in modifying federal agency policies to adapt them to this principle since the issuance of that report. We urge continuing review of such policies in the same direction; only thus can the nation be prepared for the future.

10. In surveying the practices and regulations of the several federal agencies engaged in support of basic research, we find an extraordinary diversity. At the same time we find a growing tendency to provide the same principal investigator with multiple grants and contracts, often from different agencies, to support closely related facets of his work.

We recognize the advantages of some variation in the practices of the several agencies, and of multiple sources of support where a principal investigator is engaged in research toward several objectives. We believe, however, that the present situation forces investigators to devote too much time to detailed accounting and other non-productive administrative matters. We urge that vigorous efforts be undertaken (a) to simplify and align the requirements of the several agencies regarding preparation of research proposals, accounting, progress reporting, and similar matters, and (b) to reduce the need for multiple support by more inter-agency agreements designating a single agency to provide total support of an investigator's work in a given scientific area.

CONCERNING THE UNIVERSITIES

11. A clearer recognition by university administrations of the purpose of federal project grants and contracts for basic research is an essential requirement.

12. In dealing with federal agencies, university administrations should assert more clearly and emphatically the central purpose of American universities: the advanced education of American youth integrated with the scholarly activities of teachers; in the natural sciences these activities take primarily the form of scientific research. This purpose is not inconsistent with the purpose of the federal government in providing grants and contracts for basic research. It should be stated and restated lest both the

government's purpose and the purpose of the universities be obscured by the administrative practices of the agencies.

13. University administrations, certainly no less than federal agencies, can defeat the basic purpose of federal grants or contracts for project research by their policies; for instance, by imposition of unnecessary bureaucratic controls and red tape on principal investigators, or by neglect of the investigator's problems in dealing with federal agencies. We urge a more consistent policy of positive cooperation between university administrations and the faculties engaged in research under federal sponsorship. The specific organizational forms such a policy calls for depend upon local circumstances. One form, which we believe could be widely useful, is a joint committee or board, made up of representatives of the administration, the faculty engaged in research, and supporting staff.

Some of the responsibilities that should be assumed, or acted upon more consistently, by university administrations are as follows:

a. There should be a clear definition of the mutual responsibilities and authority of university administrations and principal investigators under grants and contracts.

b. There should be a review of research proposals by faculty personnel to ensure only that they are not inconsistent with the concept of the university as a community of scholars engaged in both education of youth and the advancement of knowledge.

c. There should be assistance to faculty personnel in the preparation of research proposals, to ensure that the wording of the proposals will not place undue restrictions on the scientific freedom of principal investigators.

d. Principal investigators should be educated in the responsibilities that they assume when using federal funds in support of research.

e. There should be an explanation to faculty personnel, primarily principal investigators, of the purposes for which overhead funds and institutional grants are being spent. Understanding of this will reduce rather widespread misunderstandings among faculties and assist in developing more harmonious relations between faculties and university administrations.

f. Principal investigators should be relieved of as much budgetary work as possible, kept informed of the status of and commitments under grants and contracts, alerted to the possibility of disallowance of certain expenditures, and in other ways apprised of essential fiscal requirements.

CONCERNING THE SCIENTIFIC COMMUNITY

14. We believe that understanding of the purpose of the federal support of basic research by the project grant/contract system is not sufficiently widespread in the scientific community. Grants and contracts are given as trusts to institutions for a purpose, which is substantially as described by the

principal investigator in his proposal. The investigator assumes a major responsibility in accepting federal funds and has an obligation to account for their proper use. Acceptance of a grant commits him to a conscientious effort to achieve its stated purpose; he acquires no other rights to the granted or contracted funds.

15. To make the project grant/contract system consistent with essential freedoms of scientific research, the substance of project proposals must be properly formulated. We have described (conclusion 4) the general form of proposals that should be acceptable to federal agencies and that should minimize the problem of overly restrictive interpretation of the purpose of a grant. We urge the scientific community to present proposals in accordance with the recommendations contained in conclusion number 4.

16. The quality and effectiveness of the project grant/contract system can be no better than the scientific community makes it, by conscientious and enlightened service on panels, study sections, and other advisory bodies and as consultants in the selection of the best research proposals. We urge the scientific community to see such service in this light and to give time willingly to it.

17. In concluding our findings, we want to remind that part of the total scientific community to which we address ourselves that they, being part of the university community, are part of a society of scholars; that they have an obligation to their society: to share in the education of youth as well as in advancing scientific knowledge.

The federal government, the universities, and the scientific community have entered into an enlightened partnership whose common purpose is the advancement of scientific knowledge and the upbringing of younger cadres to continue this task. This report is but a reminder of this central fact and an attempt to set out a few simple guidelines that should reduce some mutual irritations and help the partnership in its grand purpose of advancing the welfare of our nation and of all mankind.

Committee on Science and Public Policy

George B. Kistiakowsky, Harvard University, Chairman
Lawrence R. Blinks, Stanford University
H. W. Bode, Bell Telephone Laboratories
Frank Brink, Jr., The Rockefeller Institute
Melvin Calvin, University of California, Berkeley
Leo Goldberg, Harvard College Observatory
Frank L. Horsfall, Jr., Sloan-Kettering Institute for Cancer Research
A. L. Lehninger, The Johns Hopkins University

Donald B. Lindsley, University of California, Los Angeles
Saunders Mac Lane, University of Chicago
William W. Rubey, University of California, Los Angeles
Harry L. Shapiro, American Museum of Natural History
T. M. Sonneborn, Indiana University
Alvin M. Weinberg, Oak Ridge National Laboratory
Robert E. Green, National Academy of Sciences, Executive Secretary
A. Hunter Dupree, University of California, Berkeley, Consultant
Don K. Price, Harvard University, Consultant

The Committee wishes to acknowledge its great indebtedness to Professor Dupree and Dean Price for their valuable contributions as active participants in its deliberations and in the preparation of this report. It acknowledges also its appreciation of the financial support of this study by the Ford Foundation.

Federal Expenditures and the Quality of Education

HAROLD ORLANS

What, since World War II, has been the relation of federal expenditures to the quality of higher educational institutions, of instruction, and of research, and what changes, if any, should be made in the present pattern of expenditures?

Such large questions can hardly be answered simply or to everyone's satisfaction, and if I am so foolhardy as to answer them, it is not from a vain illusion that my answers are all correct (and, still less from an illusion that they are the only correct ones), but from a conviction that the questions are important. My conclusions are drawn mainly from a study of the effects of federal programs on departments of science, social science, and the humanities at 36 universities and colleges, undertaken by the Brookings Institution for the U.S. Office of Education (1). Better federal policies for higher education and research will come only from a continuing evaluation of present programs and a continuing effort to reconcile their actual effects, what we really want, and what is practicable.

FUNDS HIGHLY CONCENTRATED

With the decline of the broadly distributed expenditures for veterans education, federal funds during the past decade, devoted largely to scientific research, have been highly concentrated at a few of our strongest universities and institutes of technology. This is not to say that the correlation between research expenditures and the quality of scientists at particular institutions is necessarily high; still less, that the faculty of one physics department with ten times the research volume of another is ten times as good; too many transitory and historical factors of special government and faculty interest supervene to make for so simple a relationship. (For example, good as they are, I doubt that the scientists at Iowa State University would claim to be inherently superior to their colleagues at Harvard or Yale, but for a variety

Reprinted from *Science*, Vol. CXLII, No. 3600, December 27, 1963, pp. 1625–1629, with the permission of the author, the Brookings Institution, and the publisher. Dr. Harold Orlans is Senior Research Associate in Governmental Studies at the Brookings Institution in Washington, D.C. He recently published *The Effects of Federal Programs on Higher Education*, Washington: The Brookings Institution, 1962.

of reasons, going back to Frank Spedding's pioneering work in casting high-
purity uranium at Ames in the spring of 1942 and the subsequent estab- .
lishment on campus of a major atomic research center, Iowa State has
received more money from the Atomic Energy Commission than either of
those Ivy League schools.) But, overall, relying on the best professional
judgment of scientists in evaluating the merit of research proposals has
served admirably to maximize the strictly technical aspect and to minimize
the irreducible personal and political factors in research allocations.

Comparison of representative institutions that have a large volume of
federal research with those that have a small volume demonstrates this convincingly. Among the former, one will find a few flabby Goliaths whose
strength is attributable to their size rather than their temper, and among
the latter, some stalwart Davids. But, taken as a whole, the institutions with
a large volume of federal research are patently superior, in the quality of
their faculty and their students, on most available measures, including the
judgment of department chairmen and faculty at institutions with less
money to spend on research. Nor can it be claimed that their superiority
has been achieved simply because of federal money. Although that money
has not hurt, these schools were famous before the war and had a high level
of research, supported from private and state sources, long before the government entered upon the scene.

What, then, have been the educational effects of the large but concentrated federal spending for research and development, which ran well over
a billion dollars last year?

GOOD EFFECTS FAR OUTWEIGH BAD

As I later discuss some harmful effects, I want to start by stating as emphatically as I can that the good effects have far outweighed the bad. The present strength of our national scientific and technological enterprise has its
roots in the talent, knowledge, and ideas engendered at our great institutions of learning, and should federal aid to these institutions be curtailed
without compensation from other quarters, that enterprise would wane. Federal programs at universities have enormously enlarged our knowledge in
the basic and applied sciences; have fashioned and outmoded whole industries; have brought each of us great rewards (and 15 minutes' notice of
death) ; and have, as a by-product, raised the prestige, the influence, and the
income of scientists. What is wrong with the present pattern is not that it
bestows benefits upon certain institutions and most sciences but that these
benefits have not been shared adequately by important groups of institutions
and nonscientific disciplines, and that excessive concentration on research

has substantially reduced the return in ideas from each additional dollar and has had some harmful effects on education, even in the sciences.

One group of institutions neglected by federal programs has been the good liberal arts colleges. The best of these have students as able as those of any university and maintain a sense of community and a degree of personal contact between senior faculty and undergraduates which has been or is being lost at even the best universities. These colleges can facilitate precisely the kind of individual research and authorship needed as a corrective to the collective scholarship our free-enterprise society so strangely generates. For these and other reasons one can confidently advise many students in the humanities and social sciences to choose a good college over a good university; however, the science student will usually be better off at a university. The pace of scientific progress is so rapid that science instruction at colleges often lags far behind that at universities; government money has improved the equipment, enlarged the number, enhanced the status, and reduced the burdens of scientists at universities far more than at colleges. Indeed, while at universities the current teaching load of scientists is well below that of humanists, at colleges it is higher. Altogether, it is understandable that the shortage of faculty at liberal arts colleges is most acute in the sciences, and federal policies have surely contributed to the problem. A comparatively small investment in scientific research, facilities, fellowships, and education at good colleges should now yield greater dividends in scientists and scientific ideas than the same investment at our universities.

STATE UNIVERSITIES NEGLECTED

Another group of relatively neglected institutions is the great state universities. A few, such as Michigan, Illinois, Minnesota, and Wisconsin, have not done badly, while the University of California and the laboratories it operates at Berkeley, Livermore, and Los Alamos constitute an educational and scientific endeavor so vast that it can more readily be compared to that of a nation like Great Britain than to activities of other American institutions. But for that very reason, gross statistics on federal research funds at public universities can be misleading. In fact, the present rank order of federal research dollars at our 20 leading universities is not significantly correlated with the relative number of doctorates in science these universities award. This is another way of saying that state universities do not participate in these research programs to the extent that their preponderant importance in graduate science education would lead one to expect. This has long been recognized by the Association of State Universities and Land Grant Colleges, which has more than once proposed that some research funds be awarded on a quota system based upon student enrollment or degrees conferred in the sciences. The danger of the present situation is that most students will receive mass-produced, low-priced, and relatively low-quality science degrees at state-operated educational plants, high-quality education being reserved for a minority at a few favored institutions.

Although federal policies have aggravated some of the problems of state universities and liberal arts colleges, clearly the government cannot alone be blamed for, nor alone solve, these problems. State legislatures, state taxpayers, and local citizens bear an obvious responsibility. Thus, the American Association of University Professors' report on 1961–62 faculty salaries observes (2):

> *Whereas five private independent universities were in the highest [salary] category, no state university reached the very top level.*
>
> *But even this is not as serious as the fact that almost half of all public universities are in category D on a scale that ranges from AA to F. Only 3 percent of the independent institutions range so low. . . .*

There are some institutions where research grants remain unspent, and many more where they are not requested, because faculty members teaching 12 or 15 classroom hours a week cannot find time for anything but their classes, and additional staff members can simply not be recruited at dimestore wages. A wage paid monthly for 9 months in the year does not constitute a professional salary.

The main charge to be leveled against the government is not that it is responsible for the low quality and poor conditions at so many institutions but that, by overemphasizing scientific research, it has devaluated undergraduate teaching and has lowered the status of nonscientific fields and the quality of scientific research itself. In doing so, of course, the government has not acted alone as a foreign force; other powerful social and educational forces have been at work toward the same ends. But the government has been their willing mistress, and if the government and university science are now living in a state of sin, it is, despite occasional bickering, a contented state which two adults have entered upon willingly and which each is reluctant to leave.

UNDERGRADUATE TEACHING DEVALUED

Need it be argued that there is at present a devaluation of undergraduate teaching? A Brookings Institution survey of over 3000 faculty members showed that in colleges as well as universities, small and large, in the humanities and social sciences as well as the natural sciences, faculty members at every rank, regardless of how little time they devoted to undergraduate teaching, wished to reduce that time still further, although all groups wished to increase the time devoted to graduate instruction and especially to research (1, p. 316). The devaluation of undergraduate teaching that has accompanied the government-primed upsurge of graduate education and research has produced a virtual cleavage in the faculties of larger universities: a fifth of the faculty now teaches only undergraduates, while another fifth teaches only graduate students.

The cleavage between university faculty members and students is more severe. Over half of university scientists know the names of few or no seniors majoring in their department, while a fifth do not even know the names of advanced graduate students. Over half of university faculty members have never had a lower-classman in their homes. How many of our foremost scientists and scholars would speak today as William Osler did in 1892 (3), of his "deep autumnal yearning" for teaching, "not unnatural in a man the best years of whose life have been passed with undergraduate students, and who has had temporarily to content himself with the dry husks of graduate teaching"?

Undoubtedly the sheer numbers of students and faculty and the increase in the size of classes have contributed more to the depersonalization of higher education than government action has. But the government has abetted the process by the lures it extends to research workers and the reduction in teaching hours it has bought for so many faculty members. (One is reminded of the exemption from military service which can be bought in some armies for a fee.) I would not want to be caught telling a group of university faculty that a further reduction in their teaching hours can be bad, although it is evident that *college* faculty members are in greater need of reduced hours, and I do not see how the average of six classroom hours a week for science faculty of all ranks in the spring of 1961 at 12 major universities (it was 4 to 5 hours at three institutions) can be held excessive. But, clearly, graduate students and not undergraduates are the main individual beneficiaries of all the extra time faculty members now devote to research. Admittedly, some people consider the view that meaningful personal contact between teacher and student plays *some* part in the educational process to be not only uneconomic but antiquated. Some people have a wonderful ability to explain why what is, is good. They will doubtless be delighted when higher education is completely taped and programmed audiovisually, and when diplomas, untouched by human hand, are delivered automatically upon receipt of the requisite responses and fees, as divorces are delivered by machine in Reno, 6 weeks after deposit of the requisite silver dollars.

Things have come to such a pass at some of our larger schools that seniors may not know faculty members well enough to give the references required on applying for a graduate fellowship, and special counselors have been designated to talk to them long enough to arrange for this. Eminent professors devote so little time to teaching (or should I say lecturing), and that time is arranged so much to their convenience (their other time being spent more profitably at home, in the laboratory, in attending to private business ventures, or in Washington), that their own graduate students often have considerable difficulty getting to see them. The relation of the government to the university scientists is disturbingly like that of the farmer to the goose that laid the golden eggs.

In one particular the government's responsibility for lowering the quality of instruction is evident. Federal agencies have provided so many of the best graduate science students with fellowships and research assistant-ships that only the poorer students are content to serve as teaching assistants in undergraduate laboratory sections, and it is widely conceded that laboratory instruction has, therefore, either definitely suffered or, at best, not improved as much as laboratory equipment and graduate science faculties have.

THE HUMANIST IS NOT BEATEN

The position of the humanist today recalls that of the emancipated Negro on a good plantation. If he works hard, he is fairly well housed and fed, and not beaten; and while this is hardly enough to evoke a sense of elation, where else can he go? Unlike the scientist who can find interesting and well-paid scientific work in government or in industry, if he is displeased with his university salary of $15,000 or $20,000, the humanist must either remain on the academic plantation or change his profession. Since his dean is aware of this situation, his bargaining power is considerably reduced. Now, the government is not responsible for the American people's dearth of history and their ignorance of the little they have; for the aversion the children of immigrants have shown for their parents' language (be it Germanic, Romance, Slavic, or English) and their inability to relearn it in school; or for the constitutional proscription of a peerage and for a busy, practical people's lack of interest in classical learning and other cultural accoutrements of landed gentry and monastic scholars. But the government is in good part responsible for the prosperity of the academic scientist, and, quite obliviously and unintentionally of course, the humanist's nose has been rubbed in the scientist's success to their mutual discomfiture.

Not only is the scientist younger than the humanist (3 to 5 years younger at each rank, at major universities), because the government has sped him through graduate school, and not only does he teach less (2 hours less on an average), because the government pays him not to teach, but he is paid more for teaching less (at 43 of 56 universities for which information was available, the salary of the philosophy department chairman was less last year than that of the physics department chairman) (4). He is paid by the government, besides, for his summers, and often for his assistants, his secretary, his equipment, his publications, his travel—for virtually everything but his entrance into heaven, and that, I suppose, will ultimately become an allowable part of overhead.

One charge commonly leveled against the government is not, I think (or not yet) warranted: that it has induced the best students to go into the sciences, leaving only the second-best for the humanities and social sciences (this, it is often added, is a reason for the turgidity of these fields). This charge suggests, on the one hand, a certain naive conceit on the part of scientists (*obviously* they are brighter than other people, including, presumably, their nonscientific parents and children) and, on the other hand, a low opinion of our brightest youth—the view that their careers are determined not by their heart but by their purse.

It is a charge which the available information on student ability by field simply does not substantiate. The data show the mean I.Q. of recent Ph.D.'s in the humanities and social sciences to be identical with that of the Ph.D.'s in the natural sciences (5). What has probably been misleading is the very high ability of graduate students and Ph.D.'s in physics and mathematics. One overlooks two points in jumping from this observation to the conclusion that the government is diverting talent to the sciences: (i) students of physics and mathematics were as bright before the war (that is, before the government paid their way through graduate school) as they are now; and (ii) the ability of students in certain populous sciences heavily financed by the government (most notably, the biological sciences) is well below par for the natural sciences, social sciences, and humanities. Therefore, we must reject the thesis that the government has bought for science an undue proportion of our best brains; its vast expenditures have demonstrably failed even to increase the proportion of either bachelor or doctoral degrees awarded in the natural sciences over the last two or three decades. It is the social and not the natural sciences that have gained from the relative decline in the number of degrees awarded in the humanities during this period.

"COMPETENCE" REPLACES MERIT

The final, and in some ways most damaging, charge to be brought against the government is that excessive appropriations are now diluting the quality of research and that mediocrity (or, in the jargon of Washington, "competence") is replacing merit as the standard of support. "Competence" as a standard may in fairness be contrasted with the standard advanced by the Seaborg panel of the President's Science Advisory Committee (6): "In the advancement of science the best is vastly more important than the next best. Mediocre research is generally worse than useless." With some effort, authority can still be arrayed on both sides of this charge, but negative observations about a decline in the quality of government-sponsored research have increased and, I believe, now decidedly outweigh claims that quality has improved. Among recent public critics of the quality of much government-sponsored work in physics may be listed Hans Bethe, Polykarp Kusch, Melvin Schwartz, Roman Smoluchowski, and Alvin Weinberg (7, 8); among critics of the quality of biological and medical research are Max Finland, Basil O'Connor, Herbert Ratner, John Russell, and Paul Weiss, not to mention the House Committee on Government Operations, which observed that between 1956 and 1960 the proportion of National Institutes of Health research grants rated by reviewers in the "highest quality" class fell from 40 to 24 percent (9, 10).

Let me quote two of these criticisms. Alvin Weinberg, director of the Oak Ridge National Laboratory, remarks (8):

> ... our operating budget for science has increased since 1950 by a factor of almost 5, whereas the number of Ph.D.'s in science and engineering has increased by only a factor of 2.... I know of no evidence to show that our people are smarter now than they were a decade ago; we merely heap more money on them, and therefore we use each dollar less efficiently.

And Paul Weiss of the Rockefeller Institute says (10):

> ... biological experimentation, at the height of success, is beginning to drift ... into habits that threaten to place bulk ahead of brains, and routine exercises ahead of thought.... [As] research has grown in volume it also has grown softer by loss of self-restraint, lowered selectivity, blurring of research targets.

Much work of the highest quality is also, of course, being done and, in important fields of science, greatly expanding, although we are too close to judge the long-run trend and the evidence is sometimes contradictory. Thus, Gerald Holton tells us (see 11) that:

> ... throughout history, transforming ideas, as well as great ideas only one magnitude less high, have not appeared in science at a rate equal to a fraction of the present rate.

On the other hand, Hans Bethe declares (*12*) that:

> *the pace of basic discoveries in physics was far greater in the first*
> *thirty years of this century than it has been in the second thirty*
> *years. . . . Many very important details . . . have been discovered in*
> *this second period, but it is all a lot of detail, important but*
> *nothing you cannot summarize in one or two sentences.*

The appearance of epochal thinkers like Newton and Einstein cannot
be ordained by any program, government or private, because such men
represent a unique conjunction of ungovernable talent, opportunity, and
possibility. Perhaps the likelihood that Einsteins will arise is greater as enlightened efforts are made to recognize and encourage them; and perhaps
not. The outcome may depend more on the nature of the problem, of our
society, and of our luck than on the extent of our effort.

Below the pinnacle, it seems clear, there has been an enormous expansion of both high-quality and pedestrian work, and the absolute volume of
both is now so great that it is unrewarding to ask (even if it were possible
to get an accurate answer) just how the relative proportion today compares
with that in the 1930's, in Colonial times, or in ancient Greece. The important question is: Is it really necessary or desirable to sustain so much pedestrian work in order to bring forth the excellent and the good?

The edifice of science, some say, is built brick by brick, and one can
never tell in advance the value a humdrum fact may have; therefore, all
"competent" science should be supported. This argument is, to my mind,
unacceptable as a basis for public policy, for, in principle, it would justify
any and every careful inquiry, could readily result in absorption of the gross
national product, and equates science with the ditty bag of an idiot.

DESIRABLE SHIFTS IN EXPENDITURES

One need not deny that *some* good may occasionally come from the mounting public investment in second-rate scientific research conducted by second-
rate scientists at both first- and second-rate institutions to ask, Is this really
the wisest investment that can be made of these large sums? The answer, I
think, is "No," and *some* shift in emphasis at the present level of expenditure (and certainly at any higher future level) is in order, away from scientific research and toward scientific education, toward the humanities and
neglected sectors of the social sciences, and toward the good colleges.

Over two-thirds of university scientists themselves agreed, in the Brookings survey, that some redistribution of present funds was desirable to "give
the humanities somewhat more and the sciences somewhat less, but still the

major portion." However, I must in all honesty report that a majority of university scientists reject—or rejected, 2 years ago—my view that federal expenditures should be shifted somewhat toward teaching. Roughly 60 percent of scientists at universities with a large volume of federal research then felt that "the present concentration on research should continue," although scientists at universities with a smaller volume of research were squarely divided between this position and the view that "Federal funds should be more evenly balanced between research and teaching" (*1*, pp. 66, 105).

The perceptible lowering of standards in federal research programs has resulted, in part, from the conscious use of these programs by administrators, scientists, and the Congress as a politically convenient means to aid higher education. We all know the difficulties sectarian interests in education and the Congress have experienced in trying to agree upon desirable legislation. So long as these interests remain unresolved and the nation does not establish satisfactory policies to meet directly our urgent educational needs, so long are we likely to witness efforts to meet these needs indirectly.

It is easier for an observer to advocate a pure course of action than for a congressman, a university president, or a federal administrator or his scientific advisers to pursue such a course under heavy political pressures. I certainly cannot subscribe to the opinion, all too prevalent in some academic circles (the more uninformed the circle, the more prevalent the opinion), that these men are either villians or fools. In my experience they are generally able, well-intentioned, and politically sophisticated.

Nevertheless, I believe they have been mistaken, and that they risk their long-term interests in pursuit of immediate gain. I would, in particular, charge those scientists who review research proposals and help set prevailing research standards with (for the best of motives) failing to meet their professional obligation to maintain high quality in federal research grants. Nothing would be more effective toward this end than an increased rate of rejection in certain federal programs, accompanied, if necessary (and I believe it would be necessary, initially, in some programs), by the return of unexpended funds to the treasury.

Five years ago a distinguished committee of the National Science Board, composed mainly of presidents of leading private and public universities, enunciated the following as the first principle for federally sponsored research (*13*):

> *Problems of Government-university relationships in the Federal support of research at colleges and universities should be explicitly and completely dissociated from the budgetary needs and crises of the institutions and from the general issue of Federal aid to higher education. In the consideration and administration of*

these relationships there should be no implication that Federal
sponsorship of research is a convenient subterfuge for Federal aid
to institutions of higher learning.

The more this principle is breached, the more apparent will become its merit in directing us toward two vital but separate national goals: the maintenance and improvement of quality in scientific research and the maintenance and improvement of quality in higher education. To merge these goals out of political expediency is to endanger both.

SUMMARY

The great expansion of federal scientific research expenditures and their concentration at a few leading universities and institutes of technology has brought enormous benefits to higher education, science, and the nation. It has also contributed to a devaluation of undergraduate teaching and to an expansion of mediocre research. Some reorientation of expenditures toward state universities, liberal arts colleges, science education, and the humanities, and a reaffirmation of standards of quality rather than of mere competence in research, are needed.

REFERENCES AND NOTES

1. H. Orlans, *The Effects of Federal Programs on Higher Education* (Brookings Institution, Washington, D.C., 1962).

2. New York *Times* (29 Apr. 1962), sec. 4, p. 9.

3. From an address at the University of Minnesota cited by Harvey Cushing in *The Life of Sir William Osler* (Clarendon, Oxford, England, 1925), vol. 1, p. 367.

4. See J. H. Comroe, Jr., Ed., *Research and Medical Education* (Assoc. of American Medical Colleges, Evanston, Ill., 1962), pp. 181–82.

5. See L. R. Harmon, *Science* 133, 679 (1961).

6. *Scientific Progress, the Universities and the Federal Government* (President's Science Advisory Committee, Washington, D.C., 1960), p. 14.

7. See *Science, An Interview by Donald McDonald with Hans Bethe* (Center for the Study of Democratic Institutions, Santa Barbara, Calif., 1962), p. 25; P. Kusch, quoted in *Current* (July 1962), p. 52; M. Schwartz, *Am. Behavioral Scientist* **1962**, 35 (Dec. 1962); R. Smoluchowski, in *Proceedings of a Conference on Academic and Industrial Basic Research* (National Science Foundation, Washington, D.C., 1961), p. 38.

8. A. M. Weinberg, *Science* 136, 27 (1962).

9. See M. Finland, quoted in *Saturday Review of Literature* **1960**, 38 (1 Oct. 1960); B. O'Connor, "Science and government: the perilous partnership," address to the 3rd International Symposium on Immunopathology, LaJolla, Calif., 1963; H. Ratner, *Medicine* (Center for the Study of Democratic Institutions, Santa Barbara, Calif., 1962), p. 11; J. Russell, in *Research and Medical Edu-*

cation, J. H. Comroe, Jr., Ed. (Association of American Medical Colleges, Evanston, Ill., 1962), pp. 101–04; *Health Research and Training* (Second Report by the House Committee on Government Operations, Washington, D.C., 1961), p. 28.

10. P. Weiss, *Science* **136**, 468 (1962).
11. G. Holton, *Daedalus* **91**, 371 (Spring 1962).
12. *Science, An Interview by Donald McDonald with Hans Bethe* (Center for the Study of Democratic Institutions, Santa Barbara, Calif., 1962), pp. 20–21.
13. *Government-University Relationships in Federally Sponsored Scientific Research and Development* (National Science Foundation, Washington, D.C., 1958), p. 21.

PART VI

Prologue to the Future

The changes within science as well as the changing interrelationships of science and government will inevitably lead to changing emphases within science and within societies. Some of these problems can already be anticipated on the basis of present developments. It is quite clear, for example, that science and technology will be much more closely linked to the economic development, the general welfare, and the goals and priorities of the society in general. Within the institution of science itself, it is quite likely that the present trend toward large-scale organizations will continue. Many more of these organizations are likely to be international in scope. At the same time, there is likely to be little diminution in the current concern to protect and preserve a solid role for the individual scientist who prefers, and perhaps needs, to work alone and not in a large organization. Science and technology will undoubtedly play a significantly increasing role in the development of the poorer and new nations of the world.

Science is now without question the business and the proper concern not only of the scientists but of the citizens of all nations. Science can no longer be left on a pedestal or swept under the rug to be ignored or forgotten. Public support for science must be accompanied by greater and deeper understanding of the nature of science and its implications. Public understanding of at least some of the fundamental ideas of science is both necessary and desirable. The technical complexities of most subspecialties will be beyond most of us, as indeed they are beyond most scientists not in the same or closely allied subspecialties. Equally important are the necessity and desirability for greater understanding, by laymen and scientists alike, of the social arrangements governing the conduct of science. It is not enough to understand the Second Law of Thermodynamics, as C. P. Snow once suggested. One must also understand something about the social conditions and the social arrangements which foster the scientific creativity involved in producing great as well as ordinary science.

In the first selection, Alexander King, a pioneer in seeking and developing national and international science policy machinery, presents an analysis of the major trends in the development of research and scientific education in Europe. Despite the many rapid changes in science in recent years, much of its organization is still based on established traditions and outmoded conditions which were true of scientific research at least fifty years ago. But as the role of science in society becomes increasingly important, and is so recognized, changes in its organization can be expected. European patterns have been shaped by a strong tradition of academic freedom, the academies of science, central government control of education and research facilities, and a high degree of political and economic fractionation. The high cost of science and the high level of industrialization of most of the European nations coupled with the small political unit size of these nations made some form of regional and international cooperation essential. A primary need today is the development of policies which will guide both internal scientific development and international cooperative ventures.

As King pointed out in passing, science now has, and will continue to have, a very important role in the development of the new nations. In the next essay, Stevan Dedijer discusses the question of how to bring the "pre-research" cultures and societies into the modern age of science and technology. Dedijer suggests that the social science approach be used to help accomplish this goal. He distinguishes three stages in the scientific revolution of a nation, the first being intellectual recognition of its importance, the second being economic capacity to carry on research, and, finally, the political will and capability to organize and coordinate such an effort. The developing countries, no less than the older and more industrialized nations, must have an explicit research policy.

In a paper on a related theme, P. M. S. Blackett discusses the role of science in aiding the underdeveloped countries. It is not enough, in his view, to provide the developing nations with foreign aid; there must be effective machinery to absorb this aid and, even more important, a modern educational system. The first task for such new nations is to learn to *apply* existing scientific knowledge rather than try to develop their own new knowledge in competition with the scientifically established nations. Three conditions are necessary: there must be the determination to bring about the change; financial resources must be adequate; and there must be adequately trained personnel. Blackett suggests that perhaps the British universities (this was written primarily although not exclusively for a British audience) can and should play a part in helping to provide trained personnel by sending professionals to work in these nations.

While the more scientifically advanced countries have an important role to play in helping the newer countries to develop their own scientific establishments, the search for new ideas and new organizational methods to cope with the changing character of science must continue everywhere. One trend, which has already been noted in several of the previous papers, is toward the establishment of international institutes. While the need seems to be obvious, and the potential return great, the establishment of international institutes is still no easy matter in the world of today. Apparently, there are still many political and social obstacles to be overcome before such international understakings become more thoroughly acceptable. The international institute discussed in the next selection, which many scientists apparently felt was an exciting and worthwhile proposal, remains an unfulfilled idea at this writing. The proposal is included here not so much to remind us of the apparent failure of its implementation, but rather because of the new ideas presented. Certainly the barriers to innovations in the organization of scientific research and training are no less important than are the many other kinds of barriers to innovation in other fields of human endeavor.

In this selection James Killian outlines some of the major reasons for considering the establishment of an international institute of science and technology. In doing so he raises a number of issues which are likely to become increasingly important in the years ahead. Among these are: the possibility of having such an institute grant a degree which would be international in status and be recognized by the member nations; the explicit combination of science and technology; the concentration on doctoral and postdoctoral students; the combination of the research institute idea with the idea of a center for advanced studies; and, finally, the breaking down of traditional university departmental patterns of organization. Certainly in the foreseeable future, and perhaps even beyond that, many of these issues raised by Dr. Killian are likely to be at the forefront of attention of those interested in the evolving organization of scientific research.

Yet another problem likely to become increasingly important to both the developed and the less developed nations of the world is that which concerns the relationship between the results of science and economic growth. Despite the vast progress which has been made, the use of science for the benefit of society is still not very well understood. As the next selection by J. Herbert Hollomon argues rather convincingly, a nation's research and development effort does not inevitably, as it is sometimes claimed, lead to national prosperity. Hollomon notes that "modern myth says that science, through magic, converts itself into useful products of society." In this paper Hollomon suggests a number of concrete mechanisms which might replace our faith in magic and might provide greater assurance that science can be converted into useful products for the society. He suggests for example that we might try to think along the same lines as the land-grant college and extension service system with a view to applying these lines to industry. He cautions us against the danger of overreacting against the practical and pragmatic in our desire to encourage vitally necessary work in basic research.

Dr. Hollomon's paper is concerned primarily with making more explicit and improving the linkages between science and economic benefit for the society. Implicit in this paper is a general problem much more fundamental in nature. This problem might be summed up simply as: Science for what? The impact of science is likely to be greater, and to be more explicit than it has ever been before. This raises the question for all of us: What do we really want? The emphasis in one society can be on better gadgets and higher tail fins on more glamorous cars, or it can be on more truly *useful* products and services. For the first time in human history, probably, it may become possible to choose among alternative definitions of the good life rather than among various alternatives of subsistence and survival. These are some of the questions to which Dr. Seaborg addresses himself in the next selection. As he notes in these excerpts from his Harrelson lecture: "By the most conservative estimates, profound social and economic changes are in progress through the impact of science." It is of considerable interest and concern that all too few social scientists are involved in speculating about the kind of world in which we shall be living within the coming century.

While many of us tend to think of the "impact of science" as good or bad (the bomb is bad, curing a disease is good) the next paper by Rene J. Dubos illustrates forcefully the difficulties in trying to make such simple assessments. It also indicates the hard choices which must be faced as we continue to progress (or what we think is progress) especially in the field of medical research. For example, the problems of human ecology raise questions about whether new knowledge of disease will ease the burden of medical care in the future or whether new problems of disease will arise endlessly and require ever increasing scientific and social efforts. In Dubos' view, it will "continue to take all the running we can do to remain at the same place." Medical ethics may have to be reconsidered perhaps even in the harsh light of economics as well as other considerations. This may be the case, for example, in the necessity to decide whether *very expensive* procedures are truly worth while and for whom. Dubos concludes that sociological aspects of medicine may become far more important as time goes on. Dubos is clearly not suggesting, as some antiscience groups sometimes do, that scientific progress is destroying the "good old days." He is suggesting that scientific progress in medical research has brought with it, and will continue to bring with it, many serious and often unanticipated problems. Our recent experiences with pesticides are but one of many such examples.

In the remaining selections included here we return to the problems and impending changes in the internal organization of science and in the relations of science and scientists to society. Alvin Weinberg, in the next selection, raises three main questions about new developments within science: (1) Is big science ruining science? (2) Is big science ruining us [the society] financially? (3) Where is big science taking us?

Weinberg contends that there certainly is a danger of big science ruining science. This would be especially true if it were permitted to invade the universities which would then be diverted from their primary purposes. It is also true to the extent that scientists are now spending money instead of thought and are in danger of becoming fat and lazy especially in certain areas. In answer to his second question, Weinberg agrees with most other observers that the current rate of expansion cannot continue. The leveling off of the support for science will face us with hard choices. As for the direction in which science is moving, Weinberg would prefer a shift away from the more glamorous (and usually expensive) areas of concentration into those bearing more immediately on human welfare.

In a related paper Norman Storer calls attention to still other important dangers in the changing nature of science. In particular he is concerned with the effects of these changes on the traditional value system of science and on the effects it will have on professional recognition. In Storer's view professional recognition is being replaced by the rewards of the society at large including money and social prestige. As this happens, the old institutional reward system of science is breaking down. Our notions of basic research are also becoming adulterated, and Storer expects that applied research will eventually dominate science although this will be done under the guise of supporting and encouraging basic work. In a word, the fundamental character of science as a social system is undergoing considerable change. Big science tends to lead toward increased stratification of scientists, an oligarchic elite leadership, and a greater splintering of areas of specialization. Science will become much more like a federation than the old-fashioned community. To foster basic research in the future it will be necessary to increase the number of career investigatorships and of unrestricted grants to universities and to encourage generalists within science.

In the final selection on the interrelations of science and society, Leland Haworth stresses the importance of scientists assuming responsibility for disseminating and interpreting science to the government in particular and to the layman in general. In one of his first public addresses since assuming the office of Director of the National Science Foundation, Haworth outlines the broad objectives of the federal government with respect to science and technology. The importance of basic research as in intellectual and cultural value must be reaffirmed in addition to its importance for technological advance and for our educational system generally. The complete political process involves the interrelationship of government and science which means that there must be much more open communication between scientists, laymen, and the government to preserve our democratic institutions.

Science and Technology in the New Europe

ALEXANDER KING

INTRODUCTION

The new measures of economic cooperation and integration in Europe and the political consequences inherent in them are closely tied to the explosive development of science and technology of the past few decades. Contemporary industry, based on a complex technology derived in turn from scientific research, can operate only through large units of plant and organization and requires resources of research and development which, unless above a specific threshold value, are uncompetitive on a world scale. In other words, modern technology can be productive only in terms of large markets which an economically and politically fractionated continent is incapable of supplying. Measures of economic harmonization and integration are thus inevitably demanded by a highly developed and rapidly growing technology.

Equally, however, the closer political and economic ties which are now being created between neighboring countries provide conditions propitious for accelerated scientific growth, and it is inevitable that the new economic arrangements in Europe will directly influence the extent and vigor of scientific effort in the countries concerned in much the same ways as the size, political unity and economic strength first of the United States and later of the Soviet Union have produced massive research and development.

For such a development, the European countries possess at the outset an enormous asset in their scientific tradition. The natural sciences have in fact their origin in western Europe, and until after World War II by far the greatest proportion of significant scientific discovery came from European laboratories. The argument behind "Science, the Endless Frontier," which Vannevar Bush submitted to the President in 1945, was, in fact, that the United States had until then relied too much on the scientific product of western Europe and had need therefore to make a relatively much greater effort in fundamental scientific research.

In Europe the industrial revolution was caused by the same spirit of

Reprinted from *Daedalus, Journal of the American Academy of Arts and Sciences,* Winter 1964, Vol. XCIII, No. 1, pp. 434–458, with permission of the author and the publisher. Dr. Alexander King is Director for Scientific Affairs of O.E.C.D. (Organization for Economic Cooperation and Development) in Paris.

inquiry which marked the beginning of contemporary science. This approach, based on the experimental method, was indeed a delayed flowering of the Renaissance and had a strong flavor of universalism in it. Yet, in reality, early science was able to contribute little to the industrial revolution, which depended essentially on empirical invention; and during the nineteenth century science and manufacturing technology grew further and further apart until the natural sciences had accumulated a substance of fact and principle sufficient to found the science-based industries of the present century. During much of this period European science, despite its strength and its glory, often tended to be somewhat remote from everyday life and from practical application, while on the other hand European industry as a consequence of tradition and of its very success was often less ready to incorporate new scientific ideas. This situation, in spite of many notable exceptions, persisted until World War II; in some countries industry was much less competent than that of the United States in the development phase of innovation typified by the engineering prototype and the chemical pilot plant. This deficiency, contrasted to American mass production techniques, was undoubtedly encouraged not only by the smaller domestic markets of the various European countries, but also by the prolonged success of traditional European products on the world market, a success which appeared to make innovation unnecessary.

This phase of industrial history is past. Contemporary European industry, with its prospects of larger "domestic" markets and its new managerial consciousness, is well prepared for a full exploitation of technology. Furthermore, European industry is open to change to an extent unthinkable during the last century and a half. The coming into existence of the Common Market has necessitated the abandonment of many long-held ideas and has brought about a willingness on the part of managements, workers and the public at least to consider new concepts, new approaches, new methods—a change perhaps more significant for the future than all the immediate mercantile consequences of economic integration. In science as in industry, extensive changes are taking place, through the building of greater research resources, government encouragement and a rapid expansion of universities that reflects not only the increasing levels of education needed by the economy but greatly enhanced social demands.

The extent, organization and objectives of science in Europe are thus moving very quickly as a result of the particular political and economic development on that continent. They are perhaps even more influenced, however, by the inherent changes in the nature of science itself as it develops throughout the world. It is this double influence which is bringing about the fundamental changes in European research and scientific education today.

To understand the evolving scientific scene in Europe, it is necessary to examine these world trends and then to consider them in terms of the European environment.

I. WORLD TRENDS IN THE POSITION AND FUNCTIONING OF SCIENCE

The great extension of research activity of the last few decades, its evident and direct importance for economic advancement and defense, its prestige value and its high costs, have completely changed the position of science and of the scientist in national and international life. Yet the organizations of science, while gradually modifying to meet the new circumstances, are in most countries largely based on long established tradition suited to conditions of scientific research of fifty years ago, and on institutional models long since outmoded. In order to understand how these institutions are evolving, it is necessary to enumerate some of the circumstances and trends in scientific work today which render such development necessary.

A public image of science has emerged as a power compounded of good and evil. There is general comprehension of its role in both war and peace which has given rise to widely different and even contradictory attitudes. Science, the creator of the hydrogen bomb, intercontinental missiles and potential space weapons, has naturally enough produced a violent popular revulsion against the misuses of discovery. Yet there is widespread recognition of its importance for human well-being and of its decisive role for the future of the race. It is unfortunate that it has been the more dramatic developments of technology, with their potentialities for both destruction and human welfare, that have raised the prestige value of science in the eyes of the public and of its governments, rather than the multitude of less dramatic but in the aggregate more solidly useful contributions to national and individual life.

The political prestige as well as the obvious economic and defense value of science and technology make it increasingly difficult for the scientist to work quietly in the corner of his laboratory without excessive interest being focused on his actions by governments and industrialists. Indeed the large funds which he requires for his experiments have in many cases produced cracks in the ivory tower; many individual scientists have shown little reticence in commenting on the political consequences of their work. This situation is but another example of the difficult balance of privilege and responsibility which will have to be established through good sense and understanding on both sides if circumstances propitious to the maintenance of scientific creation are to be preserved with long-term advantage to those who enjoy its fruits.

Equally important is the influence on science of economic pressure for improved technology. The arising of the science-based industries has already changed the pattern of the economy and of trade quite brutally and has made accessible new materials, drugs, equipment and devices of all kinds which have altered the daily lives of men and women throughout the world. Meanwhile, industry generally is becoming technologically much more complex, highly capital-intensive, requiring large units of production for economic operation and large research efforts to ensure the future; the gap between discovery in the laboratory and application in production is rapidly diminishing.

This increasing technological complexity throws a great burden on management and necessitates the presence of scientific and engineering skills in the board room as well as in the production shop. Industry is in fact entering a new phase of development which succeeds the earlier stages, first of invention, and later of application of the physical sciences, for innovation is now determined not only by discoveries in the laboratory but also by a complex of economic and sociological considerations. In many aspects of automation, for example, not only is basic scientific discovery sufficient for considerable practical advance, but opportunity for technological development is equally ripe. Increasingly in the future, social and economic factors are likely to be equally important with new science as determinants of change, and much development of research in the social sciences will be necessary if the prerequisites of innovation are to be understood and its social consequences intelligently allowed for.

Increasing recognition of the value of science for industry will tend toward the acceptance of research expenditure as a normal company investment requiring as careful assessment of possibilities, selection between alternatives and sound management as any other investment item. It will also have an increasing influence in Europe, as in the United States, on demands for supporting fundamental research.

Science has potentially as great contributions to make to the developing as to the underdeveloped areas of the world. Problems of raising living standards in the underdeveloped regions of the world are essentially those of making possible greatly increased rates of technological innovation, whether these may take the form of a simple improvement such as the replacement of the wooden plow by a steel instrument or the introduction of a degree of industrialization. Scientific discovery has the greatest importance for such areas through agricultural improvement, the conquest of disease and the availability of new forms of energy. As in industrialized societies, more primitive conditions still call for a balance of technological, economic and social forces for effective change, and transfer of technology from advanced to subsistence economies demands much more than conventional technical assistance. Science can and will provide an impulse to rapid development in these areas, and this development is likely to require the skills of a quite considerable proportion of the scientific and engineering manpower of the donor nations in the next few decades. It becomes increasingly more clear, however, that such help can be effective only when it is conceived in terms of integrated economic development, the growth of societies, the evolution of permanent local institutions and, above all, a coherent and balanced educational plan.

Help in development will become an increasingly important political necessity and will require much more than conventional financial and technical aid. Real progress from the subsistence level can be achieved only through industrialization, which the advanced countries will have to encourage without reserve. This will mean a change in the pattern of their own industries away from the traditional; and the simpler manufacturers will have to encourage the production of complex products of high added value in skills and research.

The amount of scientific research undertaken is increasing very rapidly not only in the highly industrialized areas but throughout the world, so that there is likely to be much less dominance in the future by the scientific achievement of any one region. Nevertheless, areas of high industrialization and high per capita income, such as Europe, are well favored for the still further extension of their scientific resources, particularly if these are developed with a sensible balance of effort in the context of a deliberate national policy.

Not only is the total amount of research increasing, but the cost per unit of research is becoming very high, owing to the need for special instruments and equipment, especially in fundamental research fields such as high energy physics and radio-astronomy. In an increasing number of cases, including those just mentioned and still more for space research, fundamental research relies on the development of highly complex and costly technologies which may not have any direct utility for the economy, thus reversing the normal chain of events in which fundamental scientific discovery precedes applied research, which in turn leads through technological development to production. In some fields, the demand for expensive equipment is already excluding the smaller political units by economic limitations from participation altogether, except where means for international cooperation and cost sharing are available. This difficulty will become increasingly serious until certain activities become possible only in terms of total world effort— and even then the limits are in sight.

Fashions in science are as dominant as in other realms of activity and may, through prestige considerations, distort the balance of scientific advance to the extent that some countries can neglect the less glamorous subjects and give insufficient attention to subjects on which national well-being depends. It is most unfortunate that excesses of scientific fashion should be encouraged by the highly science-based countries with regard to the development of new nations to which such luxuries, although even less easy to afford, are tempting for reasons of international status.

There are profound changes in research work itself. It is widely recognized that the breakthrough discoveries of fundamental science are due to a very few men of scientific genius whose creative ability can never be replaced by regiments of more pedestrian workers, however well trained and competent they may be. It is realized as important by all political systems that such pioneers of the future must be provided with facilities to work in the directions chosen by their genius and given conditions which preserve their creativity. Rapid advances of knowledge have, however, greatly encouraged specialization, so that few universities can longer pretend to universality in their teaching. Furthermore, progress in many of the new fields of discovery lies on borderlines between different sciences and can be successfully assured only by teams of scientists from different disciplines. Conditions of scientific work are changing in many other ways: for example, in activities which require very expensive equipment, their technology will necessitate an understanding of the basic engineering problems posed by research needs, and the research leader will have to work in harmony with those who develop and maintain his equipment. In such cases too the approach to a scientific problem can often not be easily modified once the work has begun, because of the extremely heavy capitalization necessitated by the scientist's cerebration. We know very little as yet as to the influence of such change on the emergence and maintenance of the creative research worker.

II. THE INSTITUTIONS OF SCIENCE

While it is generally agreed in Europe, as in the United States, that the university provides the best environment for fundamental research, and that applied research for industry is most effectively carried out by the individual enterprises, great differences exist nevertheless between the patterns of institutional organization which have developed in different countries. These differences result from factors of history and environment, or they have a political origin.

Among features of the European scene which have helped to shape the nature of European scientific organization are the long tradition of academic freedom and status derived without a break from medieval learning; the great influence of academies and learned societies which help to maintain and extend this tradition and to enhance the status of fundamental research; the existence of massive concentrations of industrialization, often all too inbred; the strong and sometimes centralized authority of government frequently determining educational policy in detail and operating its own research facilities; and above all the high degree of political and economic fractionation which has persisted until now. These circumstances explain many features of the European institutions; a few of them will be subject of brief comment.

During the earlier phases of scientific history, the individual scholar, the research worker and indeed the university were largely supported by rich or noble patrons. The social changes which followed the industrial revolution gradually altered this system, although the emergence of large foundations financed by the fortunes of rich and successful industrialists is to some degree an extension of the individual patronage of earlier centuries. Until recently, however, foundations have not had as important a role in Europe as in the United States, although since the war the Nuffield Foundation in the United Kingdom and the Gulbenkian Foundation located in Portugal have made their mark, while the new Volkswagen Foundation in Germany may well be important for scientific development. The great increase in expenditure on science has taken it quite beyond all reliance on private patronage. There is indeed no alternative to major financing of science by governments and by industry. The very term "patronage" disappears, of course, as soon as these expenditures are regarded as investments, and the concept must be replaced by considerations of enlightened self-interest. In education too, with increasing costs, inflation and rapid expansion, university endowments are grossly insufficient and have had to be augmented massively with government funds.

In Europe therefore research and scientific education have become recognized as aspects of national investment. Already during the first decade of this century, governments began to appreciate the practical consequences of research and assumed responsibility for institutions such as the Kaiser Wilhelm Institute in Germany and the National Physical Laboratory in England. The 1914–1918 war gave a great impulse to this movement and encouraged governments to promote industrial research and to set up their own scientific institutions for specific fields. These activities increased markedly between the two world wars, to the extent that government influence and operation have now become a dominant feature in the organization of science in Europe.

At present, all European countries with the exception of Austria, Switzerland and Greece possess central national scientific organizations of some sort. These vary greatly in character, function and influence from country to country. In some instances they are great and powerful organs of the state, operating networks of national laboratories; in other instances their function is largely advisory or their main task may be the distribution of government funds in the form of fellowships and grants for research to individual scientists or to academic institutions. They form, in some cases, part of the conventional civil service; they may be largely government financed, but advised and managed independently for reasons of efficiency and of easier contact with the academic and industrial worlds. They may concentrate exclusively on the support of fundamental research or they may cooperate with industry in the promotion of applied research and development. History plays a great part in shaping scientific organization, and those countries which have large defense commitments necessarily have a more complicated scientific system. In the United Kingdom and France, for example, military research contracts have greatly helped to build up electronics and precision engineering industries—for civil as well as for defense products—while in countries such as Austria, where defense science plays little part, the place of government in science remains ambiguous.

The existence of central research councils and similar bodies does not avoid the creation, in most countries, of scientific organizations both separate and attached to individual departments of government; the following survey indicates the wide range of functions in science which the average European government has assumed.

A. SCIENCE EDUCATION

Primary and secondary education being accepted as a universal human right, they become a central charge on government, while a large proportion of the finance for higher education also comes from central and local governments. Education is regarded still mainly in terms of basic social and cultural objectives and only secondarily in terms of its vocational importance to the individual and its economic function in creating the necessary scientific and engineering manpower for future national needs.

B. RESEARCH IN UNIVERSITIES AND OTHER CENTERS OF HIGHER LEARNING

In many countries such research is made possible as part of general university financing by the state or by regional bodies through the provision of fellowships to enable a substantial number of graduate students to be trained in research, although the extent of such support varies greatly from nation to nation. The dual objectives of such support are to provide trained research workers for the government's own purposes and for industry as well as to contribute to the extension of knowledge.

C. DEFENSE RESEARCH

Only governments can assume responsibility for the complex military technology of today, and in Europe it is mainly carried out in defense science laboratories, although at the development stage much is done by contract in industry. In the United Kingdom, defense research forms a very substantial proportion of the total effort, as in the United States. It is also important in some other countries, such as France, but it is proportionately much less significant in most of the other European countries.

D. RESEARCH FOR PUBLIC UTILITIES

Since in the modern state government activity is so extensive, it requires the undertaking of research and development work in fields where the government is a direct user of the results. Examples are forestry, geological survey, water resources and their purity, prevention of air pollution, road research, fire preservation, loose-bed hydraulics, and insect control. In European countries such topics are generally the concern of governmental or semigovernmental institutes.

E. MEDICAL RESEARCH

Although much medical research is done in universities and their medical schools in close proximity to great hospitals, many governments support special medical research councils, such as that in the United Kingdom, which maintains central laboratories and achieves a balanced research effort by financing research units for particular topics in hospitals and universities.

F. INDUSTRIAL DEVELOPMENT AND RESEARCH

In many European countries a great many sectors of the economy are nationalized, particularly the railways and other transportation services; coal, iron and steel; and gas, electricity and nuclear energy. In addition particular industrial enterprises such as Renault in France are state owned. All of these undertake research in much the same way as the ordinary industrial corporation under private enterprise, that is to say with little direct state intervention. Outside the government's own productive effort, however, there is much influence on industry, and industrial policies are often framed in such a way as to encourage development and technological innovation. Fiscal policies are important instruments to this end but can, if badly conceived, have a contrary influence. There is also a tendency, only now becoming important, for the stimulation of industrial change by the granting of research contracts for firms, or groups of firms, to undertake particular developments deemed to be in the national interest, in much the same way as for defense technology.

A further industrial preoccupation of many governments is to speed up the development of scientific discoveries in the laboratory, through applied research and development, to production; some governments have therefore set up special organizations to scan the output of national science, to select topics of potential economic importance and to facilitate their exploitation. The National Research Development Corporation of the United Kingdom is a well-established and successful organization of this type. It is an independent organization with government capital and a board of industrialists, bankers and professors, expert not only in technological forecasting but in the legal and organizational problems of facilitating development. Through international cooperation among European countries, there is a healthy exchange of experience on this subject, which becomes increasingly important with ever greater research expenditures of governments.

Many governments undertake directly background research of utility to industry as a whole, such as experimental investigations related to the maintenance of standards of weight, electricity and radioactivity, and provision of reference materials such as exceptionally pure chemicals; many often conduct researches on metallurgy, corrosion, etc. Increasingly too, governments undertake research for industries where the average unit of production is very small, such as in agriculture and building; where the individual firm or the small contractor respectively cannot be expected to undertake their own research; and where, even could they do so, the result would be excessive duplication and waste. Such production elements are unable in most cases even to select and apply relevant research done by others, and hence most countries have created for such sectors a complex network of specialist research institutions and extension services.

The role of governments in stimulating research activity on a cooperative and sector by sector basis has been particularly important in Europe, and it is described on page 471 in relation to industrial research in general.

A particular feature of many European countries is the extent to which governments are content to delegate responsibility for the expenditure of national funds to specialist groups. This is particularly true of the universities. European universities, which in some countries are directly under ministries of education, or which in any case receive most of their funds directly from the state, have for long maintained a very high level of academic attainment, and they enjoy an honorable status in society. Their long traditions, together with the relatively small proportion of Europeans who have until recently had the privilege of higher education, have enabled the universities to pursue for the elite their aims of scholarship and to resist a too narrowly vocational education. Nevertheless, in the engineering, medical and other schools and as a result of the pressures exerted by a rapid expansion, much instruction of a directly utilitarian nature, albeit of a high quality, has crept in. European universities have striven hard to maintain their levels of quality despite their very rapid postwar expansion, and they have very largely succeeded. High uniformity of attainment is controlled in many instances by systems of examination determined nationally or by the use of examiners from sister universities, who are able to insist on enforcement of the generally recognized standards. There is in fact little in the way of a pyramid in European higher education to compare with that of the United States, with what appears to many Europeans to be an excessive variety of institutional methods and quality, or with that of the Soviet Union, where a large proportion of higher education is carried out by institutes for particular subjects such as agriculture, mining or medicine, which, although teaching at a very high level are admittedly vocational in their objectives.

Further, considerable expansion of the universities is envisaged in the next decade, and there is every reason to question if this will or indeed should permit the maintenance of uniform standards and academic bias as at present. There are many indications of change and of greater flexibility in European university planning, and of a more practical orientation. The last few years have seen a very marked tendency, discussed on pages 477–478, to attempt to relate educational investment to long-term economic needs and social objectives. The increasing demand in economic activity for the services of large numbers of educated persons is leading to a new concept of education, planned to benefit the individual and yet in the joint interest of himself and of the economy, to make sure that such education (and to a lesser extent, higher training) is suited to future employment patterns.

Technical high schools of great achievement have existed for years, especially in Germany, Switzerland, Holland and Scandinavia, and it is interesting to note recent decisions for example in the Netherlands, where new technological universities are being planned as consquences of national policy ·to intensify industrialization. In France too demographic changes, technological advance and social pressures are leading to radical modification of the educational structure. For example, fourteen colleges of science and seven of arts have recently been set up to relieve the pressure on the already too large University of Paris. These are mainly restricted to the preparation for short-term (two-year) diplomas, specially created. Many long held traditions of French education are being questioned in relation to their suitability to meet contemporary needs, and in the engineering schools, for instance, openings are provided, much as in Russia, for candidates from factories and workshops. Interesting experiments are being made in many other places, such as in Yugoslavia, where a novel three-cycle system is being tried out to provide the pyramid of skills needed by the economy and at the same time designed to provide the elite of scholarship and research.

It should not be assumed that these changes will result in a narrowly utilitarian concept of education. Attempts to relate the educational process to long-term economic objectives (or, as far as the individual is concerned, employment prospects) give great importance to the adaptation of a man's knowledge and skill throughout his career to the quickly changing tasks which result from a dynamic technology. This continuous learning process will be fruitful only if the initial, formal education is sufficiently developed and focused on principles, and above all if it develops permanent equipment to allow for learning at later stages. Paradoxically then, really enlightened approaches to vocational needs stress true education in contrast to training for immediate tasks.

European governments generally accept the university as providing the best environment for fundamental research and for long maintenance of the creative proportion of fundamental investigation in government and industrial laboratories, therefore, by far the greatest effort remains in academic surroundings.

Increased costs of research and particularly of equipment in fields such as nuclear physics and radio-astronomy have also led in most countries to the provision of special funds for the purchase and often the maintenance of such equipment, which can hardly be provided through normal university budgets without causing grave unbalance among different fields of learning. Government support of research in European universities is mainly in the form of fellowships and grants rather than as contracts for specific research projects, as is so common in the United States. There is, in fact, a strong feeling in Europe that the best way to encourage research is to back well-established research leaders and young scientists of promise and to discourage project research since, however germane it may be to the normal work of a university institute, it tends to inhibit the creative development of research which depends so much on the free choice of the professor to follow the lines of his own genius. On the whole much greater importance is given in Europe than elsewhere to the right, and indeed to the duty, of the professor to choose his own research topics undiverted by the attractions of research projects offered by government departments, military or civil, and by industry. This, of course, encourages the trends of fashion; and in some countries a corrective has been applied to assure the investigation, in the national interest, of important research fields not at the moment à la mode. This has been achieved in France by the National Center for Scientific Research, and in Great Britain by the Medical Research Council by the insertion of special research units associated with, but financially independent from, existing university research departments. Such units offer great advantages over other forms of aid for oriented fundamental research in that they involve no new institutions or capital equipment; if they are successful, these units gradually become assimilated into the university research fabric.

The extent and cost of research in the natural sciences also present many problems of balance of discipline, and the increasing extent of specialization renders true universality, within a single university, impossible. There are as yet few centers of university cooperation for research on expensive topics on the Brookhaven model, but international institutions such as the European Council for Nuclear Research (see page 475), have somewhat the same function although they are intergovernmental, rather than interuniversity, in character. An interesting "growing points" scheme is being attempted in Scandinavia, where a number of specialized science institutes of the universities of the three countries have been selected by the research councils of the countries concerned to receive priority support and to serve the needs of the whole area for the specializations concerned. This experiment is of general significance because of the attempt of too many European universities to provide too wide a coverage of subjects, with the result that for some subjects, research centers are too numerous and individually too weak.

European industrial research also differs greatly from that of the United States, mainly for a pattern of industry reasons and because of the existence of so many small political units. European industry is extremely heterogeneous in character, ranging from huge corporations of the most advanced type with operations throughout the world and generally supported by sound and extensive research programs, to small family-controlled business often survivals from the successful industrialization of the middle of the last century. On the whole, however, industry in Europe has been technologically less aggressive than its American counterpart, less concerned with the dangers of obsolescence and often quite indifferent to needs for innovation. This attitude was understandable during the long period when possibilities of economic expansion ceased to be disucussed, and it was entrenched by an accumulation of marketing tradition, ingrown management tradition, product range and process stability which had been successful for so long.

Management in many European countries has been until recently dominantly mercantile in its approach. In some areas control has been firmly in the hands of the accountant and of the lawyer, although in Germany the engineer has played a big part—a sign of the success of the technical high school system. Science in European industry has been usually "on tap"— although only at a trickle, and seldom "on top"—with the consequence that in too many instances new scientific and technological ideas were unable to penetrate the financial sanctity of the board room.

This situation is rapidly breaking up; wartime destruction rendered inevitable the replacement of old buildings, old machinery, and often of old managements. Social change, the broadening of education, the general prestige of science, completely new managerial attitudes with technological awareness infiltrating from the large science-based corporations and through association with the United States—these things and the general hurricane of change which economic integration or its threat is blowing through all the board rooms of Europe, and also, it should be whispered, through many of the trades union headquarters too—are producing an expansive and forward-looking industry in Europe, likely to be aggressively competitive and fully aware of the possibilities offered by the application of science.

In the process, research resources are being built up and, what is even more important, technological appreciation is becoming widely evident at board level. Attitudes to research in industries such as chemicals, pharmaceuticals, electronics, and the precision engineering sectors are much the same in Europe as in the United States, while in some countries, such as the United Kingdom and France, defense science contracts have speeded their building up. The lowering of trade barriers with consequent prospects for larger "domestic" markets is encouraging association among firms in different countries of the Six for research and design cooperation or for the exchange of technical ideas, a very necessary movement in view of the rising thresholds of research expenditure above which alone investment yields from science are statistically likely to prove profitable.

The high degree of density of industrialization in much of western Europe, which has led to the concentration of many firms engaged in the same type of manufacture in a particular area, has encouraged the evolution of cooperative research schemes which are a uniquely European growth unlikely to find extensive emulation in the United States, if only for the practical reason of the much greater distances there between industrial units. In Great Britain, for example, there are upwards of fifty research associations for particular industries undertaking cooperative work to raise the general technological level of the sector in question. This system, which had its origins at the end of World War I, is in fact a financial partnership between government (through the agency of the Department of Scientific and Industrial Research) and industry, and represents a significant part of British industrial research. Not only is research successfully undertaken for an industry as a whole, and its results made available to the contributing member firms, but great stress is laid on the communication to the individual firms of relevant new scientific and technological information, including know-how from sources throughout the world by means of information services, field liaison schemes, demonstration methods and the like. Similar schemes exist also in the Netherlands, France, Germany and Belgium, while in countries such as Norway, novel schemes of government-industry cooperation for research have been created which are adapted to particular national conditions.

The cooperative research movement is particularly successful for the more traditional sectors such as textiles and the metal industries and is much less important in newer branches, where large firms with their own highly evolved research facilities dominate. It is generally found that in an industry where the research association is strong and aggressive, the scientific activities of the individual member firms build up quickly with the initial role of enabling use to be made of the technological experience from the association. The cooperative research approach should therefore be regarded as a stimulus and complementary to, rather than as a substitute for, the competitive research of the individual enterprise. Some research associations, particularly those of the Dutch TNO Organization, conduct research under contract for individual firms in addition to their broader cooperative work; and it seems that confidential work, which becomes the property of the firms which buy it, is compatible within the same institute with cooperative research leading to results which are commonly owned. Since the war, a number of private or nonprofit-making industrial research institutes have sprung up in Europe, while some of the United States-sponsored research organizations, such as Batelle, have established overseas branches. These initiatives have met with some success, but this type of system has not grown as quickly as was initially expected.

III. INTERNATIONAL COOPERATION IN RESEARCH

The rising costs and astonishingly quick growth of scientific research make it difficult for any country to keep abreast of scientific development along the whole extending frontier of knowledge. This is especially the case in those fields of fundamental research where unit equipment costs are beyond the possibilities of the smaller countries. Nevertheless, bridging the gap between the promise held out by science and the resources available to undertake it is gradually becoming a general and more difficult problem. It has been argued in some quarters, and has even become national policy in a few instances, that smaller countries should rely for fundamental scientific discovery on the outpourings of the great research efforts of the United

States, the Soviet Union, and the larger western European countries. This is, however, a doubtful policy in the interest of a nation, since applications of productive value from such research can be very great and in quite unexpected directions. Furthermore, unless a country possesses scientists with some experience in new specializations and novel techniques, the applied research and productive technology of the future can be acquired only slowly and with difficulty. This means in effect that all countries with ambitions of progressive industrialization are tempted to undertake research work on a broad front and to deploy their limited scientific resources over too many subjects.

This problem is particularly acute in Europe as a result of high levels of industrialization and small political unit size. The basic overheads of science have to be met separately by each state, with the result that there is much useless duplication and subthreshold effort. The situation is much the same as if, in the United States, each state of the Union were to attempt individually to provide the whole apparatus of the contemporary scientific effort. This problem can be solved satisfactorily in Europe only by some degree of political integration, but in the meantime much has already been achieved through cooperative effort. The close proximity of European countries and a considerable identity of objectives make the growth of regional cooperative research particularly attractive, and in fact they present the only means at present available for small progressive countries to participate in some of the newer and most quickly advancing fields of scientific investigation. This movement has already proceeded to the extent that some of the smaller countries expend a considerable proportion of their total research budgets on cooperative research undertaken beyond their frontiers; on the other hand they may receive in the form of international research contracts more money than they disburse. There is thus gradually emerging among European countries, it would seem, a "balance of payments" position for scientific effort.

It must be admitted, however, that participation in such schemes, important and costly as it may be, is often a matter of individual enthusiasms or of prestige rather than a decision of policy. The extent and direction of this international movement is of sufficient interest for other areas of the world for some of the major institutions to be described.

Apart from the United Nations specialized agencies, such as UNESCO, which have world membership and are more and more preoccupied with the problems of underdevelopment, there exist for European countries a number of important intergovernmental organizations wtih a practical interest in science, or at least in its promotion, each of which has different general objectives, different membership and quite different approaches to the problems of science.

One of the most important of these is the Council of Europe, with sixteen members, which, in addition to its important parliamentary assembly, receives annual reports on the scientific work of other European bodies. This organization has an important cultural program supervised by a Council for Cultural Cooperation. Important problems of university development, equivalence of university degrees and improvement in the teaching of particular subjects are discussed here. The Council of Europe also provides the Secretariat for occasional conferences of the European ministers of education which are organized independently. In quite a different category is the North Atlantic Treaty Organization (NATO), whose thirteen European members, together with the United States and Canada, are bound by defense treaty obligations. NATO operates an important Science Committee concerned with the general health of European science, and not specifically with defense problems. Its main science activities are to operate a large fellowship scheme, which in 1963 will amount to two and a half million dollars, the support of summer schools in European universities on advanced scientific topics and the provision of grants for university research. The strength of NATO science lies in its Atlantic constitution; its weakness in the absence of "neutral" European countries such as Sweden and Switzerland, which nevertheless contribute greatly to the fabric of the European security effort.

Yet another "Atlantic" organization which has scientific interests is the Organization for Economic Cooperation and Development (OECD), which has eighteen European members (including the "neutrals"), the United States and Canada, with Jugoslavia as an associate; it will shortly accept Japan as a full member. OECD is concerned with objectives of high rates of economic growth and the encouragement of economic development. It has two scientific committees, one for Scientific and Technical Personnel, and one for Scientific Research, whose work is directly related to these purposes. Each committee has a substantial program of operation, the first including important studies and actions to make possible planning of educational investment in relation to future economic and social needs, programs for the reform of secondary school science and mathematics curricula and the introduction of new educational technology; the second committee, among many activities, is encouraging the provision of national research and development expenditure data, studying the relationship between research investment and economic advancement and organizing cooperative research between member countries on specific topics, mainly of an applied character. This functional approach to research cooperation allows groups of institutions interested in a specific subject to plan a comprehensive program for which each laboratory takes responsibility for a particular element. The object is to obtain a much higher research yield from a particular effort, and it is only in exceptional cases that new research institutions are advocated. This network of cooperation is growing rapidly and at present includes the work of well over 1000 researchers, the overhead costs being trivial.

OECD also possesses a semi-autonomous agency for nuclear energy (the European Nuclear Energy Agency, or ENEA), which was set up to encourage the development of nuclear energy for peaceful purposes in Europe. ENEA has created a number of joint undertakings in research and development, such as the Halden (Norway) boiling heavy water reactor project, the Dragon (U.K.) high temperature, gas-cooled reactor project, and the Eurochemic Company in Belgium for the reprocessing of irradiated nuclear fuels. In each instance, the scheme is financed by a group of countries specifically interested, without commitment to participate in other ENEA schemes, Although each undertaking is independently managed from the scientific and technical point of view, connection to the parent body is maintained on matters of general policy and financial negotiation.

The six countries of the European Economic Community have not yet created permanent machinery for general research purposes, but the two sister organizations have important activities in research, development and dissemination of technical information as well as discussing social and economic implications of their research. Euratom, which employs a research staff of nearly 2000, runs a Joint Nuclear Research Center with branch establishments in Italy, Belgium, Germany, and the Netherlands; it has also placed some 250 research contracts and has been responsible for plans to create a new European University at Florence.

In addition to the above examples of international cooperation within intergovernmental organizations of a general character, western European governments have come together to finance a number of specialized research bodies, some of which are of considerable importance. The oldest and most striking of these is the European Council for Nuclear Research (CERN), situated at Geneva, with a membership of fourteen European countries. CERN undertakes research on high energy particle physics of a fundamental scientific character and has no concern with applied nuclear energy. Its main projects are a 25/28 GeV proton synchroton and a 600 MeV synchrocyclotron, together with work on theoretical nuclear physics, cosmic ray research, etc. The main arguments for the establishment of CERN were economic, and its common facilities are certainly far beyond the financial possibilities of most of its members working separately. The enterprise, which has been particularly successful, has furthermore demonstrated that the intellectual cross-fertilization made possible by the working together of scientists from different countries under a dynamic leadership is in itself ample justification for international cooperation.

Two additional independent organizations of considerable magnitude have started work more recently. The European Space Research Organization (ESRO), housed in Paris, is an attempt to organize major programs of space research which are well beyond the means of the individual members. It is unlikely that ESRO will develop a large central establishment of the CERN type, but it is more favorable to the concept of promoting its work in a group of institutions devoted to various aspects of space technology, data processing, etc. The European Launching Development Organization (ELDO), a complementary body which includes Australia as well as western European countries, has as its objective the development of suitable rocket vehicles for the launching of European satellites.

This enumeration, which is greatly simplified, indicates that the growth of cooperative scientific activity in Europe is considerable in scale, somewhat haphazard in conception, and valuable both in itself by making available entry to research fields which would otherwise be barred to many countries, and as a large-scale experiment in international technique with many lessons for the future. Many governments are beginning to be confused and even irritated by this random growth, which is exaggerated in some instances by the fact that national policy is communicated fractionally and in contradiction through different departments of state—education, science, defense, economic, and finance—frequently without sufficient coordinative machinery to enable coherent national views to be sought. The bills which are regularly presented are becoming bigger each year, amounting to a considerable part of the research budget of some countries; furthermore some members, and especially the smaller countries, feel that they have little control over the expansion and direction of these international activities which demand so high a proportion of their national research budgets. Some rationalization will certainly be demanded before long, but the whole problem is dominated by overall political uncertainty—will scientific cooperation in Europe be on the scale of the Six, of the greater Europe, on an Atlantic level, or on a world basis? In fact, all are necessary. Needs vary from case to case according to the nature of the problem, its scale, cost level, adequacy of existing resources and other factors. Problems which involve the environment of the whole earth, as in oceanography or meteorology, are most intelligently attacked on the full international scale; other problems are, for practical purposes, most conveniently handled between a group of neighboring countries.

Scientific cooperation in Europe is no longer a marginal activity; it represents a major and perhaps the only means for the smaller countries to keep in touch with the rapid advances of science, especially in expensive fields. The present arrangements are in rapid transition; through them much is being learned as to techniques of collaboration. Rationalizations will come about through evolution; the primary need is for a policy.

IV. EDUCATION, SCIENCE, AND THE ECONOMY

An important feature of the new Europe is increasing interest in economic planning. Most countries have now moved far from their initial repugnance to this idea, which after the war was regarded essentially in doctrinaire terms. The success of the French Comissariat au Plan has gradually built up a conviction that a degree of planning through consultation is possible, and even desirable, in a liberal society, and that indeed the scale and complexity of the modern, technological economy renders unsafe a too easy reliance on laissez faire. The Swedish concept of a labor market policy closely integrated with the changing nature of the economy is another instance among many. Planning is gradually being recognized as a technique and not as a dogma. This trend is greatly encouraged by the acceptance of the concept of economic growth and the examination of the various factors which control its rate. The decision of the OECD ministers at the end of 1961 to aim at a 50 per cent increase in the gross national product of the region by 1970 is germane.

These ideas have, of late, become quite important when considering questions of education and research policies. The *quality* of the two input factors of the economy—capital and labor—is of the greatest significance in producing high growth rates, and this quality is largely a matter of the education and training of individuals and of optimum innovation decisions. Such thinking throws great importance on the investment aspects of education and research and, since both are essentially long-term processes, on the need to plan them many years ahead and in terms of overall national needs, including economic projections, technological promise and social aims.

Much attention has been paid in Europe, during the last two years, to education and science as national investment items which are vital and related elements of economic and social progress representing a commitment on national resources as necessary as investments in factory buildings and machinery. This concept is not to be understood in any narrow or technocratic sense, nor is it in any way incompatible with appreciation of the need to develop education and science in their own right for the cultural and general benefit of the individual as well as his society. In this sense education, as research, is one of the main beneficiaries of economic growth, and long-term arrangements are desirable in order that the appropriate share of growing national resources are allocated to it. A manpower study on "Targets for Education in Europe in 1970," made by Professors Svennilson, Edding and Elvin, was the basis for a policy conference of OECD educational and finance policy representatives held in October, 1961, which considered the dimensions and the principal characteristics of the task facing education in the next decade to meet the needs of social and economic progress in the area as well as to be effective in answering requests for help from the underdeveloped countries. There was general agreement with the order of magnitude of the proposed targets for educational expenditure which represented a very great expansion during the next decade, necessary if advantage was to be taken of economic possibilities.

Practical and detailed planning of such investment needs up to 1975 has now been undertaken in six countries of the Mediterranean—Greece, Italy, Portugal, Spain, Turkey and Yugoslavia—in terms of demographic trends, economic plans and evolving social policy, and a start has also been made to similar assessment of technological and research needs. This Mediterranean Regional Project of the OECD has been undertaken by groups of planning economists of the countries concerned, reinforced by consultants from abroad and by frequent meetings of the directors of the various national teams to exchange experience and to develop a common methodology. It is expected that this activity will assist governments and particularly ministers of education in establishing or strengthening the educational planning function on a continuing basis, whereby detailed proposals based on demographic, economic, social and cultural considerations can be translated into practical plans for educational development. The corresponding studies of technological and research needs are designed to assist on the achievement of more rapid and systematic innovation and to throw light on how techniques can be more quickly and soundly transferred from industrialized to less developed economies. This investment approach of educational planning with its basically dynamic approach was discussed by the European ministers of education in October, 1962, and was unanimously endorsed by them. The Mediterranean experiment has attracted much attention and activity along the same lines as is being undertaken in a number of the more industrialized countries of Europe, both separately and in consultation with one another.

The corresponding approach to the investment value of research is as yet only at its beginning. There are no research and development statistics which enable accurate comparisons of effort between countries to be made, although agreement among the OECD countries as to definitions on which such statistics might be collected has recently been achieved. Furthermore the economic significance of research expenditure is confused by the large military and space budgets of some countries in contrast to their absence in others. Broadly speaking, countries with a high per capita gross national product have a substantially higher research ratio than those with a low per capita GNP. Advanced, industrialized countries typically spend more than 1 per cent of their GNP on research and development, while underdeveloped countries spend less than one quarter of 1 per cent; high rates of economic growth appear to be accompanied by high increases in research budgets. These matters are now receiving much attention, especially in relation to national economic plans.

V. SCIENCE AND POLICY

In the complex mosaic of the European scientific and educational scene, with all its new experiments and changing attitudes, the dominant feature is a recognition of the great promise for individual and national well-being offered by science, and at the same time the insufficiency of resources to exploit these possibilities to the full—a world problem indeed, but aggravated in Europe by political fractionation. Both within each country and among all of them, there is a compelling need to establish policies with regard to science. These are required in three senses: policy within each country on the allocation of science resources of trained manpower and of finance to provide the best possible balance of effort in the broad national interest; policies for a more rational augmentation of the total resources of the region through international action; and, finally, a continuing and systematic review of the impact of evolving scientific knowledge on other elements of national policy.

So far, the greatest attention has been paid to the first of these; the science policy function is recognized in a number of countries, for instance by the creation of a ministry for science in the United Kingdom, France, Germany and Italy, and the establishment in Belgium and Sweden of Science Policy Councils under the chairmanship of the prime minister. In some instances, the European science bodies are insufficiently strong to evolve and enforce a thorough coordination and balance among different elements of national science activity, and even that of different departments of government; methods of scientific and technological forecasting, of establishing a balance of effort which favors an optimum rational development are scarcely developed; the relations among scientific effort, educational development and general economic development planning are understood as yet in only the most general terms. In spite of these inadequacies, however, the concept of a national science policy and the thinking processes of the bodies set up to create it is utterly different from the working of science councils a decade ago with their simple task of distributing relatively small government funds for fundamental research on the single criterion of scientific promise.

The science policy of the contemporary industrialized state is then a matter of determining broadly the extent and balance of its research effort, scientific manpower plans and technological development schemes in terms of long-term economic, social, defense, and cultural objectives. The establishment of such a policy will require much background data—comprehensive statistics of research and development expenditure, knowledge of other elements of national policy and planning and of raw material possibilities, energy reserves and other assets, and information concerning existing or planned legislation, fiscal or otherwise, which may influence research or innovations. Those concerned with such a policy would have to possess a deep understanding of the way research works, an appreciation of the fact that fundamental research, probably the most important investment of all, is essentially long-term in its unfolding and requires special conditions of freedom of choice, of protection against the compulsion to consider directly the practical value of its fruits. It is not easy for the authorities to understand that much fundamental research has no direct practical product, but that its addition to knowledge may throw back the frontiers of human understanding in directions not to be envisaged at the outset, with economic possibilities in directions which could not possibly be guessed when the original research was begun.

There is no necessary conflict between the acceptance of a comprehensive and intelligent policy for science aiming at a general balance of effort and the freedom of the individual research worker in fundamental science to follow the lines of his own scientific interest and intuition within it; no well-advised government would attempt to regiment the work of university laboratories and other fundamental research institutions. Nevertheless, the relationship between the work of the creative scientist on the one hand, and national or general human needs on the other, is an increasingly complex matter requiring understanding and tolerance on the part of both scientists and governments. If the scientist is to accept the responsibilities which accompany his privileges, governments must equally respect the nature and demands of research from which they can expect so much if they are willing to throw their bread upon the waters. These are compelling reasons for science itself to assume the initiative in the creation of the science policy of each nation.

The development of international or regional science policies is much more difficult to achieve. The creatively haphazard state of the European scientific organizations, useful as it has been in finding new ways of effective collaboration, will inevitably have to approach some degree of rationalization. This is unlikely to succeed in isolation, and it will probably have to await the evolution and simplification of the political structures themselves. It is possible, however, at least to review the situation and to formulate its problems. For this purpose the OECD has scheduled a meeting in October, 1963, of the ministers of its member countries responsible for science policy to consider national and international aspects of the subject as well as the influence of science on the growth of the economy.

CONCLUSIONS

European science with its long tradition is an essential element in the construction of the new Europe. The vitality of fundamental research in Europe remains, and although the fractionation of the continent into small political units has made it difficult to provide sufficient resources for some important—and expensive—fields of rapid development, resources are in general increasing and institutional methods of international cooperation are being found which can enable it to make a major contribution in these fields also. In applied research and development, progress is very rapid and adjustment is being made to the needs of the economy and of the evolving social structure. In science education too, experiments of all kinds are in train, and institutions of new types are being built up, combining new thinking with an inborn respect for learning.

The most significant result of the strivings of the last decade toward a closer relationship among European countries is probably not to be found in the halting approaches to a new political pattern, or even in tariff reduction and the economy expansion it may bring, but in a new-found openness and willingness to look at new ideas. Through the desperation of war and the subsequent reconstruction of the continent, the average European has had to cast off much in the way of backward-looking tradition and complaisancy. Whether politician, civil servant, industrialist, or trade unionist, he has had to face up to major change, and he continues to be able to do so. This new attitude is reflected in European science and its institutions, the development of which is inextricably linked with that of Europe itself.

Research and the Developing Countries—
Problems and Possibilities

STEVAN DEDIJER

"My hopes for the future of the human race can be summed up in three main points: the destruction of the inequality among nations; the progress of equality of the people within each country; and finally, the real improvement of man. All nations will reach one day the state of civilization attained by the peoples who are the most enlightened, the most free, the most liberated from prejudices . . . . The march of these nations will be more rapid and more certain than ours, because they will receive from us what we had to discover; in order to learn these simple truths (for progress), these sure methods which we found after long wanderings, these nations will simply make their own the developments and the proofs contained in the words and the books of our own countries." *

Today I shall consider how the undeveloped countries can begin to make research the motor of their social progress and how the developed countries can help them in that.

First, let us see what is the problem.

There is one feature of the present world situation on which Mr. Khrushchev and Mr. Kennedy are in complete agreement. They both say: we are living in a scientific-technological revolution. They both act on the belief that scientific research is a sine qua non condition for the welfare and for the very existence of their countries. In most of the developed nations today every product and service is increasingly based on research; in some of them the research potential is increasing exponentially; the percentage of the national income spent annually on research is doubling every few

Reprinted from *Tek. Vetenskaplig Forskning*, 1962, Vol. XXXIII, No. 1, pp. 1–13, with permission of the author and the publisher. Paper read at a meeting arranged by the Royal Swedish Academy of Engineering Sciences in Stockholm, November 13, 1961. Stevan Dedijer has been Director of the Boris Kidrich Institute of Nuclear Science in Belgrade and later worked at the Boshkovich Institute in Zagreb. Since 1954 he has devoted himself mainly to the problem of the development of research in underdeveloped countries. He has been with the Institute of Theoretical Physics at the University of Lund in Sweden while continuing to explore problems in scientific policy.

* "*Les progrès futurs de l'esprit humain.*" Oeuvres Complètes de Condorcet, Volume VIII, Paris, *1797,* p. 329.

years; research policy is becoming one of the most important components of their national policies.

So much for the most developed countries. And what is the situation in the rest of the world? Recently UNESCO published[1] estimates of the world's research potential and the world's research effort: a potential of some 300,000 senior scientists and an effort of about 20,000 million dollars annually. Yet when this research potential and this research effort are plotted on a map of the globe, we see that about two-thirds of the world's nations, inhabited by two-thirds of its population, are passive bystanders in the scientific revolution. Most of these countries belong to what sociologists would call pre-research cultures.

The present division of the world into developed and undeveloped countries is largely due to modern science. Of late, economists have signaled a rapidly growing gap in the rates of economic growth of the developed and of most of the undeveloped countries. Scientific research and its continuous creation of new technologies is one of the principal social forces increasing this gap. This is simply because the developed countries are more and more using research in a socially planned way as the motor of their social progress, while the undeveloped countries are still cultures without this motor. Until recently, most leaders of the undeveloped countries did not know how this motor worked, nor even that it existed.

Although, as we shall see, exact estimates of research expenditure are very difficult to make because of the many factors involved, nevertheless an order of magnitude comparison can be made of the gross national product percentages spent annually on research. This is done in Table I.

TABLE 1. An Order of Magnitude Comparison

Country	Per cent of gross national product spent on research	A comparative scale	Year
U.S.A.	2.74	17	1959
U.K.	2.35	15	1959
U.S.S.R.	>2.0	13	1959
Australia	0,6	4	1959
Norway	0,7	4	1960
Yugoslavia	<0,5	3	1957
Ghana	0,19	1	1960
Philippines	≤0,15	1	1960
Pakistan	0,14	1	1960
Israel	?		
Sweden	?		
Argentina	?		

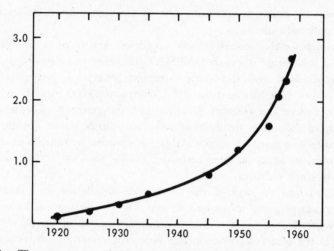

Figure 1. The percentage of the Gross National Product of the U.S.A. spent on research since 1920.

This should be compared with the curve shown in Fig. 1, giving the increase in the Gross National Product percentage spent on research by the U.S.A. since 1920.

From these partial data we see: the less a country is developed, the smaller is its rate of investment in science and hence its rate of scientific growth. To this one should add that this increase in research effort in the developed countries is being added to an already existing research potential incomparably greater than that of the undeveloped countries. If all of this is correct, and it seems to be, a number of disturbing conclusions can be drawn. One is that the solution of particular technological problems, no matter how important, in undeveloped countries by foreign aid does not basically solve the problem as a whole. The undeveloped countries must quickly learn to build and use *their own* research.

Until quite recently there was almost complete silence on this one-sided development of the world's research work. It was put on the international order of the day for the first time in August 1960 when Israel organized at Rehovoth the conference on "Science and the New States." In the spring of 1963 it is expected that the United Nations will hold in Geneva the first world conference on science and technology in the developing countries.

THE NEED FOR AN IMPRACTICAL APPROACH

The general ideas on how to start to couple the developing countries to the scientific revolution can be drawn from social science. One naturally asks: why attempt to lean on such a weak staff as social science seems to be? Why be so impractical about a basically practical problem? To answer this, one has only to notice, for example, how many such countries have under way very ambitious projects in fields like nuclear science, while they lack an elementary scientific survey of the country's resources; or how many big institutes they are building, which for years will be isolated from the problems of the country while research at the universities is completely neglected. It is interesting to note that the same pattern of such practical and yet wasteful endeavours is repeated in numerous countries without a tradition in science and without a research policy based on study.

At the same time a growing need is being felt in many international and national organizations to consider the problem of aid to undeveloped countries on a broad, studied line of approach. This is because many technically well conceived projects begun by them in the undeveloped regions have often led to waste and ill will.

The need for a theoretical approach has a third and simple cause: research and its social effects are growing extremely rapidly in the developed countries themselves. This has given rise to, and requires a deepened study of, the interaction of science and society. Thus, for example, the National Foundation of Science announces that in 1960 there were in U.S. institutions 216 research projects concerned with a study of the interaction of research and economy.[2]

The final reason for a social science approach is the growing tendency everywhere—including the strongholds of rugged individualism—toward a planned change of society. And this can be done only by using the knowledge of social behaviour as systemized by social science. Consider, for example, the strong sociological flavor of the U.S. Government document, An Act for International Development[3] of June 1961, where it is said:

"By providing long term support for development plans, created by the less developed nations themselves, the United States can during the decade of the sixties, help decisively a large number of these nations along the road to economic growth . . .

"The process of fostering the development process requires many things:

"First, a recognition of the range and the scope of development needs including those for the surveying of a country's resources, the improvement of its manpower skills, the creation of new organizations and institutions, and the acquisitions and acceptance of new ideas.

"Second, a recognition that countries pass through various stages of development and that priorities for any country must take into account the unique stage of development of that particular country."

"Third, the preparation of an overall integrated development plan for each country in order to avoid a piecemeal approach."

The principal aim of this studious approach to the problem of research in the undeveloped countries is to derive certain general rules or ideas. By means of these ideas one should not expect to be able to make particular decisions. The general aim is to minimize the probability of making big errors in developing science. And by big errors I mean when the output in social return is incomparably smaller than or at variance with the effort expended.

The problem of developing science is now being studiously approached at different levels of abstraction:

as the problem of formation and execution of a research policy,

as the solution of a social problem by means of the applied social sciences, especially the applied sociology of science,

as an attempt to apply such branches of science as operations research, mathematical theory of decision processes, basic ideas of cybernetics to the problem of growth of undeveloped countries.

From all these points of view our problem could be formulated as follows:

how to bring the undeveloped countries from their initial state without science to a state of developed and socially effective science.

WHAT IS AN UNDEVELOPED COUNTRY?

Any studious approach of our problem must start by asking and analyzing what are the initial conditions, what is an undeveloped country. Here we shall merely say that the old definition of an undeveloped country as a country with primitive economy has been proved by practice to have grave limitations. This is especially true when considering the problem of research. A sociological definition of an undeveloped country gives a much clearer picture of the social goal to be reached by planned development, of the initial conditions, and how the first can be reached from the second. We shall, therefore, define an undeveloped country as an undeveloped culture. Here we define culture sociologically as "all ways of doing things which men have learned or have invented," such as technology, ways of working, social institutions, customs and practices, ways of thinking etc. Undeveloped countries can then be classified into categories of cultures at different levels of development: some of them are basically fifty years, others a hundred, and some even more than a thousand years behind the cultures of the most developed countries. Although the initial conditions differ for countries within each category, we shall present here some general ideas about developing research valid for all of them.

Development then consists in carrying out with the aid of the outside world, but primarily by their own forces, a planned, rapid and simultaneous change of most traits of their existing cultures in the general direction of the developing world culture. I shall illustrate what this means by one of the many existing examples, by the one I know at first hand, that of Yugoslavia. In the complex and planned change since 1945 millions of Yugoslavs are ceasing to be peasants, living on a subsistence level, and are becoming farmers or urban dwellers, learning to work with machines, or in factories, changing their eating habits, their dress, their leisure habits, their family structure, and most of the patterns of their social behaviour. In the process the forces of production of the country, its social structure, is changing rapidly. The population of Yugoslavia has changed from 70 per cent peasant to less than 50 per cent, while at the same time the ways of living of these 50 per cent are rapidly changing also. The way of thinking, of looking at the world, the social behaviour of millions of Yugoslavs are changing beyond recognition. This cultural revolution has been going on for 15 years and in many respects Yugoslavia has ceased to be an undeveloped country. Recently it has started a vigorous research policy in order to couple itself to the scientific revolution.

THE THREE STAGES OF THE SCIENTIFIC REVOLUTION

Sooner or later all undeveloped countries will change from their role of bystanders to that of active participants in the scientific revolution. And to see what exactly this often used but rarely defined term "Scientific revolution" means we must again turn to social science.

Science today is a giant with one natural body and two social heads, both looking at the same world but seeing mostly different things. But surprisingly, when looking at science, the social scientists both of East and West see approximately the same thing. Thus, for example, both the western and the Soviet sociologists roughly agree on what is science. Although the two social sciences do not agree on the sources of the scientific revolution, they agree on its social effects and on its principal historical stages.

Like most revolutions, this one came unannounced and unexpected by everybody both in East and West.

Many social thinkers since Bacon have considered the interaction of science and society, but one above all stressed its revolutionary effect. "Science," said Engels at the grave of his best friend in 1883, "was for Marx a force changing history, a revolutionary force." Also, as was pointed out at the M.I.T. sesquicentennial celebration, it was Engels who in 1843 first saw that science increases proportionally to the total previously accumulated knowledge: in other words exponentially. Recent researches in the science of science have brought this feature out clearly. Thus, for example, Professor Derek Price of Cambridge has brought to light[4] that the number of scientific journals has increased exponentially (Fig. 2). But although many indicators of science and its effect on society increase exponentially, there are periods

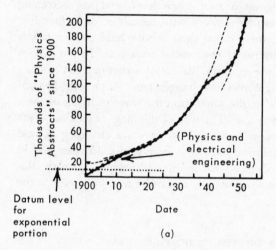

(a)

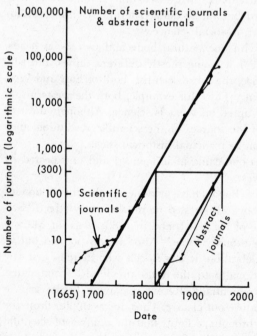

(b)

Figure 2. (a) Total number of Physical Abstracts published since January 1, 1960. The full curve gives the total, and the broken curve represents the exponential approximation. Parallel curves are drawn to enable the effect of the wars to be illustrated.

(b) Number of scientific journals and abstract journals since 1665.

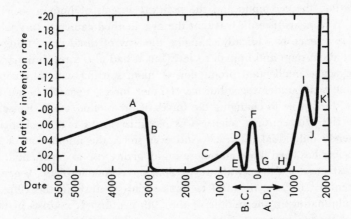

Figure 3. The relative invention rate. The height of the curve at any date represents the percentage increase in man's mechanical equipment occurring on the average in one year. When the curve is high, progress is rapid; when it is low, progress is slow. The technological revolutions may be said to have taken place at points where the rate of invention starts to increase rapidly, namely at points E.H.J.

when new, discontinuous, revolutionary changes take place. This can be seen clearly from Fig. 3,[5] where the relative rate of invention is plotted against time. We see here that since the discovery of the scientific method in the 17th century there is an extremely rapid increase in the rate of invention. The creators of the new method were fully aware of the revolutionary effect of their discovery. Galileo in his "Discources Concerning Two New Sciences" [6]† says: "The door is now opened, for the first time, to a new method, fraught with new and wonderful results, which in future years will command the attention of others minds." And R. Coates in his famous preface to the 1713 edition of Newton's Principia said: "The gates are now set open, and by the passage he (Newton) has revealed we may freely enter the knowledge of the hidden secrets and wonders of natural things." Using Galileo's language we can say that during the next three and a half centuries there were three principal "new and wonderful" results of the new method of making discoveries which affected society: it revolutionized one after the other the

† "Note the word "new" in the title of Galileo's book. As Dyksterhuis points out in "The Mechanisation of the World Picture," Part IV, the word "new" occurs in many titles of scientific books of the period. Thus, for example: J. Kepler— "Astronomia *Nova.*" William Gilbert—"De Magnete Magneticiisque Corporibus et de Magno Magnete Tellure Physiologia *Nova,*" William Gilbert: "De Mundo Nostro Sublunari Philosophia *Nova,*" Patrizzi: *"Nova* de Universis Philosophia,"* Francis Bacon: *"Novum* Organum.*"

intellectual, the economic and the political aspects of human society. The first such wonderful result was that the new method caused a veritable revolution *in* science by radically changing the way of discovering things about nature, about man and human society. But it had also a revolutionary effect on the whole intellectual production of man, starting with philosophy. At the same time, under the influence of other forces, research began to play a more direct role in changing the forces of production. As B. Russell said: "From the 17th century, science was recognized as a matter of social and not merely individual interest." And ever since, the interaction of science and society has been more and more rapid, giving rise to exponential curves. The next stage of the scientific revolution, the economic phase, began in the 17th century, became manifest to some social scientists in the 19th, and is now culminating in the middle of the 20th century. It consists in this: all parts of the old processes of production were submitted to research analysis and every new product was fathered by research. As was repeatedly pointed out by the "prophet" of this stage of the scientific revolution, Karl Marx, the social force of profit motive and competition coupled science to production and drove both, enabling the present developed countries to forge rapidly ahead in changing their culture and in imprinting it on the rest of the world. Today, in the middle of the 20th century, after the intellectual and the economic, we have entered the political stage of the scientific revolution: science has finally become a paramount concern of society and is strongly influencing every one of its traits. This stage may be said to have started under the impact of the success of various, planned, state-supported research projects of the Western powers during the First and especially during the Second World War, and under the influence of the successful, planned development of research in the Soviet Union. Today, scientific research is acting simultaneously as a revolutionary intellectual force, as a force revolutionizing the production of goods and services, and as a political force influencing the social and political behaviour of men.

During every one of the stages of the scientific revolution men invented new social institutions typical of each particular stage. In the 17th and 18th centuries these social inventions were scientific societies, scientific periodicals, and the laboratories of gentlemen scientists. In the 19th century there appeared the first university laboratories like those of Leibig, Tait's at Edinburgh and Maxwell's at Cambridge, inventors' laboratories like those of Edison and Tesla, industrial research laboratories and the first international scientific societies and congresses. In this, the political phase of the scientific revolution, new social inventions are being brought forth to increase the productivity of work in science and the productivity of the social effect of science. The most important social invention at this stage is the planned development of science on a national scale by means of the set of decisions called "research policy." As a matter of fact, there is a growing trend toward a world research policy. The "research policy" stage of the scientific revolution is now in process in most countries. And during all this time, since the 17th century, there was a corresponding accumulation of know how in dealing with science which was transmitted through unwritten tradition from generation to generation of leaders of science, administrators and political decision makers. And it is through and as a part of this traditional way of doing things that the research policy is developing in the developed countries. As Churchill says somewhere in his Memoirs: "and so we decided to undertake certain actions, and through experience with action slowly a policy emerged."

Before considering more closely what is research policy, certain important conclusion can be drawn. The first is this: Since research work is one of the key elements missing from the culture of the undeveloped countries and one of the key factors for social progress, the development of research must be one of the key tasks of their cultural revolution.

Second: all three phases of the scientific revolution—the intellectual, the economic and the research policy stages—are equally important and strongly dependent on each other. But the undeveloped countries will have to carry out all three stages without having what the developed cultures have: the traditionally accumulated and difficult to transmit know how in dealing with science.

Third: the decision makers in such new countries must from the start apply the new social invention made for the effective interaction of science and society, the invention of the research policy. Only thus can they carry out simultaneously all phases of the scientific revolution.

Research policy is a very recent invention. The literature on it is scanty, its definition still uncertain. As late as 1954 the OEEC complained that in very few of its member states "serious thought has been given to the formulation of a national research policy." [7] The situation has rapidly changed since then. Research policies are now being formulated in dozens of the developed and some of the undeveloped countries. In this work are participating the highest political decision makers, the administrators of science, representatives of various scientific bodies and government departments, the universities, research councils, associations of industry and agriculture, economic institutions and others.

THE SOCIAL ENGINEERS OF SCIENCE

Before considering a bit more closely what is research policy, we must consider who is going to engineer the development of research in the new states. This is extremely important to bear in mind in devising plans for the advance of science in these countries.

Both the general world environment and the internal social forces of most undeveloped countries are pushing into power new groups determined to engineer the cultural revolution. They constitute the new social elites in these countries. They make all the important decisions, including those on science. A power elite uninterested in or passive to the problem of development will not stay long in power. Reactionary elites or backward looking decision makers in such countries are finding less and less support from abroad. Conscious that I am committing the grievous sin of generalization, I shall list some social and psychological traits of these elites as described in recent studies by sociologists.

The first trait, as noted, is that these elites consist to a large extent of men determined to carry through rapidly the cultural revolution in their own country.

As the victorious minority, fresh in power after difficult personal and political struggles, they are extremely confident of themselves. They insist on doing things in their own way. They are extremely jealous of their independence and consider the right to make their own mistakes an inalienable right of a sovereign country. They insist on a complete political equality with the developed states, no matter how large and powerful.

Although many of them are devotees of western revolutionary ideologies and are all, or most of them, western trained, all of them are essentially a part of their own social culture. They believe they know best about their own country's problems and its people, including how to introduce changes into their society. It is worth remembering that, although their goals and plans sometimes prove to be megalomaniac, they often achieve more than the experts from the developed countries believed possible.

They consider the maintenance of political stability the first condition for carrying out the cultural revolution. They consider most of the problems of their country from this point of view. And hence they are liable to neglect the importance of developing channels for social communication necessary for the definition of goals, for the formulation and efficient execution of policies. They tend to forget that democracy is an invention made by the developed countries for the efficient growth and life of society.

Except in making political revolutions, these decision makers have as a rule very little knowledge and know how of social decision making in such fields as economy, education, science, etc.

The process of developing a country means importing and grafting modern civilization—the most advanced stage of man's culture—into a social environment alien to it and resisting change with great social inertia. Under the triple pressure of this social inertia, of the need for the cultural revolution and of their own lack of experience, the decision makers are prone to accept and act from ideologies based on the idea that social change can be best brought about by considering and treating society as consisting of masses moving under the action of social forces and according to "laws of motion of human matter." Both this attitude and the complementary one of ignoring the need for social communication in effecting change leads to inefficient social development. And nowhere is such an ideological approach as ineffective as in research, which is based on individual creative work.

It is extremely important to remember that the key decisions on science are today everywhere the result of the work of at most a few dozen men. In the undeveloped countries this work will have to be done exclusively by members of these new elites—by a few political decision makers, newly appointed administrators of science, by the small scientific community—all of them with little or no experience in decision making on science, and importing the scientific outlook and scientific work into a society alien to it and its traditional ways. To forget what type of people these decision makers are liable to be can render ineffective every help proffered.

RESEARCH POLICIES: ELEMENTS AND TRENDS

When we examine the growing literature on research policies in the USA, China, USSR, India, United Kingdom and half a dozen other countries, we note that we are essentially dealing with the same social invention irrespective of the social system where it is applied. The basic elements and the very terminology used to describe this tool for the planned interaction of science and society are the same for all. In all these countries research policies consist of the following sets of decisions:

The decisions on the principal national policy goals which can be reached by means of the research potential.

The decisions on developing the "physical elements" of the research potential: personnel, finances, buildings, equipment.

The decisions on the long range research program: the distribution of the scientific potential with respect to the main scientific and social goals; for example on the relation of basic and applied research, on the work in special fields like nuclear energy, military research, automation and others.

The decisions on social institutions needed to make science and society interact productively. This calls for legislative action in regard to science, for the formation of research councils, research associations, for decisions on centralized and/or dispersed industrial research establishments and others.

The time distribution of scientific effort and the time sequence of goals according to priorities.

Finally, decisions on socio-political measures and behaviour which will make research productive by creating the proper atmosphere within the scientific community and in its relations with other sectors of society.

In all the more developed countries there is a growing trend—in some more and in others less rapid—to form central bodies for deciding on research policy. Such bodies with responsible leaders are charged with the following tasks:

> to help coordinate the search policy with the general national policy;
> to coordinate the work of bodies deciding on different kinds of research (basic, applied, development) or its different fields (industrial, agricultural, medical, military, etc.);
> to plan the development and initiate new essential branches of research;
> to propose new institutions which may improve the social productivity of science and the productivity in science;
> to develop and implement a foreign research policy;
> to collect and analyze by means of social sciences the information on the state of the research potential, the scientific effort, on the effectiveness of the research policy measures, etc.

Finally such bodies have the task of using the sociology of science, the policy sciences and others, to study the development of interaction of science and society at home and abroad in order to improve continually the formation and the execution of their research policy. This process, called by the Soviet Academy of Sciences "continuous planning of research" [8] is going on in such developed countries as the United States, the USSR and the United Kingdom.

In undeveloped countries research policy has and must have certain specific traits. In advanced countries research policy is developing on the basis of experience, through a gradual increase of planning and a greater coordination of the activities of already existing institutions. Their research policy is based on a cumulative traditional know how of making decisions about science through the cooperation of leaders of government, science, industry, agriculture, education and other fields. In the undeveloped countries both the general policy making and the know how of dealing with science are in most cases non-existent. As the experience of many such countries shows, when there is no studied approach, and if there are no open channels of social communication, research will be beset from the start with two dangerous diseases: anarchy and bureaucracy. These diseases, so prevalent in some undeveloped countries, greatly lower the efficiency of using scientific effort to increase the scientific potential. And in considering the implications of Table 1 this element must be taken into account.

One of the most important components of the research policy of new countries must be their "foreign research policy." Its principal goal must be to gain international help from all possible sources in training not only its young researchers, but its research policy makers, administrators of science, leaders of laboratories, and leaders of the scientific community.

HOW TO MAKE SCIENCE A SOCIAL PROBLEM

Having very sketchily considered the initial conditions, the goal and the social tools needed to reach these goals, we have to ask perhaps the most important question of all: has the problem of science become a social problem in such countries? This is not an idle, academic question. Anyone who has anything to do with research in such countries knows its importance.

According to social science: "For a social problem to exist, two conditions must be fulfilled. First there must be a wide recognition of some condition that affects adversely the welfare of large numbers of people. Second, there must exist a belief that this condition can and should be changed." [9] Hence we can and must ask: is there in the undeveloped countries an awareness of the lack of science and its consequences? Are they aware of the present state of their research potential, the rate at which they are increasing it? Are they aware which of the culture traits of their society and which of their own policies act favorably and which act adversely on the development of research? Have they ever asked themselves: what exactly is our research policy?

The best way to hold up to them such a mirror is to present data on the comparative development of research, including data on the awareness or the lack of it in their own country. All measurements about science are still very difficult: simply, perhaps, because so few have been made so far. The situation until recently was as described in 1956 by the Advisory Council of the Scientific Policy of the U.K.[10]: "This is a field in which it is difficult to obtain precise and comprehensive statistics" and warned "that any comparison should be made with considerable reserve." However, such measurements can be made if one is interested only in making rough comparisons of orders of magnitude. For undeveloped countries, where there is so little scientific work and science in general, this is not difficult. The position is shown in Table II.

TABLE II. A Relative Comparison of the Research Potential and Effort and of the Awareness of Research (per Inhabitant) 1960

| Country | Income | Research potential | | Research effort | | Awareness |
		Total scientists and engineers	Expenditure on research 1945–1960	Annual expenditure on science	Rate of production, scientists and engineers	
A	1	1	1	1	1	1
B	3	8	45	40	10	50
C	10	56	900	960	40	300

The awareness of science as a social problem is here assumed to be correlated to the amount of information exchanged within the public domain of a society on problems concerned with the interaction of research and that society. This information consists of the amount of documents, publications, articles, government reports, books, records of public discussions and other printed matter on the problems of developing research. For two of the countries, the least developed A and the underdeveloped B, this quantity of printed matter can be and has been estimated fairly exactly. The magnitude of this quantity for C is certainly underestimated.

From these and similar data we may conclude:

The less a country is developed, the smaller is its rate of development of science.

The developing countries at present lag in the rate of development of research, perhaps more than in any other field.

Since the exchange of information on research, as well as their experience, is smaller than in the developed countries, one can assume that their research effort and research potential are less productively used than in the developed countries.

The most important conclusion from all this is that the political decision makers in new nations must find ways and give an energetic initiative to increase the social awareness in their country of the need for the development of research and of methods of doing it effectively. Many observers have noted that the newly formed research councils in such countries have devoted little or no attention to this question.

Of course, as regards all these aspects of developing research, there exists quite a variety of situations and conditions among countries at the same stage of growth. Some undeveloped countries, especially those in the British Commonwealth, are devoting considerable attention to developing adequate research policies. Others have neglected the development of research altogether, simply because their decision makers were not aware of it. In such countries we often see that the economic development is much more rapid than the growth of science.

HELP FROM ABROAD

It is from the angle of these basic questions of awareness of science and of the need for a research policy that we shall consider the possibilities of aid from the advanced nations. It is from this basis that we shall examine how the foreign research policy of the undeveloped countries meets the foreign policy of the advanced nations and consider how these two foreign policies can be related.

In the developed countries there is a growing public interest in the undeveloped countries. Private and public organizations and governments are formulating attitudes, planning actions and actively giving aid. This is done from a variety of motives: humanitarian, foreign policy, and economic.

Looking ahead, everything seems to point to the likelihood that the 70 odd undeveloped countries will push the development of their research with increasing energy and that the world research potential in the next generation will increase by leaps and bounds on this account. In these countries there is a growing need to build and equip thousands of school and university laboratories, hundreds of national laboratories, and numerous industrial ones. For at least the next generation a large percentage, almost 90 per cent, of the material needed for research will have to be imported. The undeveloped countries will need thousands of experts in various fields of research to advise and help in building scientific institutions. They will need help to train their scientific talent, to transmit the know how of research and to establish a national research tradition.

The developed countries have realized that this problem cannot be tackled haphazardly. In the United States, the United Kingdom and Germany, just to give examples, institutes are growing up for the purpose of studying all aspects of the problem, including that of how to help develop research.

It is evident, therefore, that the most effective help in developing science at this stage could be given along the following lines:

First: aid to increase the awareness and the knowledge needed to develop research. The Rehovoth Conference, attended by statesmen and decision makers from the undeveloped countries and by leaders of research from the West, was a step in this direction. It is hoped that the coming Geneva conference in 1963 will remove the problem of lack of awareness of research from the order of the day, just as the 1955 Geneva conference on nuclear energy helped a considerable number of undeveloped countries to clarify their attitude toward nuclear energy.

Second: to help develop research policies and research programs. A Ford Foundation report of 1960[11] recommends: ". . . the most significant gift which the Foundation could give to science and scientists in Argentina would be an important role in framing and carrying out a program to improve science in the country." The participation of British scientists in preparing such important documents as the "Report of the Scientific Commission of Pakistan" [12] indicates how this help can be given on the research policy level. The Commonwealth Science Conferences and the Ashby report on higher education in Nigeria are other examples of this kind of aid.

Third: work out realistic research programs in key branches of the life of the country and in conformity with its stage of development. This can be done by concentrating on the development of research programs for improving agriculture, for the prevention of disease, and in other fields. One social science problem of extreme importance is how to find ways of financing research so that industry and agriculture not only benefit from it but also are stimulated to develop and use research.

Fourth: Most of the work in developing and using research will have to be done by the decision makers in the developing countries themselves. Hence the greatest help they need is to learn *how* to develop research within the framework of their social conditions. This aid can be proffered by training government administrators of science, training research leaders in administrative duties, helping to make the work of Research Councils more effective.

Fifth and last: Aid can be given in developing research projects on the detailed problems important for the given stage of development through cooperative ventures between the two kinds of countries. Such problems have an infinite range of level and scope: from the determination of ore contents, modes of transmission of disease, to the adaptation of machines to local climatic conditions. The Brookings Institution in the USA has given attention to the question of how innovation can be initiated and devised in the developing nations. Thus J. Baranson of this Institution has proposed the establishment of "technology teams." [13] The activity of these teams, according to him, in countries least developed economically can constitute the initial steps in establishing national research programs close to the actual problems facing them. These teams should help to crystallize the technological needs of the economy and to set in motion the flow of innovation. Baranson proposes that these teams should work under the direction of applied research institutes and should tackle the most immediate problems of raising productivity in agriculture and industry. The aim of these teams should be to set up patterns of learning how an undeveloped country can set up such teams for itself.

IN THE BEGINNING THERE MUST BE IDEAS

I have attempted to illuminate some of the basic elements of the work of decision makers in the undeveloped countries in, so to say, the engineering of science. In defining work, one of the most influential books in the history of man stresses the extremely important role of ideas and says:

"We presuppose labour in a form that stamps it as exclusively human. A spider conducts operations that resemble those of a weaver, and a bee puts to shame many an architect in the construction of her cells. But what distinguishes the worst architect from the best of bees is this, that the architect raises his structure in imagination before he erects it in reality. At the end of every labour-process we get a result that already existed in the imagination of the labourer at its commencement." This thought, in Karl Marx's "Capital" [14] says in effect the same as "In the beginning was the word" of the Gospel according to St. John, from which the title of this lecture was taken.

To accomplish efficiently the extremely important and difficult work of making research a motor of their social progress, the decision makers in new countries must first of all acquire an idea of the need for research, of their initial research conditions, and of the best methods available for developing it. And the greatest help the developed countries can give them is to aid them in acquiring these ideas.

REFERENCES

[1] RODERICK, H, *Natural sciences department, UNESCO, Statement to ECOSOC* 32nd session.

[2] NATIONAL SCIENCE FOUNDATION, *Current projects on economic and other impacts of scientific research and development, 1960.* NSF 60–79. Wash. 1961.

[3] *An act for international development.* Department of State publ. 7205, Wash.

[4] PRICE, D, *The exponential curve of science.* Discovery 1956: June.

[5] LILLEY, S, *Men, machines and history.* London 1948.

[6] GALLILEI, G, *Discources concerning two new sciences,* transl. by Crew & de Salvio. p. 243. New York.

[7] *The organisation of applied research in Europe, the United States and Canada.* Publ. by OEEC. Vol. 1. Paris 1954.

[8] TOPCHIEV, A V, *Sovetskaya nauka na novom etape razvitiya.* Vestnik Akademii nauk SSSR. 1961:8.

[9] HUNT, E F, *Social science.* New York. 1955.

[10] ADVISORY COUNCIL ON SCIENTIFIC POLICY. London. *Annual report 1956–57.*

[11] KIDD, C V, *Suggestions for Ford foundation support of science and technology in Argentina.* 1960.

[12] GOVERNMENT OF PAKISTAN, MINISTRY OF INDUSTRIES, *Report of the scientific commission of Pakistan.* 1960.

[13] BARANSON, J, *National programs for science and technology in the underdeveloped areas.* Bull. atomic scientists. 1960:May.

[14] MARX, K, *Capital.* Vol. 1, p. 178. Moscow 1959.

Science, Technology and World Advancement

P. M. S. BLACKETT

I

An essential problem to be solved is the part that modern science and technology can play in the economic, social and cultural growth of those new nations which are now setting out to transform themselves from their present state of material poverty and economic backwardness into prosperous and growing societies.

During the past five years an important change has occurred in the attitude of the rich Western World to the under-developed and so poor countries: these are those which have not yet reaped much benefit from the scientific and industrial revolution which has transformed the material way of life of Europe and its overseas descendants during the past tumultuous two hundred years.

Historians do not know whether, two hundred years ago, Europe was better or worse off in material wealth than China; nor is it known whether Europe was better or worse off than it was in classical times. Craft technology did not, in fact, make many major advances between classical times, or even earlier, and about the seventeenth century. Then came the birth of modern science which produced modern scientific technology.

One of the fascinating unsolved questions of history is why the scientific and industrial revolutions of the seventeenth and eighteenth centuries happened in Europe rather than in one of the great ancient civilizations of the Near and Far East. Craft technology may be said to have evolved to a very high level about five thousand years ago in the river-valley civilizations of the Near East, and in India and China. By 2000 B.C. the level of building, woodwork, fine metal work, shipbuilding and transport had reached a level which was not surpassed for nearly three thousand years. Then, for one reason or another, the great civilizations of north India, Egypt, Meso-

Reprinted from *Nature,* February 3, 1962, Vol. CXCIII, No. 4814, pp. 416–420, with the permission of the author and the publisher. Substance of the Irvine Memorial Lecture delivered at the University of St. Andrews on November 3, 1961. Professor P. M. S. Blackett, F.R.S., is at the Imperial College of Science and Technology, University of London. He was awarded the Nobel Prize in Physics in 1948. Professor Blackett was recently appointed Deputy Chairman of the newly formed Advisory Council of Technology.

potamia became static and finally declined. Then China rose and was socially and technologically pre-eminent from 500 B.C. to A.D. 1500, when Europe started the extraordinary movement which produced the Scientific and later the Industrial Revolution, which were, in three centuries, to transform man's life on Earth. The essential foundation on which this revolution was based was the high level of craft technology which was largely of Near and Far Eastern origin. What it was that prevented these ancient civilizations from making the scientific breakthrough is not fully understood. There is no evidence to suggest that there are any demonstrable differences of innate ability between the different races of the world. There may be some yet to be discovered, but it would be anyone's guess what would be the order if the races of the world were listed according to innate ability.

The only sound working rule is that the different people of the world, even though they are now at very different levels of development, have the same innate capacity for science and technology, as the rich and proud Western Europeans who created the scientific revolution. Thus the vast differences between the material wealth of Europe, North America and Australia on one hand, and India, China, the Middle East, Africa and most of South America on the other, cannot be ascribed to racial differences. Almost certainly the differences were of complex social origin. For not very clear reasons Europe produced in the seventeenth and eighteenth centuries the social conditions which welcomed and rewarded scientific and technical innovation: these conditions seemed not to have been present either in the contemporary Moghul Empire of India or in China. Thus, these two outstanding civilizations remained static or even declined somewhat during recent centuries, while Europe and America shot ahead.

In the century and a half since A.D. 1800 the material standard of life of Europe has been multiplied by ten, and by much more in North America, while that in China and India has stood still or fallen somewhat. To-day there are some 400 million people in Europe, North America and Australia, and the white parts of Africa and South America, with an average income a head of some £400 a year. On the other hand, in Asia, Africa and South America there are some 1,000 million people (excluding China) with an income a head of less than £40 a year.

Nearly all these materially poor countries are now attempting to become richer and more prosperous by making use of modern scientific technology: and they are in a hurry. Few of their Governments will survive for long unless they provide a steadily rising material standard of life. To achieve this a very great increase of investment in roads, transport, electric power, houses, schools, factories and industrial plants is essential. All these are expensive, and the countries are poor with very little available resources over and above that to keep the population at a subsistence level. Moreover, many of these things have to be bought from the already industrialized countries with foreign exchange which is nearly always in short supply. It is the poverty of these countries in general and their shortage of foreign exchange in particular which makes essential the giving of generous financial aid by the rich countries of the world.

For this aid to be effective the recipient country must have the will and the administrative machinery to carry through the social and political changes without which the process of modernization cannot succeed. There are only too many cases where foreign aid has been poured in, very often for political and military reasons, to countries without either the will or the social system to make good use of it. But there are many countries—India is an important example—where both will and social conditions are present, and where the main check on progress is financial stringency. For such countries generous foreign aid is urgent. The survival of parliamentary democracy may well depend on the amount and the speed with which this aid is given.

To carry out this process of social and industrial modernization a developing country needs a modern educational system capable of producing the necessary teachers, administrators, civil servants, industrialists, doctors, scientists and agriculturists. Without these, development cannot take place. At the early stages of growth, some of these essential trained people will have to be engaged from the already advanced countries. However, this is expensive and the supply precarious. So a major objective in all these countries must be to train their own people to produce their own native born intelligentsia.

There is now in the world a vast amount of scientific knowledge and technological information ready to be applied for the purpose of raising the standard of life of the poorer countries. So the first task of such a country is to learn to apply existing knowledge: then will come the task of adding to knowledge, especially in those fields such as, for example, tropical medicine and agriculture, where the required knowledge is not available. But, by and large, the first requirement in order to raise the material level of a poor country is the application of known technology, rather than to wait for new discoveries. For example, an adequate supply of doctors and nurses, piped water, main drainage and public health measures generally are necessary before even known medical methods can be applied. So economic and social planning must be based primarily on existing technology; energetic efforts must be made to improve this technology, especially in relation to local problems and there must always be readiness to make use of radical new developments should they arise. But development should not wait on new discovery.

II

In order that a country which is now poor and under-developed shall be able to transform itself into a growing and dynamic one, able to profit by the scientific and technological revolution of the past two hundred years, there are at least three requisites. There must exist in the country a determination to bring about such a change and to face up to all its complex social implications: the financial resources to make the change must be provided somehow, and finally, adequate trained personnel must be available.

At the outset it is important to remember that different under-developed countries have very different needs. India, for example, has had a modern university system for very many decades and so can now supply the major part of the intelligentsia, professional, scientific, technological, managerial and teaching personnel which are essential for the implementation of the national plan for economic and social advancement. India's vital need is for financial resources to carry out her plans; she has both the political determination and all but a small fraction of her needs for trained man-power: however, because of her large population, this small fraction may mean a considerable number.

However, many of the new emergent countries, particularly those in Africa, are in a very different situation. An acute shortage of locally born trained personnel exists at almost all levels, from technicians to professors. Thus such a country, even when it has the first two requisites, the will and the money, will still need the help of foreign-born professionals for many years. Even with the most rapid achievable growth of the whole educational system, elementary, secondary and higher, many years must elapse before some of these countries can supply all their needs. In fact, it is the building up of an educational system adequate to produce the essential locally born intelligentsia, which needs at the start the help of foreign-born professionals. While fully aware that this problem is world wide in scope and involves the general relationship of the already rich industrial powers to all the now poorer and under-privileged ones, so that international action on a wide scale is essential and is, in fact, in train, through many agencies, I will here confine myself to the problem of what part British universities could and should play in this task.

In 1946, as a result of the Asquith Report, a big plan of expansion of university education in the major British colonies was initiated by the British Government. Directly or indirectly, the pattern to-day of university education in the Universities and University Colleges of Malta, Hong Kong, Malaya, Ghana, Nigeria, West Indies, Uganda, Sierra Leone and several other institutions was set up by the recommendations of the Asquith Commission on which Sir James Irvine was an active member. In 1960, in these overseas university institutions (about twelve in number) there are nearly 10,000 students and an academic staff of more than 1,500. Of these some 700 were British-born. The fraction of local-born staff is low in the African colleges—10–30 per cent. Many or most of the British staff took up their posts in African colleges when these countries were still under Colonial rule, but many stayed on when the countries became independent.

Most of these newly independent countries still find it convenient to make use of the administrative machinery available in Britain for the recruitment of foreign-born staff, especially the Inter-University Council for Higher Education Overseas. To show the scale of activity of the Council, it is interesting to note that in 1960 it advertised 400 academic vacancies, received more than 2,000 applications, and finally recommended more than 300 appointments. Of these, nearly a half were British-born, about a quarter local-born and the rest from other countries. In all these cases the overseas university paid the full salary from its own resources. The British Council performed an analogous part in relation to some other overseas university institutions, mainly in non-Commonwealth countries. There may be about 100 British-born academic staff in posts overseas through the machinery of the British Council. The British Council has funds to supplement salaries, but the Inter-University Council has not.

I give these figures to emphasize that Britain has already a big stake in the higher educational systems of many developing countries, particularly of those in the Commonwealth. It is essential that Britain should be prepared to continue and extend this role in the future—if, and only if, the newly independent countries want us to do so. A first task is for Britain to find ways of maintaining the supply of able university staff under the new conditions of independence of these new countries, so as to make good the losses of existing staff, as they move on to other posts in the United Kingdom or elsewhere. The second task is to be prepared to increase the supply markedly to compete with the great expansion of higher education which is bound to take place when these newly independent countries begin to stride forward into rapid economic and social progress.

The scale of expansion of output of trained people in a new nation on the march is indicated by some figures taken from the Ashby Report on educational needs of Nigeria. The need is estimated as some 2,000 university graduates a year compared with the present output from University College of 200. Two other universities are now being formed. In addition, there may at present be some 600 returning each year from training overseas.

In Britain there is one university student to every 500 population—a low figure by the standard of most advanced countries: in Nigeria it is 1 in 20,000 and in Ghana 1 in 10,000. So it is clear that a great increase of university education, as a part of a planned increase of education as a whole, is a necessity in all the newly developing countries. Compared with some other colonial powers Britain can claim that it did initiate local higher education on a substantial scale—the total number of students now in these colonial and ex-colonial countries is more than three times what it was ten years ago. Considerable as this achievement is, it is far below the real needs of these emerging countries.

If then the need of the emergent nations for rapidly expanding higher education is accepted and likewise the duty of the rich and developed countries to help, the question then arises as to how this can best be done. First we note that one of the objectives of the expansion of the higher education systems of these new countries is to provide enough trained men and women from their own population so as to be able as soon as possible to dispense with the use of large numbers of foreign staff. As we have seen, this is already the case with India: in spite of its great poverty it does produce the majority of the trained people it needs. The ratio of university students to population in India is about the same as in Britain, though it is true that the standards are considerably lower in some Indian institutions.

It would probably be reasonable to assume that many of the emergent African countries will remain dependent on ex-patriate university staff for a substantial fraction of their needs for a decade or more.

In discussing the part which British universities could play in this inevitable educational advance, it is important to remember that these newly independent countries have no obligation whatever to look to Britain rather than to other countries for their ex-patriate staff. They can and do shop elsewhere. However, our historic relations with these former Colonies, and the fact that their common language is English, does provide a reason why many Britons would be welcomed, especially when they throw themselves wholeheartedly behind the aspirations of these new nations for social growth and progress.

In Colonial days most of the British-born academic staff in these overseas universities and colleges were appointed for life, though in fact many only stayed in their posts for a limited number of years. Now when these countries are independent, and incidentally hoping soon to be producing their own local-born candidates for these posts, there is much to be said for making administrative arrangements in Britain for men and women to take these overseas posts for a limited period of say, up to five years, with a guaranteed post in Britain to return to. There could be advantages also in this for the overseas university: for it often might not be wise for them to appoint a foreigner for life when equally good or better local-born candidates might be available within a decade or less. But the main advantage of working out some form of secondment for overseas service, rather than relying, as generally in the past, on finding candidates willing to take life appointments, even if they do not intend to stay for life, is that one should be able to widen the application lists and so to allow the selection of abler people.

Though many academics who might welcome a period of work in an overseas university, either from a sense of adventure or because it would give him special opportunities to pursue his research interests—as, for example, geologists or biologists, or medicals or social scientists, or simply from a sense of service, akin to the motives of the religious and medical missionaries of earlier decades—they might often be deterred from accepting a life appointment. The climate might not suit him or his family: education facilities for his children might not be available: or unwelcome political changes might ensue. Any of these circumstances might throw him, perhaps in middle age with wife and family, on the academic labour market.

Many more might be willing or keen to take these posts if they were assured of a post to return to after five years or so. In a Civil Service, appointment to overseas service presents little difficulty and is, of course, usual in the Foreign and Consular branches. Since British university staffs are not civil servants—they are in France, so secondment would be easier—other ways must be found. It has often been suggested that the universities should be given extra funds to enable them to have continually some fraction, say 5 per cent, of their staff at any time on overseas service. Unfortunately there seems little chance that such funds will be available at any rate for several years. So consideration must be given to possible ways in which individual universities can act on their own without waiting on government action.

Now the main difficulty in arranging such long-period secondment of a senior academic has lain in the past in the problem of replacing his role in the university department while he is away. Suppose a reader is seconded to an overseas university for five years as a professor. If he is replaced at home by another reader, then, when the first man returns to his readership, there will be two, not one, readers on the staff. So this procedure effectively earmarks one additional readership to the department concerned at the end of the five years. Even in an expanding university, this might be hard to justify; in a static one it would be very difficult.

However, there is another method which avoids this difficulty and which is most easily applicable in fairly large university departments, particularly perhaps to large science and mathematics departments. This is simply to use the salary saved to replace the teaching and administrative role of the absent senior member of the staff by one or more temporary appointments at a junior level. Almost every such large department has a number of able young men and women keen to start up the early steps of the academic ladder, assistant lecturers on short-period appointments, research fellows, academic research assistants, etc. From such a reserve stock of potential academic teachers, it is generally easy to find some who would jump at the chance of a junior academic post for a year or more. For example, a temporary assistant lecturer could be offered a fourth year extension at the end of his normal three year appointment: or an Imperial Chemical Industries Fellow, for example, could be offered a temporary teaching post.

The essential steps in making such an arrangement are that the university concerned must be willing to give long-period deferment, up to, say, five years, and the university department must be willing to use the salary saved to make suitable short-period appointments. This procedure has already been put in operation. The University of London has given one of its readers leave of absence without pay for up to five years to fill a chair at an overseas university. He is free to return at any intervening year, if circumstances were to make this his wish, and while abroad his name remains on the departmental list and College Calendar as 'Seconded to University X.' If at the end of the five years the overseas university wanted to retain his services for life he would be free to accept: he would then resign from his home university. This procedure appears to offer great advantages, particularly because it imposes no financial burden on the home university and because it is flexible in operation, and only necessitates relatively minor administrative changes within a large department.

The Secretary of the Inter-University Council has told me that he thinks that if this method were to be widely adopted in British universities it would greatly ease the task of his Council of finding the best possible candidates to fill all the very many posts now vacant in overseas universities. At the present time the Council is attempting to fill more than 200 academic vacancies in all subjects in 12 university institutions overseas: of these vacancies nearly 40 are professorships. The position of the British Council is similar, but on a much smaller scale. The number of posts to be filled overseas in non-Commonwealth countries, particularly in medicine, is showing signs of rapid increase.

It is of interest to compare the present 800 or so British-born academics now in overseas university posts in under-developed countries with the 12,000 university teachers now in the British universities. So those in overseas posts are now about 7 per cent of those at home. In order to compete with the big rise in numbers in the overseas universities as the countries' development plans make progress, one might hope that this fraction might rise to nearer 10 per cent—assuming, of course, that the overseas universities still welcome British candidates: they will only do so if, in the long run, British candidates are at least equal to the best available from elsewhere. As with other exports, Britain must be competitive in quality.

If we suppose that in a few years' time, say, 5 per cent of British academic staff would be seconded overseas, it would mean that in a medium-sized department of 20 staff there would on the average be one member seconded for overseas service: in a large department with 40 or more staff, there would be on the average two or more away. That this does not involve an impossible organizational problem to a department is shown by the number of academics who now do go abroad with one year leave of absence. Moreover, any university which has a regular seven year sabbatical leave of absence must be able to compete organizationally, in principle, with 13 per cent of their staff absent.

In small departments there is less flexibility and probably here the institution of supernumerary posts might be necessary. So, in spite of the fact that the secondment scheme from big departments does not involve extra financial resources, a considerable annual sum is probably required to make possible the secondment of staff from the universities as a whole. Presumably this in the future will come through the Department of Technical Co-operation.

If able university staff are to be attracted to periods of overseas service, it is important that they should be able to obtain facilities to carry on their own researches. In some cases the local universities can produce what is required, but in many cases they cannot. In England we have found the great importance of having money for special researches available direct to the research worker from an outside body. It is satisfactory to note that the grants for special researches from the Research Grants Committee of the Department of Scientific and Industrial Research are available for British subjects on secondment to Commonwealth countries from permanent posts in this country. On the other hand, under present regulations such grants are not available to British subjects overseas on permanent appointments. I hope that the Department of Technical Co-operation will take the initiative and remove this anomaly.

If Britain and also the other affluent members of the Commonwealth are to play their part in the development of university education in the now poor countries of the world, then I think two things are vital. First, it is important that the governing bodies and senates of the universities work out administrative arrangements for seconding a few of their staff and encourage the use of this machinery. Then I would like to see growing up among the academic staff of our universities, both senior and junior, a greater readiness to envisage working overseas for a period of their career. Of course, to-day, overseas service of all kinds, as a contribution which the affluent West can make to the growth and prosperity of the newly developing nations, is much in the news: President Kennedy's Peace Corps is a much publicized example, but many other important schemes are in operation in Great Britain or elsewhere. There is a desperate need in the developing countries for all types of trained people, particularly in the technical and technological fields. National schemes must be worked out to ensure their supply. This will cost a lot of money and must be accepted as part of our national obligation to give generous aid to these countries.

Here I have concentrated on the university aspect, partly because I know this field best and partly because I think that much can be done by the local initiative of universities and individuals through making use of the secondment method. In the jargon of to-day one might call this suggested method an administrative 'do it yourself' trick. How many academic pundits have bewailed—in my view falsely—the alleged lack of initiative of the modern generation, and the undue reliance on Government action. Here is a chance for the academic world as a whole to show that much can be done without waiting on Government initiative.

An International Institute of Science and Technology

J. R. KILLIAN, JR.

Every so often, an idea appears or a proposal is made that stirs one's imagination deeply because of its fresh potentialities, its importance, its intellectual spirit, and its appropriateness at a particular moment in time. Such a proposal in my estimation was the suggestion made to NATO in 1960 that they should examine the possibility of establishing in the Atlantic Community of nations an International Institute of Science and Technology as a co-operative centre of research and advanced education in the sciences and technology.

The idea emerged in 1959 in the discussions of the Study Group[1] set up by the NATO Science Committee in co-operation with the Ford Foundation and the Fondation Universitaire of Brussels; M. Louis Armand was Chairman of this distinguished group. After some discussion of the scope and objectives of such an Institute, the Study Group recommended a feasibility study of this proposed technical university in their report: 'Improving the Effectiveness of Western Science.' Specifically, they recommended that a small working-group be formed to develop concrete plans that might then be considered by NATO governments.

PRIMARY MOTIVATIONS

The reasons for the emergence of this idea and the Study Group's support of it are complex. I was not a member of the Group, but in subsequent consideration of the subject and discussion with those who were, it became apparent that the primary motivations are a mixture of educational, scientific, engineering, economic, and political objectives, with the emphasis on the educational, scientific and engineering. We have in the Atlantic Community a great tradition of scientific achievement. With this to build upon, we have a scientific and technological potential that is unmatched. We see

Reprinted from *NATO Letter*, April 1962, Vol. X, No. 4, with the permission of the author and the publisher, NATO Information Service in Paris. Dr. J. R. Killian, Jr., is Chairman of the Corporation of the Massachusetts Institute of Technology. He was the first Special Assistant on Science and Technology appointed by President Eisenhower in 1957.

[1] *NATO Letter*, October 1960.

some fields in which this full potential is being realized, but in others, and in relation to the challenge faced by the West, we can say that we are not in general realizing to the full what we are capable of doing. It is not primarily a matter of the West's striving to excel another bloc of nations such as the Soviet; it is rather a matter of the Atlantic Community being deserving of itself by releasing its full resources of talent, energy, imagination—and freedom.

The reasons for the gap between our accomplishments and our potential in science are many—the need for greater co-operation among Atlantic nations, the need for new institutions to demonstrate unity, the rapidly changing character of scientific research as its instruments become more expensive and the fields more interrelated, the ever more demanding intellectual requirements of higher education, the need for training greater numbers of scientists and engineers, and a host of others. Clearly, a single new Institute could not normally have much impact on a problem of such variety and magnitude. An Institute of this kind, however, might be different and this is where the excitement and challenge of the idea became evident to me and to many others. Such an institution, unachievable anywhere in the world probably except in the Atlantic Community, might provide the first positive demonstration that higher education is a domain of common interest to the Western nations.

Through the creation of an Institute under the joint auspices of the Atlantic nations, it might be possible to set a new pattern of advanced education in the sciences that was essentially novel to all nations of the West, and at the same time that would demonstrate the enormous advantages of real co-operation in research among the scientists of Western nations. Of course, the Institute could also be in the scientific forefront in the fields it emphasized: its educational outlook could always be directed toward the future. It would also augment the educational facilities that are clearly needed. But its real justification, I and others believed, would go far beyond the normal measurable output.

"TRADITION OF THE FUTURE"

For some time I have felt that the cause of science and engineering education would be served by the creation of new university-level institutions. By starting fresh, these new institutions would be free to devise new patterns of education, uninhibited by the traditions and embedded policies to be found in every existing institute, however great. I had felt, particularly, that it would be helpful to all existing institutions, as they sought to adapt themselves to the future to have before them a new unfolding institution which sought to draw the best methods and ideas from existing institutions and to achieve a new blend. Such an institution, fresh in spirit, innovative in practice, and dedicated to 'the tradition of the future' could be a stimulus to other institutions and help them in their efforts to try new and updated approaches to education. The fact that most of my career has been devoted to an American institute of technology which has been notably willing to experiment has not diminished this conviction. On the contrary, I felt that such a new-style university could be a help to my own institution and not a threat.

I also had become convinced that the Western world was short of educational capacity to prepare enough high-talent scientists and engineers. Almost every country on both sides of the Atlantic was faced with the need to double the number of its scientists and engineers.

LOCATION IN EUROPE

In the United States scientific community I also found great enthusiasm for this concept, and a willingness to advocate it, even though the institution was to be located in the European area, as all agree it must.

An additional important factor highlighted by M. Armand's Study Group was the need to develop, particularly in Europe, much closer substantive relationships between industry and universities on scientific and technical matters. In this respect, I believe the United States has been more successful than Europe, primarily I would say because of the more recent development of universities in my country where many of them came into existence during our industrial revolution and were closely tied to it. This situation is changing in Europe, I understand, but the Study Group felt that it could be enormously speeded by the creation of the Institute in Europe which would have this as one of its primary objectives.

STRONG WORKING GROUP

When the Study Group submitted its report, the recommendation for the Institute was immediately singled out and passed to the North Atlantic Council for action, and on 2 November 1960 the Council voted to establish the small group proposed, with a mission ... 'to study the question of the establishment of an International Institute of Science and Technology' and to formulate 'recommendations on specific possibilities and their feasibility.'

I was honoured, and frankly challenged, when M. Spaak, then Secretary General, asked if I would accept the Chairmanship of the Working Group, and was particularly pleased when I realized what a strong group we would have. Two members—Sir John Cockcroft and Dr. H. B. G. Casimir—were members of M. Armand's previous Committee, and the others were Dr. P. Piganiol, Professor A. Rucker, Professor P. Caldirola and Dr. W. A. Nierenberg, the Assistant Secretary General for Scientific Affairs of NATO. The Working Group was established in the same way as that of M. Armand with a portion of the financial support supplied by the Ford Foundation through the Fondation Universitaire of Brussels.

The deliberations of this Working Group were lively and were enriched by discussions outside the Group and with a large number of scientists, educationalists and government officials throughout the Atlantic nations. The Group itself had full plenary meetings in Cambridge (Mass.), Paris and Bellagio. I think all of the members feel that we carefully examined the idea and possible ways of implementing it. It was exciting to me to observe the way the Group, notwithstanding the very different conditions in each of our countries, was able to narrow the discussions until we all felt that we understood each other and had a clear idea of what we wanted to accomplish and the best way we could see to proceed to bring it about.

UNANIMOUS CONCLUSION

Our conclusion was unanimous, and I can do no better than quote from our report:

'It is the unanimous conclusion of the Working Group that it is both feasible and desirable to establish in Europe an International Institute of Science and Technology devoted to graduate and post-doctoral studies and operating at the pinnacle of the university system; and that the benefits which such an institution could bring to science, engineering and education, and thus to the welfare and security of the Western countries, make its establishment urgently important.

'The Working Group concludes, further, that today the widely recognized advantages of international efforts in science, together with the growing facility and effectiveness with which Western countries undertake group efforts for the common good, provide an unprecedentedly favourable climate for the establishment of an international educational institution devoted to science and technology. The increasing interdependence of nations—in part the result of science and technology—and the importance to scientific progress of free and cultivated international exchange set the stage for new joint efforts among nations.'

The institution we finally proposed in some detail to the NATO Council is based on the considerations I have already mentioned, on some that emerged from our deliberations, and on the advice received from others we consulted.

PATTERN OF GROWTH

In developing the organization of the Institute it should break away from the traditional framework of conventional departments and adopt a pattern along the lines of the inter-disciplinary research fields. We have proposed a small number of research centres in specified research areas which represent important fields combining both the sciences and technology and which require integration of diverse disciplines. Specifically, we have proposed centres in Applied Mathematics and Theoretical Physics, Technological Processes and Systems, Materials Research, Earth Sciences, and Life Sciences. We also recognize in this proposal the danger of simply substituting a new, fairly rigid pattern for the conventional academic organization. Accordingly, it is our hope that the Institute can ensure, through flexible organization and procedures and good communications between the centres, a pattern of change and growth that can accommodate to changing needs.

The pattern proposed is but one of several that are possible, though it seemed the best to the Working Group. The kinds of people selected to lead and build the institution should really determine its pattern. It will derive from their taste, insight and judgement.

CENTRE FOR ADVANCED STUDY

We have suggested that a Centre for Advanced Study be created as an essential part of the Institute; in fact, as the first part to come into existence, to provide an environment attractive to visiting scholars and available for conferences and other activities contributory to scientific intercourse and international exchange. Such a centre for Advanced Study could assist the Institute in its development. We do believe most firmly that the idea of inter-disciplinary centres should be maintained, but would, at the same time, hold that the Institute be so deeply imbued with the importance of adaptability and change that it will have the courage to drop centres and programmes if more important ones emerge that should replace them.

Through pooling of resources, as at CERN, the Institute could emphasize special fields requiring large-scale facilities, not easily available elsewhere. High-speed computers and equipment for providing high magnetic fields are examples of such large-scale facilities.

Throughout, we believe it essential that the Institute emphasize the intimate interrelation of research and teaching.

We recommend location at a central place, complete with research centres, administrative building, staff and student housing and other facilities. Association might well be provided with existing research centres in various countries which have programmes relevant to the interests of the

Institute. It is my personal hope to see CERN associated with the Institute in some way. Among ourselves we ventured the hope that some country, even several, would offer to provide certain basic needs for land and buildings.

EIGHT-YEAR PLAN

As I have said, special emphasis would be given to relations with industry and with governments. Summer courses for professional personnel are a possibility, as are special studies, conferences or seminars on important technical questions. Co-operative programmes of education or research in management of science and organization of science would also be natural subjects for the Institute to be concerned with.

As far as size is concerned, the Working Group contemplated an Institute with a student body—doctoral candidates and post-doctoral fellows—of about 1,000, an academic staff of 400, and supporting staff of 1,000. Our estimates of the costs, carefully considered and compared with the costs of comparable existing institutions, were for ultimate capital investment totalling some $55 million and average annual operating costs close to $16 million.

Recognizing that such an Institute could not spring full-blown into being, and should not, we have considered a phased build-up that will allow step-by-step growth, gradual selection of staff, and an even requirement for funds. Such a phased approach we estimate should be planned over an eight-year period.

NO DUPLICATION

One of the most frequent questions raised about the Institute bears on this last point; that is, the drain on the staffs of existing institutions that would be caused by the creation of the new Institute with the goal of scientific excellence we have recommended. Some staff members most certainly could be drawn from the scientific establishment of industries and governments as well as from universities. The Working Group, most of whose members are closely associated with universities, has the strong conviction that such an Institute would supplement rather than duplicate the science and engineering departments of existing universities and institutes. If a gradual build-up is adopted, the requirement for academic staff would not be large at first, and many could come as one- or two-year visitors, especially in the Institute for Advanced Study. In time, from the pool of countries participating, and from the students the Institute itself has trained, adequate staff should be obtained without serious effect on any existing university or research laboratory.

The full details of the administrative arrangements recommended by the Working Group, and of the substantive research areas we believe appropriate for the early stages of the Institute are contained in our report. Two points are worthy of special mention, however. One is the importance of establishing among the participating governments a means whereby the degree awarded by the Institute will be accepted in all countries for teaching purposes. This is obviously fundamental to the ability to attract students. I believe it is fair to say that it would be important today, independently of the proposed Institute, if such a provision could be adopted to advance the international equivalence of university degrees.

The second point is that the Working Group believed the Institute should be established so that it could be ultimately independent of any existing international organization. It must have a life of its own if its viability is to be assured and if the true spirit of a university is to be achieved. It cannot depend directly on the military, political or economic considerations that necessarily determine the course of other organizations.

ELEVEN OBJECTIVES

The most effective summation I can provide is to quote, from our report, the eleven primary objectives our Working Group developed as our view of the Institute:

'1. To be in the fullest sense an international institution, representing the sponsorship of a group of nations and the bringing together of scholars, both students and staff, from many countries. Through its organization, spirit and motivation, it could attempt to imbue in its students a wider understanding of science and technology, and indeed of all learning, through appreciation of the positive values which an international milieu would provide.

2. To recognize the growing interrelationships among different fields of learning and research. In its structure and in all of its programmes, the Institute should stress the unity of knowledge and seek to achieve a flexibility which promotes easy interrelationships among fields, and which avoids rigidly organized departments.

3. To pitch its programme at the pinnacle of university education.

4. To build a research programme of such quality and comprehensiveness that it will provide the richest possible environment for the nurturing of scientists and engineers of exceptional creative ability. In all of its plans and policies the Institute should recognize that research and education are inseparable, that each reinforces the other, and that its success will depend upon its doing both superlatively well. The Institute should always be alert to identify important new fields of research and to educate scientists in those fields.

5. To seek a close association between pure and applied science, recognizing the contribution which each can make to the other, and avoiding the separation which frequently works to the disadvantage of both science and engineering. Especially should there be recognition of the need in Europe for an institute that (a) brings into close association the education of both scientists and engineers, (b) achieves a productive relationship between science and technology, and (c) emphasizes and facilitates the transition from new knowledge to its application.

6. To respond to the need in the West for greater stress on graduate education in engineering as well as in science, and for engineers of greater versatility and adaptability. Industry, for example, increasingly demands qualified scientists and engineers who possess not only a mastery of the latest developments and techniques, but also a deep understanding of the underlying disciplines. They must be able to master new ideas and new technologies throughout their working careers.

7. To establish close relations with industry, and thus to facilitate the rapid application of new ideas arising out of basic research.

8. To become an international centre for scientific conferences and the interchange of ideas, and a mecca for outstanding scholars by the formal provision within the institution for a centre for advanced study.

9. To include as an ultimate objective, even though not formally provided for at first, a strong programme devoted to the relation between science and society and the cultivation of the humanities and social sciences as partners of science and engineering. As indicated later, much can be done from the very start to develop and contribute to these fields.

10. To provide for freedom of scholarly opportunity at all levels and thus to encourage individual development and initiative. The Institute should aspire to achieve an environment universally recognized by scholars to be superlatively attractive for their work and professional growth.

11. To limit the enrolment to exceptionally talented students by maintaining uncompromisingly high standards of admission . . .'

EXCITING TESTAMENT

I find the prospect of the creation of the International Institute of Science and Technology a moving and exciting testament to the inventiveness of Western society.

I believe the achievement of such a university, located in Europe, but serving and being supported by the entire Atlantic Community, could be another one of those 'transforming' institutions contributing uniquely to the cultural, economic and political resources of the region. These institutions may well provide an unmatched example to all the world of the strength and appeal which derives from the free exchange of ideas, the promotion of comity among nations of like interests and objectives, and the steady striving of international forces to release the full intellectual and imaginative energies of free peoples.

Science, Technology, and Economic Growth

J. HERBERT HOLLOMON

The relationships between science and technology and economic growth are not at all clear to many of those engaged in science or to those who participate in the business of "growing" the economy. It is a strange paradox that, although the human intellect has been capable of great achievements in science and its pursuit, the translation of science to use by society is not well understood. Indeed, the glittering successes of science have dimmed our perception of the details of the complex process by which man's understanding of the universe finally enters the world of industry and commerce.

That there is misunderstanding is clear from the frequent claims that the large research and development expenditures and the large commitment to science in our country lead inevitably to national prosperity and well-being. Consider for a moment our recent expenditures for research and development and the rate of growth of our gross national product. The enormous increases in funds for science and for the development of technology have not been followed by a corresponding increase in the rate of growth of our economy. Indeed, nearly the reverse has been true. In the period 1947 to 1954, the average annual rate of growth was 3.7 percent. From 1954 to 1960, the average rate dropped to 3 percent. All this occurred during the period when our expenditures for R&D tripled and the percentage of our gross national product spent for R&D doubled (rising from 1.4 to 2.8 percent). During this time, there have been loud and strident claims of the great social benefits that were to come from this large commitment to science and to research and development.

However, the enormous increase in R&D was stimulated mainly by the requirements of national programs not particularly directed toward the increase of industrial productivity or toward innovation in civilian technology, both of which are so important in increasing our rate of economic growth or in improving the variety of our society. Moreover, the people, institutions,

Reprinted from *Physics Today*, March 1963, Vol. XVI, No. 3, pp. 38–40, 42 and 46, with the permission of the author and the publisher, American Institute of Physics. Dr. J. Herbert Hollomon is Assistant Secretary for Science and Technology in the Department of Commerce. Before coming to Washington in 1962, he was with the research laboratories of the General Electric Company where he became General Manager of the General Engineering Laboratory.

and environment necessary for the health of technology pertinent to the civil needs have not been well supported.

The development of technology is clearly influenced by the pressures and demands of the times. Even science has its fads, encouraged by the interests, needs, and amusements of its patrons. Solid-state physics claims its practical application to materials, and much of the justification of nuclear physics derives from the awesome power of the atom.

Of the annual R&D expenditure of 2.8 percent of our gross national product, about 2 percent is spent for space, defense, and atomic-energy purposes, with only 0.8 percent for all other purposes, including those to increase productivity and stimulate innovation. Other major industrial countries, such as Japan, West Germany, the Netherlands, and Sweden, spend an average of about 1.25 percent of their gross national product for R&D, little of it aimed at military or space objectives. In terms of manpower, 0.4 percent of the West German labor force are scientists and engineers devoted directly to activities that either relate to science itself or are pertinent to the development of industry and commerce. The comparable figure for the United States is 0.2 percent.[1] While it is evident that economic growth depends upon many factors other than research and development, during recent times the rate of growth of almost all the industrial nations of the world exceeded our own. This gives cause for serious concern about the effectiveness of the use of science and of the resources we apply to the development of civilian technology. The United Kingdom and Canada, the other industrialized countries having relatively low rates of economic growth, are also concerned about the development and use of scientific and technical resources for their own national objectives.

The rate of growth of the Soviet gross national product was 6 to 7 percent in the 1950's, and is expected to reach 8 percent in the 1960's. In terms of productivity, the Soviet gross national product per man-year in this decade is expected to grow at 4 percent per year, almost double ours. Here it is important to note that, despite large space and military programs, the Soviet Union has enjoyed a high productivity growth rate by committing nonmilitary and nonspace R&D to the development of basic heavy industry rather than to the development of consumer goods and services.

It is clear that the effort to break the way technologically may be greater and the risks higher than they are for the adaptation of demonstrated accomplishment to the needs of another society or circumstances. Thus, as the front runner, our relative effort should be much greater than that of other nations.

---

[1] This figure is obtained by subtracting from the U.S. effort the technical people engaged in the space and military programs that only indirectly benefit the civilian economy, and even then not without the additional technical effort of translation.

We must be concerned not only with how our economy and our society use science but also that the means for its use are healthy and effective. In the long term, the development of science depends upon the support of the society in which it flourishes. As Bacon said, "The true and lawful goal of science is that human life be endowed with new powers and inventions." If the economy is not healthy, science itself cannot be healthy. If science claims too much or is misused, it may not be able to demand the conditions of free inquiry and healthy support that it needs. Thus, it is important to understand the relationship of science and technology to the growth of the economy, and to examine those things that need to be done to insure that our scientific and technical houses are in order and that the best use is being made of the rare resources and capabilities of unusual people.

You know well that science is international. A scientific discovery made in the United States—or in Britain or France—is more quickly communicated, and its significance more swiftly appreciated, throughout the international scientific community than it is to those who use it for practical ends. The knowledge of the great discoveries of biophysics and biochemistry concerning the structure and character of living matter and the discoveries of the nature of atomic forces spread quickly through the "open" society of science. Science is common property available to all nations with even a modest scientific effort.

Science is free to all. The economy or our way of life benefits only after someone puts science to work for the practical benefit of man. Modern myth says that science, through some magic, converts itself into useful products of society. The great achievements of science in changing the modern world and broadening the character of our society have obscured the activity that is engaged in its use. The activity that puts science to use to meet the needs of society proceeds almost independently of the advancing science. The technology of the Gothic period did not use science, nor does the construction of modern shelter depend much on the immediate advances in atomic, quantum, or nuclear physics.

It is also true that the knowledge and understanding that are associated with the technology of pertinence to our civilian economy and to the improvement of the character of society are not necessarily the same as those which are thought to be needed for our military or space efforts. The science of possible pertinence to the improvement of housing or to the elimination of air pollution is not likely to be the same as that related to space travel. Nor does the activity through which science is made useful happen by itself. It requires a special environment, people with a special education and outlook, and institutions that encourage invention, innovation, and the diffusion of technology. Basic to the art of invention and the technique of innovation is the art of design and synthesis, using science, economics, practice, and lore. The two activities are symbiotic—advances in science benefit the development of technology, and the tools developed from new technology open new vistas for the advancement of science.

However, economic progress stems from increased productivity based on new technology; then, the resulting increased income provides the purchasing power for new products and new services. The broadening of the economic choice and the improvement in our way of life that are made possible by increased productivity come from the introduction of new goods and services. More frequently than not, the introduction of these new goods awaits the ability of the society to purchase them. The sale of washing machines to Nigeria is not limited by technology, nor was the sale of automobiles that recently increased so rapidly in the Netherlands.

The process by which science is used to benefit the economy occurs by an extraordinarily complex process of the development and diffusion of new technology throughout the whole of industry and commerce. It depends upon a close interaction between the known and the unique demands of the times. The mechanics of technological change require perceptive and technically trained management to comprehend the potential of the new technology and to know about the interaction among production, science, marketing, distribution, and technology.

It is often assumed that the spectacular results of atomic energy (which have so radically changed concepts of national defense), the transistor (which led to miniaturization and the reliability so important to space vehicles), and radar (so crucial to modern travel) have made substantial contributions to our economy. Actually, their contribution to gross national product has been small, and they have not as yet made substantial contributions to an increased efficiency in the use of capital and of labor. Probably the greatest recent impact of technology on our economy has come from the increase in agricultural productivity. The most fundamental change in the character of our society in the last five decades has been the change from an agricultural to an industrial economy—from a rural to an urban society.

The rise in agricultural productivity provided the increased income to allow the purchase of products and services other than those which fulfill the simple necessities. Just as in agriculture, the great force that will further increase our economic growth, improve the environment for science, and lead to new products and services for the consumer, is the increase in the productivity of industry and commerce. Last year only about 10 percent of the huge total of $15 billion spent on research and development was devoted to improving productivity.

In our society, innovation is often first introduced by industries and enterprises that can afford the high costs of modern technical resources and can appreciate and exploit the results of new science and the opportunities provided by advancing technology. But the society generally benefits only when these technological improvements diffuse rapidly to the less efficient firms. This rate of adaptation depends on an effective means of rapidly diffusing technical knowledge. Japan and Russia, for example, appreciate the importance of this diffusion as basic to the development of their economy, and seek to exploit the best practices of others and use their own technical resources for their own special needs.

This problem of diffusion is critical to our effective use of science and to the growth of the economy. Of the 300,000 manufacturing companies in the United States, about 300 perform 80 percent of industrially sponsored research and development. The same 300 companies account for 60 percent of the sales of all manufacturing companies and 61 percent of total manufacturing employment. They also spend about 2.75 percent of their sales on research and development, while the remainder of the 300,000 spend 0.9 percent, about one-fifth as much. This disparity reduces the ability of the smaller enterprises to compete in the world economy. As companies become less profitable, they spend less on research and development. This tends to make them comparatively less productive and still less profitable.

The ability of the small company either to undertake innovation on its own, or to take advantage of the innovations of large companies, is determined first by the availability of new technology and second by the facility with which the small company can profitably exploit the possibilities it provides. Unlike the diffusion of agricultural technology, which was effectively accomplished by land-grant colleges and extension services, there is no special mechanism of assuring the diffusion of technology to the 3.3 million industrial and commercial firms in America, even though that figure means there are almost as many individual companies as there are now farms.

Let us look at another aspect of the relationship of scientific and technical effort to the economy. Reassuring justification of the enormous federal programs for research and development is that there will be results deriving from it that will be of substantial direct benefit to private industry and the public. The argument runs something like this: We don't have to worry about our economy since the results of the government-supported technical effort will be so useful to civilian technology that they justify the huge expenditures. These efforts to develop military equipment, atomic power plants, and space vehicles may well be providing the basis for a whole new technology of complex systems made up of highly reliable parts, but the translation of this technology to the economy through industry and commerce is neither direct nor cheap—nor inevitable. In fact, the translation requires specially trained people with a special point of view and an industry that understands and appreciates the possibilities of the new technology and can afford to use it. These people come from the same pool of scientists and engineers who provide the advancing technology to meet the threat to our national security.

Government-sponsored activity is becoming increasingly dependent on a sophisticated science and technology peculiarly suited to very specialized military and space objectives, and thus more and more unlikely to be of important direct benefit to the economy, to the improvement of our transportation system, to urban development, to food, shelter, and clothing, or to education. Moreover, the results that can be used require further research and development to adapt them for civilian needs. Essential to that adaptation process are technically competent people able to carry out the additional research and development and institutions to produce and distribute the resulting product in a competitive market at a profit. It is also well to recognize that technically competent people are required to develop a market for a product as well as to develop the product itself. The establishment of an efficient service organization or the determination of the need of an industrial customer for new products are examples.

Crucial to the development and use of science for any of our social, economic, or national needs is an adequately growing supply of scientists and engineers, and the technicians that work with them. We, in our country, have not made a sufficient commitment to education. Our unemployed are those of our people who are the least skilled and with the least education. An earlier investment in education would have made them available to fill the openings so widely advertised for teachers, nurses, technicians, engineers, and scientists. We are also failing to provide the people for research and development, particularly in fields important to our civilian economy.

The 1963 increase in the supply of scientists and engineers engaged in research and development is expected to be almost 30,000. But the increase in support for research and development for space alone will require about the same number, and that number is equivalent to 20 percent of the total now doing research and development supported by industry, and equivalent to half the total of those doing research and development in universities.

The number of engineering graduates this year declined to an annual average of 35,000. Yet it is the engineer that conceives, designs, builds, launches, and controls the complex space vehicles that orbit the earth and reach for the moon. And, it is the technician who backs up the engineer who backs up the scientists. For lack of adequately trained technicians, we waste the talent of both scientists and engineers. For lack of engineers to implement the results of scientific research, we delay the practical benefits from scientific discovery.

The education of engineers to carry on the development and advancement of technology today is inadequate. Few of our schools provide the enthusiastic challenge that the big problems of our time pose, nor do many show the young man the opportunities for applying science to the civilian economy. There are few schools in the country that provide a professional graduate education for engineers or recognize that the art of design and the understanding of social need and opportunity are basic to engineering while providing the science and mathematics that are the engineers' working tools.

The overwhelming concentration of research and development on space and defense projects, the relatively small amount done for private industrial purposes, and the even smaller fraction designed to increase productivity, determine the distribution of our technically trained manpower. With the demand for that scarce resource exceeding total supply, we must make more efficient use of our technical people, or increase the supply, or modify our national goals.

Increasing the supply depends upon the capacity of our educational institutions, both in physical plant and teachers, the financial rather than scholastic ability of students to stay in school, and the encouragement of careers in science and engineering without starving the other disciplines.

If we are to improve the supply, we must increase the proportion of baccalaureates going on to graduate study. In mathematics, physical sciences, and engineering, the most critical fields to many of our national aspirations, only 3000 PhD's are graduating each year, and of these, only 1000 are engineers. If scholastic ability were the limiting factor, there could be ten times as many in engineering, five times as many in mathematics, and twice as many in the physical sciences. The chief obstacle to further study seems to be money—either a lack of funds to pay for the additional education, or the decision to increase immediate income by taking a full-time job.

Redistribution of the current activity is a complex matter. Of the 1.4 million scientists and engineers in America, 400,000 are doing research and development, most of them (280,000) on government-sponsored projects such as space and defense. The remaining 120,000 work in industry for civilian objectives.

The enormous increase in federal support for research and development has already brought about a significant redeployment in technical manpower. There is little doubt that scientists and engineers have been diverted from such fields as teaching, management, supervision, and production to work in research and development. For example, the annual increase in scientists and engineers is about 6 percent a year, but the increase in the number engaged in research and development is 10 percent, whereas the increase of personnel in other areas of activity is only 3 percent.

Educational institutions and government are finding it increasingly difficult to recruit and to hold competent technical people. The fraction of technical people who manage the vast government-sponsored technical programs—who influence policy decisions involving science and technology—

the fraction of these with PhD's is declining. The fraction of college science teachers with PhD's is also decreasing.

We need to recognize that there are some fundamental steps required to improve the health of the economy and provide the adquate and proper support for science. Concerted action by physicists as individuals and through their professional institutions is required to insure public understanding and the political force to meet the problems of our time.

First, we must urge that all aspects of education be strengthened. College and postgraduate training is as important today as secondary-school education was 50 years ago, and deserves and needs the same public support.

Support for education at all levels and in all fields is probably the most important national investment that can be made. Future generations will be better equipped intellectually to cope with the enormously complex technical and social problems, an ability indispensable to the survival of democracy in this technological age. This investment in education is the capital for future economic growth.

This support must be provided directly both to individuals and to institutions for education itself, and not limited to the indirect route of research grants and contracts. This latter form of support, coming largely from the military and space agencies, has biased our teaching and learning toward their special needs.

Secondly, we must recognize that after two centuries of emphasizing the practical and the pragmatic, we are now in great danger of over-reacting. Not only are we neglecting the pragmatic aspects of society but we teach our best students to look down upon practical or useful activities as being intellectually demeaning or inferior. We must provide the climate and the support for work in universities related to the broad practical needs of our civilian economy and society.

Thirdly, we must encourage the establishment of the institutions and the environment that most effectively puts science to practical use, diffuses the results of technology throughout the society, and encourages even higher levels of innovative activity. What is needed is additional support for research and teaching in those fields and in those disciplines that undergird the civilian industrial needs and the technical requirements that an increasingly urbanized life demands. Means must also be found to provide support and stimulation to increase the technological work required for better productivity and the development of new products and services for our people. Industry is aware of the need for this work and has knowledge of its pertinence. In some cases, however, industry either cannot afford (or consists of units too small) to support adequately the development and spread of the technology. Support must be made available for industry, probably through associations, to do work of broad application.

Fourthly, those of us with technical training have a particular responsibility to understand and explain the complex relationship among the elements and factors involving science, technology, invention, and innovation, on the one hand, and the social, economic, political, and cultural needs of our society, on the other. A worthwhile precedent is the important contribution made by physicists after World War II in explaining the physical, social, and political implications of atomic energy.

In summary, we must address ourselves to the task of providing the climate and support required both for science and for that separate activity which puts science to use. Science cannot prosper nor can our nation be secure without a healthy, growing economy based upon a system of free enterprise.

Science and the General Welfare in a Democracy

GLENN T. SEABORG

I have spoken on other occasions of the Third, or Scientific, Revolution and how it is affecting in the most pervasive and intensive way the fabric of modern society. It is the Third Revolution of Science that concerns us today as in earlier days the Democratic Revolution called into service the architects of our national political institutions and as the Industrial Revolution engaged the best talents and energies of those who fashioned the great industrial system of America during the last century. With the advent of the Third Revolution, science has become so important to our national welfare, not only in terms of national defense but also for our economic growth and social well-being, that the relationship between science and government is for us in our day a matter of profound significance.

There was the foreshadowing of such a relationship as early as the Civil War, and a yet stronger indication during the first World War. No one, however, could fail to see at the conclusion of World War II that the contributions of science had been fundamental to national survival in our greatest crisis. Later, the shifting of alignments and the prolongation of latent hostilities in the shape of the Cold War meant that the Federal Government had perforce to become more and more heavily involved in the support of science. These factors account for much of the Government's continued role in setting national objectives in science and influencing progress toward these objectives.

But as we responded to the persisting demands of the Cold War and the needs of national security, we awakened also to a more significant realization. We found that we could not abandon the productive fusion of forces that emerged during the war years. We discovered that the powerful focusing of basic and applied science, engineering development, and industrial production which accomplished so much for us in wartime had equally profound implications for our peacetime future. The advancement of peaceful national goals, for example, economic expansion, the improvement of

The Harrelson Lecture delivered at North Carolina State, University of North Carolina, Raleigh, March 11, 1964, with permission to reprint selected excerpts from the author. Dr. Glenn T. Seaborg is Chairman of the United States Atomic Energy Commission. He is a Nobel Laureate in Chemistry (1951).

health, the development of adequate energy resources and assistance to other nations—all these were recognized to rest upon a continuation of the machinery of concerted scientific-technological efforts.

Before considering more directly the problems that confront us with regard to the structure of our national science policy as it affects our general welfare, I want to explore in somewhat greater depth the circumstances of the Scientific Revolution, the manifold possibilities we are offered and the sobering responsibilities with which we must grapple as modern people in a changing world. Though the forces that have brought about this manifold transformation of human capabilities have been developing for several centuries, it was the discovery of nuclear fission that unmistakably marked our transition into a new world. The sinister aspect of this event was that man had now become capable of drastically modifying the total ecology of his native planet in less time than it will take me to deliver this speech. We have in our hands negative potentialities for destruction that approach infinity; the constructive potentialities for amelioration of the human condition are no less. Perhaps we should look at both in their broad outlines.

As a general condition applicable more or less across the board, we should note first the factor of *amplification*. In every phase of modern technology, the potentiality for phenomenal degrees of amplification forces us to consider the whole planet and even its surrounding regions in space as a closely coupled system. On the terrestrial level, a devastating flood or earthquake in the remotest region of the globe can almost instantly, through modern means of communication and transportation, marshal the enormous resources of our own and other technologically advanced nations to assist the beleaguered inhabitants of that region. The effects of a drought in some part of the world resonate throughout the economies of the major grain-producing nations with an almost imperceptible time-lag. In the reaches of outer space, a scientific experiment by one nation becomes the concern of the international community of scientists even before it can be performed. Today in the strictest sense of their truth we can quote John Donne's words that "no man is an island unto himself." Certainly with the increasing unity of world science, no nation of great power can shape the future of its own scientific and technological development without profoundly affecting also the future of all mankind.

The policy such a nation adopts with regard to the development of its energy resources, for example, will of necessity be watched with interest by developing nations in need of the help that new forms of energy can provide for their emerging economies. We have some distance to go with the development of nuclear power, and later perhaps with controlled thermonuclear power, before every inhabitant of the world can flick a switch and have electrical energy derived from the atom at his command. Nevertheless we are certain such a day will come if humanity is sufficiently endowed with patience, good will and wisdom.

The widespread use of radioisotopes has already done much through medical applications to alleviate human suffering and prolong life, and, in addition, these new materials now available in substantial quantities provide tools of great value for the improvement of industrial processes and agricultural productivity. What we have accomplished in the span of only a few years should convince us that nuclear energy can also revolutionize maritime transportation, quench the thirst of arid nations, lengthen the shelf life of perishable foods, provide the electrical power in space satellites needed to make world-wide radio and television a reality for this generation, and in the not-too-distant future propel us on missions of exploration to other planets.

The consequences of the misuse of nuclear energy, on the other hand, can place us all in jeopardy. The threat of rockets armed with nuclear warheads imposes new burdens upon man's capacity for rational conduct. In the present conflict it is not men who are in jeopardy—it is man.

Powerful and dangerous as nuclear energy can be when pointed toward destructive ends, it is not strange that the applications of this force in peaceful pursuits also require of man that he proceed always on the basis of precise knowledge and with the greatest respect for the possible consequences of his undertakings. With the exploitation of nuclear energy for power, we must concern ourselves increasingly with the safe disposal of large quantities of radioactive waste materials. With the ever-widening employment of radioisotopes for industrial, medical and research purposes, we need widespread sophistication among the scientists, physicians, and technicians who handle these remarkably potent substances. As we prepare to use the enormous potentialities of nuclear explosions for such projects as forming canals or cutting passes through mountains, we cannot safely neglect any expense or care needed to assure that we will accurately and reliably achieve the objectives we have planned. At the same time we should have the courage to make the best use of these new instruments in their right relation to other technological developments when the need arises.

Not only do we have these tremendous new energy resources well on their way to successful exploitation, we are also rapidly mastering the revolutionary technology of high-speed computers and automation. Amplification is very much in evidence in this field: unprecedented amplification of the rate of production and equally unprecedented amplification of our thought processes, leading to the solution of problems of remarkable scope and complexity. The potential effects of this technology are of such significance that we must restudy, and perhaps may have to reshape, what we had thought were unchanging economic concepts and principles.

Equally profound changes have taken place in the life sciences, especially in their relationships to physics and biochemistry. The possibilities of transforming microorganisms, plants and animals in such a manner as to improve our ecological and economic situations are so nearly infinite as to dwarf description. There are millions of species, and the routes of artificial evolution through which any one of them may be educed into new forms are diverse, ever-branching and virtually endless. We may expect that inevitably our recently acquired knowledge of the genetic code will be applied also to the improvement of the human species which Julian Huxley said recently so badly needs to be done. He says that our species is deteriorating "thanks to the keeping alive of genetic defectives . . . and thanks to new mutation-causing agents." But once we have the ability to determine the genetic characteristics of a human infant, who will step forward with sufficient wisdom to choose those traits most beneficial to the man of the future?

These possibilities, together with the urgent problems of an exploding world population, force us to consider the fundamental question—what are people for? We will need to answer this question at the same time that we are struggling with the multitude of other problems brought about by the population explosion. Science must play the key role in the solution of these problems. We may expect, for example, that our present farm surpluses will soon disappear and we shall require all the skill of our soil scientists, agronomists and agricultural experts to raise productivity to the required levels. These difficulties are sure to be further increased by the withdrawal of appreciable acreages of our best farm lands from cultivation to be used for urban developments, freeways, military installations, factories, etc. New methods of food processing and means to reduce waste and spoilage will have to be devised so that we may more completely utilize our plant and animal crops. Our diminishing reserves of forests and minerals will force the adoption of adequate conservation policies, and the development of substitute materials will assume a new urgency. We shall find ourselves increasingly dependent on the desalting of sea water to fill urban reservoirs. The congestion of our cities will intensify present problems and create new ones in transportation, utilities, water supply, waste disposal, public health and recreation, mental health and the entire range of social behavior.

Fortunately we have the potent instrumentality of the new techniques in automation to help us with the solution of many of these problems. Not only does this new computer-based technology provide the means of tremendously increasing production but it also will enable us to operate the systems of great complexity which we will need for the simultaneous control and harmonizing of the many factors affecting our expanding urban civilization. The extremely great capability of the new computer technology brings with it, however, the threat of major social and economic distortions. One freewheeling mathematician believes that the rise of automation will propel us into an entirely novel kind of world where 2% of our population, working in factory and on farm, will produce all the goods and food that the other 98% can possibly consume. Faced with this overabundance of leisure, an economist predicts that we may have to keep the unemployed portion of our population under more or less constant sedation unless we can figure out something better for them to do.

Sedation as an answer may already be old hat because of the startling development of new chemotherapeutic drugs which upon further development hold promise for the alleviation of mental suffering and perhaps also for the beneficial readjustment of personality and our more transient moods. We would hope that, valuable as these drugs may prove themselves to be, their use on any extensive scale will be no more than a passing phase in our history, giving way in due time to a finer adjustment in the relations between the individual and society. It is possible that by the combined attack of improved human genetics and the development of more sophisticated social sciences and psychology we may someday be able to empty our medicine cabinets. However this may be, we can imagine the grave political consequences, even apart from war, should these psychotherapeutic drugs be used as psychochemical weapons for coercion and control. Since self-control is essential for non-violent resistance, peaceful Gandhian methods could be rendered ineffectual by mood-altering drugs; in such a nightmare existence, brainwashing might become a specialty of chemists.

We need not accept the probability of such extreme predictions concerning our future to realize that by the most conservative estimates profound social and economic changes are in progress through the impact of science. There can be no doubt that the kinds of jobs people will be doing in the future will be very different from those being performed by the majority of us today. Indeed there has already been a great increase in the number of jobs based on providing services and recreation—a trend that is certain to be magnified with further increases in national productivity and the accompanying increase of leisure time.

The most remarkable testimony to the unsinkable buoyancy and optimism of mankind is that over the centuries with possibilities and problems of this magnitude facing him, man has nevertheless begun to feel restless within the confines of his local planet and has sent spacecraft with their human cargo beyond the atmosphere. We have now mustered and coordinated the massive resources of our whole technology in an effort to reach our moon and ultimately the neighboring planets of our solar system. The horizons of human vision have shifted from a horizontal to a vertical orientation. More and more often as we think of the future, our gaze turns toward the immense regions of outer space.

Against this background of the impact of science on our future perhaps we are ready now to consider the question—how well are we equipped as a nation to enter upon this new age of Science, the Third Revolution? There is at this point, I think, no question but that we must face the problems of our time and must assume the responsibilities that our new knowledge and technology are forcing upon us ever more urgently. Before we become too scholarly about the question, however, I must say that some have managed to look at the lighter side of our situation. A few of the more irreverent individuals, scientists I suspect, have compared our management of science policy in recent years to a ship with a thousand helms all connected to one rudder with rubber bands. Another of these whimsical images would have Federal science and its leaders as a colony of ants riding a rolling, tossing log down a flooded stream. As each new twist of the log brings a different bunch of ants out of the water and on top of the log, the ants then able to see daylight proclaim to the others that they have the situation well in hand and know exactly which way to steer the vehicle.

As to where we presently stand with respect to a national policy toward science, there is no better way of gaining a perspective than to review briefly the genesis of science in our government. The growth of our national policy affecting science and our programs for furthering this policy have been the resultant of many forces and events over the span of our history. Looking at the course its development has followed, some have described the evolution of our national policy as the product of a struggle between factions aiming at unified control—those tending toward a monolithic system —and opposing forces striving to preserve pluralism.

*   *   *

. . . While our system of modified pluralism with all of its imperfections has worked remarkably well during a number of crucial years in our nation's history, we have come to the point at which we must grapple with basic issues, questions both as to the management and the support of Federal science. The degree of our preparedness as a people to meet the new challenge of the Third Revolution can be measured by our ability to cope with these issues of the management of science in a democracy. . . . Despite welcome progress, we may yet have a considerable distance to go before the desired balance between pluralism and a more nearly integrated viewpoint can be achieved. Though our current practices have the pluralistic advantage of greater flexibility, we continue as a nation to be plagued by a persistent myopia as to our long-term national goals in science.

*   *   *

As we reflect in this brief and very general discussion on the problems our nation confronts at this stage of its progress into the Third Revolution,

I believe we cannot fail to agree on one major conclusion: if we are to make our way into the future with any degree of assurance that we are on the right path, we will have to give nothing less than our best efforts and wisdom to planning and carrying into effect our long-term national goals in science. We cannot in good conscience treat this aspect of our national well-being with the crisis-to-crisis approach that has so frequently been followed in the past.

Obviously, then we all have a lot to do. Like it or not—we are living in the 20th century. Our country and the world are undergoing a period of change in which the influence of science reaches throughout the fabric of society, shaping nearly every aspect of our lives and our institutions. In our generation a man can no more ignore science than Medieval man could ignore the Christian church or the feudal system. To be fully alive today is to be a conscious participant in forwarding the creative evolution brought about by man's increasing knowledge of his environment.

For the scientist the onus of his new social responsibility cannot be lightly regarded, and it is time that all of us as citizens helped occasionally to remind him of this fact. We should do all that we can to encourage people of scientific capability to enter Government. Nor should we be deterred by the once-popular image of the scientist as a scrambled egghead or an amateur human being. For all his human failings, the scientist also is capable of having some of the talent found in people with other backgrounds and training. Not all scientists, certainly, are practical; not all of them are persons with unusually good judgment. I have even known a few who were not good administrators. But many have this potentiality, and I suggest that, if we have not already done so, we discard the stereotype of the absent-minded professor along with other relics of the past. The Government will continue to need scientists of stature and competence to help administer the great technical programs on which we are embarked. Our official policy and public attitudes should be directed toward achieving this end.

In the academic world more than ever before, scientists and educators bear the responsibility for assuring that the new generations of scientists now coming up through our schools, colleges and universities receive education of the highest degree of excellence. In the pursuit of basic research, so significant for our future, the Federal Government and the university are partners, each necessary and neither sufficient in itself. I would repeat that basic research and graduate education should reinforce each other in a variety of ways. They belong together at every possible level. It is up to all of us involved in the affairs of science to see that this reinforcement is made a vital thing.

The universities, and in particular the scientist in the university, must go even further—they must go beyond the limited task of offering professional education to scientists and look also to the problem of educating a citizenry for an age of science. In this task the problem is not one of seeing that every college graduate is a scientist of some kind. The task is rather to see that every person who comes out of our institutions of higher learning to become a responsible member of our national community has some background in science and understands as thoroughly and as broadly as possible the significance of science for the modern world.

More than ever before we must be prepared to work with all the means and media at our disposal to increase the general level of scientific literacy in this country. Much progress has been made at the grammar school and high school levels, but much more needs to be done to improve the elementary and secondary school curricula and especially to enrich the scientific content at the collegiate level of liberal education.

We are all in this together, and I for one believe that we shall see a growing community of thought extending throughout all groups of our increasingly mobile social structure. I would not underestimate the present growing degree of sophistication of the man in the street about scientific matters. In addition to the excitement over our new breed of astronauts, there has been a very natural and effective dissemination of science and technology, due in part to the close association many members of our growing population of technicians have with these matters on a daily basis. We are recognizing now that there may be a need to provide an additional two years of education beyond high school for many of our young people who can profit from such training. And as we go on to develop an intermediate level of higher education I think we shall see a beneficial interaction between this new group of students and those engaged in baccalaureate programs in the sciences and the arts and humanities.

The program of education for the future must also of necessity include the practice and support of continuing education for our adult population. We have already begun to give emphasis to the significant trends in this direction through educational radio and television and through increased offerings in university and college extension courses. It is by means of these developments in our national educational process that we may hope for genuine progress in the growth of the scientific understanding so necessary to guide our future as a nation.

I want to say, in closing, that I feel very strongly about our need also to strengthen the humanities and arts at every level in the nation's educational programs. This need is not simply a question of giving the humanities a degree of support commensurate with that given to science and technology. I have tried to emphasize throughout this discussion that the shape of our future depends not only upon our strong pursuit of excellence and understanding in science. We are brought face to face with many alternatives by our new capabilities for controlling our environment in all its aspects—physical, social and spiritual. But the use we make of these alternatives, the means we use to direct them toward achievement of the most exalted human objectives, will depend on the values we are able to create for ourselves as we live and grow into a newer world. If we are to achieve humanity in terms of its greatest fulfillment, individually and as a nation, we need to share deeply in the varied experiences which can be reached only through the arts and humane letters. For we know that so long as we are able to see our images reflected clearly and with great validity in these lasting mirrors of the human adventure, by just so long we need not fear to ask with the Scotch poet: "O wad some Power the giftie gie us / To see oursels as ithers see us."

Medical Utopias

RENE J. DUBOS

1

Medicine has been called the mother of sciences. In the minds of most medical men the "basic sciences" are identified with the physical, chemical, and biological theories and techniques used in the laboratory. And indeed, it is apparent that the laboratory has provided the most successful opportunities for the interplay between medicine and basic science during modern times. True enough, the study of psychoses has also revealed fascinating phenomena that throw light on other aspects of human nature, but few of these can as yet be studied in the laboratory. It is probably for this reason that the study of the mind does not rate high among "basic sciences."

The present subject occupies an even lower place in the pecking order of sciences. My thesis is that the study of disease has contributed much to the understanding of man as part of the social body, and therefore to the science of human ecology. An epigram published in the London *Spectator* shortly after the First World War defines succinctly some important aspects of medical sociology.

> *Science finds out ingenious ways to kill*
> *Strong men, and keep alive the weak and ill—*
> *That these a sickly progeny may breed*
> *Too poor to tax, too numerous to feed.*

The problems of human ecology, so well summarized in this epigram, are too complex to be dealt with in a single article, and I shall limit my discussion to a very narrow aspect of the field. Perhaps the easiest way to define my topic is to present it to you—very crudely—in the form of two alternatives. Can we hope that the knowledge gained by the study of disease

Reprinted from *Daedalus, Journal of the American Academy of Arts and Sciences,* 1959, Vol. LXXXVIII, No. 3, pp. 410–424, with permission of the author and the publisher. Dr. Rene Dubos has been with the Rockefeller Institute of Medical Research since 1927 where he did his pioneer work in the field of antibiotics. In addition to his monumental contributions to the biological sciences, Dr. Dubos has written many books and articles on related subjects, including *Pasteur and Modern Science* and the *Mirage of Health* among many others.

will greatly lighten the burden of medical care in the future? Or will new problems of disease endlessly arise and require ever increasing scientific and social efforts, making of medical Utopia a castle in the air that can exist only in the Erewhon of political Utopia?

It is my impression that the first alternative is the one most generally regarded as probable. In fact, it is clear that the lay and para-medical organizations established during the past fifty years to deal with problems of health are based on the optimistic assumption that, given enough time and financial resources, science can develop techniques to prevent or cure most diseases, and that only social and economic limitations will in the future stand in the way of ideal health. Anyone who has dealt with Congressional appropriation committees knows that the present flow of public money for medical research is based on the conviction that science will provide ways to eliminate disease. I wonder whether the attitude of fund-granting agencies would be as generous as now if they knew that it will continue to take all the running we can do to remain at the same place.

To state it bluntly, my personal view is that the burden of disease is not likely to decrease in the future, whatever the progress of medical research and whatever the skill of social organizations in applying new discoveries. While methods of control can and will be found for almost any given pathological state, I believe nevertheless that disease will remain a problem, and will merely change its manifestations according to social circumstances. Threats to health are inescapable accompaniments of life.

Health is an expression of fitness to the various factors of the total environment, and fitness is achieved through countless genotypic and phenotypic adaptations to these factors. Any change in the environment demands new adaptive reactions, and disease is the consequence of inadequacies in these adaptive responses. The more rapid and profound the environmental changes, the larger the number of individuals who cannot adapt to them rapidly enough to maintain an adequate state of fitness and who therefore develop some type of organic or psychotic disease. "It is changes that are chiefly responsible for diseases," wrote Hippocrates in Chapter XV of *Humours,* "especially the great changes, the violent alterations both in seasons and in other things." And he stated again in *Regimen in Acute Diseases,* "The chief causes of disease are the most violent changes in what concerns our constitutions and habits."

A perfect policy of public health could be conceived for colonies of social ants or bees, whose habits have become stabilized by instincts. Likewise, it would be possible to devise for a herd of cows an ideal system of husbandry with the proper combination of stables and pastures. But unless men become robots, their behavior and environment fully controllable and predictable, no formula can ever give them permanently the health and happiness symbolized by the contented cow. Free men will develop new urges, and these will give rise to new habits and new problems, which will require ever new solutions. New environmental factors are introduced by technological innovations, by the constant flux of tastes, habits, and mores, and by the profound disturbances that culture and ethics exert on the normal play of biological processes. It is because of this instability of the physical and social environment that the pattern of disease changes with each phase of civilization, and that medical research and medical services cannot be self-limiting. Science provides methods of control for the problems inherited from past generations, but it cannot prepare solutions for the specific problems of tomorrow because it does not know what these problems will be. Physicians and public health officials, like soldiers, are always equipped to fight the last war. Before proceeding further with this theme, however, it is only fair that I outline briefly the more optimistic attitude taken by many of the social philosophers and scientists in the course of history.

2

Some of the thinkers of classical Greece certainly believed that reasonable men could achieve the millennium of health by the exercise of wisdom. Witness the cult of Hygeia, which symbolized the faith that men could enjoy *mens sana in corpore sano* if they lived according to reason. Carrying this doctrine to its logical conclusion, Plato wrote that the need for many hospitals and doctors was the earmark of a bad city; there would be little use for them in his ideal Republic. In Imperial Rome, Tiberius asserted in a similar vein that anyone who consulted a doctor after the age of thirty was a fool for not having yet learned to regulate his life properly without outside help. In contrast, medieval Christianity had little faith in the possibility of creating a medical Paradise on earth. But after the Renaissance, Thomas More and all the utopists that followed him popularized imaginary states so well organized that their medical needs could be foreseen and provided for just as certainly as their political and economic problems. Describing the ideal society he imagined on the moon, Cyrano de Bergerac asserted, "In every house there is a Physionome supported by the state, who is approximately what would be called among you a doctor, except that he only treats healthy people." [1]

The French Encyclopedists believed that all health problems could be solved by science, and Condorcet envisaged an era free from disease, in which old age and death would be infinitely postponed. Echoing this faith, Benjamin Franklin wrote to Joseph Priestley that "all diseases may by sure means be prevented or cured, not excepting that of old age, and our lives lengthened at pleasure even beyond the antediluvian standard." Continuing the traditions of the Enlightenment, Rudolph Virchow preached in his journal *Medizinische Reform* that misery was the breeder of disease, and that the key to the general improvement of health would be found in the improvement of social conditions. In one form or another, projections of Utopia have continued until our time. In James Hilton's *Lost Horizon,* the lamas living in Shangri-La, miles from corrupting influences, had mastered the secret of long life. In his book *My First Days in the White House,* Huey Long listed high on his program a plan to provide adequate medical care for the whole country—giving the job to the Mayo brothers!

Faith in the powers of man to eradicate disease had been greatly strengthened, of course, by the spectacular scientific achievements of the nineteenth century. In 1900 Hermann Biggs, then Commissioner of Health of New York State, adopted for his department the motto "Public Health is Purchasable. Within Natural Limitations Any Community Can Determine its Own Death Rate." In 1958 the same faith was repeatedly expressed on the occasion of the tenth anniversary of the World Health Organization. The authors of the WHO pamphlet *Ten Years of Health Progress* recognized, of course, that large problems remained to be solved, and that "as one disease is eradicated . . . others grow in importance," but Dr. Axel Hojer voiced their collective confidence that through the technique of scientific knowledge "man seems to have found out how to make his dreams of a paradise on earth come true." And still more recently, Dr. M. G. Candau, Director-General of WHO, affirmed:

> *If the great advances gained in science and technology are put at the service of all the people of the world, our children will live in an age from which most of the diseases our grandparents and parents took for granted will be banished. It may no longer be Utopian to envisage a new chapter in the history of medicine.*

Medical scientists may be skeptical of social Utopias designed on the basis of political theories, but they rarely doubt that mankind would soon achieve the millennium if their own theories derived from "basic sciences" were put into practice.

The widespread conviction that health is purchasable, not only in limited areas but also on a world scale, seems to be substantiated by the advances made during the past half-century in the fields of nutrition and infection. In reality, however, it has not yet been shown that these achievements justify the wide extrapolations made from them. Indeed, there is overwhelming historical evidence that the evolution of diseases is influenced by many determining factors that at present are not, and may never become, amenable to social or medical control. The changes that have spontaneously occurred in the prevalence of various diseases during the past few centuries should serve as warning that it is unwise to predict the future from the short perspective of the past decades.

Granted the lack of precise information, it is clear nevertheless that many diseases have undergone ebbs and flows in their prevalence and severity. Plague invaded the Latin world during the Justinian era. Leprosy was prevalent in Western Europe until the sixteenth century. Plague again reached catastrophic proportions during the Renaissance. Several outbreaks of the sweating sicknesses terrorized England during Tudor times. Syphilis spread like wildfire shortly after 1500. Smallpox was the scourge of the seventeenth and eighteenth centuries. Tuberculosis, scarlet fever, diphtheria, measles, took over when smallpox began to recede. Today virus infections occupy the focus of attention in our medical communities. And long before viruses had become scientifically fashionable, pandemics of influenza at times added a note of unpredictability to the pattern of infection.

Awareness that diseases come and go for mysterious reasons is not new. Malthus had sensed the phenomenon when he wrote in 1803, "For my part, I feel not the slightest doubt that, if the introduction of the cow pox should exterminate the small pox we shall find a very perceptible difference in the increased mortality of some other disease." More recently, the historical and geographic aspects of the problem were documented by August Hirsch in his monumental *Handbook of Geographical and Historical Pathology*.[2] The matter was interestingly discussed by Charles Anglada in *Etudes sur les maladies éteintes et sur les maladies nouvelles,* and by Maurice Nicolle in his famous book *Naissance, Vie, et Mort des Maladies Infectieuses* showing that such events are often governed by forces independent of conscious human intervention. Most explicit perhaps was the statement made in 1873 by William Parr in his letter to the Registrar General:

> *The infectious diseases replace each other, and when one is rooted out it is apt to be replaced by others which ravage the human race indifferently whenever the conditions of health are wanting. They have this property in common with weeds and other forms of life, as one species recedes another advances.*

I have selected infection to illustrate ebbs and flows in the prevalence of disease because of my greater familiarity with this field. But anyone with specialized knowledge could provide just as telling examples in other areas of medicine. With regard to nutrition, Lucretius was already aware of the problem when he wrote two thousand years ago, "In the old days lack of food gave languishing limbs to Lethe. On the contrary, today surfeit of things stifles us."

Coming now to our times, who could have dreamt a generation ago that hypervitaminoses would become a common form of nutritional disease in the Western world? That the cigaret industry and the use of x-rays would be held responsible for the increase in certain types of cancers? That the introduction of detergents and various synthetics would increase the incidence of allergies? That advances in chemotherapy and other therapeutic procedures would create a new staphylococcus pathology? That alcoholism would become widespread in the Western world? That patients with all forms of iatrogenic diseases would occupy such a large number of beds in the modern hospital?

We may take it for granted, I believe, that the pattern of disease will continue to change, and that as new types of pathology arise the solutions worked out for the problems of yesterday and of today will not be entirely applicable, if applicable at all, to the problems of tomorrow. For the sake of illustration, let me try to imagine a few of the problems that may be anticipated in the near future.

In the field of infectious diseases, we need not go far for examples because the future is already with us. While mortality from acute bacterial infections is at an all-time low, chronic disorders of complex and ill-defined microbial etiology loom larger and larger on the horizon. In England chronic bronchitis is at present the second in causes of death and the largest cause of disability. It claimed 37,000 lives in 1951, and accounted for the certified loss of 26.6 million working days among the insured population. Chronic bronchitis illustrates the fact that air pollution and many other factors associated with life in urbanized and industrialized areas can give to otherwise trivial infections of the respiratory tract certain pathological characters that make them impervious to drug treatment and other methods of therapy.

As to the part to be played by viruses in the future, it need only be mentioned that the development of modern sanitation has begun to bring about a progressive shift of childhood diseases into adult life—with consequences that we are only now beginning to recognize. Even with regard to uncomplicated bacterial infections, the time is probably approaching when many of the chemotherapeutic agents presently in use will lose their effectiveness. The case of the staphylococcus is in everybody's mind; recent reports from Poland, England, Japan, and Denmark reveal that the gonococcus is becoming resistant to penicillin; and there is no doubt in my mind that the indiscriminate use of isoniazid, particularly in the underdeveloped parts of the world, spells the end of convenient drug control of tuberculosis within a very few decades. New drugs will of course be dicovered, but it is unlikely that discovery will keep pace with need. In this regard, it seems relevant to quote here the conclusion reached by S. W. Simmons in a recent critical review of "The Current Status of Insecticide Resistance":

It is evident that the extermination of vectors with residual insecticides is probably not feasible. We appear to be in an endless cycle of synthesizing, at an ever increasing cost, more and more insecticides to which vectors become more and more resistant. Thus, it seems we cannot go on forever relying on insecticides. A more final and permanent solution to the vector-borne diseases problem might lie in ecologic control.[3]

In contrast to infectious diseases, the field of nutrition would at first appear to hold few surprises for the future. There is reason to believe that nutritionists have identified most if not all the growth factors required by man, and that they can devise formulae satisfactory for all ages of life and for the various occupations. But the application of this knowledge is proving more difficult than its acquisition. Both qualitatively and quantitatively, human requirements vary with the pattern of daily life; and habits as well as tastes change so fast that there is no time for orderly adjustments. Shakespeare made Nerissa say in *The Merchant of Venice,* "They are as sick that surfeit with too much as they that starve with nothing." Only now is it becoming a problem of general concern that what used to be a reasonable diet for a physically active man can be ill-balanced for the citizen wheelborne in the modern world. Dietary habits that were adequate yesterday may come to constitute a national danger in the era of television and automation.

For the largest part of the world, of course, the real concern is not overnutrition, but rather shortage of food. And this is rapidly creating new problems of disease in poor countries where death rates have been cut by partial control of infection. Agricultural and industrial technology will no doubt provide new sources of carbohydrates, fats, proteins, amino acids, and vitamins in amounts sufficient to meet essential human needs. But it can be surmised also that the consumption of new kinds of food will bring in its train new types of medical problems. Nutritional disease can arise not only from qualitative or quantitative deficiencies, but also from toxic effects, which are often slow in manifesting themselves. For example, algae are much spoken of as economical synthesizers of foodstuffs, but there are several reports that the continued consumption of large amounts of algae by farm or laboratory animals has resulted in a hepatic toxicity of unknown mechanism. Other examples of hepatic toxicity that became apparent only after long-term use of certain new foodstuffs have been reported in a recent symposium on Human Requirements and their Fulfillment in Practice.[4] Scientific knowledge is not yet sufficient to replace the biological wisdom derived from the countless centuries during which mankind has engaged in the empirical trial of foodstuffs.

Many examples could be quoted to support the statement that technological advances carry with them threats to health revealed only by long experience, and often too late. These threats extend from mere inconveniences like allergies, to the delayed carcinogenetic effects exerted by radiation and by the various types of synthetic substances with which modern man increasingly comes into contact. Most industrial processes pollute the air, the water, and the rest of the environment with countless new chemicals and thereby prepare for the future various pathological disorders of types as yet unsuspected. Even air-conditioning may turn out to have physiological and pathological consequences that have not yet been recognized.

Changes in social patterns also will contribute their share of unpredictability to the health problems of the future. As our population grows and our natural resources decrease proportionally, there will be need for ever increasing organization, regulation, and even regimentation in our lives. It is hard to believe that the physiological and psychic effects of this transformation of collective life will all be favorable to physical and mental health. There is already evidence that the boredom engendered by automation is creating new forms of psychosis, and it will become increasingly difficult for society to manage a proper balance between its intake of tranquilizers and of energizers.

More dramatic in its implications, because so intimately involved in our system of ethics, is the fact that the very medical and social advances of which we are so justifiably proud are likely to create difficult if not insoluble problems for the generations to come. Speaking of our "load of mutations," H. J. Muller has repeatedly emphasized that, as medical science becomes more effective in permitting the survival of biologically defective individuals, there will be an increase in the frequency of detrimental genes allowed to accumulate in our communities. If this trend continues, in Professor Muller's words:

> *Instead of people's time and energy being mainly spent in the struggle with external enemies of a primitive kind such as famine, climatic difficulties, and wild beasts, they would be devoted chiefly to the effort to live carefully, to spare and to prop up their own feeblenesses, to soothe their inner disharmonies and, in general, to doctor themselves as effectively as possible. For everyone would be an invalid, with his own special familial twists.*[5]

In a recent essay on "The Control of Evolution in Man," Darlington expressed tersely the same thought:

> *Those who were saved as children return to the same hospital with their children to be saved. In consequence, each generation of*

*a stable society will become more dependent on medical treatment
for its ability to survive and reproduce.*[6]

It is misleading, of course, to speak of biological defectives without
regard to the environment in which the individual lives and functions. Medical techniques can make up for genetic and other deficiencies that would
be lethal in the wilderness; by controlling the environment, and with the
help of modern medical resources, man can live and function effectively in
our world even though he is tuberculous, blind, diabetic, crippled, or psychopathic. But fitness bought at the cost of medical care has economic implications that have not yet been precisely determined. There is no doubt that a
large percentage of individuals are now unable to pull their full weight in
our communities, and we may assume that their numbers will continue to
increase at an accelerated rate, precisely by reason of medical progress. Furthermore, it is also likely that the cost of medical care will continue to soar
because each new discovery calls into use more specialized skills and expensive items. At the present time the cost of medical care in the United States
amounts to more than 10 per cent of the national income. There is certainly
a limit to the percentage of its resources that society can devote to the maintenance of its medical establishments; and a time may come when medical
ethics will have to be reconsidered in the harsh light of economics.

The use of anticoagulants for the prevention of coronary thrombosis is
a case in point. Although the value of this procedure has been established
beyond doubt (see recent survey by the Medical Research Council in
England), its application will be limited by its cost, for example by the labor
involved in the determination of blood-clotting time. In other words, the
medical justifications for the use of anticoagulants will need to be influenced
by social criteria. Surgery for the repair of congenital heart defects provides
another striking example, by reason of its exacting requirements in nursing
care, hospital space, elaborate equipment, and technical skill. Finally, it must
not be taken for granted that the power of science is limitless. After all, it is
only during the past few decades that medical treatment has permitted the
victims of genetic disabilities to survive and to reproduce on such a large
scale. Should the trend continue, it is far from certain that therapy can keep
pace with the problems that will have to be met to avoid biological extinction. Indeed, I would be surprised if the medical geneticist of the future did
not rate the sociological aspects of his science as more important than its
contribution to biochemistry.

3

The political Utopias devised by Plato, Thomas More, and their imitators
have no chance of success because they are based on a static view of the

world and of men. H. G. Wells defined the problem clearly in his book *A Modern Utopia:*

> *The Utopia of a modern dreamer must needs differ in one fundamental aspect from the Nowheres and Utopias men planned before Darwin quickened the thought of the world. Those were all perfect and static forces, a balance of happiness won for ever against the forces of unrest and disorder that inhere in things. But the Modern Utopia must be not static but kinetic, must shape not as a permanent state but as a hopeful stage.*[7]

Similarly, it is impossible to acquire in advance all the specialized knowledge and techniques that will be required to deal with the diseases of the future. What may be worth asking, however, is whether medical science can help the individual and society to develop a greater ability to meet successfully the unpredictable problems of tomorrow. This is an ill-defined task for which there is hardly any background of knowledge. Traditionally, medicine is concerned with retarding death and also with preventing pain and minimizing effort. Its achievements in this field have added greatly to the duration, safety, and charm of individual existence. While scientific medicine has continued to emphasize the detailed study of particular diseases and specific remedies, it has placed less emphasis on the nonspecific mechanisms by which the body and soul deal with the constant and multifarious threats to survival. The question is whether it is possible to increase the ability of the individual and of the social body to meet the stresses and strains of adversity. In this regard it may be worth considering that preoccupation with the avoidance of threats and dangers does not have the creative quality of goal-seeking. It is at best a negative attitude, one that does not contribute to growth, physical or mental. In our obsession with comfort and security, we have given little heed to the future, and this negligence may be fatal to society and indeed to the race.

Whatever the theories of physicians, laboratory scientists, and sociologists, it is of course society that must decide on the types of threats it is most anxious to avoid and on the kind of health it wants—whether it prizes security more than adventure, whether it is willing to jeopardize the future for the sake of present-day comfort. But this decision might be and should be influenced by knowledge derived from a study of the manner in which different ways of life can affect the future fate of the individual and of society. Although this knowledge does not yet exist, a few general remarks appear justified.

It is a matter of common experience that, while man's physical and mental resources cannot develop to the full under conditions of extreme adversity, nevertheless a certain amount of stress, strain, and risk seems essential to the full development of the individual. Normal healthy human beings have long known, and physiologists are beginning to rediscover, that too low a level of sensory stimulation may lead to psychotic disorders, and that man functions best when a sufficient number of his neurons are active. Analogous considerations seem to be valid for the lower levels of biological functions, and two recent studies illustrate that at least some of the mechanisms involved in training and in adaptability are not beyond experimental analysis.

It has been shown by Dr. Curt P. Richter and his associates that the domesticated laboratory rat differs from its wild ancestor, the Norway rat, in many anatomic and physiologic characters that can be measured by objective tests. As a result of selection and of life in the sheltered environment of the laboratory, the domesticated rat has lost most of the ability of its wild ancestor to provide for itself, to fight, and to resist fatigue as well as toxic substances and microbial diseases. The domesticated rat has become less aggressive in behavior but also less able to meet successfully the strains and stresses of life, and therefore it could hardly survive competition in the free state. As a result of domestication, in Dr. Richter's words:

> *(1) the adrenal glands, the organs most involved in reactions to stress and fatigue, and in providing protection from a number of diseases, have become smaller, less effective . . . (2) the thyroid— the organ that helps to regulate metabolism, has become less active . . . (3) the gonads, the organs responsible for sex activity and fertility, develop earlier, function with greater regularity, bring about a much greater fertility. . . . The finding of a smaller weight of the brain and a greater susceptibility to audiogenic and other types of fits, would indicate that the brain likewise has become less effective.*[8]

While some of these changes may be phenotypic, it is probable that most of them are the expression of mutations selected by life in the laboratory. But whatever their mechanism, the effects of domestication on the wild rat are not without relevance to the future of mankind. Human societies made up of well-domesticated citizens, comfort-loving and submissive, may not be the ones most likely to survive.

The study of so-called germ-free animals has revealed other aspects of this problem. Animals born and raised in an environment free of detectable microorganisms can grow to a normal size and are capable of reproducing themselves for several generations, but they exhibit extraordinary susceptibility to infection, even to the most common types of microorganisms that would be innocuous for animals raised in a normal, exposed environment. Furthermore, germ-free animals produce only small amounts of lymphoid tissue, and their plasma is extremely low in gamma globulin—deficiencies that may be of little consequence in the protected environment of the germ-free chamber, but that become fatal under normal conditions of life.

These types of experimental situations illustrate the fact that a sheltered life alters in many ways the ability of the organism to cope with the stresses of life. "Let a man either avoid the occasion altogether, or put himself often to it, that he may be little moved with it," Bacon wrote in his essay *Of Nature in Men*. While Bacon's aphorism is a picturesque statement of an important sociomedical problem, the solution that it offers hardly fits the modern world. Man cannot "put himself often to threats" the nature of which he cannot anticipate. But he can perhaps cultivate the biological mechanisms that will permit him to respond effectively when the time of danger comes.

4

Thus, a type of knowledge that bears on social philosophy is slowly emerging from preoccupations with medical problems. After a semifacetious debate held in London on 17 November 1952, the Hunterian Society voted 59 to 47 "that the continued advance in medicine will produce more problems than it solves." In reality, most of the new problems continuously arising are not the products of medical advances, but manifestations of the fact that our society becomes more complex as it grows in size and age. We cannot escape these problems, but we should give more thought to the long-range effects of the solutions that we devise to meet them.

We must have the courage to discuss the wisdom of retaining individual longevity as the dominant criterion of social and medical ethics. We must be prepared to recognize that an excessive concern wtih security, with comfort, and with avoidance of pain and of effort, has dangerous economic and biological implications—that such concern may, in fact, amount to social and racial suicide. I realize that any attempt to deal with these problems will involve painful conflicts with personal interests and with religious and moral convictions. Yet we have to formulate the problems in a forthright manner if we are to find their solutions. Unless we discover methods for producing a higher level of adaptive power in the individual and for preventing genetic deterioration of the race, the likely alternative is that more and more in the future we shall have to run frantically from one protective and palliative measure to another, trying to lengthen life at the cost of sacrificing its wholeness and many of its values.

Before closing, I must acknowledge that I have never taken care of the sick and am not a physician—a fact that has prevented me from apprehending with all their compelling force many of the human and practical aspects of medicine. Though fully aware of my lack of judgment arising from these deficiencies, I cannot refrain from quoting here a few lines from G. K. Chesterton, brought to my attention by a humane physician who is also a scientist:

> *The mistake of all that medical talk lies in the very fact that it connects the idea of health with the idea of care. What has health to do with care? Health has to do with carelessness. In special and abnormal cases it is necessary to have care. . . . If we are doctors we are speaking to exceptionally sick men, and they ought to be told to be careful. But when we are sociologists we are addressing the normal, we are addressing humanity. And humanity ought to be told to be recklessness itself. For all the fundamental functions of a healthy man emphatically ought not to be performed with precaution or for precaution.*[9]

Chesterton was neither a scientist nor a physician, and as a sociologist he was prone to substitute brilliant paradox for logic and knowledge. Yet it seems to me that his flippant remarks help to quicken attention to an aspect of medicine that bids fair to become of increasing social importance in the future. Medical advances do not arise in a social vacuum. They are products of the sparks between the scientific knowledge of the time and the demands of the community. But what the community demands is determined to a large extent by publicity, apparent or hidden—in this case by the implied promises of medical science. We must beware lest we give the illusion that health will be a birthright for all in medical Utopia, or a state to be reached passively from effortless directives given by physicians or from drugs bought at the corner store. In the real world of the future, as in the past, health will depend on a creative way of life, on the manner in which men respond to the unpredictable challenges that continue to arise from an ever changing environment.

The study of specific pathological problems requires the use of laboratory techniques and contributes to the advancement of laboratory knowledge. But the field of medicine transcends this kind of knowledge because it deals with man as a spiritual being and also with the future of the human race. Medical science is concerned not only with the control of individual diseases, but also with the long-range effects of its products on the total performance and happiness of the individual, on the social problems of the community, and on the adaptive powers of the race. Unless medical scientists are willing to take a long-range view of the consequences of their activities, some day they may have to confess like Captain Ahab in *Moby Dick,* "All my means are sane . . . my object mad." They may come to know the anguish that atomic physicists experienced as they watched the tragic effects of their scientific triumphs. Because medicine is an aspect of social technology, its ethics and its goals are the products of the interplay between scientific understanding and human aspirations.

REFERENCES

[1] Cyrano de Bergerac, *Histoire comique des états et empires de la lune.* Paris, 1656.

[2] August Hirsch, *Handbook of Geographical and Historical Pathology.* London, The New Sydenham Society, 1885–1886.

[3] Samuel W. Simmons, "Current Status of Insecticide Resistance," in *Industry and Tropical Health* III (Proceedings of the Third Conference, Industrial Council for Tropical Health, Harvard School of Public Health; Boston, 1957), pp. 34–41.

[4] J. C. Waterlow and J. M. L. Stephen, eds., *Human Protein Requirements and Their Fulfilment in Practice* (proceedings of a conference in Princeton, New Jersey, 1955). Bristol, England, John Wright & Sons, Ltd, 1956.

[5] H. J. Muller, "Our Load of Mutations," *American Journal of Human Genetics, 2* (1950), 111–176.

[6] C. D. Darlington, "Control of Evolution in Man," *Nature, 182* (1958), 14–17.

[7] H. G. Wells, *A Modern Utopia.* London, Chapman & Hall, 1905.

[8] Curt P. Richter, "Rats, Man, and the Welfare State." Address before the American Psychological Association, Washington, D.C., 1957.

[9] G. K. Chesterton, *Heretics.* New York, Dodd, Mead & Co., 1905.

Impact of Large-Scale Science on the United States

ALVIN M. WEINBERG

Throughout history, societies have expressed their aspirations in large-scale, monumental enterprises which, though not necessary for the survival of the societies, have taxed them to their physical and intellectual limits. History often views these monuments as symbolizing the societies. The Pyramids, the Sphinx, and the great temple at Karnak symbolize Egypt; the magnificent cathedrals symbolize the church culture of the Middle Ages; Versailles symbolizes the France of Louis XIV; and so on. The societies were goaded into these extraordinary exertions by their rulers—the pharaoh, the church, the king—who invoked the cultural mystique when this was sufficient, but who also used force when necessary. Sometimes, as with the cathedrals, local pride and a sense of competition with other cities helped launch the project. In many cases the distortion of the economy caused by construction of the big monuments contributed to the civilization's decline.

When history looks at the 20th century, she will see science and technology as its theme; she will find in the monuments of Big Science—the huge rockets, the high-energy accelerators, the high-flux research reactors—symbols of our time just as surely as she finds in Notre Dame a symbol of the Middle Ages. She might even see analogies between our motivations for building these tools of giant science and the motivations of the church builders and the pyramid builders. We build our monuments in the name of scientific truth, they built theirs in the name of religious truth; we use our Big Science to add to our country's prestige, they used their churches for their cities' prestige; we build to placate what ex-President Eisenhower suggested could become a dominant scientific caste, they built to please the priests of Isis and Osiris.

The emergence of Big Science and its tools as a supreme outward expression of our culture's aspirations has created many difficult problems, both philosophic and practical. Some of the problems concern science itself, some the relation between science and our society. I shall address myself to

Reprinted from *Science*, July 21, 1961, Vol. CXXXIV, No. 3473, pp. 161–164, with the permission of the author and the publisher. Dr. Alvin M. Weinberg is Director of the Oak Ridge National Laboratory. A physicist by training, Dr. Weinberg has published many papers in recent years on the wider implications of science policies.

three specific questions, all of which arise from the growth of Big Science: first, Is Big Science ruining science?; second, Is Big Science ruining us financially?; and third, Should we divert a larger part of our effort toward scientific issues which bear more directly on human well-being than do such Big-Science spectaculars as manned space travel and high-energy physics? These questions are so broad, and so difficult, that I cannot do more than raise them here. Since they involve the issue of the scientist's responsibility to his science and to his society, I believe I shall have done some service merely by urging scientists to think seriously about them.

IS BIG SCIENCE RUINING SCIENCE?

The English astronomer Fred Hoyle recently set off a lively controversy by arguing against the United Kingdom's going into large-scale space research. His argument, which applies to much of Big Science, is twofold: first, that the intrinsic scientific interest of space research is not worth the money and manpower that goes into it and certainly does not justify spending more on it than on any other branch of science; and second, that wherever science is fed by too *much* money, it becomes fat and lazy. He claims to see evidence that the tight intellectual discipline necessary for science is, especially in America, being loosened. I shall touch later upon Hoyle's first point: Is Big Science giving us our money's worth? For the moment I want to discuss his second point, which can be paraphrased as, "Is Big Science ruining science?"

I confess that I share Hoyle's misgivings. In the first place, since Big Science needs great public support it thrives on publicity. The inevitable result is the injection of a journalistic flavor into Big Science which is fundamentally in conflict with the scientific method. If the serious writings about Big Science were carefully separated from the journalistic writings, little harm would be done. But they are not so separated. Issues of scientific or technical merit tend to get argued in the popular, not the scientific, press, or in the congressional committee room rather than in the technical-society lecture hall; the spectacular rather than the perceptive becomes the scientific standard. When these trends are added to the enormous proliferation of scientific writing, which largely remains unread in its original form and therefore must be predigested, one cannot escape the conclusion that the line between journalism and science has become blurred.

In the second place, one sees evidence of scientists' spending money instead of thought. This is one of the most insidious effects of large-scale support of science. In the past the two commodities, thought and money, have both been hard to come by. Now that money is relatively plentiful but thought is still scarce, there is a natural rush to spend dollars rather than thought—to order a 10^7 nuclear reactor instead of devising a crucial experiment with the reactors at hand, or to make additional large-scale computations instead of reducing the problem to tractable dimensions by perceptive physical approximation. The line between spending money and spending thought is blurring.

Finally, the huge growth of Big Science has greatly increased the number of scientific administrators. Where large sums of public money are being spent there must be many administrators who see to it that the money is spent wisely. Just as it is easier to spend money than to spend thought, so it is easier to tell other scientists how and what to do than to do it oneself. The big scientific community tends to acquire more and more bosses. The Indians with bellies to the bench are hard to discern for all the chiefs with bellies to the mahogany desks. Unfortunately, science dominated by administrators is science understood by administrators, and such science quickly becomes attenuated if not meaningless.

But it is fruitless to wring one's hands over the bad effects of Big Science. Big Science is an inevitable stage in the development of science and, for better or for worse, it is here to stay. What we must do is learn to live with Big Science. We must make Big Science flourish without, at the same time, allowing it to trample Little Science—that is, we must nurture small-scale excellence as carefully as we lavish gifts on large-scale spectaculars.

In respect to Big Science, huge laboratories like Oak Ridge play a central role. They were established to encourage Big Science yet to segregate it and prevent it from taking over Little Science. Big-scale science's triple diseases—journalitis, moneyitis, administratitis—have always been with us in the big laboratories. Being aware of these pitfalls we have made conscious efforts to cope with them—by requiring internal review of each publication, by occasionally sending an administrator back to his laboratory, by subjecting large expenditures to enough scrutiny so that money is not as easy to get as it may outwardly seem to be. I do not believe that we at Oak Ridge, or I suspect at other such institutions, are completely successful in these efforts. We do the best we can, however; and at least, by confining Big Science to such institutions, we prevent the contagion from spreading.

What really bothers me is the evidence that Big Science is invading the universities. One need not look far to find Bev accelerators and megawatt research reactors on many campuses. The justification for putting these devices on university campuses is that such gadgets of Big Science are now needed to perform large parts of basic research, and that basic research is best done in conjunction with education. But I think there is a very grave danger to our universities in this incursion of Big Science. A professor of science is chosen because he is extremely well qualified as a scientist, as a thinker, or as a teacher. If he becomes too involved with Big Science he will have to become a publicist, if not a journalist, an administrator, and a spender of big money. I do not for a moment suggest that college professors are less able big-time administrators than are professional administrators. I merely point out that the proper function of a professor is to be a professor; that once Big Science has invaded his precincts and he becomes an operator (even though a very effective one), his students and his intellectual eminence and proficiency are bound to suffer. Thus, though my question "Is Big Science ruining science?" is irrelevant, since Big Science is here to stay, I do believe that Big Science can ruin our universities, by diverting the universities from their primary purpose and by converting university professors into administrators, housekeepers, and publicists.

Are there ways of bringing Big Science into the educational stream other than by converting our universities into National Laboratories? One way which is tentatively suggested in the report of the President's Science Advisory Committee, "Scientific Progress, The Universities, and The Federal Government," is to strengthen the already close relationships between the government laboratories and the universities. I would go a step further and propose the creation of technical universities close to or in conjunction with the large government laboratories. One advantage of such a scheme would be that the National Laboratories have already made their peace with Big Science—the onerous housekeeping function, the layer of inevitable administrators and publicists, is already in being. Professors in such collaborating universities, who might be drawn in part, but not wholly, from the existing scientific staffs of the big laboratories, would not have to get involved so strongly in activities not related to their science as they would if they had to start Big Science from the beginning. In addition, the big government laboratories have facilities and technically trained personnel that are not now pulling their full weight in the educational job which must be done.

Exactly what pattern should be established would vary from institution to institution. The Rockefeller Institute for Medical Research has recently been rechartered as the Rockefeller University—this is the most extreme possibility. I think that a more generally appropriate pattern would involve, first, a great expansion in the use of short-tenure, postdoctoral fellows at the big laboratories, and second, the establishment of independent graduate schools of technology in close proximity to the big laboratories, and with some interlocking staff. Such schools would have as much claim to federal support as do the universities which receive money for direct educational purposes as part of their payment for conducting research.

IS BIG SCIENCE RUINING US FINANCIALLY?

My second question is, Is Big Science ruining us financially? The present federal expenditure on research and development is 8.4×10^9, which is about 10 percent of the federal budget, about 1.6 percent of the gross national product. The money spent on research and development is the largest single *controllable* item in the federal budget in the sense that, unlike wheat subsidies or interest on the national debt, it can be changed at the President's discretion. It is not surprising, therefore, that the Bureau of the Budget has taken such an interest in our research and development budget.

The rate of change of our research and development budget, averaged over the past ten years, has been 10 percent per year; this corresponds to a doubling time of seven years. Since the doubling time of the gross national product is about 20 years, at the present rate we shall be spending *all* of our money on science and technology in about 65 years. Evidently something will have to be done or Big Science will ruin us financially.

The amount that we spend on research and development is only one-fifth of our military budget—and of course over 80 percent of the 8.4×10^9 is for military purposes. There are many analogies between research expenditures and military expenditures. In neither case can one guarantee that anything useful will come of a specific expenditure; yet, on the average, we know that we must spend money for science and for defense. In both cases there is a high rate of obsolescence. Both our military and our scientific might are instruments of national policy. It therefore seems to me that the general principles which have guided our military-fiscal policy should be useful in guiding our science-fiscal policy.

We have decided, though implicitly, that our military budget shall represent about 10 percent of our gross national product. In the same way we ought soon to decide to devote a certain fraction of our gross national product to nondefense science rather than pay for each scientific expenditure on an *ad hoc,* item-by-item basis. At the moment science grows much more rapidly than does the gross national product. I suggest that we settle on some figure—say something less than 1 percent of the gross national product —as the long-term bill for federally supported, nondefense science, and that we stick to it for a period of, say, 15 years. Our science budget will then increase only as fast as our gross national product does, but we scientists shall have to get used to that idea.

If we settle on an over-all science budget which is geared to the gross national product, we shall have to make choices. At present each scientific expenditure is considered separately. The merits of desirable projects are argued by interested and clever proponents, but the relative merit of a project in high-energy physics as compared to a project in space or in atomic energy is not weighed in the balance. The system works because the science budget is expanding so fast. Fortunately, the President's Science Advisory Committee and the Federal Council for Science and Technology give us a mechanism for establishing an over-all science budget and for making the hard choices when we shall have to make them. These choices, which will require weighing space against biology, atomic energy against oceanography, will be the very hardest of all to make—if for no other reason than that no man knows enough to make such comparative judgments on scientific grounds. The incentive for creating a favorable public opinion for a pet scientific project will become much greater than it now is; the dangers of creating a political "in" group of scientists who keep worthy outsiders from the till will be severe. Nevertheless, it is obvious that we shall have to devote much more attention than we now do to making choices between science projects in very different fields.

CAN WE DIVERT THE COURSE OF BIG SCIENCE?

As an example of the kind of choice which we shall have to make, let us consider whether there are alternative scientific fields which ought to have prior claim on our resources, ahead of manned space flight or high-energy physics.

It would be naive, if not hopeless, to argue that we should not use scientific achievement as a means of competing with the U.S.S.R. Major Gagarin's feat has caught the world's fancy, and we may as well face up to it. The question is, are we wise in choosing manned flight into space as the primary event in these scientific Olympic Games? I shall argue against doing so, on three grounds—hazard, expense, and relevance.

It is my impression that the hazard of space flight, particularly the radiation hazard, is not fully assessed as yet. An admirable analysis of the radiation hazard of manned space travel is given by T. Foelsche of Langley Field. Foelsche's estimates are given in Table 1.

TABLE 1. SUMMARY OF SHIELDING ESTIMATES AND RADIATION DOSES. THE LD_{50} FOR MAN IS ABOUT 500 REM (*not* REP); THE MILITARY TOLERANCE IS 25 REM. [FROM T. FOELSCHE, "PROTECTION AGAINST SOLAR FLARE PROTONS," A PAPER PRESENTED AT THE 7TH ANNUAL MEETING OF THE AMERICAN ASTRONAUTICAL SOCIETY, DALLAS, TEX., 16–18 JAN. 1961]

Shield weight (g/cm^2)	Radiation dose			
	inner belt (D)		Flares (D) (rep)	
	rem/hr	rep/hr	Low energy (<500 Mev)	High energy (<20 Bev)
2	21	12	2500–25,000	80–400
15	7.5	4.2	18–180	23–80
25	4.5	2.5	6–50	23–50

It is obvious from these figures that the radiation shielding for a space craft could be formidable. To shield an entire capsule against high-energy solar flares with shielding of 25 grams per square centimeter might require about 10 tons of material; to shield a man individually would require about a ton. These figures are not catastrophic. Yet I find them disturbing for several reasons. First, the measurements of the solar-flare radiation, if not of the Van Allen belt radiation, are still very uncertain. Second, the values used in all of the calculations on space shielding for relative biological effectiveness of fast heavy particles have been much lower than those used in estimates of the shielding required for the manned nuclear aircraft. This difference is usually justified by the difference in energy of the radiations in the two cases; the space radiation, being harder, has a low linear energy transfer and therefore should have low relative biological effectiveness. However, the total experimental evidence on the relative biological effectiveness of very fast particles is not very large; in any event, the secondary particles produced in spallation processes, such as occur with energetic primaries, are in the binding-energy, not the 100-Mev, region. Finally, the biological effects of extremely energetic heavy particles are not fully understood. Although Curtis's experiments on nerve cells suggest that these particles are not too dangerous (1), the matter is not really settled.

The radiation hazard does not clearly make space an intolerable environment for man; on the other hand, it makes space a much more hostile environment than we had suspected even five years ago. That man can tramp about without shielding for extended times on the moon's surface seems to me quite unlikely. The Lord, so to speak, provided His children with a marvelous radiation shield, the atmosphere, and He did not intend them to poke their heads into His unshielded reactors. The corollary I draw is that, on the basis of what we now know, manned space travel is not definitely feasible in the sense that we can now really place a firm upper limit on the cost of a round trip to the moon; the estimates of 20×10^9 to 40×10^9 for this mission are so large and cover so wide a range as to make the outsider doubt their validity on a priori grounds. May I remind you that about ten years ago the Lexington Project predicted that the cost of the nuclear-powered aircraft would be 1×10^9 and the time required, ten years. As it turned out, after ten years and an expenditure of 1×10^9, we have words, not nuclear airplanes, flying. Just because a project is very big and very expensive does not mean that the project will be very successful.

The other main contender for the position of Number One Event in the scientific Olympics is high-energy physics. It, too, is wonderfully expensive (the Stanford linear accelerator is expected to cost 100×10^6), and we may expect to spend 400×10^6 per year on this area of research by 1970.

The issues with which such research deals have greater scientific validity than those dealt with in the *manned* space program, but its remoteness from human affairs is equally great. It has the advantage, from our point of view, that we are ahead of the Russians in high-energy physics.

But even if it were possible to generate around high-energy physics the same popular interest that arises naturally in connection with manned space travel, I am not persuaded that this is the battleground of choice. I personally would much rather choose scientific issues which have more bearing on the world that is part of man's everyday environment, and more bearing on man's welfare, than have either high-energy physics or manned space travel.

There are several such areas, and we are generally very far ahead in them. The most spectacular is molecular biology—a field in which the contribution from the East is minimal. We have learned more about the essential life processes—growth, protein synthesis, and reproduction—during the past decade than during all previous history. In my opinion the probability of our synthesizing living material from nonliving before the end of the century is of the same order as the probability of our making a successful manned round trip to the planets. I suspect that most Americans would prefer to belong to the society which first gave the world a cure for cancer than to the society which put the first astronaut on Mars.

I mention also the group of economic-technical problems which arise from the increasing pressure of population on resources. Of these, nuclear energy is the best known. Here the Western lead is clear, and it is important to consolidate the lead. There are others—the problem of water, or atmospheric pollution, or of chemical contamination of the biosphere, for example. Each of these is a technical issue which can lay claim to our resources—a claim that will have to be heard when we make choices.

But it is presumptuous for me to urge that we study biology on earth rather than biology in space, or physics in the nuclear binding-energy region, with its clear practical applications and its strong bearing on the rest of science, rather than physics in the Bev region, with its absence of practical applications and its very slight bearing on the rest of science. What I am urging is that these choices have become matters of high national policy. We cannot allow our over-all science strategy, when it involves such large sums, to be settled by default, or to be pre-empted by the group with the most skillful publicity department. We should have extensive debate on these over-all questions of scientific choice; we should make a choice, explain it, and then have the courage to stick to a course arrived at rationally.

In making our choices we should remember the experiences of other civilizations. Those cultures which have devoted too much of their talent to monuments which had nothing to do with the real issues of human well-being have usually fallen upon bad days. History tells us that the French

Revolution was the bitter fruit of Versailles and that the Roman Colosseum helped not at all in staving off the barbarians. So it is for us to learn well these lessons of history: we must not allow ourselves, by short-sighted seeking after fragile monuments of Big Science, to be diverted from our real purpose, which is the enriching and broadening of human life.

REFERENCE

1. H. J. Curtis, *Science* **133**, 312 (1961).

The Coming Changes in American Science

NORMAN W. STORER

Prediction does not necessarily provide for control, but it can be of vital importance in enabling us to compensate for unavoidable events. The forces now impinging upon American science are producing fundamental changes in the scientific community which, whether we approve of them or not, must be known before we can act intelligently in achieving the best possible adjustment to them.

Alvin M. Weinberg's well-known article "Impact of large-scale science on the United States" (1) is a perceptive discussion of some of these changes. It appears to stop short, however, of facing the full consequences of science's new position in society. In discussing the possibility that Big Science will "ruin" science, for instance, Weinberg suggests that by "nurturing small-scale excellence as carefully as we lavish gifts on large-scale spectaculars," we may "prevent the contagion from spreading." Needed now is a better picture of what is happening to all of science and how it is happening. To do something about such symptoms as "journalitis, moneyitis, and administratitis," we must understand the deeper changes that are resulting from science's enhanced ability to command support from society and to exert appreciable influence upon policy decisions at the highest levels.

I would like to argue that Weinberg has examined the top of the iceberg very well but has not seen clearly the greater part which is submerged. This greater part is hidden both in the slowness of time, which disguises important trends, and in the implicit assumption that quantitative change is unrelated to qualitative change. His discussion centers upon the consequences of the increased support of science. To complement his analysis, I examine here some of the other factors which are at work today and cast the problem in a larger framework.

AMERICAN SCIENCE BEFORE 1940

Twenty years ago and more science received relatively little support and

Reprinted from *Science*, October 25, 1963, Vol. CXLII, No. 3591, pp. 464–467, with the permission of the author and the publisher. Professor Norman W. Storer is in the Department of Social Relations at Harvard University. He was the first Ph.D. at Cornell University who combined a major in the sociology of science with a minor in the history of science.

approbation from the rest of society. Salaries were low, research was done on shoestring budgets, and the prospects of even modest wealth, social position, or community influence were not promising for a young man entering science. Under these conditions, science tended to attract two largely over-lapping groups of people—those who were completely committed to re-search, and those for whom membership in even this low-ranking sector of society represented a rise in social status.

In her study of eminent scientists, all of them men who had entered science before 1940, Anne Roe notes (2) that "[after] the discovery of the possibility of doing research . . . absorption in the vocation was so complete as seriously to limit all other activity. . . ." Knapp and Goodrich found that rural backgrounds were overrepresented among their subjects (3). For men from rural areas, science provided a way of moving up in life; perhaps this was due to its connection with academic life, but still it attracted them. It should be remembered, too, that the values of rural life, like those of Prot-estantism (4) seem particularly to fit a person for a scientific career. The scientific community, made up generally of these two types of people, shaped itself to accommodate them.

The insularity of their interests was reflected in their condemnation of applied research, the idealization of curiosity, and a single-minded commit-ment to the development of science. Such values not only expressed these men's personal feelings but served as well to protect science by reinforcing its members' distinction from the rest of society. Strong barriers were erected to keep scientists from succumbing to temptations that would make them desert the community or compromise its integrity.

The picture here is of course exaggerated, but in the main these seem to have been the conditions that existed. When the members of this group were devoted to their work, and when no other rewards for it were avail-able, the primary reward which was available and could be used within the group was professional recognition. This reward, the affirmation by one's colleagues that one has made a contribution to a body of knowledge, was entirely appropriate to science (5).

In other fields—law, medicine, engineering—where the practice of one's profession requires interaction with laymen and yields tangible results, pro-fessional recognition is important primarily as it signifies ability; it forms the basis of one's reputation and proclaims one's potential for excellent performance in the future. But in science, without regular relationships with nonscientists and often without tangible results, it signifies achieve-ment. Despite increasing tendencies to make recognition important to the scientist as a basis for obtaining further research support, the original im-portance of recognition was in validating the scientist's own creativity. Thus, particularly in science before World War II, professional recognition was looked upon as an end rather than a means. The importance of priority, especially as commemorated in the practice of eponymy, testifies to this.

In a social setting where science received little support, it became, to a high degree, a closed system, since both research output and its rewards were contained in the same community. Basic research flourishes under such conditions, which ensure progress along all fronts and provide maximum opportunity for heuristic cross-fertilization. With practically no other market for one's work besides one's colleagues and with little outside support for any research, there was no more reason to work in one area than in another except for those reasons inherent in the development of science itself, plus personal predilection. The success of science in a democratic society may be due as much to its being relatively ignored as to the felicitous agreement between the basic values of science and democracy.

That such a community was able to survive in this relatively closed form depended upon its having a relatively small number of members and stringent criteria for membership. Many older scientists today remember nostalgically their professional meetings of the 1930's, when they could identify almost everyone in attendance and knew something of each man's work. The difficulties of going through graduate school then, and of finding employment afterward, meant that these men were automatically selected on the basis of deep devotion to their work. The sharing of such common hardships forged another link in the bonds uniting scientists.

This intimacy within science meant that professional recognition was reasonably easy to gain when one had done good work. It was possible for everyone interested in a given field to follow and evaluate nearly all new research in it—and without such feedback, a scientist would have had difficulty in satisfying himself that he had accomplished what he had set out to do. The moral obligation to provide this feedback, to "keep them honest"— the obligation called "organized skepticism" by Merton (6)—was supported by the nature of the reward which perforce had to be important in science; the other side of the coin of professional recognition is professional criticism.

Lack of outside support, then, and relative smallness were the major factors which shaped American science in the decades before World War II. Employing the currency of professional recognition, the community was able to encourage its members to carry out basic research, to report it, and to maintain the system of double-checking its validity. These three elements of science are necessary for the production of new empirical knowledge, but they do not define the character of what is produced.

I have argued elsewhere (7) that the traditional values of science are actually rooted in the requirements for continued, adequate allocation of professional recognition rather than in the utilitarian relationship of these values to the goal of science. It follows that as the basic currency changes, these values will be weakened.

CONSEQUENCES OF INCREASED SUPPORT AND GROWTH

I suggest that in American science today this older currency is being gradually replaced by coins minted in the larger society: money, prestige, and power. The new coins will "buy" the three necessary activities (production, dissemination, and evaluation) just as the old ones did, but in themselves these activities do not make up genuine science as we have known it. My argument is that the new coins coming into greater use within science today are having consequences of the utmost seriousness for the fundamental character of science itself.

The new coins are a product of the larger society; society's increased support of science has made them available for use within science. Scientists are members of this larger society as well as of their professional community, and they are accustomed to the use of these currencies. Because we have Big Science, graduate fellowships in abundance, larger research grants, and more interest in learning scientists' opinions on the great political issues of the day, there is more opportunity to spend these currencies within science. The need for more scientists to administer Big Science and to act as ambassadors to the public in order to maintain the flow of support has been recognized. The need to control the allocation of research funds, resulting in the creation of more and more study sections, has been noted. But one further consequence of the increase in public support must be recognized as well. This is the atmosphere in which new scientists are being trained.

With more money available, it is a rare thing now for a competent young man to have to put himself through graduate school by his own earnings (other than those earned through teaching or research assistantships). He *expects* to be supported, and he may even choose a graduate school on the basis of the financial aid it offers rather than by the quality of its professors. From the beginning, he is entering science with the expectation that it will yield a respectable living. This is a major factor in the gradual replacement of professional recognition by rewards native to the rest of society.

The increasing availability of consulting and advisory work, which carries with it a fair amount of social prestige, is providing scientists with another means of "earning" more of society's coins. Research administration, both formal and informal, as when a man receives a large grant, is increasingly a legitimate career for the scientist. And slowly, the size of a man's research grant is coming to mean more to him and to others than the findings it pays for. These new activities of the scientist—consulting in Washington, becoming an administrator of research, and receiving large grants—are coming to be defined by younger scientists as marks of success in the scientific career. They are easier to come by than a Nobel prize; they are negotiable in the larger society—Gresham's law indeed!

In this way the central importance of professional recognition in the scientific community is being challenged, and the values of science based upon it, which have given shape to American science in the past, are changing as well. Not only is the coinage of science being challenged, it is also becoming more scarce. With the growth of the scientific community, professional recognition is no longer so easily obtainable.

For one thing, the larger number of scientists [the number of doctorates per year in the sciences near quadrupled between 1932 and 1957 (8)] has meant a vast increase in the amount of scientific material being published. No one can expect a single article in a given field to be read by anything like the proportion of scientists in that field who formerly read each new article. A senior scientist once remarked to me that the major difference between his day and the present is that young scientists today no longer even hope to master the literature of their fields. And as one's confidence in his command of the literature decreases, he may become more hesitant about proclaiming the fact of another's priority.

Add to this the continuing policy of secrecy in many areas of defense and industrial research and it is obvious that the coin of professional recognition is becoming scarcer. Much of the current concern with information retrieval may be as much related to the problem of getting one's own work read as to that of finding others' work which is pertinent to one's own. The outcry against "publish-or-perish" policies in some parts of academia and elsewhere may be seen in one sense as resistance to making professional recognition a means rather than an end.

Second, the larger number of scientists means that there are relatively fewer opportunities for the old system of controls to operate effectively. Published criticism by a colleague may not be so important to a scientist now, for he can find many other scientists who have not read the criticism or who may not care. With the increased tempo at which science is moving today, such criticism may be lost in the shuffle, or may be thought unnecessary because in the next few months other men will have found the right answer. It may not be forthcoming at all (9). While the flow of publication swells, the techniques by which scientific truth was formerly ensured may be more frequently replaced by other means which do not involve the alter ego of professional recognition, professional criticism. The rapidly decreasing lead time between discovery and application may even presage a return to Francis Bacon's criterion: "works themselves . . . as pledges of truth. . . ."

Finally, there are the consequences of a growing tendency to turn to "basic" research to solve specific problems. I know of medical researchers who are now doing "basic research on heart disease" because, as practicing M.D.'s, they were frustrated by the lack of knowledge in this area. Such research is essentially a broadening of the area covered by research that seeks the solution to a practical problem, and it leads to a blurring of the real distinction between basic and applied science. When greater numbers of scientists are concentrating their efforts in the few areas designated "major problems," the audience for research that is genuinely basic in nature—research in the interstitial areas of science which apparently will not have practical consequences—is likely to be diminished. And with less opportunity to gain professional recognition through such work, either as means or as end, there is a natural snowballing of interest in those areas where recognition may be obtained. Thus threatened by a powerful imposter, "basic research *on a problem,*" the vital concept of the disinterested quest for knowledge is in danger of being stifled as a legitimate form of inquiry.

In sum, I am suggesting that the new position of science in society has engendered internal conditions which are rapidly altering its entire structure. The two sources of change—increasing support from outside and increasing growth inside—are operating to open wide the older, closed-system scientific community which we may still be assuming, or hoping, will be preserved. I suggest that it will *not* be preserved, and that we must accept this and bend our efforts toward preserving what we can of it in the new situation which is already upon us. An attempt to predict the new shape which American science will take is necessary. After making such a prediction I shall suggest some countermeasures that I think must be undertaken to protect the essential character of our scientific community.

NEW STRUCTURE OF AMERICAN SCIENCE

Most subtle, perhaps, but of far-reaching significance, is the decline of the informal atmosphere within science. In a very concrete sense, this change is similar to the sudden growth of a small town during a boom. The older citizens remember the days when everyone knew each other and when the town's stability was maintained through informal controls. Most of the new people, though, do not know each other personally, nor do they care. The police, welfare department, and city government must take on new and heavier responsibilities. The boundaries between social classes become chasms instead of fences. The pressures of public opinion play a smaller part in the maintenance of an orderly civic life.

The same thing is happening within the scientific community. One of the graduate student's real traumas is his first professional convention, where he first sees just how many people there are in his field. His implicit hope that all these people will someday become friends is shattered. His feelings that he will be a welcome member of a small band are replaced by the fear that he will never be able to make his mark in such a vast company.

Like relationships among people in a metropolis, relationships among scientists will assume a more businesslike character. They will be restricted more and more to the exchange of specific information and will lack the warmth and the assumption of mutual sympathies, which was so typical before World War II. Within a given organization this will not be true, but in the same way that his neighborhood and his place of employment are the places where a person finds friends in the city, so will university departments and research centers or divisions come to mark the boundaries within which a scientist may automatically expect to find warm relationships. He no longer can assume that the holder of a degree in his field will respond naturally to overtures of friendship; before he will feel free to make these overtures, more specific credentials will be required.

With this breakdown in the small-town atmosphere of science will come also a greater amount of stratification in the community. There will be fewer and weaker lines of communication between the bottom ranks and those at the top. The top ranks—the scientific elites—will become more isolated at the same time that they assume greater responsibilities. That the oligarchic "government" of science has not yet been openly criticized may be due to its general responsiveness to science as a whole (10); but in coming years we may expect more complaints about "dictatorial powers" possessed by the small number of senior scientists who control the allocation of research funds and the access to desirable positions. The only response that can be made to such complaints is to raise the standards by which men are deemed acceptable for such positions and to make sure that these men keep in touch with all sectors of the scientific metropolis.

At the same time that these changes are going on we may expect an increase in the splintering of science into subdivisions. The appearance of more specialized journals, the need to restrict one's training and reading to narrower areas, and the establishment of research organizations focused upon more tightly defined fields all point in this direction. Just when the continuous subdivision of science will stretch the lines of communication to the breaking point cannot be estimated precisely, although the present feeling in some quarters that medical research is developing an ethos different from that of other areas may be a forerunner of such breaks.

It seems likely that, in the future, science will become a federation instead of a community, or even an aggregate of specialties whose unity lies more in their being classified together by the public than in their own feelings of interdependence and mutual support. How much, after all, do civil engineers today feel that they have in common with electronics engineers?

SOME POSSIBLE COUNTERMEASURES

It is obvious that a science characterized by this type of structure will lack many of the things which have facilitated the growth of knowledge through the encouragement of creativity and of genuinely basic research. In addition to trying to make sure that only the most broadly competent and humane men continue to reach positions within science where they will influence the internal distribution of its support from outside, I think special efforts must be made to provide an enclave within this structure where the conditions that foster basic research are maintained.

There must be a rapid increase in the establishment of "career investigatorships" along the lines being explored now by the National Institutes of Health and by some private foundations, where a man is guaranteed a reasonable income with yearly increments for a period of 10 or more years and is left absolutely free to study whatever he wishes. More unrestricted grants to university departments and laboratories must be made—not so much larger grants to some groups as middle-sized grants to many. We must remember that basic research must have enough support to "get off the ground"; without the expectation that a fair number of other scientists will be interested in his work, a man often seems to lack motivation to work in really unexplored areas. The small-scale and random support of a few men to do such research is not enough.

Finally, there must be found ways and means of encouraging "generalists," men who are admittedly jacks-of-all-trades who have chosen breadth rather than depth and who can thereby strengthen the lines of communication among different disciplines. A promising development along this line already is the increasing importance of the computer programmer, a man who by his detailed acquaintance with several fields and through his continuing connections with them is in an excellent position to engage in this sort of cross-fertilization.

I think we must expect to find that basic research will become the tail rather than the dog in coming years. Unless knowledgeable efforts are made now to protect it, we may find it being wagged right on the dog without our being aware of it. Huey Long's famous dictum, "When fascism comes to America, it will come under the guise of anti-fascism," has its parallel in our own situation: "When applied research comes to dominate science, it will come under the guise of basic research." If we do not recognize the coming changes in American science, we shall be poorly equipped to preserve the creative essence of science—science whose purpose is, in Weinberg's words, "the enriching and broadening of human life."

REFERENCES AND NOTES

1. A. Weinberg, *Science* **134**, 161 (1961).
2. A. Roe, *Psychol. Monogr.* **67**, 49 (1953).
3. R. Knapp and H. Goodrich, *Origins of American Scientists* (Univ. of Chicago Press, Chicago, 1952), pp. 292–293.
4. R. Merton, *Osiris* **4**, 360 (1938).

5. ———, *Am. Sociol. Rev.* **22**, 635 (1957);
   ———, in *Recognition of Excellence* (Free Press, Glencoe, Ill., 1960), pp. 297–328; H. Shepard, *Phil. Sci.* **23**, 48 (1956).
6. R. Merton, *Social Theory and Social Structure* (Free Press, Glencoe, Ill., rev. ed., 1957), pp. 560–561.
7. N. Storer, *Am. Behavioral Scientist* **4**, 27 (1962).
8. Naval Research Advisory Committee, *Basic Research in the Navy* (Little, Cambridge, Mass., 1959), vol. 2, pp. 36–39.
9. M. K. Hubbert, *Science* **139**, 884 (1963).
10. B. De Jouvenel, in *The Logic of Personal Knowledge: Essays Presented to Michael Polanyi* (Free Press, Glencoe, Ill., 1961), pp. 139–140.

The Scientist and Society

LELAND J. HAWORTH

It is a great pleasure to be here this evening on the occasion of your Annual
Meeting and to share, in a small way at least, the efforts of the Institute to
advance the cause of science education. It is interesting and gratifying that
the Institute perpetuates the tradition of the public science lecture. I fear
that with the modern competition of television, radio, and movies, the science lecture does not have the same entertainment appeal it had in the great
days of Agassiz and Gray, Huxley and Darwin, Burton, and Speke. But the
fact that it survives at all is extremely gratifying. The nineteenth century
could have no way of foreseeing the extent to which science and technology
were beginning to shape the modern world. But the public sensed the vast
stirrings of something new and flocked to hear the scientists and explorers
of the day relate their experiences and expound their theories from public
platforms. In the twentieth century the evidence is so overwhelming and so
complex that we search for means of understanding and using wisely the
same forces they discussed. The science lecture is only one of the ways that
are now available to us for bringing a message, but it is still one of the most
satisfying, for it has the warmth and intimacy of face-to-face encounter.

The mutual responsibilities of scientists and society as a whole are important to our survival in that both government and citizenry should understand something of the capabilities and potentialities of science, and that we
scientists join our efforts to those of the public media to bring about such
an understanding.

Public issues involving science and technology crowd upon us from
every side. For example, take the field of health. The problem of radioactive
fallout from weapons testing has happily been solved. But there are many
others.

Recently the U.S. Public Health Service released the report of the
President's blue ribbon panel on the relationship of smoking to health. So

This paper was delivered at the Annual Meeting of The Franklin Institute,
January 15, 1964. Reprinted from the *Journal of the Franklin Institute,* April 1964,
Vol. CCLXXVII, No. 4, pp. 382–392, with permission of the author and the pub-
lisher. Dr. Leland J. Haworth, a physicist, is the Director of the National Science
Foundation in Washington, D.C. He was formerly the Director of the Brookhaven
National Laboratory.

great was its expected impact that prior to its release the report was closely held to prevent its premature disclosure; and long before its release, columnists were speculating on its possible effects on American Industry.

Two years ago, in her book, *Silent Spring,* Rachel Carson attracted the attention of the American public in a wholly unprecedented way to the problems created by the widespread use of pesticides and a wide variety of chemical pollutants. Public interest led to action at the very highest levels of the government. President Kennedy commented on the book in a press conference, and at his request the President's Science Advisory Committee analyzed the situation and issued a special report: *The Use of Pesticides.*

The tragedies resulting from the use of the drug Thalidomide by expectant mothers provoked nationwide controversy regarding the need for stricter control of drugs. A few years ago the discovery of a chemical contaminant in a cranberry crop produced a major crisis over a national dish. These are some of the more spectacular occurrences that have made the headlines. Back of the headlines, however, are such continuing issues as the struggle between conservation and industrial growth, the growing problem of air and water pollution, the mounting problems of a continually-expanding world population, and so on through an unending list of issues in which the forces of science and technology are either marshaled to make life better for man or to threaten him with new and awesome means of destruction. For always in the background is the all-pervasive threat of nuclear war— the greatest danger that we face today.

GOOD AS WELL AS EVIL

Clearly, science and scientists have changed the world. They have created untold opportunities for good and enormous potentialities for evil. As a result of their effort we enjoy longer and healthier lives; we have such conveniences and tools as abundant electricity in the home; safe and speedy surface and air transportation; nuclear reactors propelling surface and subsurface ocean-going vessels; instantaneous communication, including live television from Europe via communications satellites; space vehicles travelling millions of miles to inspect the planets and to relay their observations back to the earth; giant accelerators probing deep into the sub-nuclear world; ultra-high speed computers solving complex problems in science, in business and in many other spheres.

But science has also made possible intercontinental ballistic missiles with nuclear warheads, world-ranging submarines armed with similar weapons, and a wide variety of death-dealing devices making use of biological and chemical agents. These levels of technical sophistication have been achieved in a world whose inhabitants are not all intellectually mature. We are still "growing up," and growing up can be dangerous. Throughout the centuries history has shown us that the human race never moves forward uniformly; hence increasing scientific knowledge brings both opportunity and danger. Only by the most arduous efforts can opportunity be strengthened and danger lessened.

It is clearly the responsibility of scientists to assist their fellow-citizens in every possible way to chart the course of society between shoals of danger, through the channels of peace and human well-being. The best and possibly the only lasting way to accomplish this is to protect, maintain and strengthen the deeper human values that make life worthwhile everywhere.

Therefore, I would like to discuss specifically a question I have raised before: "How can scientists make maximum contributions to significant and lasting human values?" I do not pretend to have answers to this question. Rather, by posing additional questions I hope to stimulate further thought on this far-reaching and important subject.

Certainly a partial answer to my question is to be found in the realization that the scientist has the dual mission of uncovering the facts of nature and of interpreting these facts to his fellow-men. A great deal more effort and attention should, indeed *must*, be given by the scientist to present a true picture of science, in the most meaningful form, to the public, both at the level of the citizen and at the level of the government. The aspirations, the potentialities and the limitations of science must be made known to the people so that they can meet the responsibilities of progressive citizenship called for in the world today; they must be made known to government so that decision-makers can act rationally within the framework of reality.

How can a government be responsible in matters involving science if those guiding its course do not really understand how their acts will affect individual citizens? How can the general welfare be promoted, or the blessings of liberty be generally secured, through government action on scientific affairs, without a proper understanding in both quarters?

Additionally and importantly, how is it possible to instill in the individual citizen an understanding of the fundamental truths of nature yielding intellectual and cultural rewards that are among the greatest of the lasting human values?

PUBLIC MADE TO UNDERSTAND

It is also important that the public learn to understand the scientists themselves, that they are simply highly-educated men working in a special field. Today there is no question as to the skill, capability, efficiency and natural endowment of American scientists and engineers. The public is proud of the remarkable achievements they have made. Their successes have instilled in the average citizen a feeling that scientists and engineers can accomplish almost anything. This image of the scientist is, of course, exaggerated. Scientists cannot produce miracles. You and I know this—but does the average citizen?

The citizen actually yearns for the truth. He wants to learn how to utilize science properly so that nature can be made to serve him. Only people such as we have the ability to help him.

There is a second popular misconception concerning scientists—that their inherent characteristics, together with their specific training, in some mysterious way have rendered them incapable of other tasks. It is commonly accepted that a lawyer, a businessman, a farmer, a labor-leader, or a soldier —indeed, almost anyone—can, if given opportunity, become a successful executive, or Congressman, or government official; but not a scientist. This last, of course, is arrant nonsense. But let me give you an example. For two months in 1962 the Atomic Energy Commission was reduced to three members, all with scientific educations. The fear was expressed in many quarters, including articles by leading journalists, that these "callow"—the word is mine—these callow scientists might mismanage the whole atomic energy establishment, that managerial experience and sense were clearly lacking. But actually one Commissioner had headed the several largest oil companies in the country; another had been Chancellor of the largest and one of the greatest universities; the third had directed a large, successful laboratory. Certainly this was pertinent experience.

I am convinced that the citizen wants to know more about our scientific achievements. Certainly he deserves to know. In the final analysis, the labor and toil of the citizen has paid for the freedom of the scientist to conduct research with dignity and honor. The citizen, in turn, also has a responsibility to make a real attempt to acquire sufficient knowledge of the basic principles of science to enable him to understand the implications of its discoveries and their significance to him. This requires time and effort, and the average citizen tends to avoid this kind of responsibility; so it becomes part of the task of the scientist to persuade him to make the effort to acquire such knowledge.

In the past, scientific research was such a purely academic pursuit and government involvement in such research was so minor that neither impinged to any substantial extent on the public consciousness. Today, however, over-all national expenditures for research and development amount to more than $16 billion per year of which the Federal Government is the source of approximately two-thirds. Federal expenditures of this magnitude have quite properly attracted the attention of Congress, and the question is being raised as to whether expenditures in this area could not properly be reduced. But most of the public and many of the lawmakers have fallen into the fallacy of thinking of research and development as a single entity. A wide spectrum of activities, from very basic research to the routine testing of devices, is erroneously lumped together under the heading of science. It is a matter of the gravest importance that this misunderstanding be corrected. Actually, research and development must be thought of in terms of the many individual purposes for which they are conducted. In testifying before one of the committees of Congress recently, I expressed the view that the broad objectives of the Federal Government in science and technology are about three in number.

The first is to assure that the scientific and technological health of the country is first-rate.

A second objective is to develop, or have developed, end items—hardware, processes, etc.,—that the Federal Government needs directly for its own purposes. These fall mostly, at the present time, in the areas of defense and space.

Thirdly, I believe that the Federal Government should foster and encourage and, as appropriate, assist in practical developments that are in the general public interest, for which the public, as distinguished from the government, is the customer. These include public health, agriculture, and developments contributing to our general well-being and economic health in such fields as energy, water, transportation, etc.

The future state of our scientific and technological health rests primarily on two factors: the maintenance and constant augmentation of a fund of scientific knowledge derived through research, especially basic research, plus a vigorous program of education in the sciences, with particular emphasis on higher education, to be sure that we have a constant stream of new, vigorous young scientists and engineers to carry out the various programs that are so essential to us.

A SEARCH FOR KNOWLEDGE

Let me speak briefly about research. The wide spectrum of scientific and technical activities is customarily divided into basic research, applied research and development, although there are no sharp boundaries between them. Indeed, different people may apply different terms to the same or similar programs. For example, what may be applied research to a university scientist working on the frontiers of knowledge may be considered very basic by an engineer desiring to utilize the results. Similarly, whereas in industry the word "development" is usually applied to work directed at end items for direct use, in public health and agriculture the same type of work is usually denoted as applied research. In spite of these overlaps, however, the designations are quite useful.

Research is, of course, a search for knowledge. As a matter of fact, one can say that science itself is a particular form of knowledge. Now in the broad sense, knowledge implies understanding as well as information. "Basic" research seeks an understanding of the laws of nature without regard to the ultimate applicability of the results. Hence, the real objective of basic research is not merely to discover a lot of separate empirical facts by measuring this or measuring that, but to develop understanding of nature —not merely how does nature behave but why does she behave that way. Such an understanding is obviously part of any complete knowledge. But it has unusual importance in science and the application of science because only with understanding can one predict. It is not sufficient to have a set of isolated facts, because if one does not understand those facts he cannot interpolate between them or expand them to new areas. The search for understanding leads in unpredictable directions. Hence it is important that the individual scientist be free to pursue those courses giving promise of greatest contribution to that understanding.

"Applied" research is carried out with a practical objective in mind, although it may be a very general one; it may range from a specific measurement yielding data needed for some engineering purpose to broad fields of research leading to knowledge of general applicability for many purposes, as for example in high temperature materials. Applied research pursues those courses deemed most promising in terms of practical results. Although important, understanding nature's laws is not a primary objective. We may sometimes seek a particular piece of information for direct application without undue concern as to why it may be so. Straightforward phenomenological measurements may then suffice.

Some of the contrasts between basic and applied research can be illustrated by an example. At the Brookhaven National Laboratory we studied the absorption of neutrons by various substances. We did this from two standpoints. In our more basic program we measured the degree to which neutrons of different velocities were absorbed by various atomic nuclei, with a view to furthering our understanding of the structure of those and other nuclei. Here we chose as our experimental materials those elements deemed most likely to shed light on nuclear structure without regard to whether such measurements would have practical utility. In another facet of the program we concerned ourselves with neutron absorption by materials used in nuclear reactors and by the products that result from nuclear fission. This was because loss of neutrons through absorption in a reactor inhibits the nuclear chain reaction, thereby reducing its efficiency. But in both cases the measurements were made in precisely the same way. Thus, on Monday an experiment might be done with materials chosen to develop fundamental understanding. On Tuesday similar measurements might be made to develop information for use by reactor engineers.

IMPORTANCE OF BASIC RESEARCH

These distinctions are, of course, not always sharp and there is overlap. Basic research is often inspired, in part at least, by the belief that information in the general field may have utilitarian value. Contrariwise, research motivated by possible applications may well be very fruitful in a basic sense.

Basic research is important in several senses: first, it has very great intellectual and cultural value; second, it is the foundation upon which rests all of our technological advances; third, it is intimately involved in the education and training of first-class scientists and engineers.

The importance of basic research to ultimate application needs a bit of explanation. In stating that basic research is the foundation upon which all technology rests, it is first necessary to understand that this is usually meant in the broad sense. Practical developments do not usually arise from a single set of basic facts or the results of one experiment. They usually arise from a mosaic of knowledge made up of a great many experiments and the understanding derived from them—just as one's house rests on a whole array of bricks or blocks in its foundation. Thus, the question "How can that particular piece of basic research possibly ever have an application?" is not a proper question. What is important from the ultimate application standpoint is the total understanding that grows out of that and many other experiments analyzed and interpreted as a whole.

Scientists have been careless in not explaining these facts more carefully. We have also fallen into the trap of trying to illustrate the ultimate utilitarian value of basic research by giving examples where a single fundamental experiment has had an important practical impact. Nuclear fission has been used as such an example for many years. Even in this case, however, a whole series of experiments preceded and followed that one discovery of fission. Without them the fission experiment alone could not have accomplished the results it did even though it was an outstanding scientific-technical breakthrough.

The role of basic research in graduate education, in the production of new and vigorous, highly-trained, highly-educated scientists is very intimate and very necessary. Not only does the search for knowledge on the frontiers of science provide experience and cultivate the student's ingenuity and resourcefulness, but it is also here that the professor-student relationship reaches its highest level of effectiveness. These relationships and their importance are well discussed in the report of the President's Science Advisory Committee in 1960 entitled "Scientific Progress, the Universities, and the Federal Government," usually known as The Seaborg Report

The point I wish to stress in giving considerations to Federal expenditures for research and development is that they must be thought of not as an entity but in terms of the objectives to which they are directed. We must ask ourselves how much we can afford to spend on the latest weaponry essential to national defense; how much we can afford to spend on the conquest of cancer and heart disease; and how much we can afford to spend for the maintenance of a healthy state in our science and technology, particularly in terms of basic research and education.

These, then, as I see them, are the basic issues involving science and technology in relation to the Federal Government and the reasons why public understanding of the role of science is not only desirable but essential.

An informed citizenry can best be achieved by reaching the individual in his formative years—while he is still in school and before the excitement and wonder of learning about nature have been dulled and discouraged through contact with the indifferent world of adults.

To this end, considerable progress has been made in the past decade in improving the course content and the methods of teaching science and mathematics in the school systems. Much of this progress has been brought about by leading scientists who have taken the time and expanded the effort required to bring our new knowledge into proper focus in the minds of youth. The true measure of our improvement in the teaching of science is the level of competence and understanding retained by the students five to ten years after they have completed their basic studies. Obviously we must continue our efforts to improve the teaching of science in our secondary schools by such means as are employed here at The Franklin Institute.

But to educate the public thus as a whole will require many decades. Meanwhile we cannot wait. We must create an understanding by methods that reach adults. Scientists have only partially succeeded in this task. Often we have simply satisfied ourselves that we have informed the citizen of our activities by repeating our own shop talk and catch phrases in our public appearances and press releases. When asked for further details we have gratuitously provided copies of our highly condensed and sophisticated technical papers and let the matter drop. This is not enough.

Scientists have the great and often irksome responsibility of interpreting science to the layman, through simple articles and talks, through sympathetic and careful help to the journalists and others who reach the public through newspapers, magazines, radio and television. By helping in this way scientists not only serve society as a whole, they also serve themselves.

INFORMED CITIZENRY URGED

An informed citizenry will ultimately insure an informed government, for government officials are merely citizens in a special category. But in the governmental process there is need for deeper understanding of science, especially in certain fields. Moreover, the informed citizenry does not now exist. Here then lies another responsibility of scientists this time to government— to assist responsible officials to gain as far as possible this deeper understanding of the scientific and terchnological facts and their implications.

But even this is not enough. No matter how well informed, the government official cannot in many instances appreciate and understand the implications of his actions when science and technology are involved. It is essential that he have the continuing advice of competent and experienced scientists. There are many mechanisms to this end—advisory committees made up of scientists from outside the Government, such as the President's Science Advisory Committee, the General Advisory Committee of the Atomic Energy Commission and the Disarmament Agency, the many boards and committees advising the Department of Defense, the National Science Foundation and other agencies. The scientists of the country have given unselfishly and effectively of their time and effort to serve on such committees.

But, useful as they are, part-time committees in turn do not suffice. Advice is needed when decisions must be made. Intimate, continuing and up-to-date knowledge of all the facts may be essential to the giving of advice in many instances. Hence there is need for many full-time scientists to serve as staff advisors to the most responsible officials of the government. A growing recognition of this need is found throughout the government. Increasing numbers of men of scientific stature are playing important roles—the Special Assistant to the President, who also heads the Office of Science and Technology, advisors at the senior level in the Departments of Defense, Interior, State, Commerce and many others.

Within many agencies there is, of course, the need for scientists and engineers to administer scientific and technological programs. The Atomic Energy Commission, the Department of Defense, the National Science Foundation, the National Institutes of Health, and the National Aeronautics and Space Administration all have requirements for large numbers of such men. It is in the interest of both science and the general public that these men be highly qualified.

The appropriateness of using scientists to administer the scientific programs of the government has long been recognized. It first came for technical agencies such as the National Science Foundation and the Atomic Energy Commission which are headed by scientists.

The trend is broadening. Scientists are found at the assistant secretary level in agencies of a more general nature. These men and other experts are playing increasingly important roles in making and executing public policy, not only with respect to our scientific and technological programs, but across the entire spectrum of government affairs. Political, economic and scientific implications are discussed on equal terms by composite groups of experts from various fields, with no sharp barriers to participation regardless of the individual's specialty. In short, it has become clear that scientists can have valid and useful thoughts beyond the realm of science, that they can contribute to painting the picture as a whole. This is as it should be. For science is increasingly enmeshed with all the other disciplines and activities that together make up society and hence concern the government in their over-all impact.

Thus, there is great and continuing need for mature and experienced scientists to devote a few years of their working lives to full-time service in the government. You may well ask "Why should any scientist want to make this sacrifice?" The pace is difficult, the criticism constant and the pay is only adequate. However, I can assure you that such service can be an enriching experience for the individual. The satisfaction that one finds in feeling that he has made a contribution toward channelling the affairs of government in directions serving best the public interest can be great indeed.

A friend of mine has drawn an analogy between the scientist in government and the lawyer who is a public attorney or a judge. It would be a marked advance if the practicing scientist and the general public would recognize the similarity and honor the scientific public servants as they do the legal ones.

The responsibilities I have outlined are common to all citizens. Scientists differ from others only in the nature of their skills and knowledge, and in the great importance that science holds today. But in another way, science —especially basic science—has a relationship to society that is more or less peculiar. Through government, the general public now supports financially a major fraction of all research—without direct and obvious financial return. It is well understood by scientists that in addition to the enormous cultural and intellectual values, this research is ultimately the basis for all material progress, but this is not necessarily understood by the individual citizen. He sometimes feels that his money is being improperly diverted to serve the selfish interests of the scientists rather than the interests of society as a whole.

This brings me to another formulation of the basic question, "How can scientists make maximum contributions to human values of lasting significance?" Perhaps I could state it as follows: "How can scientists in our universities, with Federal Government financial support and control, assist in the preservation of the values and processes essential to scientific inquiry under conditions which will preserve the fundamental values and processes of a responsible democratic government?"

My own belief is that the individual scientist can make his most effective contribution to his cause if he is able to carry into his public life those fundamental tenets of thoughtful analysis and intellectual honesty which guide him in his scientific endeavors. I think that the scientist can, by extension of his methods, contribute to general progress in a significant way.

I have devoted all of my now lengthy adult life to service in universities, in scientific laboratories, and in government. The more I become acquainted with each of these institutions, the more I am convinced that each can learn something from the others. I believe, however, that thoughtful people from each of these institutions adhere to about the same sense of values and have their eyes on about the same goals, but without fully understanding each other.

I think that scientists, after seeing political compromise in action, are often apt to conclude that government is composed of individuals whose actions are sometimes stupid or self-serving. The scientist, accustomed to the logic of the scientific process, is sometimes impatient with the seemingly slow, and, to him, often illogical and unintelligent, actions of government officials.

On the other hand, the harried government legislator or administrator, not always understanding fully the information he has available, is likely to interject into his official actions his own attitudes and experience. If he cannot solve his immediate problems on this basis, he is apt to rely heavily on the actions of powerful groups or the advice of influential individuals. Thus, when the official is faced with conflicting advice from competing groups, he often becomes cautious and less responsive to the real needs of the scientist. Worse still, he begins to attribute unintended motives to scientists; he is prone, mistakenly, to decide that all scientists are intellectually dishonest when removed from their laboratories. We must find ways to communicate with these individuals so that our motives become self-evident.

The government official and the academic leader must learn more about the proper role which scientists at home can play in a democracy. Granted that this should be done, the entire realm of political philosophy immediately presents itself to us for reflection. The nature of man and his relationship with the state; the problems of political obligations, of rights and responsibilities, of authority and of freedom; the meanings of abstract principles such as liberty, justice, equality, public interest; means and ends, the form and substance of government processes—all these, and more, become germane.

THE COMPLETE POLITICAL PROCESS

The proper role of government in the affairs of science and the proper role of the scientist in the affairs of government, is surely the complete political process. Government decisions on large and small items—on accelerators, on space, on medicine—are composites of many decisions by many individuals and groups, both within and out of the government. Conflict is built into the decision-making process in our society which permits contesting interests to exercise openly their power of influence at the decision-making centers of government. In this process, no activity is ignored, no tenet unchallenged, no doctrine sacred.

Few people will deny that the democratic principles of the United States are on trial today. The entire nation—especially its leaders—is now faced with a critical challenge as to whether our increasingly complex society can continue to have a government which fosters the essential conditions of democracy.

Individual liberty and human dignity, the very cornerstones of democracy, bear brief examination here. It is easy for us as scientists valuing, as we do, our academic freedom to say that individual liberty is best served by a passive government, but as national problems increase in complexity, the needs of the nation and the rights of the individual are more and more being thrown into conflict. The question of war now involves the issue of human survival. Accordingly, the dictates of national defense pervade every area of our national life and therefore of our individual liberty.

Those within the government who assist in formulation of the problems or in reaching the policy decisions, can do so effectively only if scientific advice is freely and promptly given by the scientific community and given in a form uncolored by real or imagined "political" implications.

The intricate web of relationships between government and society is too little known to express even in general terms.

Therefore to return to my original point, we must develop a better system of communication between the scientist and the layman. We must educate the general public and the government to an understanding of the basic facts of science and we must inculcate in ourselves the realization that individual scientists must play increasing general public roles. Only by striving in these ways and making the necessary sacrifices can we insure that science and scientists will make their maximum contribution to significant and lasting human values.

Bibliography

This bibliography is designed to provide the reader with a reasonably good start toward further exploration of the problems and issues raised by the many authors included in this volume. In addition to the specific items included here, its main usefulness is to indicate the very wide variety of types of sources—especially among journals—in which relevant material has been published. Even specialists working in one or another area concerned with science and society are often unfamiliar with related work stemming from those in quite distant academically defined specialties. So for both the specialist and the nonspecialist, this list should provide an idea of the range and variety of sources which may be examined.

It goes without saying that this bibliography cannot be considered comprehensive and that the listing of a particular item under one of the general organizing categories of this volume is often quite arbitrary. Because of space limitations, it is restricted almost exclusively to a selection of work in the last five years or so, and many highly significant works which appeared earlier have not been included here. However, a number of sources with quite extensive bibliographies covering various time periods may be found listed below. Finally, some readers may find the review essay by Norman Kaplan[1] a helpful guide to a considerable body of literature on the sociology of science which appeared in the last decade. This essay also notes other bibliographies and sources of information.

I. *Prologue to Present*

Barber, Bernard. *Science and The Social Order* (Glencoe, Ill.: The Free Press, 1952).

Barber, Bernard. "The Sociology of Science," in Robert K. Merton, Leonard Broom and Leonard S. Cottrell, Jr. (eds.) *Sociology Today* (New York: Basic Books, Inc., 1959).

Barber, Bernard, and Hirsch, Walter (eds.) *The Sociology of Science* (Glencoe, Ill.: The Free Press, 1962).

Ben-David, Joseph. "Akademische Berufe und die Professionalisierung." *Kölner Zeitschrift für Soziologie und Sozialpsychologie,* Sonderheft 5, 1961, 104–119.

Ben-David, Joseph, and Zloczower, Awraham. "The Idea of the University and the Academic Market-Place." *European Journal of Sociology,* II, 1961, 303–314.

[1] "Sociology of Science." Chapter 22 in *Handbook of Modern Sociology,* Robert E. L. Faris (ed.) (Chicago: Rand McNally & Company, 1964, pp. 852–881).

Beer, John J., and Lewis, W. David. "Aspects of the Professionalization of Science." *Daedalus,* XCII, No. 4, Fall 1963, 764–783.

Bronowski, J. *Science and Human Values* (New York: Julian Messner, 1956).

Burlingame, Roger. *Scientists Behind the Inventors* (New York: Harcourt, Brace and Co., 1960).

Cannon, Walter F. "John Herschel and Idea of Science." *Journal of the History of Ideas,* XXII, No. 2, April–June, 1961, 215–239.

Cardwell, D. S. L. *The Organisation of Science in England: A Retrospect* (London: William Heinemann, Ltd., 1957).

Cardwell, D. S. L. "The Development of Scientific Research in Modern Universities: A Comparative Study of Motives and Opportunities." Chapter 22 in *Scientific Change* (London: William Heinemann, Ltd., 1961), pp. 661–677.

Dubos, Rene J. "Scientist and Public." *Science,* CXXXIII, April 21, 1961, 1207–1211.

Dupree, A. Hunter. "Influence of the Past: An Interpretation of Recent Development in the Context of 200 Years of History." *Annals of the American Academy of Political Science,* CCCXXVII, January 1960, 19–26.

Dupree, A. Hunter. "Public Education for Science and Technology." *Science,* CXXXIV, 1961, 716–718.

Dupree, A. Hunter. *Science in the Federal Government* (Cambridge: Harvard University Press, 1957).

Gillispie, Charles Coulston. *The Edge of Objectivity* (Princeton: Princeton University Press, 1960).

Hartley, Sir Harold, F. R. S. (ed.) *The Royal Society: Its Origins and Founders* (London: The Royal Society, 1960).

Hartley, Sir Harold, F. R. S. "The Tercentenary of the Royal Society." *American Scientist,* XLVIII, 1960, 279–299.

Jewkes, John, Sawers, David, and Stillerman, Richard. *The Sources of Invention* (New York: St. Martin's Press, 1958).

Machlup, Fritz. *The Production and Distribution of Knowledge in the United States* (Princeton: Princeton University Press, 1962).

Rosenberg, Charles E. "The Adams Act: Politics and the Cause of Scientific Research." *Agricultural History,* XXXVIII, No. 1, 3–12.

Rosenberg, Charles E. "On the Study of American Biology and Medicine: Some Justifications." *Bulletin of the History of Medicine,* XXXVIII, No. 4, July–August 1964, 364–376.

Seitz, Frederick. "Science and Government." *Physics Today,* XVI, No. 12, December 1963, 28–30, 32.

Shizume, Eri Yagi. "How Japan Introduced Western Physics in the Early Years of the Meiji (1868–1888)." *Scientific Papers of the College of General Education,* University of Tokyo, IX, No. 1, 1959, 163–174.

Toulmin, S. "Science and Our Intellectual Tradition." *Advancement of Science,* May 1963, XX, No. 83, 28–34.

Vucinich, Alexander. *Science in Russian Culture* (Stanford: Stanford University Press, 1963).

II.   *Science as a Changing Institution*

Ashby, Sir Eric. *Technology and the Academics* (London: St. Martin's Press, 1958).

Auger, Pierre. *Current Trends in Scientific Research* (New York: United Nations, 1961).

Avery, Robert W. "Enculturation in Industrial Research." *IRE Transactions of the Professional Group on Engineering Management,* EM-7, No. 1, March 1960, 2–24.

Barber, Bernard. "Resistance by Scientists to Scientific Discovery." *Science,* CXXXIV, 1961, 596–602.

Barber, Bernard. "Tension and Accommodations Between Science and Humanism." *American Behavioral Scientist,* VII, No. 3, November 1963, 3–8.

Beardslee, David C., and O'Dowd, Donald D. "The College-Student Image of the Scientist." *Science,* CXXXIII, No. 3457, March 31, 1961, 997–1001.

Ben-David, Joseph. "Roles and Innovations in Medicine." *American Journal of Sociology,* LXV, No. 6, May 1960, 557–568.

Ben-David, Joseph. "Scientific Growth: A Sociological View." *Minerva,* Summer 1964, II, No. 4, 455–476.

Brown, J. Douglas, and Harbison, Frederick. *High-Talent Manpower for Science and Industry* (Princeton, N.J.: Princeton University, Industrial Relations Section, 1957).

Brownson, Helen L. "Research on Handling Scientific Information." *Science,* CXXXII, 1960, 1922–1931.

Cole, Charles C., Jr. *Encouraging Scientific Talent* (New York: College Entrance Examination Board, 1956).

Cooley, William W. "Attributes of Potential Scientists." *Harvard Educational Review,* XXVIII, No. 1, Winter 1958.

Dedijer, Stevan. "Measuring the Growth of Science." *Science,* CXXXVIII, No. 3542, November 16, 1962, 781–788.

Dooley, D. J. "Science as Cliché, Fable and Faith." *Bull. Atomic Scientists,* XV, 1959, 372–375.

Dubarle, Dominic. "Toward a World Community of Scientists." *Bull. Atomic Scientists,* XV, No. 5, May 1959, 178–180.

Eiduson, Bernice T. *Scientists: Their Psychological World* (New York: Basic Books, Inc., 1962).

Flexner, A. "The Usefulness of Useless Knowledge." *Journal of Chronic Disease,* II, 1955, 241–246.

Fortune, Editors of. *Great American Scientists* (Englewood Cliffs, N.J.: Prentice-Hall, Inc., 1961).

Fox, Renée C. "Symposium on the Study of Drugs in Man: Part IV. Some Social and Cultural Factors in American Society Conducive to Medical Research on Human Subjects." *Clinical Pharmacology and Therapeutics,* I, 1960, 423–443.

Fox, Renée C. *Experiment Perilous: Physicians and Patients Facing the Unknown* (Glencoe, Ill.: The Free Press, 1959).

Glass, Bentley. "The Academic Scientist, 1940–1960." *Science,* CXXXII, 1960, 598–603.

Goldfarb, Albert M. "On the Education of Physicists in Three Foreign Countries." *American Journal of Physics,* XXVIII, 1960, 179–186.

Gray, George W. "'Which Scientists Win Nobel Prizes?" *Harper's Magazine,* CCXXII, May 1961, 78–82.

Greenewalt, Crawford H. "The Fickle Fashions of Science." A speech before the Society of the Sigma Xi and Scientific Research Society of America at the Annual Meeting of American Association for Advancement of Science, Indianapolis, Ind., December 27, 1957. Printed by E. I. duPont de Nemours & Company.

Hagstrom, Warren O. "Anomy in Scientific Communities." *Social Problems,* XII, No. 2, Fall 1964, pp. 186–195.

Hagstrom, Warren O. "Traditional and Modern Forms of Scientific Teamwork." *Administrative Science Quarterly,* IX, No. 3, December 1964, 241–263.

Hirsch, Walter. "The Autonomy of Science in Totalitarian Societies." *Social Forces,* XL 1961, 15–22.

Hirsch, Walter. "Knowledge, Power, and Social Change: The Role of American Scientists." In *Explorations in Social Change,* George K. Zollschan & Walter Hirsch (eds.) (Boston: Houghton Mifflin Co., 1964) pp. 798–816.

Holton, Gerald. "Models for Understanding the Growth and Excellence of Scientific Research." In *Excellence and Leadership in a Democracy,* Gerald Holton & S. R. Graubard (eds.) (New York: Columbia University Press, 1962).

Holton, Gerald. "On the Recent Past of Physics." *American Journal of Physics,* XXIX, No. 12, December 1961, 805–810.

Kemeny, John G. "Once the Professor Was a Teacher." *New York Times Magazine,* June 2, 1963.

Kidd, Charles V. "The Implications of Research Funds for Academic Freedom." *Law and Contemporary Problems,* XXVIII, No. 3, Summer 1963, 613–624.

Kistiakowsky, George B. "Basic Research: An Industrial Responsibility." *Research Management,* III, No. 2, Summer 1960, 69–76.

Klaw, Spencer. "The Affluent Professors." *The Reporter,* June 23, 1960.

Kuhn, Thomas S. "The Function of Dogma in Scientific Research." In *Scientific Change: Historical Studies in the Intellectual, Social and Technical Conditions for Scientific Discovery and Technical Invention from Antiquity to the Present,* A. C. Crombie (ed.) (London: William Heinemann, Ltd., 1961), pp. 347–369.

Kuhn, Thomas S. "Historical Structure of Scientific Discovery." *Science,* CXXXVI, June 1, 1962, 760–764.

Kuhn, Thomas S. *The Structure of Scientific Revolutions* (Chicago: The University of Chicago Press, 1962).

Lehman, Harvey C. "The Age Decrement in Outstanding Scientific Creativity." *American Psychologist,* XV, 1960, 128–34.

Lenher, Samuel. "The Scientist as a Person." A speech at the Tenth Annual Management Conference, Graduate School of Business and Public Administration, Cornell University, April 18, 1958. Printed by E. I. duPont de Nemours & Company.

Lodge, R. M. "Choice and Valuation in Industrial Research." *Advancement of Science* XV, No. 59, December 1958, 211–216.

McClelland, David C. "On the Psychodynamics of Creative Physical Scientists." In *Contemporary Approaches to Creative Thinking,* Howard E. Gruber, Glenn Terrall, and Michael Wertheimer (eds.) (New York: Atherton Press, 1962), pp. 141–174.

Merton, Robert K. "Basic Research and Potentials of Relevance." *American Behavioral Scientist,* VI, No. 9, May 1963, 86–90.

Merton, Robert K. "Priorities in Scientific Discovery: A Chapter in the Sociology of Science." *American Sociological Review,* XXII, No. 6, December 1957, 635–659.

Merton, Robert K. "Recognition and Excellence: Instructive Ambiguities." In

Recognition of Excellence: Working Papers (Glencoe, Ill.: The Free Press, 1960), pp. 297–328.

Merton, Robert K. "Resistance to the Systematic Study of Multiple Discoveries in Science." *European Journal of Sociology,* IV, 1963, 237–282.

Merton, Robert K. "Singletons and Multiples in Scientific Discovery: A Chapter in the Sociology of Science." *Proceedings of the American Philosophical Society,* CV, October 1961, 470:486.

Merton, Robert K., and Barber, Bernard. "Sorokin's Formulations in the Sociology of Science." In Philip J. Allen (ed.) *Pitirim A. Sorokin in Review* (Durham, N.C.: Duke University Press, 1963) pp. 332–368.

Merz, Louise Elizabeth. "The Graduate School as a Socializing Agency: A Pilot Study of Sociological Aspects of Graduate Training in the Physical Sciences." Unpublished Ph.D. dissertation, Cornell University, June 1961.

Motz, Annabelle Bender. "The Roles of the Married Woman in Science." *Marriage and Family Living,* November 1961, XXIII, No. 4, 374–376.

Oppenheimer, Robert. "Communication and Comprehension of Scientific Knowledge." *Science,* November 29, 1963, CXLII, No. 3596, 1143–1146.

Orowan, Egon. "Our Universities and Scientific Creativity." *Bulletin of the Atomic Scientists,* XV, No. 6, June 1959, 236, 239.

Pierce, J. R. "Freedom in Research." *Science,* CXXX, September 4, 1959, 540–542.

Polanyi, Michael. "Passion and Controversy in Science." *Bulletin of Atomic Scientists,* XIII, No. 4, April 1957, 114–119.

Shepard, Herbert A. "Basic Research and the Social System of Pure Science." *Philosophy of Science,* XXIII, No. 1, January 1956, 48–57.

Shepard, Herbert A. "Social Change in Science and Engineering." *IRE Transactions on Engineering Management,* EM-8, 1961, 11–14.

Shryock, Richard H. "United States." In *The Status of University Teachers,* Reports from Sixteen Countries Prepared with the Assistance of UNESCO, International Association of University Professors and Lecturers (Ghent, Belgium: Secretariat General: Rozier 6, 1961) pp. 179–194.

Stein, Morris I., and Heinze, Shirley J. *Creativity and Individual: Summaries of Selected Literature in Psychology and Psychiatry* (Glencoe, Ill.: The Free Press, 1960).

Tuve, Merle A. "Basic Research in Private Research Institutes." In Dael Wolfle, (ed.) *Symposium on Basic Research* (Washington, D.C.: American Association for the Advancement of Science, 1959) pp. 169–184.

Weaver, Warren. "The Imperfections of Science." *Proceedings of the American Philosophical Society,* CIV, No. 5, October 17, 1960, 419–428.

West, S. S. "The Ideology of Academic Scientists." *IRE Transactions on Engineering Management,* EM-7, June 1960, 54–62.

III. *Scientific Research and Laboratory Organization*

Back, Kurt W. "The Behavior of Scientists: Communication and Creativity." *Sociological Inquiry,* XXXII, No. 1, Winter 1962, 82–87.

Barton, Allen H. "The College as a Social Organization." *College Admissions 10: The Behavioral Sciences and Education* (New York: College Entrance Examination Board, 1963).

Boring, Edwin G. "Cognitive Dissonance: Its Use in Science." *Science,* CXLV, No. 3633, August 14, 1964, 681–685.

Dennis, Wayne. "The Age Decrement in Outstanding Scientific Contributions: Fact or Artifact?" *American Psychologist,* XIII, 1958, 457–460.

Fell, Honor B. "Fashion in Cell Biology." *Science,* CXXXII, No. 2440, December 2, 1960, 1625–1627.

Folsom, R. G. "The Academic Institution's Concern with Future Patterns of Research." *American Scientist,* XLVI, No. 2, June 1958, 169–175.

Glaser, Barney G. "Attraction, Autonomy, and Reciprocity in the Scientist-Supervisor Relationship." *Administrative Science Quarterly,* VIII, No. 3, December 1963, 379–398.

Glaser, Barney G. "Comparative Failure in Science." *Science,* CXLIII, No. 3610, March 6, 1964, 1012–1024.

Glaser, Barney G. "The Local-Cosmopolitan Scientist." *The American Journal of Sociology,* LXIX, No. 3, November 1963, 249–259.

Glaser, Barney G. *Organizational Scientists: Their Professional Careers* (Indianapolis, Ind.: Bobbs-Merrill, 1964).

Glaser, Barney G. "The Impact of Differential Promotion Systems on Careers." *IEEE Transactions of the Professional Technical Group on Engineering Management,* EM-10, No. 1, March 1963, 21–24.

Glaser, Barney G. "Variations in the Importance of Recognition of Scientists' Careers." *Social Problems,* X, 1963, 269–276.

Gordon, Gerald. "The Problem of Assessing Scientific Accomplishment: A Potential Solution." *IEEE Transactions of the Professional Technical Group on Engineering Management,* EM-10, No. 4, December 1963, 192–196.

Gordon, Gerald, Anderson, Odin, and Marquis, Sue. "Organization for Scientific Productivity." *The American Behavioral Scientist,* V, No. 4, December 1961, 35–37.

Gordon, Gerald, and Marquis, Sue. "The Effect of Differing Administrative Authority on Scientific Innovation." Paper presented at the Institute for Social Research, University of Chicago, May 1963 (mimeographed), 13 pages.

Gordon, Gerald, Marquis, Sue, and Anderson, O. W. "Freedom and Control in Four Types of Scientific Settings." *The American Behavioral Scientist,* VI, No. 4, 1962, 39–43.

Harington, Sir Charles. "Leadership in Scientific Research." Sir David Russell Memorial Lecture delivered November 12, 1957 at the University of St. Andrews (London: Oxford University Press, 1958), 27 pages.

Hill, Karl (ed.) *The Management of Scientists* (Boston: Beacon Press, 1964).

Hirsch, Irving, Milwitt, William, and Oakes, William J., Jr. "Increasing the Productivity of Scientists." *Harvard Business Review,* XXXVI, No. 2, March–April, 1958.

Kaplan, Norman. "Organization: Will It Choke or Promote the Growth of Science?" Chapter 5 in *The Management of Scientists,* K. Hill (ed.) (Boston: Beacon Press, 1964), pp 103–127.

Kaplan, Norman. "The Relation of Creativity to Sociological Variables in Research Organizations." in Calvin W. Taylor and Frank Barron (eds.) *Scientific Creativity: Its Recognition and Development* (New York: John Wiley & Sons, Inc., 1963).

Kaplan, Norman. "Some Organizational Factors Affecting Creativity." *IRE Transactions on Engineering Management,* EM-7, 1960, 24–30.

Kornhauser, William (with the assistance of Warren O. Hagstrom). *Scientists in Industry: Conflict and Accommodation* (Berkeley: University of California Press, 1962).

Marcson, Simon. "Role Adaptation of Scientists in Industrial Research." *IRE Transactions on Engineering Management,* EM-7, 1960, 159–166.

Marcson, Simon. *The Scientists in American Industry: Some Organization Determinants in Manpower Utilization* (New York: Harper & Bros., 1960).

Menzel, Herbert. "The Information Needs of Current Scientific Research." *Library Quarterly,* XLIV, No. 1, January 1964, 4–19.

Mottley, Charles M. "Managing Innovation for Growth." *Stanford Research Institute Journal,* V, 1961, 58–66.

Orth, Charles D., Bailey, Joseph C., and Wolek, Francis W. *Administering Research and Development: The Behavior of Scientists and Engineers in Organizations* (Homewood, Ill.: Richard D. Irwin & Co., 1964).

Paterson, T. T. "Administration of Research." *Nature,* CXCVIII, May 11, 1963, 520–525.

Pelz, Donald C. "Dither and Time in the Motivation of Scientists." *Chemist,* XL, No. 4, April 1963, 139–149.

Pelz, Donald C. "Freedom in Research." *International Science and Technology,* No. 26, February 1964, 54–66.

Pelz, Donald C. "Some Social Factors Related to Performance in a Research Organization." *Administrative Science Quarterly,* I, No. 3, April 30, 1956, 310–325.

Pelz, Donald C., and Andrews, Frank M. "Diversity in Research." *International Science and Technology,* No. 31, July 1964, 28–36.

Pelz, Donald C., and Andrews, Frank M. "Organizational Atmosphere, Motivation, and Research Contribution." *American Behavioral Scientist,* VI, No. 4, 1962, 43–47.

Peres, Leon. "Research Organization and the Control of Incentives: The Case of an Australian Scientific Organization." *Public Administration,* (Australia) XXII, No. 4, December 1963, 330–349.

Price, Daniel O. *University Research Administration Policies* (Atlanta, Ga.: Southern Regional Education Board, 1962).

Randle, C. Wilson. "Problems of R & D Management." *Harvard Business Review,* January-February 1959, 128–136.

Reich, Irving. "Creativity in Research Organizations." *Research Management,* III, No. 4, Winter 1960, 217–226.

Rhenman, E. and Svensson, S. *Research Administration: A Selected and Annotated Bibliography of Recent Literature* (Stockholm, Sweden: Aktiebolaget Atomenergi, 1961).

Roe, Anne. "The Psychology of the Scientist." *Science,* CXXXIV, No. 3477, August 18, 1961, 456–459.

Royer, George L. "Performance Evaluation of Research Personnel." *Industrial and Engineering Chemistry,* XLIX, No. 8, August 1957, 42A–47A.

Rubenstein, Albert H. "Research on the Research Process." *IRE Transactions on Engineering Management,* EM-6, 1959, 87–88.

Rubenstein, Albert H. "Setting Criteria for R & D." *Harvard Business Review,* XXXV, No. 1, January-February 1957, 95–104.

Shepard, Herbert A. "Patterns of Organization for Applied Research and Development." *Journal of Business* of the University of Chicago, XXIX, No. 1, January 1956, 52–58.

Stein, Morris I. "On the Role of the Industrial Research Chemist and Its Relationship to the Problem of Creativity." Unpublished manuscript.

Taylor, Calvin W., and Barron, Frank (eds.) *Scientific Creativity: Its Recognition and Development* (New York: John Wiley, 1963).

Taylor, C. W., Smith, W. R., and Chiselin, R. "A Study of the Multiple Contributions of Scientists at One Research Organization." *IRE Transactions on Engineering Management,* EM-8, 1961, 194–200.

Thomson, Sir George P. *The Strategy of Research,* The Fourth Fawley Foundation Lecture (Southampton: Camelot Press, Ltd., for the University of Southampton, 1957).

IV. *National Science Establishments*

Audrieth, Ludwig F., and Chinn, Herman I. *The Organization of Science in Germany* (Washington, D.C.: National Science Foundation, Office of International Science Activities, June 1962).

Ballard, B. G. "Organization of Scientific Activities in Canada." *Science,* CXXIX, No. 3351, March 20, 1959, 754–759.

Ben-David, Joseph. "Scientific Endeavor in Israel and the United States." *American Behavioral Scientist,* VI, No. 4, 1962, 12–16.

Cagle, Fred R. *Federal Research Projects and the Southern University* (Atlanta, Ga.: Southern Regional Education Board, 1962).

Calkins, Robert D. "Government Support of Higher Education." The Brookings Institute Reprint No. 38, Washington, D.C., 1960.

The Carnegie Report. "Twenty-Six Campuses and the Federal Government." *Educational Record,* XLIV, No. 2, April 1963, 95–136.

Cleaveland, Frederic N. *Science and State Government* (Chapel Hill: The University of North Carolina Press for the Institute for Research in Social Science, 1959).

Davydovskii, I. V. "Questions of Organization and Planning of Medical Science: A Prospective Plan for the Most Important Problems of Medical Science 1959–1965." *Vestnik Akademii meditskinskikh nauk USSR,* XIII, No. 7, 1958, 46–61. (Translated at the National Institutes of Health, Bethesda, Md., February 13, 1959.)

DeWitt, Nicholas. *Education and Professional Employment in the U.S.S.R.* (Washington, D.C.: National Science Foundation, 1961).

DeWitt, Nicholas. "Soviet Brainpower." *International Science and Technology,* No. 1, January 1962, 33–38.

DeWitt, Nicholas. "Soviet Science: The Institutional Debate." *Bulletin of Atomic Scientists* XVI, No. 6, June 1960, 208–211.

Encel, S. "Financing Scientific Research in Australia." *Science,* CXXXIV, July 28, 1961, 260–266.

Field, M. G. "Soviet Science and Some Implications for American Science and Society." *Journal of International Affairs,* XIII, No. 1, 1959, 18–33.

Gates, David M. "Basic Research in Europe." *Science,* CXXVIII, 1958, 227–235.

Gibello, Henri. "Research and Development Activities in France." *Research Management,* V, No. 6, 1962, 475–483.

Gillespie, D. T. C. "Research Management in the Commonwealth Scientific and Industrial Research Organization, Australia" (mimeographed copy).

Hiscocks, E. S. "Organization of Science in the United Kingdom." *Science,* CXXIX, No. 3350, March 13, 1959, 689–693.

Ismail, Abdel Fattah. "Current Trends in Science Policy in the United Arab Republic." *Impact of Science on Society,* XII, No. 3, 1962, 103–118.

Jablonski, Henryk. "Polish Academy of Sciences in 1962." *Review of the Polish Academy of Sciences,* VIII, No. 3 (31), July-September 1963, 1–15.

Jones, Sir Harold Spencer. "The International Council of Scientific Unions." *Endeavour,* XVIII, 1959, 88–92.

Jubilee of the Max-Planck-Gesellschaft, *Endeavour,* XX, 1961, 59–60.

Kane, Henry. "Research as an Aid to Industrial Development." *State Government* (Oregon), Spring 1962, 105–11.

Kidd, Charles V. *American Universities and Federal Research Funds* (Cambridge: Harvard University Press, 1959).

Kidd, Charles V. "New Government-University Relationships in Research." *Higher Education,* XVI, No. 8, April 1960, 3–6, 18–19.

Korol, Alexander G. *Soviet Research and Development* (Cambridge: Massachusetts Institute of Technology Press, 1964).

Lindsay, Dale R., and Allen, Ernest M. "Medical Research: Past Support, Future Directions." *Science,* CXXXIV, December 22, 1961, 2017–2024.

Lindbeck, John M. H. "The Organization and Development of Science." In *Sciences in Communist China,* Sidney H. Gould (ed.). Pub. No. 68 of the American Association for the Advancement of Science, Washington, D.C., 1961, pp. 3–58.

Mackay, Alan. "An Outsider's View of Science in Japan." *Impact of Science on Society,* XII, No. 3, 1962, 177–201.

Major, Robert. "Organization of Scientific Activities in Norway." *Science,* CXXIX, No. 3350, March 13, 1959, 694–700.

McCrensky, Edward. *Scientific Manpower in Europe* (New York and London: Pergamon Press, 1958).

McElheny, Victor K. "Biological Research in Czechoslovakia." *Science,* CXLV, August 21, 1964, 799–802.

McElheny, Victor K. "Research Climate in Italy." *Science,* CXLV, No. 3633, August 14, 1964, 690–693.

National Science Foundation, 1962–1964. Scientific Manpower from Abroad (Washington, D.C.: National Science Foundation, 1962).

Orlans, Harold. *The Effects of Federal Programs on Higher Education* (Washington, D.C.: The Brookings Institution, 1962).

Orleans, Leo A. *Professional Manpower and Education in Communist China* (Washington, D.C.: National Science Foundation, 1961).

Price, Don K. "Organization of Science Here and Abroad." *Science,* CXXIX, No. 3351, March 20, 1959, 759–765.

Prywes, Moshe (ed.) *Medical and Biological Research in Israel* (New York: Grune & Stratton, 1960).

Rahman, A., Ghosal, A., Sen, N., Rajagopal, N. R., Das Gupta, Mrs. S., Hussaini, S. H. M., and Roy, A. K. "A Study of Government Expenditure on Scientific Research" *Journal of Scientific and Industrial Research,* XXII, No. 12, 1963, 479–486.

Robbins, Lord. *Higher Education.* Report of the Committee appointed by the

Prime Minister under the Chairmanship of Lord Robbins 1961–63 (London: Her Majesty's Stationery Office, October, 1963, Cmnd. 2154, with 5 vol. appendices).

Rosenberg, Herbert H. "Research Planning and Program Development in the National Institutes of Health: The Experience of a Relatively New and Growing Agency." *Annals of American Academy of Political and Social Science,* CCCXXVII, January 1960, 103–113.

Royal Society. *Emigration of Scientists from the United Kingdom* (London: Royal Society, February 1963).

Shils, E. A. *Torment of Secrecy: The Background and Consequences of American Security Policies* (Glencoe, Ill.: The Free Press, 1956).

Slamecka, Vladimir. *Science in Czechoslovakia* (New York: Columbia University Press, 1963).

Slamecka, Vladimir. *Science in East Germany* (New York: Columbia University Press, 1963).

Swain, Donald C. "The Rise of a Research Empire: NIH, 1930 to 1950." *Science,* CXXXVIII, No. 3546, December 14, 1962, 1233–1237.

Thompson, H. W. "Science in China." *International Science and Technology,* No. 18, June 1963, 86–95.

Trend, Sir Burke. "Committee of Enquiry into the Organisation of Civil Science." Presented to Parliament by the Prime Minister and First Lord of the Treasury by Command of Her Majesty, October 1963 (London: Her Majesty's Stationery Office, Cmnd. 2171).

Uyeki, Eugene S., and Cliffe, Frank B., Jr. "The Federal Scientist-Administrator." *Science,* CXXXIX, No. 3561, March 29, 1963, 1267–1270.

Watson, Earnest C. *Organization of Scientific Activities in India* (Washington, D.C.: National Science Foundation, Office of International Science Activities, June 1962).

Wilgreen, Dana. "China's Forward Leap in Science." *Discovery,* XXI, 1960, 464–473.

Zarechnak, Galina. "Academy of Medical Sciences of the USSR; History and Organization, 1944–1959." United States Public Health Service, Washington, D.C., 1960.

V. *Science and Policy*

The Administration of Federally Sponsored University Research. Six Papers Presented at the Conference on Administration of Federally Sponsored University Research (Atlanta, Ga.: The Southern Regional Education Board, 1963).

Alpert, Harry. "The Government's Growing Recognition of Social Science." *Annals of the American Academy of Political and Social Science,* CCCXXVII, 1960, 59–67.

Alpert, Harry. "The Social Science Research Program of the National Science Foundation." *American Sociological Review,* XXII, No. 5, October 1957, 582–585.

The American Assembly, Columbia University. *The Federal Government and Higher Education* (Englewood Cliffs, N.J.: Prentice-Hall, Inc., 1960).

Anderson, Clifton P., and Ramey, James T. "Congress and Research: Experience in Atomic Research and Development." *Annals of American Academy of Political Science,* CCCXXVII, January 1960, 85–94.

Berkner, Lloyd V. "Government Sponsorship of Scientific Research." *Science,* CXXIX, No. 3352, March 27, 1959, 817–821.

Berkner, Lloyd V. "The Support and Direction of Research at Academic Institutions." *American Scientist,* XLVI, No. 2, June 1958, 159–168.

Bolt, Richard H. "Statesmanship in Science." *Physics Today,* XIV, March 1961, 30–32.

Brode, Wallace. "Development of a Science Policy." *Science,* CXXXI, No. 3392, January 1, 1960, 9–15.

Brozen, Yale. "The Role of Government in Research and Development." *American Behavioral Scientist,* VI, No. 4, 1962, 22–26.

Carey, William D. "Budgeting for Science: Presidential Responsibility." *Annals of American Academy of Political and Social Science,* CCCXXVII, 1960, 76–84.

Carter, C. F., and Williams, B. R. *Investment in Innovation* (London: Oxford University Press, 1958).

Center for the Study of Democratic Institutions. *Science, Scientists, and Politics* (New York: The Fund for the Republic, 1963).

Dedijer, Stevan. "Research Policy—Its Making and Measurements." *Tek. Vetenskaplig Forskning,* XXXIV, No. 4, 1963, 134–146.

Dedijer, Stevan. "Windowshopping for a Research Policy." *Bulletin of Atomic Scientists,* XV, 1959, 367–371.

DuBridge, Lee A. "Policy and the Scientists." *Foreign Affairs,* XLI, No. 3, April 1963, 571–588.

Dupré, J. Stefan, and Lakoff, Sanford A. *Science and the Nation* (Englewood Cliffs, N.J.: Prentice-Hall, Inc., 1962).

Fondation Universitaire. *Increasing the Effectiveness of Western Science* (Brussels: Fondation Universitaire, 1960).

Freeman, Christopher, Poignant, M. Raymond, and Svennilson, Ingvar. *Science, Economic Growth and Government Policy* (Paris: Organization for Economic Co-operation and Development, 1963).

Gilpin, Robert. *American Scientists and Nuclear Weapons Policy* (Princeton, N.J.: Princeton University Press, 1962).

Gilpin, Robert, and Wright, Christopher (eds.) *Scientists and National Policy Making* (New York: Columbia University Press, 1964).

Groszkowski, Janusz, and Newacki, Witold. "Some Experiences from Work on National Plans of Scientific Research." *Review of Polish Academy of Sciences,* V, July-December 1960, 1–18.

Hailsham, Lord. *Science and Politics* (London: Faber & Faber, 1963).

Haskins, Caryl P. "Technology, Science and American Foreign Policy." *Foreign Affairs,* XL, No. 2, January 1962, 1–20.

Herring, Pendleton. "On Science and the Polity." Social Science Research Council *Items,* XV, No. 1, Part 2, March 1961, 1–6.

Honey, John C. "The Challenge of Government Science." *Annals of American Academy of Political and Social Science,* CCCXXVII, January 1960, 1–9.

Humphrey, Hubert H. "The Need for a Department of Science." *Annals of American Academy of Political and Social Science,* CCCXXVII, January 1960, 27–35.

Kaplan, Norman. "Research Overhead and the Universities." *Science,* CXXXII, 1960, 400–404.

Kidd, Charles V. "The Effect of Research Emphasis on Research Itself." Chapter 4 in *Research and Medical Education* (Evanston, Ill.: Association of American Medical Colleges, 1962), pp. 95–122.

Kidd, Charles V. "L'Essor scientifique et la répartition des hommes de science entre les nations." *Impact,* XIV, No. 1, 1964, 5–20.

Kidd, Charles V. "The Loss of Scientists from Less to More Developed Countries." In *U.N. Conference on the Application of Science and Technology for the Benefit of the Less Developed Areas* (Geneva: United Nations, February 1963), pp. 18–26.

Killian, James R., Jr. "Science and Public Policy." *Science,* CXXIX, January 16, 1959, 129–136.

Killian, James R., Jr. "Strengthening American Science." *American Scientist,* XLVII, 1959, 264–287.

King, Alexander. "Towards a National Science Policy." *Impact of Science on Society,* XII, No. 3, 1962, 157–176.

Kistiakowsky, George B. "Science and Foreign Affairs." *Bulletin of Atomic Scientists,* XVI, 1960, 114–116.

Kramish, Arnold. "Research and Development in the Common Market vis-a-vis The U.K., U.S., and U.S.S.R." (Santa Monica, Calif.: Rand Corporation, 1963).

Lang, Daniel. "Profile of Jerome B. Wiesner—A Scientist's Advice." *The New Yorker,* XXXVIII, Part I, January 19, 1963; Part II, January 26, 1963, 38–71.

Merton, Robert K. "The Role of Applied Social Science in the Formation of Policy: A Research Memorandum." *Philosophy of Science,* XVI, No. 3, July 1949, 161–181.

Merton, Robert K. "Role of the Intellectual in Public Bureaucracy." *Social Forces,* XXIII, No. 4, May 1945, 405–415.

Mesthene, Emmanuel G. "Can Only Scientists Make Government Science Policy?" *Science,* CXLV, No. 3629, July 17, 1964, 237–240.

Mukerjee, Dilip. "Indian Science: Policy, Organisation and Application." *Minerva,* II, No. 3, Spring 1964, 360–369.

Piganiol, Pierre, and Villecourt, Louis. *Pour une politique scientifique* (Paris: Flammarion, 1963).

President's Science Advisory Committee. *Scientific Progress, the Universities and the Federal Government* (Washington, D.C.: U.S. Government Printing Office, 1960).

President's Science Advisory Committee. "Strengthening the Behavioral Sciences." *Science,* CXXXVI, April 20, 1962, 233–241.

Price, Don K., Dupré, J. Stefan, and Gustafson, W. Eric. "Current Trends in Science Policy in the United States." *Impact of Science on Society,* X, 1960, 187–213.

Rahman, A. "National Basis for Scientific Research." *Link,* August 15, 1963.

Rahman, A. "Planning, Finance, Organization of Research and Related Administrative Problems; Training of Scientists; Science and the Government." Presented at Symposium on Science and Nation, Association of Scientific Workers of India, July 29, 1964.

Robinson, Sir Robert. "Science and the New Politics." *New Scientist,* XX, No. 360, October 10, 1963, 74–75.

Salomon, Jean-Jacques. "International Scientific Policy." *Minerva,* II, No. 4, Summer 1964, 411–434.

Sayre, Wallace S. "Scientists and American Science Policy." *Science,* CXXXIII, March 24, 1961, 859–864.

Schilling, Warner R. "The H-Bomb Decision: How to Decide without Actually Choosing." *Political Science Quarterly,* LXXVI, No. 1, 1961, 24–46.

Seitz, Frederick. "Science and the Government." *Physics Today,* XVI, No. 12, December 1963, 28–30.

Shannon, James A. "Science and Federal Programs: The Continuing Dialogue." *Science,* CXLIV, No. 3621, May 22, 1964, 976–978.

Smyth, Henry D. "Sponsored Research." *Princeton Alumni Weekly,* LIX, No. 27, May 22, 1959, 7–14.

Snow, C. P. *Science and Government* (Cambridge: Harvard University Press, 1961).

Storer, Norman W. "Some Sociological Aspects of Federal Science Policy." *American Behavioral Scientist,* VI, No. 4, 1962, 27–29.

Stover, Carl F. "The Government of Science." A Report to the Center for the Study of Democratic Institutions, March 1962.

Stover, Carl F., and Hatch, Lorraine. "Science and Democratic Government." Report of a Conference on the Role and Responsibilities of Science Executives in the Federal Service Center for the Study of Democratic Institutions, January 1963.

Toulmin, Stephen. "The Complexity of Scientific Choice: A Stocktaking." *Minerva,* II, No. 3, Spring 1964, 343–359.

Waterman, Alan T. "National Science Foundation: A Ten-Year Resume." *Science,* CXXXI, No. 3410, May 6, 1960, 1341–1354.

"White House Superstructure for Science." *Chemical and Engineering News,* XLII, October 19, 1964, 78–92.

Wohlstetter, Albert. "Scientists, Seers and Strategy." *Foreign Affairs,* XLI, No. 3, April, 1963, 466–478.

Wolfle, Dael. "Diversity of Talent." *The American Psychologist,* XV, No. 8, August 1960, 535–545.

Wolfle, Dael. *Science and Public Policy* (Lincoln: University of Nebraska Press, 1959).

Wolfle, Dael (ed.) *Symposium on Basic Research* (Washington, D.C.: American Association for the Advancement of Science, Publication No. 56, 1959).

Zaheer, S. Husain, Rahman, A., and Sen, N. "Investment in Scientific and Technological Research During the Fourth Five Year Plan." Council of Scientific and Industrial Research, New Delhi, India, September 14, 1964.

VI. *Prologue to the Future*

Adrian, The Rt. Hon. the Lord. "The Risks of Progress" The Sixth Fawley Foundation Lecture (Southampton: Camelot Press, Ltd., for the University of Southampton, 1959).

Allen, F. R., Hart, H., Miller, D. C., Ogburn, W. F., and Nimkoff, M. F. *Technology and Social Change* (New York: Appleton-Century-Crofts, 1957).

Apter, David E. "New Nations and the Scientific Revolution." *Bulletin of Atomic Scientists,* XVII, No. 2, February 1961, 60–64.

Barzun, Jacques. *Science: The Glorious Entertainment.* (New York: Harper & Row, Publishers, 1964).

Beck, William S. *Modern Science and the Nature of Life.* (New York: Harcourt, Brace and Company, 1957).

Berkner, L. V. *The Scientific Age: The Impact of Science on Society* (New Haven: Yale University Press, 1964).

Bethe, Hans. "Science." Interview by Donald McDonald, with a comment by James H. Douglas. (Santa Barbara, Calif.: Center for the Study of Democratic Institutions, 1962).

Calder, Ritchie. "How Much, How Many, What Sort?" *Discovery,* XXII, 1961, 30–33.

Consolazio, William V. "Sustaining Academic Science, 1965–75." *Educational Record,* XLV, No. 2, Spring 1964, 210–229.

Dedijer, Stevan. "Scientific Research and Development: A Comparative Study." *Nature,* CLXXXVII, 1960, 458–461.

Dedijer, Stevan. "Underdeveloped Science in Underdeveloped Countries." *Minerva,* II, No. 1, Autumn 1963, 61–81.

Dedijer, Stevan. "Why Did Daedalus Leave?" *Science,* CXXXIII, 1961, 2047–2052.

deHemptinne, Y. "The Science Policy of States in Course of Independent Development." *Impact of Science on Society,* XIII, No. 3, 1963, 233–247.

deJouvenel, Bertrand. "The Political Consequence of the Rise of Science." *Bulletin of Atomic Scientists,* XIX, December 1963, 2–8.

Dubos, Rene J. "Scientist and Public." *Science,* CXXXIII, April 21, 1961, 1207–1211.

Field, M. G. "Soviet Science and Some Implications for American Science and Society." *Journal of International Affairs,* XIII, No. 1, 1959, 18–33.

Gruber, Ruth (ed.) *Science and the New Nations* (New York: Basic Books, Inc., 1961).

Haskins, Caryl P. "Society and Scientific Research." *Bulletin of Atomic Scientists,* XVI, 1960, 146–150.

Hewlett, Richard G., and Anderson, Oscar E., Jr. *The New World, 1939–1946: Vol. I, A History of the United States Atomic Energy Commission* (University Park, Pa.: Pennsylvania State University Press, 1962).

Hirsch, Walter. "Knowledge, Power, and Social Change: The Role of American Scientists," In George K. Zollschan and Walter Hirsch (eds.) *Explorations in Social Change* (Boston: Houghton Mifflin Co., 1964), pp. 798–816.

Kaplan, Norman. "Sociology of Science." Chapter 22 in *Handbook of Modern Sociology,* Robert E. L. Faris (ed.) (Chicago: Rand McNally & Company, 1964, pp. 852–881).

McElheny, Victor K. "Research in Biology: New Pattern of Support is Developing." *Science,* CXLV, No. 3635, August 28, 1964, 908–912.

Muller, H. J. "Science for Humanity." *Bulletin of Atomic Scientists,* XV, 1959, 146–150.

National Science Foundation. *Investing in Scientific Progress, 1961–1970* (Washington, D.C.: National Science Foundation, 1961).

Price, Derek J. De Solla. *Little Science, Big Science* (New York: Columbia University Press, 1963).

Rabinowitch, Eugene. *The Dawn of a New Age* (Chicago and London: The University of Chicago Press, 1963).

Salk, Jonas E. "Biology in the Future." *Perspectives in Biology and Medicine,* V, No. 4, Summer 1962, 423–431.

Schonland, F. J. "The Invisible College." *International Affairs,* XXXV, No. 2, April 1959, 141–150.

Seitz, Frederick. "Science on the March" (Allerton Institute), November 6–9, 1960 (mimeograph).

Stewart, Bruce. "Science and Social Change." *Bulletin of Atomic Scientists, XVII,* 1961, 267–270, 286.

Tishler, Max. "The Government's Role and the Future of Discovery." Address delivered in accepting the 1963 Chemical Industry Medal of the American Section of Society of Chemical Industry at the Medal Dinner, September 26, 1963, Houston, Texas (mimeograph).

Toulmin, Stephen. "Towards a Natural History of Science." *New Scientist,* November 7, 1963, No. 364.

United Nations, Secretary-General Thant (1961). *Science and Technology for Development* (New York: edited and published in eight volumes by United Nations Publishing Service, 1963).

United States Papers Prepared for the United Nations Conference on the Application of Science and Technology for the Benefit of the Less Developed Areas, in *Science and Technology for Development: Vol. IX, Scientific and Technological Policy, Planning, and Organization* (Washington, D.C.: Government Printing Office, 1963).

Waterman, Alan. "Integration of Science and Society." *American Behavioral Scientist,* VI, No. 4, 1962, 3–6.

Weaver, Warren. "A Great Age for Science." In *Goals for Americans* (Englewood Cliffs, N.J.: Prentice-Hall, Inc., 1960).

Weinberg, Alvin M. "The New Estate" Commencement Address, University of Chattanooga, Chattanooga, Tenn., June 3, 1963 (mimeograph).

Weinberg, Alvin M. "The Federal Grant University and the Federal Laboratory." Commencement Address, The University of Tennessee, Knoxville, Tenn., March 17, 1964 (mimeograph).

Wilgress, D. *Cooperation in the Field of Scientific and Technical Research* (Paris: Organization for European Economic Cooperation, March 1960).

Withey, S. B. "Public Opinion About Science and Scientists." *Public Opinion Quarterly,* XXIII, Fall 1959, 382–388.

Woolf, Harry (ed.) *Science as a Cultural Force* (Baltimore, Md.: Johns Hopkins Press, 1964).

Zuckerman, Sir Solly. "Liberty in an Age of Science." *Nature, CLXXXIV,* 1959, 135–138.

West, Kelly M. (ed.) *International Biomedical Research: First National Institutes of Health International Symposium* (Washington, D.C.: Government Printing Office, 1964).

Index

Abel, F., 89
Abraham, 117
Academic achievement, decentralized competitive market for, 83
Academic freedom. *See* Universities.
Academic organization and 19th century medicine, 39–61
Academic systems, modern, growth of in Britain and U.S., 57–60
Academy of Medical Sciences (U.S.S.R.), 230–31; 239–241
Academy of Sciences (Paris), 14–15
Academy of Sciences, U.S.S.R., 303; 307–308; 494
Academy-Research Council. *See* National Academy of Sciences.
Ackerknecht, E. H., 48n
Adams, H., 278
Adams, J. Q., 158, 281
Adler, A., 114, 117
Adrian, Rt. Hon. the Lord, 593
Administrative class: Great Britain, 281–82; U.S., 281–82
Administrators, scientific, 553. *See also* Research administration.
Administrators and scientists, 284–85
Advisory Council on Scientific Policy (Britain), 363n; 495; 499
Aerospace Corporation, 290
Agassiz, A., 269, 272, 297
Aggrégation, 54
Agriculture, Department of, 158, 265, 284
Air Force, 292, 299; and government scientists, 419
Akert, K., 184
Albert (King of Belgium), 343
Allison Commission, 269–70
Allen, F. R., 593
Allen, M., 589
Alpert, H., 39n, 590
Althoff, F., 48
Amateurs: historic roles of, 52–54; declining role of, 87, 104
Ambivalence: of scientists, 112–132; toward priority of discovery, 115–124; and Eureka syndrome, 124–25. *See also* Cryptomnesia.
American science: coming changes in,

560–68; background of, 560–62; and Big Science, 563; and student attitudes, 563; and larger scientific community, 563–64; results of increased support for, 563–65; lessening of effective control in, 564; and secrecy, 564; and professional recognition, 564; and basic research, 564–65; new structure of, 565–66
American Assembly, 590
American Association for the Advancement of Science, 68, 263–64, 367–68, 400n
American Association of University Professors, 444
American Management Association, 226
American Miscellaneous Society, 300. *See also* National Academy of Sciences
American Philosophical Society, 158
American Society of Biological Chemists, 431
Ampère, 24n
Anderson, A., 76n
Anderson, C. A., 363n
Anderson, P., 590
Anderson, O., 586
Anderson, O. E., Jr., 289n, 594
Andreas-Salomé, L., 117
Andrews, F. M., 587
Anglada, C., 541
Anger, H., 63n
Aniline dye industry (Germany), as pioneer in applied science, 92–93
Applied science, conditions precedent to, 11–13; in England, development of, 86–105 *passim;* profession of: development, 86–104; education and, 89, 93–98, 104; career opportunities and, 94, 99–104; and broadening specialization, 102–103; and the open society, 104; vs. technology, 90; in Germany, development of, 91–105 *passim.*
Appropriations Committees, Congressional, 389
Appropriations, Committee on, House of Representatives, 407
Apter, D. E., 593
Argonne, 250